John W. Prados

OCTOBER 1992

Pneumatic Conveying of Solids

Powder Technology Series

EDITED BY B. SCARLETT

Department of Chemical Engineering
University of Technology
Loughborough

Many materials exist in the form of a disperse system, for example powders, pastes, slurries, emulsions and aerosols. The study of such systems necessarily arises in many technologies but may alternatively be regarded as a separate subject which is concerned with the manufacture, characterization and manipulation of such systems. Chapman and Hall were one of the first publishers to recognize the basic importance of the subject, going on to instigate this series of books. The series does not aspire to define and confine the subject without duplication, but rather to provide a good home for any book which has a contribution to make to the record of both the theory and the application of the subject. We hope that all engineers and scientists who concern themselves with disperse systems will use these books and that those who become expert will contribute further to the series.

Particle Size Measurement
T. Allen
4th edn, hardback (0 412 35070 X), about 736 pages

Powder Porosity and Surface Area
S. Lowell and Joan E. Shields
2nd edn, hardback (0 412 25240 6), 248 pages

Pneumatic Conveying of Solids
R.D. Marcus, L.S. Leung, G.E. Klinzing and F. Rizk
Hardback (0 412 21490 3), 596 pages

Particle Technology
Hans Rumpf
Translated by F.A. Bull
Hardback (0 412 35230 3), about 160 pages

Pneumatic Conveying of Solids

R.D. MARCUS
University of Pretoria,
South Africa

L.S. LEUNG
Commonwealth Scientific and Industrial Research Organization,
Australia

G.E. KLINZING
University of Pittsburgh,
United States of America

F. RIZK
BASF AG, Ludwigshafen,
Federal Republic of Germany

CHAPMAN AND HALL

London   New York   Tokyo   Melbourne   Madras

UK   Chapman and Hall, 11 New Fetter Lane, London EC4P 4EE

USA   Chapman and Hall, 29 West 35th Street, New York NY10001

Japan   Chapman and Hall Japan, Thomson Publishing Japan, Hirakawacho
          Nemoto Building, 7F, 1–7–11 Hirakawa-cho, Chiyoda-ku, Tokyo 102

Australia Chapman and Hall Australia, Thomas Nelson Australia,
          480 La Trobe Street, PO Box 4725, Melbourne 3000

India   Chapman and Hall India, R. Sheshadri, 32 Second Main Road,
          CIT East, Madras 600 035

Typeset in 10/12 Times by Thomson Press (India) Ltd, New Delhi
Printed in Great Britain by St Edmundsbury Press, Bury St Edmunds, Suffolk

ISBN 0 412 21490 3

British Library Cataloguing in Publication Data

Pneumatic conveying of solids
1. Solids. Pneumatic transport in pipes
I. Marcus, R. D. II. Series
621.8′672

ISBN 0–412–21490–3

Library of Congress Cataloging in Publication Data is available

Contents

Preface

When the four of us decided to collaborate to write this book on pneumatic conveying, there were two aspects which were of some concern. Firstly, how could four people, who live on four different continents, write a book on a fairly complex subject with such wide lines of communications? Secondly, there was the problem that two of the authors are chemical engineers. It has been noted that the majority of chemical engineers who work in the field of pneumatic conveying research have spent most of their time considering flow in vertical pipes. As such, there was some concern that the book might be biased towards vertical pneumatic conveying and that the horizontal aspects (which are clearly the most difficult!) would be somewhat neglected.

We hope that you, as the reader, are going to be satisfied with the fact that you have a truly international dissertation on pneumatic conveying and, also, that there is an even spread between the theoretical and practical aspects of pneumatic conveying technology.

We have attempted to produce a book for which we perceived a need in the market place. The book has been written taking into consideration our experiences in the pneumatic conveying industries, and also taking cognizance of the days when we started off as junior research workers in this field. In those early days, it was clear that a large amount of information pertaining to pneumatic conveying system design was not documented in the literature. Also, there was a certain amount of scepticism amongst the industry as to the effectiveness of research work carried out at universities. The fact that academics working in the field have been branded as 'one-inch' pipe technologists is indicative of the lack of confidence shown by industrialists.

As such, we have attempted to address both problems and to cater for a wide cross section of readers, including practising engineers, researchers, graduate students, plant operating personnel and the like. The text has been so arranged to accommodate those researchers who wish to gain more insight into the fundamentals, or to provide a short circuit for those readers who wish to address only the design issues relating to pneumatic conveying.

For the systems designer, it is recommended that Chapter 1 be consulted and, thereafter, the reader should study Chapters 6, 7, 9, 10 and 11. In Chapter 8 issues pertaining to the design of air-activated gravity conveyors are discussed, whilst a number of practical system design problems are solved in Chapter 14.

The researcher wishing to gain more insight into the technology is advised to consult Chapters 3, 4, 5, 12 and 13. In these chapters an attempt has been made to review the relevant literature.

Those issues which are deemed important, but peripheral to this text, are discussed in Chapter 11, where an attempt has been made to alert the reader on such issues as silo and hopper design, wear and attrition, and ancillary equipment. All these topics are subjects in their own right, and the reader wishing to gain more insight into these aspects is advised to consult more definitive texts.

We hope you find this text both useful and stimulating, and that you will reap the rewards of entering into an exciting yet complex field of fluid mechanics.

R.D. Marcus
L.S. Leung
G.E. Klinzing
F. Rizk

Foreword

Pneumatic conveying is a most important practical operation whose application is a vital and integral part in the good design of many processes. Such a book can only be written from the basis of wide experience, in this case particularly achieved by the contribution and cooperation of four authors. The book combines a complete description of all the aspects of pneumatic conveying systems as well as the technology of feeding the systems and of separating the transported particles and the gas. A basically technological subject such as this can only be systematically explained from a basis of a good understanding of fluid mechanics and fluid particle interactions. This book also includes a description of all the necessary basic laws. It is a welcome addition to the Chapman Hall Powder Technology Series.

B. SCARLETT

Nomenclature

Symbol	Description	Unit
A_0	Cross-sectional area of opening	m^2
$A = \pi D^2/4$	Cross-sectional area of pipe	m^2
	Constant or index for acceleration	
A^*	Cross-sectional area of a particle normal to flow	m^2
a	Speed of sound in a pure gas	m/s
a_s	Speed of sound in a gas–solid mixture	m/s
$C_{1,2}$	Constant with index 1, 2	
c	Average particle velocity, bubble velocity, slug velocity	m/s
c_c	Particle velocity at choking conditions	m/s
c'	Superficial solid velocity $[= c(1 - \varepsilon)]$	m/s
$C_D = \dfrac{2F}{\rho w^2 A^*}$	Drag coefficient	
$C_{D\infty}$	Drag coefficient for undisturbed and unbounded fluid	
C_N	Discharge coefficient for a nozzle	
C_t	Volumetric concentration	
C_v	Valve coefficient	
D	Pipe inner diameter	mm
D_o	Diameter of orifice or valve opening	m
D_B	Bend curvature diameter	mm
d	Spherical particle diameter	mm
d_v	Volume equivalent particle diameter	mm
$\bar{d}_v$	Volume surface mean diameter	mm
d_{vs}	Specific surface area diameter $= 4d$	mm
E_x	Electric field	N/C
F	Force	N
$Fr = v/(Dg)^{1/2}$	Froude number related to air velocity	
$Fr^* = c/(Dg)^{1/2}$	Froude number related to particle velocity	

$Fr_f = w_f/(Dg)^{1/2}$	Froude number related to particle fall velocity	
$Fr_p^* = C/(dg)^{1/2}$	Froude number related to particle velocity and particle size	
f_L	Air friction factor	
$G, \Delta G$	Bulk solid mass, element of bulk solid mass	kg
$\dot{G}$	Solid mass flow rate	kg/s kg/h t/h
$Ga = \rho \Delta \rho g (4d_v)^3/\eta^2$	Galileo number	
$Ga' = \rho \Delta \rho g d_v^3/\eta^2$	Galileo number	
$G_f = \rho v$	Gas flux	kg/m²s
$G_s = \dot{G}/A$	Solids flux	kg/m²s
$g = 9.81$	Acceleration due to gravity (gravitational constant)	m/s²
g	Index for gravitational	
H	Enthalpy	kcal/kg
I_R	Relative turbulence intensity	
K, K_1, K_2	Constants	
k	Effective pipe wall roughness	mm
$L, \Delta L$	Length, length of element	m
M	Mass of gas	kg
m_p	Particle mass	kg
n	Number of particles in an element, Number of events or as exponent	
P	Power of blower	W, kW
p	Absolute pressure	Pa, kPa
$p_{dyn} = \rho v^2/2$	Dynamic pressure	Pa, kPa
p_o	Atmospheric pressure	Pa, kPa
p_{stat}	Static pressure	Pa, kPa
Δp_g	Gauge pressure or static pressure	Pa, kPa
Δp	Pressure difference	Pa, kPa Pa, kPa
$\Delta p_Z = \Delta p_Z^* + \Delta p_G$	Additional pressure drop due to presence of solids	Pa, kPa
$\Delta p_Z^* = \lambda_Z^* \dfrac{\rho^*}{2} c^2 \dfrac{\Delta L}{D}$	Pressure drop due to impact and friction of solids	Pa, kPa
$\Delta p_G = \rho^* g \Delta Z$	Pressure drop due to gravity	Pa, kPa
$\dot{Q}$	Gas mass flow rate	kg/s kg/h
r_0	Radius of pipe	m
R	Gas constant	Nm/kgk

R_B	Radius of curvature of bend	m
$Re = vD/v$	Reynolds number related to pipe diameter	
$Re_p = vd/v$	Reynolds number related to particle diameter	
$Re_{pf} = w_{f0}d/v$	Reynolds number related to terminal velocity of particle	
$Re_{mf} = v_{min}d_v/v$	Reynolds number related to minimum fluidization velocity	
S	Entropy	kcal/K
t	Ambient temperature	°C
$V = A\Delta L$	Volume of pipe element	m^3
T	Absolute temperature	K
$V_p = \pi d^3/6$	Volume of particle	m^3
$\dot{V} = \dot{Q}/\rho$	Gas volume flow rate	m^3/s m^3/h
$\dot{V}_p = \dot{G}/\rho*$	Solids volume flow rate	m^3/s m^3/h
$v = \dot{V}/A$	Average air velocity (superficial velocity)	m/s
v_c	Air velocity at choking conditions	m/s
v_0	Fluidization velocity	m/s
$v_\varepsilon = v/\varepsilon$	Actual gas velocity in the voids or velocity of porosity wave	m/s
v_m^*	Friction velocity of mixture	m/s
v_{mb}	Minimum fluidization velocity at which bubbling occurs	m/s
v_{min}	Minimum fluidization velocity	m/s
s	Surface area of a particle	m^2
v_y	Fluctuating fluid velocity in the direction of mean motion	m/s
v_s^*	Friction velocity at saltation point	m/s
v_{s0}	Friction velocity at saltation point of a single particle	m/s
v_s	Spin velocity	m/s
v_{th}	Gas velocity in the ventury throat	m/s
W	Work	J
$w = v - c$	Relative velocity, slip velocity	m/s
w_b	Rate of rise of a single bubble or plug in a fluidized bed	m/s
$w_s = v_\varepsilon - c$	Slip velocity in a plug	m/s
w_{f0}	Single particle settling (or terminal) velocity in an undisturbed fluid	m/s

w_f	Particle settling velocity in a cloud	m/s
w_f^*	Separation velocity	m/s
w_{sl}	Slip velocity of a slug	m/s
x_{if}	Volume fraction of solid in feed with terminal velocity w_{f0i}	
x_{it}	Volume fraction of solid in tube with terminal velocity w_{f0i}	
$Z, \Delta Z$	Height, height difference	m

Greek (alphabet) symbols

α and ω	Indexes standing for initial and terminal states respectively	
$\beta_0 = w_{f0}/v$	Velocity ratio related to single particle fall velocity	
$\beta = w_f/v$	Velocity ratio related to particle fall velocity in a cloud	
$\beta_w = \tan \phi_w$	Particle/wall friction factor	
γ	Gas/cloth ratio	m/min
δ	Exponent, internal angle of friction	
$\varepsilon = 1 - \dfrac{\rho^*}{\rho_p}$	Voidage	
ε_{mf}	Voidage at minimum fluidization	
ε_s	Voidage at saltation velocity	
ε_0	Voidage of fluidized bed	
ε_p	Voidage of compact bed	
$\bar{\varepsilon}$	Voidage of gas outside clusters	
η	Dynamic viscosity	$N\,s/m^2$
η_B	Blower, compressor efficiency	
η_C	Collector efficiency	
η_F	Fractional efficiency	
η_S	Separator efficiency	
θ	Angle	degree
$\lambda = \lambda_L + \lambda_Z \mu$	Resistance factor of air and solids in a mixture stream	
λ_L	Resistance factor for air alone in pipe	
λ_Z	Additional pressure drop factor in a pipe due to solids in a flowing stream	
λ_{Zp}	Additional pressure drop factor due to air flowing through a plug in a pipe	

λ_Z^*	Pressure drop due to impact and fraction	
λ_{ZS}	Pressure drop factor for slug flow	
λ_t	Spatial macroscale between particles	mm
$\mu = \dot{G}/\dot{Q}$	$\begin{cases}\text{Mass flow ratio} \\ \text{Mass load ratio}\end{cases}$	
$\mu^* = \Delta G/\Delta Q$	Mass concentration in pipe element	
μ_w	Coefficient for sliding friction	
v	Kinematic viscosity	m^2/s
ρ	Air (gas) density	kg/m^3
$\rho^* = \rho_p(1-\varepsilon)$	Apparent bulk density	kg/m^3
$\Delta\rho = \rho_p - \rho$	Density difference between particle and fluid	kg/m^3
ρ_C^*	Dust concentration	mg/m^3
ρ_B	Bulk density	kg/m^3
ρ_m	Mean density of mixture	kg/m^3
ρ_p	Particle density	kg/m^3
τ	Relaxation time	s
τ_s	Shear stress	N/m^2
ϕ_w	Angle of wall friction	degree
ϕ	Angle of internal friction	degree
χ	Exponent	
$\psi = \pi d_v^2/s$	Sphericity	

Subscripts

atm	Atmospheric conditions
B	Bubble
c	Particle
C	Cluster
D	Drag
dyn	Dynamic
G	Gravity
H	Horizontal
IF	Impact and friction
L	Gas
mf	Choking
$\circ$	Conditions at atmospheric pressure
stat	Static
V	Vertical
ε	Voidage

1

An overview of pneumatic conveying systems and performance

1.1 INTRODUCTION

Pneumatic conveying involves the transportation of a wide variety of dry powdered and granular solids in a gas stream. In most cases the gas is normally air, however, where special conditions prevail (e.g. risk of explosion, health, fire hazards, etc.), different gases are used.

This introductory chapter has been written to provide the reader with an overview and a practical insight into pneumatic conveying technology. More specific aspects pertaining to the complex phenomenon which takes place during the pneumatic transport of solids are discussed in subsequent chapters.

1.2 WHY PNEUMATIC CONVEYING?

The concept of pipeline transportation of fluids is by no means modern. The history of its use dates back to antiquity. The Romans, for instance, used lead pipes for water supply and sewerage disposal, whilst the Chinese conveyed natural gas through bamboo tubes. The record of pipeline transportation of solids in air is more recent with the inception of fans to activate the first pneumatic conveying in 1866.

The first large scale application of pneumatic conveying was the vacuum conveying of grain in the late 19th century. By the mid 1920s, negative and positive pressure conveying of grain was common. Since that time the practice of pneumatic conveying has grown enormously and has extended to cover a wide variety of particulate solids. A survey carried out by the British Hydrodynamics Research Association [1] showed that between 1971 and 1977 the pneumatic conveying market in Britain grew by an order of magnitude and that during the one year period 1977 to 1978 a further 50% increase in the sales of equipment for pneumatic conveying systems was recorded.

1.2.1 Advantages of a pneumatic conveying system

Pneumatic conveying offers the user the following advantages:

1. Dust free transportation of a variety of products.
2. Flexibility in routing—can be transported vertically and horizontally by the addition of a bend in the pipeline.
3. Distribution to many different areas in a plant and pick-up from several areas.
4. Low maintenance and low manpower costs.
5. Multiple use—one pipeline can be used for a variety of products.
6. Security—pipelines can be used to convey high valued products.
7. Ease of automation and control.

1.2.2 Disadvantages of a pneumatic conveying system

Offset against the advantages, there are certain disadvantages which include:

1. High power consumption.
2. Wear and abrasion of equipment.
3. Incorrect design can result in particle degradation.
4. Limited distance.
5. By virtue of the complex flow phenomena which take place, there is a requirement for high levels of skill to design, operate and maintain systems.

Because of the high power consumption, pneumatic transportation systems are generally more suited to the conveyance of fine particles over shorter distances (up to a few hundred metres). The majority of existing systems have capacities within the range of 1 to 400 tonnes per hour over distances less than 1000 m with average particle size less than 10 mm.

The limitations are usually economic rather than technical. However, the economic factor is changing and recent developments have ensured the transportation of materials at lower energies. Recent applications include the conveyance of up to 40 mm coal [2] in a single lift over 300 m vertical and a small number of long distance pneumatic conveyors [3] transporting various materials over distances up to 3000 m.

With the growing increase in sophistication of pneumatic conveying systems, potential applications are increasing all the time. Thus for the transportation of solid materials, pneumatic conveying should be considered as a prime option and should be evaluated against other modes of solid transportation.

1.3 WHAT CAN BE CONVEYED?

The range of materials suitable for pneumatic conveying is extensive. Virtually all powders and granular materials can be conveyed. Table 1.1 is a partial list of materials which have been successfully conveyed pneumatically. The list is by no means exhaustive. Rocks of up to 70 mm in size, live chickens and finished manufactured parts of unusual geometry have been conveyed. Generally, the

Table 1.1 Materials suitable for pneumatic transport

ABS powder	Carbon, powdered
Acetylsalicyclic acid	Carbon black
Activated earth	Cardboard, edge trim & waste
Adipic acid	Casein
Alkali cellulose	Cast iron turnings
Altulite, powdered	Cattle feed, granulated
Alumina	Cattle feed, pulverized
Aluminium fluoride	Cellophane, edge trim and waste
Aluminium foil, trim or waste	Cellulose
Aluminium hydrate	Cellulose acetate, dry
Aluminium shavings	Cellulose acetate, wet
Aluminium silicate	Cement
Aluminium sulphate	Chalk
Ammonium nitrate	Charcoal, calibrated, dry
Ammonium sulphate	Charcoal, fine
Anthracite	Charcoal granules, activated
Antimony oxide	Charcoal, wood, fine
Apatite	Chicory roots, dry
Arsenious acid	China clay
Arsenious anhydride	Chromium sulphate flakes
Asbestos fibres or flakes	Chromium sulphate, ground
Asbestos, ground	Clay, powdered
	Cobalt ore
Bagasse (2–6 in)	Cocoa bean shells
Bagasse fines	Cocoa beans
Bakelite powder	Cocoa, ground
Baryta	Coffee beans in silver skin
Bauxite	Coffee cherries
Beetroot pulp, dry	Coffee, ground
Bentonite	Coffee, roasted
Bicarbonate of soda	Coffee, unroasted
Blast furnace dust	Coke dust
Blast furnace sinter, fine	Coke, granular
Bleach powder	Coke, granular, fine
Blende, roasted	Coke, petroleum
Bones	Colmanite
Borax, anhydrous	Copper shavings
Boric acid	Copra
Bran	Copra cakes
Brass shavings	Cork, crushed
Brick, crushed	Cork discs
Butadiene rubber crumb	Cork powder
	Corn: oats and barley also waste
Calamine	Cornflour, coarse
Calcium chloride	Cotton seeds
Calcium cyanamide	

(contd.)

Table 1.1 (*contd.*)

Decolourizing earth	Lampblack
Dextrine, powdered	Lead oxide
Diatomacious earth	Lichen, dried
Dicalcium phosphate	Lignite
Dolomite	Lime, carbonate of
	Lime, hydrated
Edible paste products (small)	Limestone
Enamel powder	
	Magnesia (magnesium oxide)
Feathers	Magnesite
Feldspar, ground	Magnesium carbonate
Flax stalk waste	Magnesium fluoride
Flint grains	Maize, broken
Flock, dry	Maize, draff
Flour, alimentary	Manganese dioxide
Flour, middlings	Marble, powdered
Flour, rye	Matches
Flour, wheat	Mataethylacetic
Fluorspar, ground	Mica
Fluorine	Milk, powdered, high fat
Fly ash	Milk, powdered, whole
Fumaric acid	Milk, skimmed, low fat
Gelatine, ground	Nickel oxide
Gelatine, strips	Nickel sulphide
Glass fibres	Nitrocellulose
Glass, granulated or ground	Nylon polymer, chips and fibres
Glue beads	
Grapes	Oilcake flour
Grape pips	Olive cake
Graphite flakes	Ossein
Graphite powder	
Groundnut cakes, granulated	Palm-nut cake
Groundnut cakes, powdered	Paper edge trim and waste
Ground rice, coarse	Papermill wood waste, wet
Gypsum, fine (anhydrous calcium	Peanut shells
sulphate)	Peat
	Peat, ground
Hemp stalk waste	Peas, frozen
	Phenol resins, crushed
Ilmenite	Phosphate, ground
Iron formiate	Phosphate, natural
Iron ore	Phosphorus pentasulphide
	Phtalic anhydride
Kaolin	Pips ground
Kisselguhr	Pitch, granulated

Table 1.1 *(contd.)*

Pitch, ground	Sodium chlorate
Plaster	Sodium chloride (table salt)
Plastic granules and powders various	Sodium citrate crystals
Polyethylene, compacted	Sodium formiate
Polyethylene, expanded	Sodium hydrosulphite
Polyethylene granules	Sodium nitrate
Polyethylene powder	Sodium perborate
Polyester, fibres and granules	Sodium sulphate
Polypropylene powder and granules	Sodium sulphate, ground
Polystyrene beads	Sodium sulphite
Polystyrene, ground	Sodium tripolyphosphate
PVC granules	Soot
PVC powder	Soya bean cakes
Pomace	Starch
Potash	Steel turnings
Potassium chloride	Straw, chopped
Potassium nitrate	Sugar, granulated
Potato chips, frozen	Sugar, icing
Potato pulp, dry	Sulphur
Potato starch	Sunflower seed husks
Pyrites, crude, ground	
Pyrites, roasted	Talc
	Terephthalic acid
Quartz powder	Titanium dioxide, grains
Quartz rock (80 mm)	Titanium dioxide, powder
Quicklime	Tobacco
	Trichlorocyanic acid
Rubber crumb	
Rubber powder	Undecanoic amino
	Uranium tetrafluoride
Salt	Urea beads
Salt cake	Urea formaldehyde granules
Sand	
Sand, coated	Vermiculite
Sawdust	Vynyl acetate
Semolina	
Silica, anhydrous ground	Wood, shredded
Silica, hydrated	Wood shavings
Silica, gel	
Slag, ground	
Slag dust	Yeast, dried
Soap powder	
Soap flakes	Zeolite
Sodium carbonate, dense	Zinc oxide
Sodium carbonate, light	Zinc, powdered

larger and denser is the material, the higher the gas velocity required for operation and the higher the power consumption. It is often stated that particles greater than 15 mm in size may not be suitable. There are, of course, exceptions to such a rule. **Another rule of thumb is that the inside diameter of the conveying pipe should be at least three times larger than the largest size of material to be conveyed to prevent blockage inside the pipe.**

The ideal candidates for pneumatic conveying are free flowing, non-abrasive and non-fibre materials. However, with the development of new types of conveyors operating at low gas velocities, cohesive, abrasive and friable materials can be handled.

1.4 WHAT CONSTITUTES A PNEUMATIC CONVEYING SYSTEM?

In essence, a pneumatic conveying system consists of four distinct zones, each requiring its own specialized hardware to effect the required operation (Fig. 1.1). The four zones are considered as follows.

1.4.1 The prime mover

The prime mover is an essential element in a pneumatic conveying system. A wide range of compressors, blowers, fans and vacuum pumps are used to provide the necessary energy to the conveying gas. Pertinent to the design of a pneumatic conveying system is the need to identify both the gas flow rate and the pressure (positive or negative) required to effect reliable transportation.

By virtue of the fact that a wide range of pressures is used for the transportation of solids, an understanding of the flow of gases through pipelines, the need for drying, cooling and filtering the gas, etc. is required.

Full details pertaining to the flow of gases in pipes are described in Chapter 2.

1.4.2 Feeding, mixing and acceleration zone

This zone is considered one of the most crucial areas in any pneumatic conveying system. In this particular zone the solids are introduced into the flowing gas stream. By virtue of the fact that the solids are essentially at rest, a large change in momentum occurs when the solids are mixed with the flowing gas.

Associated with this momentum change is the need to provide an acceleration zone. If the physical space permits, the zone normally consists of a horizontal piece of pipe of a certain length designed such that the solids are accelerated to some 'steady' flow state.

Essential to the effective operation of such a pneumatic conveying system is the selection of a feeder which meets both the requirements of the solids as well as the requirements of the system. Full details pertaining to feeder design are described in Chapter 7.

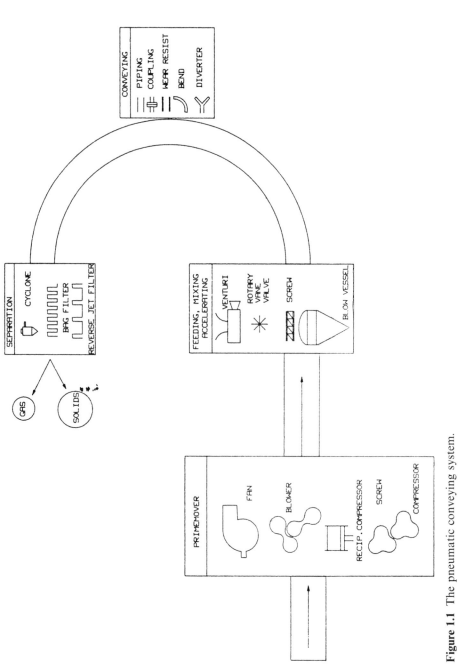

Figure 1.1 The pneumatic conveying system.

1.4.3 The conveying zone

Once the solids have passed through the acceleration zone, they enter into the conveying zone. The conveying zone consists of piping. The selection of piping is based on a number of factors including the abrasiveness of the product, pressure requirements, etc.

The conveying zone can have a number of bends and diverter valves in order to change flow direction. The selection of an appropriate bend is discussed in Chapter 11. By virtue of the fact that a bend constitutes a change of direction, the solids are decelerated as they move through a bend. At the exit of each bend an acceleration zone is normally required to re-entrain the solids.

1.4.4 Gas–solids separation zone

In this zone the solids are separated from the gas stream in which they have been conveyed. With pressure conveying systems it is only necessary to maintain a pressure drop across the collector which will be sufficient to separate the solids from the gas.

The selection of an adequate gas–solid separation system is dependent upon a number of factors, the primary factor being size of the solids requiring to be separated from the gas stream. A number of different configurations of gas–solid separation systems are used in pneumatic conveying systems. Details pertaining to the design and selection of these devices are described in Chapter 10.

1.5 MODES OF PNEUMATIC CONVEYING

For ease of classification, pneumatic conveying systems can be categorized into various modes. Perhaps the most suitable classification is based on the average particle concentration in the pipeline. In terms of this definition, pneumatic conveying systems can be classified into two distinct categories:

- Dilute phase systems
- Dense phase systems   Unstable flow regime
  Unstable/stable flow regime
  Stable flow regime

For simplicity, each phase is categorized in terms of the mass flow ratio (μ), which is defined as the ratio of the mass of solids ($\dot{G}$) to the mass of conveying air ($\dot{Q}$). Thus in terms of the above we have:

Mode	Mass flow ratio
Dilute phase	0–15
Dense phase	Greater than 15

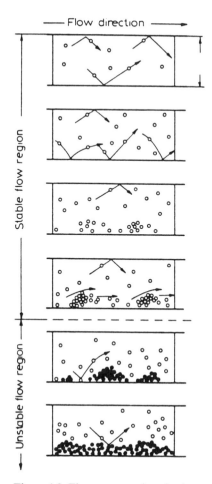

Figure 1.2 Flow patterns in a horizontal conveying pipe.

A schematic of the typical horizontal flow patterns that can take place in these various modes is shown in Fig. 1.2.

1.5.1 Dilute phase

Dilute phase (sometimes referred to as lean phase) systems in general employ large volumes of gas at high velocities. The gas stream carries the materials as discrete particles by means of lift and drag forces acting on the individual particles. Dilute phase systems constitute the most widely used of all pneumatic conveying systems.

1.5.2 Dense phase

A reduction in the gas velocity to a value lower than the saltation velocity (in horizontal flow) (Section 1.8) results in a non-uniform distribution of solids over the cross-section of the conveying pipe.

The conveying process takes place with a certain proportion of the solids flowing through the upper portion of the cross-section of the pipe together with a highly concentrated product stream, corresponding to an expanded moving layer. This moving layer progresses at a lower velocity in the lower part of the cross-section.

Depending upon the characteristics of the solids, the gas velocity, solids flow rate and such factors as pipe roughness, pipe size, etc., the flow patterns in the dense phase mode can vary from being unstable to stable or an intermediate unstable/stable regime.

Flow patterns in the dense phase mode can vary from conditions in which the solids completely pack the pipe and move as a continuous dense plug to situations where the solids on the bottom of the pipe move as a series of dunes with a dilute phase layer of solids flowing above the dunes. The stable flow situations result in a 'smooth' conveying process whilst the unstable situation is characterized by sometimes violent pressure surges as the moving layer breaks up.

Some researchers have attempted to define an intermediate 'medium' phase mode. Since this definition was confined to a limited group of solids with good 'fluidization' characteristics (Chapter 3), it is believed that the above definitions of dilute and dense phase adequately cover all flow situations.

1.6 BASIC PNEUMATIC CONVEYING SYSTEMS

In addition to classifying pneumatic conveying in terms of modes, a further classification is used to identify the type of system required to meet specific situation requirements. The particular systems described below can be designed to operate in the various modes (dilute phase, dense phase, etc.).

1.6.1 Positive pressure system (Fig. 1.3)

The positive pressure system is the most extensively used configuration in pneumatic conveying. These systems are well suited to multiple discharge applications in which material is picked up from a single point and delivered to several receiving bins. The change from one bin to another is usually effected by means of multiport diverter valves.

By virtue of their operation, positive pressure systems require feeding devices which can introduce the material which is normally stored at atmospheric pressure into a pressurized line. Depending upon the mode, and the distance to be transported, pressures up to 1000 kPa can be required for such positive pressure systems. The need for an effective solids feeding device capable of withstanding these high pressures is critical to the effective operation of such positive pressure systems.

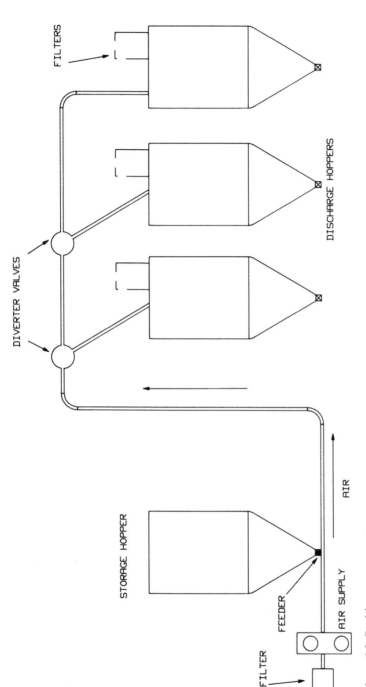

Figure 1.3 Positive pressure system.

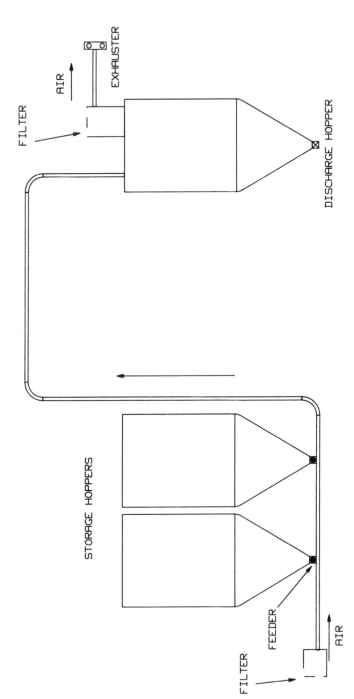

Figure 1.4 Negative pressure systems.

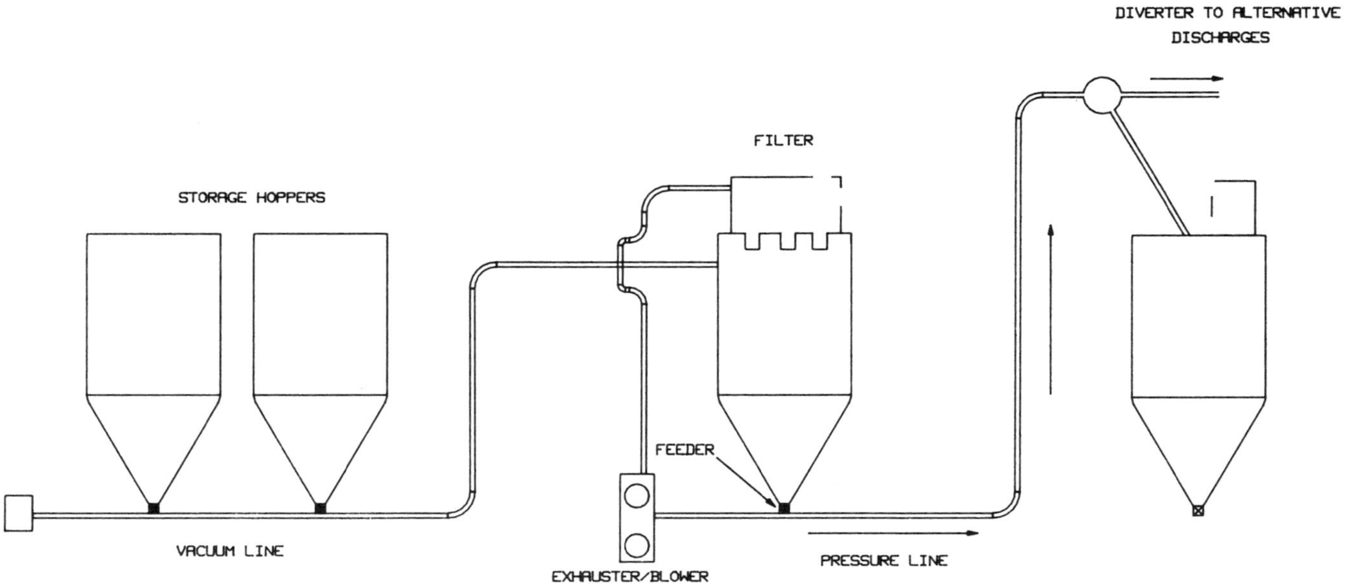

Figure 1.5 Combined negative–positive pressure systems.

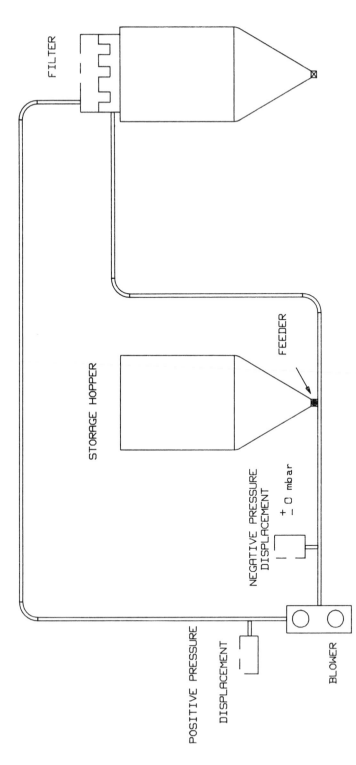

Figure 1.6 Closed loop system.

If properly designed, positive pressure systems can be arranged to have multiple pick-up points as well.

1.6.2 Negative pressure systems (Fig. 1.4)

In general, negative pressure systems are used for the transport of material from several feeding points to a common collection point. Since the operation involves the employment of exhauster systems of various kinds, such systems are limited in distance and capacity.

Negative pressure systems are extensively used in the conveyance of toxic and hazardous materials. These systems permit dust-free feeding and also provide an additional safety feature in as much as any leaks in the pipe will not result in polluting the environment due to an escape of material. With a growing awareness of the need for pollution-free operations, negative pressure systems are gaining widespread acceptance in a large number of industries.

Negative pressure systems vary in size from small industrial type cleaning operations to those used for ship unloading operations in which a capacity of several thousands of tonnes per hour is common [4].

1.6.3 Combined negative–positive pressure systems (Fig. 1.5)

When the advantages of the two systems described above are combined, a versatile pneumatic conveying system results. Such combination systems are often referred to as 'suck–blow' systems and are extensively used in many industries. By keeping the suction line as short as possible a relatively efficient handling system results. Such a system provides for the multiple intake and multiple discharge of a number of products.

1.6.4 Closed loop system (Fig. 1.6)

In the closed loop system, the conveying gas is recycled as shown in Fig. 1.6. This type of conveyor is particularly suitable for handling toxic and radioactive materials. The system also provides for the recirculation of the conveying gas and as such is well suited to such systems where gases other than air are employed.

1.7 FURTHER CLASSIFICATION TECHNIQUES

There are two additional methods for classifying pneumatic conveying systems. The classifications listed above are being rapidly accepted as the most general method of classifying pneumatic conveying systems. However, other classifications are also used by some researchers and industries alike.

1.7.1 Classification by pressure of operation

(a) Fan system—with maximum operating pressures of less than 20 kPa.

(b) Positive displacement blower system—with operating pressure in the range 38 mm Hg vacuum (about 50 kPa absolute) to 1 atmosphere gauge (100 kPa).

(c) Single stage compressor system—with operating pressures of up to 2.5 atmosphere gauge (250 kPa).

(d) High pressure system—generally with operating pressure up to 7 atmosphere gauge (700 kPa).

1.7.2 Classification by solid feeder type

(a) Controlled feed systems—the rate of solids fed into the conveying line can be controlled directly.

(b) Non-controlled feed system—in which the solids flow cannot be closely controlled (a vacuum pick-up and blow tank feed belong to this category).

1.8 DESCRIPTION AND OPERATION OF A PNEUMATIC CONVEYING SYSTEM

In an attempt to provide a general description of the transportation process which takes place in a pneumatic conveying system, the following subsections have been provided to give the reader an intuitive grasp of the process. A more detailed explanation of the various parameters is provided in the ensuing chapters.

1.8.1 State diagram (Fig. 1.7)

Perhaps the best way to introduce the gas–solid conveying process is by way of introduction to the so-called 'state diagram' (Fig. 1.7). The state diagram [5] has been drawn for a horizontal flow system and is a plot of the pressure gradient ($\Delta p/L$) at any point in the pipeline versus the superficial gas velocity (v).

It will be noted that there are various cross-sectional diagrams showing the state of the conveying pipeline at a particular point in the state diagram. In particular, the whole spectrum from dilute phase to dense phase is illustrated by means of this diagram. In Fig. 1.7 the following observations can be made.

Line AB represents the friction loss for a horizontal pipeline transporting gas only.

At an air velocity (v_1), homogeneously sized solid particles are introduced into the pipeline at a constant feedrate $\dot{G}$. As a result of drag on the solid particles and also due to particle–wall interaction (solids friction) the pressure drop increases from B to C.

Decreasing the air velocity along the path CD, the particle velocity is reduced and the mass load ratio (μ) is increased, resulting in a smaller solids frictional loss.

Point D represents the condition at which all solids can just be transported as a suspension in the dilute phase with the prevailing air velocity and the imposed solids feedrate ($\dot{G}$). At this juncture the system would just operate in a steady flow state. The critical air velocity corresponding to point D is called the **saltation velocity**.

At point D, the saltation point, a slight decrease in gas velocity will result in a

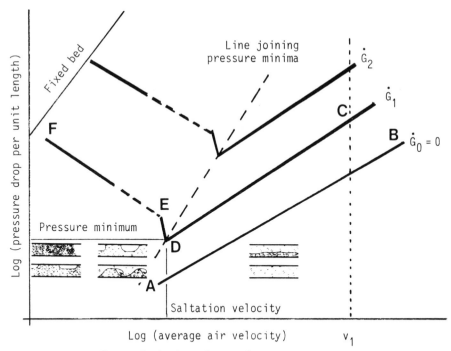

Figure 1.7 State diagram for horizontal conveying.

substantial deposition of solids (bed information). This results in an increase in the frictional resistance to point E.

It will be noted that the bed provides a reduction in the cross-sectional area of the pipe and hence promotes an area of higher velocity to effect the solids transportation.

Of importance, however, is the nature of the bed. Depending upon both the pressure available and the nature of the products, two types of beds are found in pneumatic conveying systems. The so-called stable stationary bed results in a permanent deposition on the bottom of the pipe. This bed remains intact whilst the prevailing conditions of air velocity and solids feedrate are in existence. Effectively, this bed provides the reduction in cross-sectional area of the pipe and facilitates dilute phase flow above the bed.

With some solids it is possible to effect a moving bed typical of that found in the stable dense phase mode. In this situation two types of flow prevail in the pipeline. The moving bed has a high solids concentration and above the moving bed it is common to find dilute phase transportation taking place. Depending on the characteristics of the material and the availability of a pressure head from the prime mover, often a transitionary stage occurs in which a stationary bed is transformed into a moving bed. This particular situation results in a violent pressure surge in the system and if inadequate pressure is available, blockage of the system will occur.

It can be seen that for effective dilute phase operation it is safe to operate the system at a velocity slightly greater than the saltation velocity. Further, it can be seen that there is a need for the system to operate at higher pressures resulting in the need for feeding systems which can seal to these high pressures.

With a further decrease in gas velocity (line EF), the solids flow will be partly carried out in the suspension above the solid layer and also by way of slug flow in the stationary bed itself. Once again, by virtue of the higher solids loading an increase in pressure is noted.

Superimposed upon the state diagram are curves showing the situation for higher solids mass flow rate. It will be noted that the characteristic curve for each solid mass flow rate passes through a pressure minimum at the saltation velocity.

Of importance is the curve obtained by connecting the pressure minimum for each solids flow rate condition. In particular, it can be seen that the curve moves upwards to the right thereby indicating that at higher solids loading, the saltation velocity increases. This particular aspect is of vital importance to system designers. It shows that should a system be designed to transport solids at a particular solids feedrate, and it is desired to increase the solids feedrate, it is necessary to increase the conveying velocity and hence gas flow rate to ensure stable operation. Further explanation of the state diagram is provided in Chapter 6.

1.8.2 Vertical and horizontal flow

An important factor which is not often appreciated is the difference between the flow which takes place in a vertical pipe as distinct from that which takes place in a horizontal pipe. Full details pertaining to vertical and horizontal flow are discussed in ensuing chapters. However, an intuitive feeling for the flow situation will assist with an appreciation of the transportation process.

In terms of the definition of saltation velocity described in Section 1.8.1, a similar point, the choking point, is used to define the minimum transport velocity for a vertical pipe. There is a distinct difference between the saltation velocity (horizontal pipe) and the choking velocity (vertical pipe). In Table 1.2 [6], it will be noted that the minimum safe gas velocity for a horizontal pipe is far in excess of that required to effect safe transportation in a vertical pipe.

In the case of fine particles, the horizontal conveying velocity is of the order of 3 to 5 times larger than that required for vertical conveying. It should be noted that for coarse particles the difference between horizontal and vertical safe velocities is much smaller.

1.8.3 Vacuum and positive pressure systems

Although many researchers would prefer to describe the flow mechanism which takes place in a vacuum system as being similar to that which takes place in a

Table 1.2 Minimum safe air velocity in vertical and horizontal lines for materials with different bulk densities and sizes

Material	Average bulk density (kg/m³)	Approximate size grading (mm)	Minimum safe air velocity vertical (m/s)	Minimum safe air velocity horizontal (m/s)
Coal	720	13	12.00	15.00
Coal	720	6	9.00	12.00
Wheat	753	5	9.00	12.00
Polythene cubes	480	3	9.00	12.00
Cement	1400	90	1.5	7.6
Flour	560	150	1.5	4.6
Pulverized coal	720	75	1.5	4.6
Pulverized ash	720	150	1.5	4.6
Fullers earth	640	106	1.5	6.1
Bentonite	900	75	1.5	7.6
Barite	1750	63	4.6	7.6
Silica flour	880	106	1.5	6.1
Flour spar	1760	75	3.0	9.1
Phosphate rock	1280	150	3.0	9.1
Tripolyphosphate	1040	180	1.5	7.6
Common salt	1360	150	3.0	9.1
Soda ash	560	106	3.0	9.1
Soda ash	1040	180	3.0	12.2
Sodium sulphate	1360	106	3.0	12.2
Sodium perborate	865	180	3.0	9.1
Ground bauxite	1440	106	1.5	7.6
Alumina	930	106	1.5	7.6
Kieselguhr	240	75	1.5	7.6
Magnesite	1600	75	3.0	3.0
Uranium dioxide	3520	75	6.1	18.3

positive pressure system, practice has indicated that this is not the case. It would appear that a different flow mechanism will take place albeit both flow situations can, in terms of the definition, be described as dilute phase.

Some authors [7] have described the flow in a vacuum system as being core flow in which the solids are drawn into a central core resulting in an envelope between the particles and the pipe wall. The same authors [7] have noted that in such systems the particle degradation is lower in a vacuum system than in an equivalent positive pressure system thereby substantiating their argument of a reduction in particle–wall interaction.

By virtue of a difference in gas density between a negative pressure and positive pressure system, a difference in the 'safe' gas velocity required to effect

Table 1.3 Comparison of velocities in pressure and vacuum systems for materials with different bulk densities

Material	Bulk density (kg/m³)	Velocity pressure system (m/s)	Velocity vacuum system (m/s)
Alum	800	19.8	33.5
Calcium carbonate	440	19.8	33.5
Coffee beans	672	13.7	22.9
Hydrated lime	480	12.2	27.4
Malt	449	16.8	30.5
Oats	400	16.8	30.5
Salt	1440	25.3	36.6
Starch	640	16.8	27.4
Sugar	800	18.3	33.5
Wheat	769	16.8	32.0

transportation is noted. In Table 1.3 [8] the difference in velocities can be clearly noted.

It should be noted from Table 1.3 that the transport velocity required for the safe operation of a vacuum system is greater than that required for the equivalent dilute phase positive pressure system.

1.9 PUTTING IT ALL TOGETHER

In an attempt to correlate the various factors described in this chapter, the flow of a gas–solids suspension through a typical pneumatic conveying system will be described.

In Fig. 1.8, a typical system layout including all the necessary components to ensure the transportation of solids from the feeding point to the gas–solids separation zone is shown.

1.9.1 Feeding and acceleration of solids

The solids are stored in a bunker located immediately above some form of feeding device. Downstream of the feeding device is a prime mover capable of providing gas at varying flow rates and pressures.

The solids which are stored in the bunker at atmospheric pressure are essentially at rest and are introduced into the flowing gas. A rapid change in momentum takes place with associated high pressure losses. A length of horizontal pipe is provided long enough to ensure that the particles can be accelerated from rest to some average conveying velocity. There is an acceleration pressure loss associated with the acceleration zone.

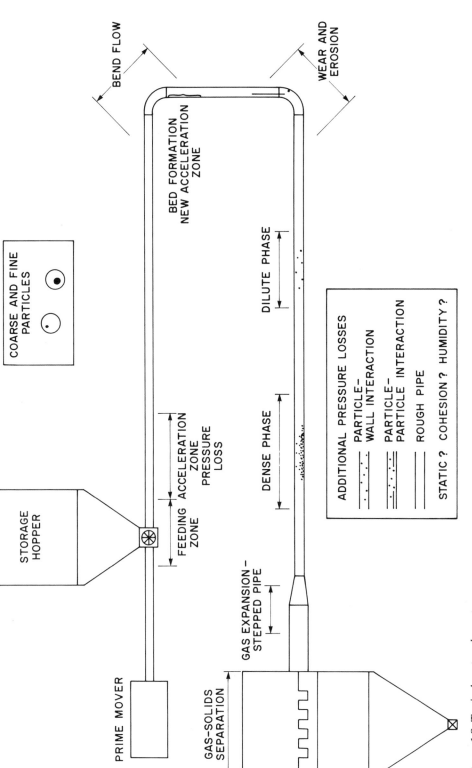

Figure 1.8 Typical system layout.

1.9.2 Factors contributing to pressure losses (Chapters 4, 5 and 6)

Once the particles have been introduced into the flowing gas stream, a number of factors come into effect. Firstly, there is a pressure loss associated with the flowing gas stream, whilst at the same time the solids themselves contribute in a number of ways to an additional pressure loss. In particular, there is a certain amount of particle–wall interaction in which the solids randomly collide with the conveying pipe wall, whilst at the same time such phenomena as particle–particle interactions take place due to the collisions between particles themselves.

In addition, it is not uncommon to find that other factors would influence the flow of the particles. Depending on the nature and the size of the particles and prevailing conditions, such aspects as static electrical forces, cohesive forces, etc. will have some influence on the overall pressure loss in the system.

1.9.3 Coarse and fine particle suspensions

The whole issue of coarse and fine particles is also of significance. There is no single definition which describes the difference between a so-called coarse particle suspension or a fine particle suspension. It has been shown that empirical and theoretical solutions to pneumatic conveying problems involving coarse particle flow cannot readily be applied to fine particle flow. Further, the vast majority of empirical and theoretical assessments have been determined for coarse particle systems. In fine particle systems a number of additional factors come into effect. Depending on the particle size, it is not uncommon for the finer particles to influence the structure of the boundary layer in the gas–solids suspension. There are examples cited in the literature where interactions between fine particle suspensions in the boundary layer have resulted in drag reduction [9, 10]. In such a situation pressure loss observations have shown that it is possible to transport dilute gas–solids suspensions at a lower pressure loss than that required to transport the gas component alone.

An average particle size of $350\,\mu$m [11] is used as the cut-off point in determining the distinction between fine particle and coarse particle suspension. However, the matter is further complicated by the diameter of the conveying pipe. It has been shown [11] that if particles, which under normal circumstances are considered fine, are transported in a small diameter pipe they behave as a coarse particle suspension. As such the so-called d/D relationship is also of importance in categorizing coarse and fine particle suspensions.

1.9.4 Horizontal movement through pipe—bed formation

Depending upon the gas velocity, the product will flow through the pipe either as a fully suspended flow (dilute phase) or flow with the presence of some form of stationary or sliding bed (dense phase).

Visual observation [12] obtained from gas–solids suspensions flowing in a horizontal pipe facilitated the categorization of a number of flow profiles. In

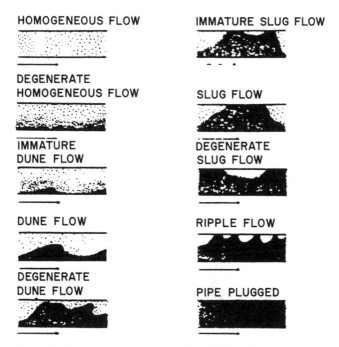

HOMOGENEOUS FLOW

DEGENERATE HOMOGENEOUS FLOW

IMMATURE DUNE FLOW

DUNE FLOW

DEGENERATE DUNE FLOW

IMMATURE SLUG FLOW

SLUG FLOW

DEGENERATE SLUG FLOW

RIPPLE FLOW

PIPE PLUGGED

Figure 1.9 Flow patterns in a horizontal pipe [12].

Fig. 1.9, a series of observed flow profiles is represented. The tests were conducted in a system in which the mass flow of solids was kept constant, whilst gas flow rate was reduced. The descriptive names for each flow pattern have not been linked with any predictive analysis. Further, the advent of such flow patterns is primarily a function of the characteristics of the solids being transported.

Stationary beds are of particular significance in pneumatic conveying systems and it has been shown that stationary beds are formed under a number of conditions.

Observations [13] of stationary bed flow indicate that solids which have been deposited at a higher velocity are more difficult to remove. Pietsch [14] reports the formation of a hard crust on the walls of a pneumatic conveyor. Several factors may account for the influence of velocity [15].

1. A faster moving particle may have a larger area of contact when it comes to rest on the bed of deposited solids because it can deform minute asperities at its contact points plastically on impact. Thus the van der Waals forces holding the particle will be much increased.

2. Because of its longer length of rolling movement over the particle bed, a fast moving particle is likely to come to rest where the bonding forces are particularly strong; it is then suddenly locked into position.

1.9.5 Bend flow (Chapter 4)

As the suspension approaches the first bend in the pipeline, a number of factors come into play. Firstly, it is common knowledge [16] that with single phase gas flow a form of double vortex flow occurs through a bend. By virtue of the presence of the high density solids, this double vortex phenomenon is further accentuated. As such the flow through a bend could consist of a double vortex type flow coupled with a series of impacts as the particle suspension moves its way through the bend. Measurements on a bend [17] have shown that some particles move

Figure 1.10 Hump profile.

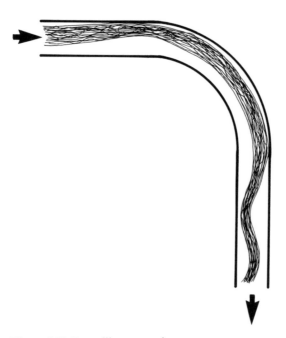

Figure 1.11 Rope like suspension.

through the bend in a zig-zag fashion. On each impact, the velocity of the suspension is reduced. Other particles move through the bend as a sliding bed.

On exit from the bend the suspension velocity can be so significantly reduced that it is quite usual to find a large bed deposit occurring immediately downstream of the bend. The formation of this bed requires the provision of an acceleration zone to facilitate the re-introduction of the solids into the flowing gas stream.

In some situations the shape of the stationary bed within a bend and immediately downstream of a bend is influenced by the double vortex flow phenomenon. A hump profile as shown in Fig. 1.10 is characteristic of a number of stationary beds [18].

By virtue of the double vortex flow at exit from a bend, gas–solids suspensions in dilute phase systems experience the so-called roping phenomenon. In this case the dilute suspension exits from the bend as a waving rope with the majority of particles concentrated in a thin rope-like suspension as shown in Fig. 1.11.

Roping causes a number of major problems in many gas–solids feeding systems. In particular, in coal burning power stations where it is required to split the gas–solids suspension into multiple streams of equal mass flow rate, the roping phenomenon will cause a non-uniform distribution in the multiple ducts. Careful design of the ducting is required to break up the rope to ensure uniform distribution of the gas–solids suspension. Bend flow is complex and is critically dependent upon bend shape, size, etc. .

1.9.6 Stepped piping systems

By virtue of the fact that solids are transported in a gas, it must be appreciated that there is a continual expansion of the gas taking place as the system moves from high pressure to low pressure. The expansion of the gas results in a continuous increase of velocity of solids in the system. In certain situations (long distance systems) it is customary to design the pipeline with an increasing pipe diameter so as to have some control on the final velocity.

1.9.7 Wear in pneumatic conveying systems

Depending upon the nature of the solids and the conveying velocity, a certain amount of wear can take place during the gas–solids transportation process. In particular, the first area which normally wears out is that of a bend. High impact forces at the so-called primary wear point result in the bend wearing out. The whole issue of adequate bend design to ensure minimal downtime as a result of erosion is described elsewhere in this monograph.

1.9.8 Gas–solids separation

The transportation process is terminated in the gas–solids separation zone. Typically the particles are decelerated and are separated from the gas stream by means of either a cyclone or some form of fabric filter. The separated solids are collected in a bunker located at the bottom of the gas–solids separations zone.

1.10 AN OVERVIEW

The selection and design of pneumatic conveying systems is often haphazard, sometimes arbitrary and never scientific. Difficulties arise from the diversity of systems available, the large choice of individual components in a system, the many competing claims of system vendors and a lack of understanding of the physics of the gas–solids flow. The scope of this monograph covers the fundamentals of gas–solids flow, description of hardware, and systems selection, design and operation. The monograph is dedicated to designers, users and vendors of pneumatic conveyors, to researchers in this field and to academics and students in Universities and Technical Colleges. In spite of its growing importance, the teaching of pneumatic conveying is still sadly missing in many undergraduate engineering courses. We hope that this monograph will provide a stimulus to encourage its inclusion in undergraduate curricula.

1.11 SOME USEFUL CONVERSION FACTORS

In order to assist the reader in transferring data based in one system of measurement to another system of units, useful conversion factors have been provided in Tables 1.4 to 1.20.

Table 1.4 Angle

(rad)	g (grade)	° (degree)	′ (minute)	″ (second)
1	63.6620	57.2958	3437.75	206 265
15.7080×10^{-3}	1	0.9	54	3 240
17.4533×10^{-3}	1.11111	1	60	3 600
0.290888×10^{-3}	18.5185×10^{-3}	16.6667×10^{-3}	1	60
4.84814×10^{-6}	0.308642×10^{-3}	0.277778×10^{-3}	16.6667×10^{-3}	1

Table 1.5 Metric system units

Length	Area	Volume	Mass
1 m	$1 \, m^2$	$1 \, m^3$	1 t (tonne)
$= 1 \times 10^1 \, dm$	$= 1 \times 10^2 \, dm^2$	$= 1 \times 10^3 \, dm^3(l)^*$	$= 1 \times 10^3 \, kg$
$= 1 \times 10^2 \, cm$	$= 1 \times 10^4 \, cm^2$	$= 1 \times 10^6 \, cm^3$	$= 1 \times 10^6 \, g$
$= 1 \times 10^3 \, mm$	$= 1 \times 10^6 \, mm^2$	$= 1 \times 10^9 \, mm^3$	$= 1 \times 10^9 \, mg$
$= 1 \times 10^6 \, \mu m$	$= 1 \times 10^{12} \, \mu m^2$		

$*(l) = $ litre (liter am.) is not used in MSU. $10001 = 1 \, m^3$.

Table 1.6 British and American units

Length	Area	Volume	Mass	
			UK	US
1 yd	1 acre	1 yd^3	1 ton	1 sh ton
= 3 ft	= 4 840 yd^2	= 27 ft^3	= 20 cwt	= 20 sh cwt
= 36 in	= 43 560 ft^2	= 46 656 in^3	= 2 240 lbs	= 2 000 lbs
			= 35 840 oz	= 32 000 oz

Table 1.7 Length (ΔL)

m	in (inch)	ft (foot)	yd (yard)	mile	nautical mile
1	39.3701	3.28084	1.09361	0.621371×10^{-3}	
0.0254	1	83.3333×10^{-3}	27.7778×10^{-3}	15.7828×10^{-6}	
0.3048	12	1	0.333333	0.189394×10^{-3}	
0.9144	36	3	1	0.568182×10^{-3}	
1 609.344	63 360	5 280	1 760	1	0.868975
1 852	72 913.4	6 076.12	2 025.37	1.15078	1

Table 1.8 Area (A)

m^2	in^2	ft^2	yd^2	acre	square mile
1	1 550	10.7639	1.19599		
0.64516×10^{-3}	1	6.94444×10^{-3}	0.771605×10^{-3}		
0.092903	144	1	0.111111		
0.836127	1 296	9	1		
4 046.86	6 272 640	43 560	4 840	1	1.5625×10^{-3}
2 589 990	$4 014.49 \times 10^6$	$27 878.4 \times 10^3$	$3 097.6 \times 10^3$	640	1

Table 1.9 Volume (V)

m³	in³	ft³	yd³	gallon (UK Imperial)	gallon (US)
1	61 023.7	35.3147	1.30795	219.969	264.172
16.3871×10^{-6}	1	0.578704×10^{-3}	21.4335×10^{-6}	3.60465×10^{-3}	4.329×10^{-3}
28.3168×10^{-3}	1 728	1	37.037×10^{-3}	6.22884	7.48052
0.764555	46 656	27	1	168.178	201.974
4.54609×10^{-3}	277.420	0.160544	5.94606×10^{-3}	1	1.20095
3.78541×10^{-3}	231	0.133681	4.95113×10^{-3}	0.832675	1

Table 1.10 Density (ρ)

kg/m³	g/cm³	lb/in³	lb/ft³
1	0.001	36.1273×10^{-6}	0.062428
1 000	1	0.0361273	62.428
27 679.9	27.6799	1	1 728
16.0185	0.0160185	0.578704×10^{-3}	1

Table 1.11 Velocity (v)

m/s	km/h	ft/s	mile/h	kn(knot)
1	3.6	3.28084	2.23694	1.94384
0.277778	1	0.911344	0.621371	0.539957
0.3048	1.09728	1	0.681818	0.592484
0.44704	1.609344	1.46667	1	0.868976
0.514444	1.852	1.68781	1.15078	1

Table 1.12 Mass

kg	lb (pound)	slug	oz (ounce)	cwt (hundred weight)	ton (UK)	sh cwt (short hundred weight US)	sh ton (short ton US)
1	2.20462	68.5218×10^{-3}	35.2740	19.6841×10^{-3}	0.984207×10^{-3}	22.0462×10^{-3}	1.10231×10^{-3}
0.45359237	1	31.081×10^{-3}	16	8.92857×10^{-3}	0.446429×10^{-3}	0.01	0.0005
14.5939	32.174	1	514.785	0.287268	14.3634×10^{-3}	0.32174	16.0869×10^{-3}
28.3495×10^{-3}	0.0625	1.94256×10^{-3}	1	0.558036×10^{-3}	27.901810×10^{-6}	0.000625	31.25×10^{-6}
50.8023	112	3.48107	1792	1	0.05	1.12	0.056
1016.05	2240	69.6213	35840	20	1	22.4	1.12
45.359237	100	3.10810	1600	0.892857	44.6429×10^{-3}	1	0.05
907.185	2000	62.1619	32000	17.8571	0.892857	20	1

Table 1.13 Temperature (T)

	Kelvin scale (K)	Celsius scale (°C)	Rankine scale (°R)	Fahrenheit scale (°F)	Physical state
Related temperature values	0	−273.15	0	−459.67	Absolute zero
	255.372	−17.7778	459.67	0	
	273.15	0	491.67	32	Melting point of ice
	273.16	0.01	491.688	32.018	Triple point of water
	373.15	100	671.67	212	Boiling point of water
Related temperature differences	1	1	1.8	1.8	
	0.555556	0.555556	1	1	

$°F = 9/5 \, °C + 32$
$°C = 5/9 \, (°F - 32)$

Table 1.14 Force (F)

N (Newton)	dyn (dyne)	kp (kilopond)	lbf (pound-force)
1	100 000	0.101972	0.224809
0.00001	1	1.01972×10^{-6}	2.24809×10^{-6}
9.80665	980 665	1	2.20462
4.44822	444 822	0.453592	1

Table 1.15 Moment of force ($F \times \Delta L$)

N m	kp m	lbf in	lbf ft
1	0.101972	8.85075	0.737562
9.80665	1	86.7962	7.23301
0.112985	11.5212×10^{-3}	1	83.3333×10^{-3}
1.35582	0.138255	12	1

Table 1.16 Pressure (p)

Pa; N/m²	bar	kp/cm²; atm	kp/mm²	Torr	lbf/m²; psi
1	0.00001	10.1972×10^{-6}	0.101972×10^{-6}	7.50062×10^{-3}	0.445038×10^{-3}
100 000	1	1.01972	10.1972×10^{-3}	750.062	14.5038
98 066.5	0.980665	1	0.01	735.559	14.2233
9 806 650	98.0665	100	1	73 555.9	1422.33
133.322	1.33322×10^{-3}	1.35951×10^{-3}	13.5951×10^{-6}	1	19.3368×10^{-3}
101 325	1.01325	1.03323	10.3323×10^{-3}	760	14.6959
6 894.76	68.9476×10^{-3}	70.307×10^{-3}	0.703070×10^{-3}	51.7149	1

Table 1.17 Energy, work (W)

J Nm, W s	erg	kW h	kp m	kcal	ft lbf (foot pound force)	Btu (British thermal unit)
1	10 000 000	0.277778×10^{-6}	0.101972	0.238846×10^{-3}	0.737562	0.947817×10^{-3}
0.1×10^{-6}	1	27.7778×10^{-15}	10.1972×10^{-9}	23.8846×10^{-12}	73.7562×10^{-9}	94.7817×10^{-12}
3 600 000	36×10^{12}	1	367 098	859 845	2 655 220	3412.14
9.80665	98 066 500	2.72407×10^{-6}	1	2.34228×10^{-3}	7.23301	9.29491×10^{-3}
4186.8	$41 868 \times 10^{6}$	1163×10^{-3}	426.935	1	3088.03	3.96832
1.35582	13 588 200	0.376616×10^{-6}	0.138255	0.323832×10^{-3}	1	1.2857×10^{-3}
1055.06	10.5506×10^{9}	0.293071×10^{-3}	107.586	0.251996	778.169	1

Table 1.18 Power (P)

W Nm/s¹, J/s¹	kp m/s	kcal/s	kcal/h	hp (metric)	hp (UK, US)	ft lbf/s	Btu/h
1	0.101972	0.238846×10^{-3}	0.859845	1.35962×10^{-3}	1.34102×10^{-3}	0.737562	3.41214
9.80665	1	2.34228×10^{-3}	8.43220	13.3333×10^{-3}	13.1509×10^{-3}	7.23301	33.4617
4 186.8	426.935	1	3 600	5.69246	5.61459	3 088.03	14 286
1.163	0.118593	0.277778×10^{-3}	1	1.58124×10^{-3}	1.55961×10^{-3}	0.857785	3.96832
735.499	75	0.175671	632.415	1	0.986320	542.476	2 509.63
745.700	76.0402	0.178107	641.186	1.01387	1	550	2 544.43
1.35582	0.138255	0.323832×10^{-3}	1.16579	1.84340×10^{-3}	1.81818×10^{-3}	1	4.62624
0.293071	29.8849×10^{-3}	69.9988×10^{-6}	0.251996	0.398467×10^{-3}	0.393015×10^{-3}	0.261158	1

Table 1.19 Energy density or specific energy consumption (W/V)

J/m³	kJ/m³ J/dm³ (J/l)	hp min/m³	kW/h m³	hp min/ft³ (hp/cfm)	kW h/ft³
1	0.001	22.6604×10^{-6}	0.277778×10^{-6}	0.632891×10^{-6}	7.86578×10^{-9}
1 000	1	22.6604×10^{-3}	0.277778×10^{-3}	0.632891×10^{-3}	7.86578×10^{-6}
44 129.9	44.1299	1	12.2583×10^{-3}	27.9294×10^{-3}	0.347116×10^{-3}
3 600 000	3 600	81.5773	1	2.27841	28.3168×10^{-3}
1.58005×10^{6}	1 580.05	35.8045	0.438903	1	12.4283×10^{-3}
127.133×10^{6}	127 133	2 880.88	35.3147	80.4613	1

Table 1.20 Viscosity

	Kinematic (v)		Dynamic (η)			
m^2/s	St (stokes)	mm/s cSt	Pa s	MPa s	P (Poise)	cP
1	10 000	1 000 000	1	0.000001	10	1 000
0.000001	0.01	1	1 000 000	1	10 000 000	10^9
0.0001	1	100	0.1	0.1×10^{-6}	1	100
			0.001	10^{-9}	0.01	1

REFERENCES

1. BHRA Fluid Engineering, Cranfield, Bedford, UK (1973) *Pneumatic Transport of Solids in Pipes* (lecture course).
2. Spronson, J.C., Gray, W.A. and Haynes, W. (1979) Pneumatic transport of coal, paper A6, *Proc. 3rd Int. Conf. on Pneumatic Transport of Solids in Pipes*, BHRA Fluid Engineering, Cranfield, Bedford, England.
3. Curten, H.J. (1982) Concept and results of pneumatic conveying of support materials in German underground mining, *Proc. Pneumatech I, International Conference of Pneumatic Conveying Technology*, Powder Advisory Centre, London, 3–5 May.
4. Vogel, R. and Marcus, R.D. (1983) The design of pneumatic shiphold discharge systems, *Bulk Solids Handling*, **3**, No. 4, 861–5.
5. Zenz, F.A. and Othmer, D.F. (1960) *Fluidisation and Fluid Particle Systems*, Reinhold, New York.
6. Engineer Equipment Users Association (1963) *Pneumatic Handling of Powdered Materials*, Constable, London.
7. Kongskilde Maskinfarbrik Als, Denmark.
8. Stoess, H.A. (1983) *Pneumatic Conveying*, John Wiley, New York, pp. 53–62.
9. Pfeffer, R. and Kane, R.S. (1974) A review of drag reduction in dilute gas–solids suspension flow in tubes, Paper F1, *Proc. Int. Conf. on Drag. Reduction*, BHRA Fluid Engineering, Cranfield, UK.
10. Marcus, R.D. (1978) An investigation into the influence of pressure pulsations on the flow characteristics of solids gaseous suspensions, *PhD Thesis*, University of the Witwatersrand, Johannesburg, South Africa.
11. Boothroyd, R.G. (1971) *Flowing Gas–Solids Suspensions*, Chapman and Hall, London, p. 129.
12. Wen, C.Y. (1959) *Flow Characteristics in Solids-Gas Transportation Systems*, US Dept of the Interior, Bureau of Mines, Pennsylvania, IC 8314, pp. 62–72.
13. Meyers, S. (1985) *The State Diagram for Fine Particle Suspensions*, Pneumatic Conveying Association of South Africa.
14. Pietsch, W. (1969) *Trans ASME* (*J. Eng. Ind.*), **91B**, 435.
15. Boothroyd, R.G. (1971) *Flowing Gas–Solids Suspensions*, Chapman and Hall, London, p. 138.

16. Boothroyd, R.G. (1971) *Flowing Gas–Solids Suspensions*, Chapman and Hall, London, p. 155.
17. Boothroyd, R.G. (1971) *Flowing Gas–Solids Suspensions*, Chapman and Hall, London, p. 156.
18. Marcus, R.D. (1974) Drag reducing flow in dilute phase pneumatic conveying, *MSc dissertation*, University of the Witwatersrand, Johannesburg, South Africa.

2
Single phase flow in pneumatic conveying systems

2.1 INTRODUCTION

The design of any pneumatic conveying system requires a basic understanding of air flow in pipes and ducts as well as an appreciation of the various prime movers used to supply air.

2.2 DEFINITIONS

The following definitions will be used in this text.

2.2.1 Free air

Free air is defined as air at the prevailing atmospheric conditions at the particular site in question. The density of air will vary according to site conditions and locality. As such, free air is **not** a standard condition. In Table 2.1 the variation of atmospheric pressure with altitude is provided.

2.2.2 Standard temperature and pressure (STP)

This is defined as air at a pressure of 101.325 kPa (abs) and a temperature of 0 °C. It is customary to assume that 1 bar = 100 kPa (error = 1.3%).

2.2.3 Standard reference conditions (SRC)

This is defined as dry air at a pressure of 101.325 kPa (abs) and a temperature of 15 °C.

2.2.4 Free air delivered (FAD)

This is the volume, rated at the site conditions, which the blower or compressor takes in, compresses and delivers at the specified discharge pressure. The compressor will deliver compressed air having a smaller volume than that at intake.

Table 2.1 Variation of standard atmospheric pressure according to NASA [1]. Values below sea level have been extrapolated

Altitude (m)	Pressure (bar)	Temperature (°C)	Density (kg/m^3)
−1000	1.138	21.5	1.345
−800	1.109	20.2	1.317
−600	1.080	18.9	1.288
−400	1.062	17.6	1.272
−200	1.038	16.3	1.249
0	1.013	15.0	1.225
100	1.001	14.4	1.213
200	0.989	13.7	1.202
300	0.978	13.1	1.190
400	0.966	12.4	1.179
500	0.955	11.8	1.167
600	0.943	11.1	1.156
800	0.921	9.8	1.134
1000	0.899	8.5	1.112
1200	0.877	7.2	1.090
1400	0.856	5.9	1.069
1600	0.835	4.6	1.048
1800	0.815	3.3	1.027
2000	0.795	2.0	1.007
2200	0.775	0.7	0.986
2400	0.756	−0.6	0.966
2600	0.737	−1.9	0.947
2800	0.719	−3.2	0.928
3000	0.701	−4.5	0.909
3200	0.683	−5.8	0.891
3400	0.666	−7.1	0.872
3600	0.649	−8.4	0.854
3800	0.633	−9.7	0.837
4000	0.616	−11.0	0.819
5000	0.540	−17.5	0.736
6000	0.472	−24.0	0.660
7000	0.411	−30.5	0.590
8000	0.356	−37.0	0.525

2.3 PERFECT GAS LAWS

An ideal or perfect gas is one which obeys the laws of Boyle, Charles and Amonton. In practice no gases behave in such a manner and the laws are corrected by taking into consideration *compressibility* factors.

	Boyles' law	Charles' law	Amonton's law
Condition	constant temperature	constant pressure	constant volume
Law	$\dfrac{V_2}{V_1}=\dfrac{p_1}{p_2}$ (2.1)	$\dfrac{V_2}{V_1}=\dfrac{T_2}{T_1}$ (2.2)	$\dfrac{p_2}{p_1}=\dfrac{T_2}{T_1}$ (2.3)

From the above we obtain the following equation:

$$\frac{p_1 V_1}{T_1}=\frac{p_2 V_2}{T_2} \tag{2.4}$$

For an ideal gas we have

$$pV = MRT \tag{2.5a}$$

where R (the gas constant) $= p_o V_o / T_o M$ and

$$\rho = \frac{p}{RT} \tag{2.5b}$$

and the subscript $_o$ stands for STP. Note the following:

(a) 1 kg air at STP has a volume $V_o = 1.292\,\text{m}^3$.
(b) For air $R = 0.287\,\text{kJ/kg/K}$.

2.4 DRYING OF COMPRESSED AIR

All air contains an amount of moisture which is dependent upon the 'site' pressure and temperature conditions. Many pneumatic conveying systems require 'dry' air and as such the designer must ensure that appropriate steps are taken to remove excess moisture.

There are two stages of air drying in a compressed air system: 1. after-cooling; 2. drying. After-cooling the air results in the air temperature being dropped below the dew point (the saturation vapour temperature at which any further decrease in temperature will cause condensation) and collecting the condensate in a trap.

Table 2.2 Cooling systems

Liquid cooled	Air cooled

Air flows through the tubes
or
Cooling water flows through the tubes
Each of the above systems has specific
  advantages and disadvantages
	Forced draught
	
	Induced draught
	Selection is made on an economic basis
	  taking into account both capital and
	  running costs

After-coolers can be categorized into two main types: 1. direct contact 2. surface. Surface after-coolers form the bulk of the systems available and include the types shown in Table 2.2.

Drying of compressed air involves the next stage of processing following the after-cooler. The use of a dryer is to further reduce the moisture content and selection is based solely on the final quality of the air required for the process. There are three basic methods of drying compressed air as detailed in Table 2.3.

After-coolers are least effective with air at low pressure. For large volumetric flow rates at low pressure, driers may have to be used if water is likely to be a hazard.

The interplay between compressing a gas, cooling and expansion is illustrated by means of an example in Section 14.2. The example also demonstrates the use of temperature/mass concentration of water in air curves (Figs 14.1, 14.2).

Table 2.3 Drying systems

Chemical drying	Absorption drying	Refrigeration drying

Deliquescent-chemical
  dissolves as vapour, is
  absorbed and must be
  replaced
	Activated alumina or silica
	  gel is used—normally a
	  dual system is used in
	  which alternative drying
	  and re-activation
	  processes take place
		Direct expansion or
		  non-cyclic type—uses
		  cold refrigerant gas to
		  produce a low temperature

Salt matrix—on exposure
  to hot air the crystal can be
  returned to its original
  form
		Indirect refrigeration or
		  cyclic type—uses a
		  secondary medium such as
		  chilled water to cool the air

Ethylene glycol liquid—
  can be regenerated using
  fuel gas or steam		

2.5 THE COMPRESSION PROCESS

In most modern pneumatic conveying systems it is generally accepted that either reciprocating or screw compressors, or a positive displacement Roots type blower is used as the prime mover. (There are still many low pressure fan systems being installed — but pressures are so low that isothermal criteria can be applied.)

Prime mover	Gas process
Reciprocating compressor (ideal) with water cooling	Isothermal
Positive displacement blower	Adiabatic

Essentially the water-cooled reciprocating compressor compresses air at constant temperature — isothermal. The positive displacement blower compresses the air 'explosively' without time for cooling and compresses the air 'adiabatically', i.e. without the transfer of heat, the energy input from the shaft work is retained in the air.

2.5.1 Isothermal compression

In isothermal compression the product of the pressure and volume remains a constant:

$$pV = \text{constant} = mRT \tag{2.6}$$

from which

$$V = mRT/p \tag{2.7}$$

$$W_t = -\int_1^2 mR(T/p)\mathrm{d}p \tag{2.8}$$

$$= -mRT\ln(p_2/p_1) \tag{2.9}$$

where W_t is the compression work done in joules (J). The amount of heat to be removed from the process is equal to the compression work.

For *fans* and *low pressure blowers*, the term for a pressure range

$$\ln(p_2/p_1) = \int_{p_1}^{p_2} \frac{\mathrm{d}p}{p} \tag{2.10}$$

In this case $p_2 - p_1$ will be small, and the logarithm term can be replaced by the term $(p_2 - p_1)/p_1$ **as long as this ratio does not exceed** 1%. Thus for *fans* and *low pressure blowers*

$$\text{Work} = p_1 V_1\left(\frac{p_2 - p_1}{p_1}\right) = (p_2 - p_1)V_1 \tag{2.11}$$

In these low pressure devices the kinetic energy required to accelerate the air cannot be omitted. In this case the total work per kilogram of gas W_T can be written as

$$W_T = \frac{v_2^2 - v_1^2}{2} + (p_2 - p_1)V_1 \tag{2.12}$$

$$= \text{velocity head} + \text{static head}$$

where v_1 is the initial velocity, v_2 the final velocity and V the specific volume.

2.5.2 Adiabatic compression [2]

In considering the gas law $pV = RT$, if the pressure remains constant whilst the volume changes by dV, the temperature will change by pdV/R. The quantity of heat absorbed for the constant pressure process is the specific heat C_p multiplied by the change in temperature $(C_p pdV/R)$.

Similarly if the pressure changes whilst the volume remains constant, the heat absorbed will be $(C_V Vdp/R)$ where C_V is the specific heat at constant volume.

For both a pressure and a volume change the quantity of heat received by the gas is

$$dQ = \frac{1}{R}(C_p pdV + C_V Vdp) \tag{2.13}$$

For a **adiabatic** process $dQ = 0$ and so

$$C_p pdV + C_V Vdp = 0 \tag{2.14}$$

Therefore

$$\frac{dp}{p} + \frac{C_p}{C_V}\frac{dV}{V} = 0 \tag{2.15}$$

Integrating this equation gives

$$\ln p = \frac{C_p}{C_V}\ln V = \text{constant} \tag{2.16}$$

Now

$$C_p/C_V = \kappa \quad \text{(ratio of specific heats)} \tag{2.17}$$

$$= 1.4 \quad \text{for air}$$

from which

$$pV^\kappa = \text{constant} = p_1 V_1^\kappa \tag{2.18}$$

if

$$p_1 V_1^\kappa = p_2 V_2^\kappa \tag{2.19}$$

or

$$\frac{p_1}{p_2} = \left(\frac{V_2}{V_1}\right)^{\kappa} \tag{2.20}$$

or

$$\frac{V_2}{V_1} = \left(\frac{p_1}{p_2}\right)^{1/\kappa} \tag{2.21}$$

2.5.3 Temperature rise during adiabatic compression

Since

$$p_1 V_1/p_2 V_2 = T_1/T_2 \tag{2.22}$$

eliminating V_2/V_1 gives the temperature rise during adiabatic comparison:

$$\frac{T_2}{T_1} = \left(\frac{p_2}{p_1}\right)^{(\kappa - 1)/\kappa} \tag{2.23}$$

Now the work done in expanding from V_1 to V_2 is

$$\int_{V_1}^{V_2} p\,dV = p_1 V_1 \kappa \int_{V_1}^{V_2} \frac{dV}{V\kappa} = \frac{p_1 V_1 - p_2 V_2}{\kappa - 1} \tag{2.24}$$

from which the work done

$$W = \frac{p_1 V_1}{\kappa - 1}\left[1 - \left(\frac{p_2}{p_1}\right)^{(\kappa - 1)/\kappa}\right] \tag{2.25}$$

when V_2 is unknown.
  Note the following:

1. The above expressions are for the total work done in changing the volume in a **non-flow** process within a cylinder.
2. For steady flow process in reciprocating compressors or positive displacement blowers, the work involved in receiving and delivering the gas and the work required to compress the gas must be taken into account.
3. If $\dot{V}$ is the volume dealt with per minute at p_1 and T_1 then

$$\text{work done per minute (actual)} = (p_2 - p_1)\dot{V} \tag{2.26}$$

4. The ideal compression process from p_1 to p_2 is a **reversible adiabatic** (isentropic) process [3]:

$$\text{work done per minute (ideal)} = \frac{\kappa}{\kappa - 1}p_1\dot{V}\left[\left(\frac{p_2}{p_1}\right)^{(\kappa - 1)/\kappa} - 1\right] \tag{2.27}$$

5.

$$\text{Roots efficiency} = \frac{\text{work done isentropically}}{\text{actual work done}} \tag{2.28}$$

$$= \frac{[\kappa/(\kappa - 1)]p_1\dot{V}(r^{(\kappa - 1)/\kappa} - 1)}{p_1\dot{V}(r - 1)} \tag{2.29}$$

where

$$r = p_2/p_1 = \text{pressure ratio} \tag{2.30}$$

also

$$\kappa/(\kappa - 1) = C_p/R \tag{2.31}$$

therefore

$$\text{Roots efficiency} = \frac{C_p}{R}\left(\frac{r^{(\kappa - 1)/\kappa} - 1}{r - 1}\right) \tag{2.32}$$

6. For a Roots type air blower values of pressure ratio, r, of 1.2, 1.6 and 2 give Roots efficiencies of 0.945, 0.84 and 0.765 respectively. These values show that the efficiency decreases as the pressure ratio increases.
7. In a Roots type blower the volumetric efficiency is a function of the internal leakage, known as 'slip'. Slip arises due to the reverse flow through the internal clearances. It depends upon the leakage area, the intake air density and the pressure difference across the leakage path.
   Slip is expressed as:

$$S = k(\Delta p/\rho)^{1/2} \tag{2.33}$$

where k is a constant for a particular machine, Δp is the pressure difference, ρ is the intake air density, and S is the slip expressed in terms of volumetric flow rate. Slip is independent of the speed of the machine.
8. The polytropic process describes those situations when there is a flow of heat ($dQ \neq 0$). In such circumstances, the adiabatic equations are used but the exponent κ is replaced by the exponent n. For air, $n = 1.3$.

2.5.4 Power requirements

(a) Isothermal compression

The power required for an isothermal compression is

$$P = p_1\dot{V}_1\ln\left(\frac{p_2}{p_1}\right) \tag{2.34}$$

where $\dot{V}_1$ is the volume of gas entering the compressor at suction. For fans, the isothermal power is determined by

$$P = \dot{Q}\left[\frac{1}{m}(p_2 - p_1)V_1 + (v_2^2 - v_3^2)/2\right] \tag{2.35}$$

Or simply

$$\text{air power} = \dot{V}p_{\text{tot}} \tag{2.36}$$

where $\dot{V}$ is the volumetric discharge of the fan per minute and p_{tot} is the total pressure (static + velocity).

(b) Adiabatic compression

$$P = \frac{\kappa}{\kappa - 1}p_1\dot{V}_1\left[\left(\frac{p_2}{p_1}\right)^{(\kappa - 1)/\kappa} - 1\right] \tag{2.37}$$

Since for air $\kappa = 1.4$

$$P = 3.5p_1\dot{V}_1\left[\left(\frac{p_2}{p_1}\right)^{0.286} - 1\right] \tag{2.38}$$

For multistage air compressors with the same inlet temperature at each stage

$$P = 3.5p_1\dot{V}_1\left[\left(\frac{p_2}{p_1}\right)^{0.286/n}\right] \tag{2.39}$$

where n is the number of stages.

In Table 2.4, the power required to compress air is shown as a function of the gauge pressure for single stage, two stage and three stage compressors.

Table 2.4 Power required to compress air [4]

Gauge pressure (bar)	Theoretical adiabatic power kW/100 dm³/s free air		
	Single stage	Two stage	Three stage
0.5	4.0	—	—
1.0	7.5	—	—
2.5	15.0	14	—
5.0	23.0	20	19
7.0	28.0	24	22
10.0	34.0	28	27
14.0	40.0	32	32

Note: 1 bar = 100 kPa

Table 2.5 Effect of altitude on compressor volumetric efficiency [5]

Altitude above sea level (m)	Barometric pressure (mbar)	Percentage relative volumetric efficiency compared with sea level	
		400 kPa	700 kPa
	1013	100.0	100.0
500	945	98.7	97.7
1000	894	97.0	95.2
1500	840	95.5	92.7
2000	789	93.9	90.0
2500	737	92.1	87.0

Compressor volumetric efficiency is dependent upon altitude. The exact location of a compressor must be taken into account when selecting a suitable machine. In Table 2.5 the effect of altitude on compressor volumetric efficiency is shown for 400 kPa and 700 kPa applications.

2.6 GAS FLOW THROUGH PIPES

The flow of gas through pipes forms an essential element of any pneumatic conveying system. In most systems, plant layouts dictate that the compressor is located some distance from the feeder. A piping system is required to connect the compressor to the feeder. Further, in order to design the actual pneumatic conveyor, an understanding of the behaviour of the gas flow through the total system is essential.

2.6.1 Types of flow

There are two basic types of flow in a pipe: (a) laminar; (b) turbulent.

(a) Laminar flow

This is characterized by streamlined concentric cylindrical layers of fluid flowing past one another in an orderly fashion. The velocity is greatest at the centre of the pipe and decreases sharply at the wall or boundary layer.

(b) Turbulent flow

This is characterized by an irregular random movement of fluid particles across the main stream without an observable frequency or pattern.

The exact limit of laminar and turbulent flow is defined by the Reynolds number (Re);

$$Re = \frac{\rho v D}{\eta} = \frac{v D}{v} \qquad (2.40)$$

where ρ is the density of fluid, v the fluid velocity, D the pipe diameter, and η the dynamic viscosity of the fluid ($N\,s/m^2$). (Viscosity in gases rises with temperature, within moderate ranges of pressure (3500 kPA) viscosity is not influenced by more than 10%.) v is the kinematic viscosity (m^2/s).

In Fig. 2.1, the variation of dynamic viscosity of air with temperature is shown for various pressures. Useful data for air at various temperatures are given in Table 2.6.

Note that a useful method of calculating the dynamic viscosity of air is by using

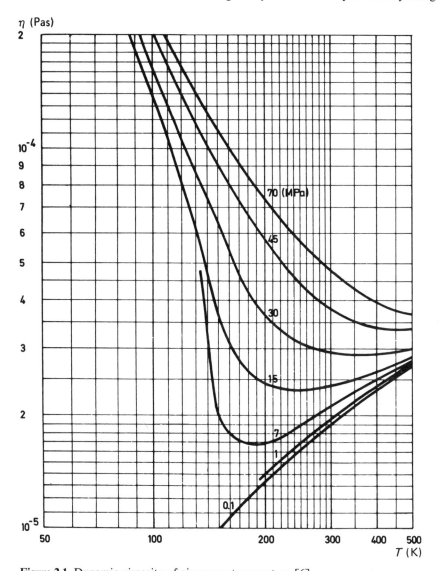

Figure 2.1 Dynamic viscosity of air versus temperature [6].

Table 2.6 Data for air as a function of temperature [8]

$T(°C)$	-20	0	20	40	60	80	100	200
$\rho(kg/m^3)$	1.4	1.29	1.2	1.12	1.06	1	0.95	0.746
$\eta(10^{-6} N\,s/m^2)$	16.24	17.16	18.12	18.93	20	20.9	21.95	26.11
$v(10^{-6} m^2/s)$	11.6	13.3	15.1	16.9	18.9	20.9	23.1	35.0
e.g. at $20°C$, $v = 15.1 \times 10^{-6} m^2/s$								

Rayleigh's criterion

$$\eta_1/\eta_o = (T_o/T_1)^{0.75}$$

where at sea level

$$\eta_o = 1.783 \times 10^{-5}\, N\,s/m^2$$

$$T_o = 288.16\,K$$

2.6.2 Pipe roughness

The absolute roughness (k) of many types of pipe materials has been approximated. A factor known as relative roughness is used to relate the internal surface conditions of a pipe to its diameter, using the ratio (k/D). Charts relating the relative roughness to the pipe diameter are available. For turbulent flow $Re > 2300$; for laminar flow $Re < 2300$. In most cases, for pressure piping the flow is turbulent.

2.6.3 General pressure drop formula

The following general formula for pressure in piping was developed by Darcy:

$$\Delta p = \lambda_L \rho L v^2 / 2D \tag{2.41}$$

where λ_L is the friction factor and L the pipe length (metres).

(a) Friction factor laminar flow

In the range $0 < Re < 2300$ the friction factor:

$$\lambda_L = 64/Re \tag{2.42}$$

(b) Friction factor turbulent flow

For turbulent flow, the friction factor can be found from Fig. 2.2 relating the friction factor to the Reynolds number.

For compressed air pipework, the following equation for the pressure drop (Δp) in a straight pipe can be used with good approximation [7]:

$$\Delta p = 1.6 \times 10^3 \dot{V}^{1.85} L / (D^5 p_1) \tag{2.43}$$

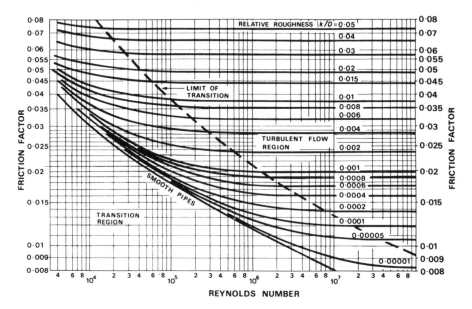

Figure 2.2 Friction factor versus Reynolds number.

where Δp is the pressure drop (Pa), $\dot{V}$ is volumetric flow rate (m³/s), L is pipe length (m), D is pipe diameter (m), p_1 is initial pressure (Pa). In equation (2.43) the temperature in the pipe is assumed to be the same as the ambient temperature. For practical situations, it can be assumed that $\lambda_L \simeq 0.02$ within a wide range, provided that $Re > 10\,000$.

There are several methods of obtaining the gas friction factor. The reader should be cautious in noting that there is a difference in definition resulting in a factor of 4 when using the Fanning friction factor (f_L) as distinctly from the friction factor (λ_L) used in the text.

For simplicity, it is recommended that the Blasius equation [8] or the Koo equation [9] be used. For $Re < 10^5$ the Blasius equation [8] states:

$$\lambda_L = 0.316/(Re)^{0.25} \qquad (2.44)$$

The Koo equation [9] for f is given by

$$f_L = 0.0014 + 0.125/(Re)^{0.32} \qquad (2.45)$$

Note that $\lambda_L = 4f_L$.

A set of curves (Fig. 2.3) produced using the Blasius equation (2.44) provides a quick method of obtaining the pressure loss for various air flow rates. For easy reference, Table 2.7 provides information pertaining to the volume of air which

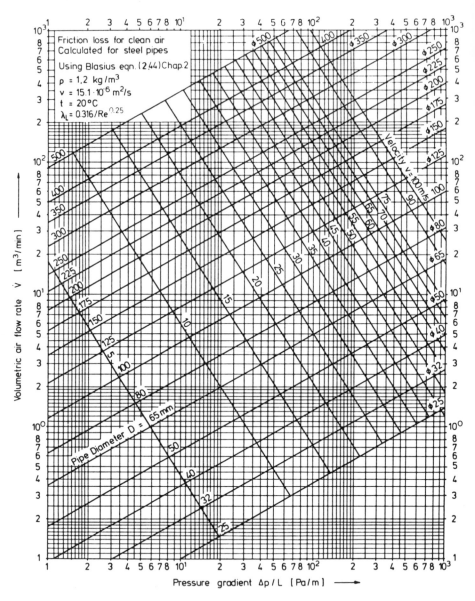

Figure 2.3 A set of curves produced using the Blasius equation.

can be carried by various sizes of pipes at given velocities. (It is common practice to size compressed air mains in a velocity range 6–9 m/s).

2.6.4. Resistance due to pipe fittings

In a system layout where a complex pipe layout is required, it is essential that the pressure losses generated by pipe fittings are taken into account. This practice is

Table 2.7 Volume of compressed air carried by medium grade steel pipes, of minimum bore, to **BS 1387**, at given velocities [9]

Velocity, v ($\mathrm{m\,s^{-1}}$)	Volume of air (10^{-3} m/s) through medium grade steel pipe, to **BS**, minimum bore, D (mm)											
	15	20	25	32	40	50	65	80	100	125	150	200
3.0	0.6	1.1	1.7	3.0	4.1	6.5	10.9	15.1	25.7	39.2	56.2	98.5
3.5	0.7	1.3	2.0	3.5	41.7	7.6	12.7	17.6	30.0	45.7	65.5	115.0
4.0	0.8	1.4	2.3	4.0	5.4	8.7	14.6	20.1	34.2	52.2	74.9	131.0
4.5	0.9	1.6	2.6	4.5	6.1	9.8	16.4	22.6	38.5	58.8	84.2	147.0
5.0	1.0	1.8	2.8	5.0	6.8	10.8	18.2	25.1	42.8	65.4	93.6	164.0
5.5	1.1	2.0	3.1	5.5	7.4	11.9	20.0	27.6	47.1	71.9	103.0	181.0
6.0	1.2	2.1	3.4	6.0	8.1	13.0	21.8	30.1	51.3	78.5	112.0	197.0
6.5	1.3	2.3	3.7	6.5	8.8	14.1	23.7	32.6	55.6	85.0	122.0	213.0
7.0	1.4	2.5	4.0	7.0	9.5	15.1	25.5	35.1	59.9	91.5	131.0	230.0
7.5	1.5	2.7	4.3	7.5	10.1	16.2	27.3	37.6	64.2	98.0	140.0	246.0
8.0	1.6	2.8	4.5	8.0	10.8	17.3	29.1	40.1	68.5	105.0	150.0	263.0
8.5	1.7	3.0	4.8	8.5	11.5	18.4	31.0	42.6	72.8	111.0	159.0	278.0
9.0	1.8	3.2	5.1	9.0	12.2	19.5	32.8	45.1	77.1	118.0	169.0	296.0

e.g. for $v = 3$ m/s and $D = 100$ mm, $V = 25.7 \times 10^{-3}\,\mathrm{m^3/s}$

Table 2.8 Resistance of pipe fittings (equivalent length in m) [10]

					Nominal pipe size (mm)					
Type of fitting	15	20	25	32	40	50	65	80	100	125
Elbow	0.26	0.37	0.49	0.67	0.76	1.07	1.37	1.83	2.44	3.2
90° bend (long)	0.15	0.18	0.24	0.38	0.46	0.61	0.76	0.91	1.2	1.52
Return bend	0.46	0.61	0.76	1.07	1.2	1.68	1.98	2.6	3.66	4.88
Globe valve	0.76	1.07	1.37	1.98	2.44	3.36	3.96	5.18	7.32	9.45
Gate valve	0.107	0.14	0.18	0.27	0.32	0.40	0.49	0.64	0.91	1.20
Run of standard tee	0.12	0.18	0.24	0.38	0.40	0.52	0.67	0.85	1.2	1.52
Through side outlet of tee	0.52	0.70	0.91	1.37	1.58	2.14	2.74	3.66	4.88	6.40

especially pertinent to low pressure air supply lines. Allowances for losses due to fittings can be accounted for by finding an equivalent length in metres for typical fittings. Table 2.8 gives the equivalent lengths for fittings in relation to pipe diameter.

2.7 ILLUSTRATIVE EXAMPLES

Example 2.1 Standard reference conditions (SRC)

A flow rate of $100 \, \text{m}^3/\text{min}$ is rated at SRC. Determine the equivalent free air flow rate at a site with atmospheric pressure $p_{atm} = 84 \, \text{kPa}$ (abs) and temperature $T = 25 \, ^\circ\text{C}$.

From equation (2.4):

$$\frac{p_1 \dot{V}_1}{T_1} = \frac{p_2 \dot{V}_2}{T_2}$$

In this example:

$$\frac{101.325 \, (100)}{273 + 15} = \frac{84 \, (\dot{V}_2)}{273 + 25}$$

Therefore

$$\dot{V}_2 = 124.8 \, \text{m}^3/\text{min (FAD)}$$

The above conversion could also have been made using the density ratio. From equation (2.5):

$$pV = mRT$$

(for air $R = 0.287 \, \text{kJ/kg/K}$). By definition density, $\rho = p/RT$

$$\rho = \begin{cases} 1.293 \, \text{kg/m}^3 & \text{at STP} \\ 1.225 \, \text{kg/m}^3 & \text{at SRC} \end{cases}$$

The 'site' density in this example:

$$\rho = \frac{84}{0.287 \times 298} = 0.98 \, \text{kg/m}^3$$

$$\dot{V}_2 = \frac{100 \times 1.225}{0.98} = 125 \, \text{m}^3/\text{min (FAD)}$$

Example 2.2 Effect of altitude on blower performance

A Roots type blower is selected at sea level conditions with an intake volume of $50 \, \text{m}^3/\text{min}$ and a pressure rise $90 \, \text{kPa}$. Temperature at site is $25 \, ^\circ\text{C}$. Determine the blower's power requirements at both sea level and at an altitude of $1500 \, \text{m}$.

(a) At sea level

The intake density $\rho = 1.18\,\text{kg/m}^3$. The slip for such a blower size $\dot{V}_s = 11.7\,\text{m}^3/\text{min}$. The displacement required would be

$$\dot{V} = 50 + 11.7 = 61.7\,\text{m}^3/\text{min}$$

A typical machine would have a speed $n = 1270\,\text{rev/min}$.
  Power required (from equation (2.38)) is

$$P = 3.5 \times 100 \times \frac{61.7}{60}\left[\left(\frac{190}{100}\right)^{0.286} - 1\right]$$

$$= 72.5\,\text{kW}$$

Temperature rise (from equation (2.23)) is

$$T_2 = T_1\left(\frac{p_2}{p_1}\right)^{(\kappa - 1)/\kappa}$$

$$= 298\left(\frac{190}{100}\right)^{0.286} = 358\,\text{K}$$

Therefore $t_2 = 85\,^\circ\text{C}$.

(b) At 1500 m above sea level

$p_{atm} = 84.5\,\text{kPa (abs)}$, $t = 25\,^\circ\text{C}$, intake density $\rho = 0.99\,\text{kg/m}^3$. For this machine slip $\dot{V}_s = 12.8\,\text{m}^3/\text{min}$. The displacement required to maintain $50\,\text{m}^3/\text{min}$

$$\dot{V} = 50 + 12.8 = 62.8\,\text{m}^3/\text{min}$$

This blower would be speeded up to $1280\,\text{rev/min}$. The power (from equation (2.38)) is

$$P = 3.5 \times 84.5 \times \frac{62.8}{60}\left[\left(\frac{174.5}{84.5}\right)^{0.286} - 1\right]$$

$$= 71.3\,\text{kW}.$$

Example 2.3 Air processes, Roots type blower

1. Determine the work input for a Roots type blower having an induced volume of $0.03\,\text{m}^3/\text{rev}$. The inlet pressure is 1.013 bar and the pressure ratio 1.5:1.

$$p_1 = 1.013\,\text{bar}$$

$$p_2 = 1.013 \times 1.5 = 1.52\,\text{bar}$$

From equation (2.26)

> Actual work done per revolution
> $$= (p_2 - p_1) \dot{V}_1$$
> $$= (1.52 - 1.013) \times 0.03 \times 10^5 = 1521 \, \text{J}$$
> $$= 1.52 \, \text{kJ (where 1 bar} = 10^5 \, \text{N m}^2)$$

2. In (1), determine the Roots efficiency.

From equation (2.27)

> Work done isentropically per revolution
> $$= \frac{\kappa}{\kappa - 1} p_1 \dot{V}_1 \left[\left(\frac{p_2}{p_1} \right)^{(\kappa - 1)/\kappa} - 1 \right]$$
> $$= \frac{1.4}{0.4} \times 1.013 \times 10^5 \times 0.03 \times [(1.5)^{0.4/1.4} - 1]$$
> $$= 1.3063 \times 10^3 \, \text{J}$$

From equation (2.28)

$$\text{Roots efficiency} = \frac{1.31}{1.52} = 86.2\%$$

3. If the inlet temperature to the blower is 15 °C, determine the final temperature after compression in degrees Celsius.

From equation (2.23)

$$T_2 = T_1 \left[\frac{p_2}{p_1} \right]^{(\kappa - 1)/\kappa}$$
$$= 288(1.5)^{0.4/1.4} = 323 \, \text{K}$$

Therefore

$$t_2 = 50 \, °\text{C}$$

Example 2.4 Power required for compression

1. If a compressor is rated at $14 \, \text{m}^3/\text{min}$ and compresses air from 100 kPa to 800 kPa, determine the power required.

For isothermal compression, from equation (2.34)

$$P = 100 \times 10^3 \times \frac{14}{60} \ln \left(\frac{800}{100} \right)$$
$$= 48.5 \, \text{kW}$$

2. If a positive displacement blower is rated to compress $14\,\mathrm{m^3/min}$ of free air to $100\,\mathrm{kPa}$, determine the power required.

For adiabatic compression, from equation (2.37)

$$P = 3.5 \times 100 \times 10^3 \times \frac{14}{60}\left[\left(\frac{200}{100}\right)^{0.286} - 1\right]$$

$$= +17.9\,\mathrm{kW}$$

Example 2.5 Pressure loss in a pipe system

Determine the pressure loss in a piping system consisting of a length $L = 200\,\mathrm{m}$ and a diameter $D = 70\,\mathrm{mm}$. The air flow rate $\dot{V} = 170\,\mathrm{dm^3/s}$ (free air), and initial pressure $p_1 = 800\,\mathrm{kPa}$ at an ambient temperature $t = 20\,^{\circ}\mathrm{C}$.

Take atmospheric pressure $p_{\mathrm{atm}} = 100\,\mathrm{kPa}$. From continuity $\dot{V} = Av$, where A is the cross sectional area of pipe $(\mathrm{m^2})$, v is velocity $(\mathrm{m/s})$ and $\dot{V}$ is volumetric flow rate $(\mathrm{m^3/s})$. The velocity at inlet to the pipe (given $\dot{V} = 170\,\mathrm{dm^3/s}$ (free air), is

$$v = (100/800) \times 0.17 \times 4/\pi \times 0.07^2$$

$$= 5.525\,\mathrm{m/s}$$

From tables the dynamic viscosity of the air is $18.08 \times 10^{-6}\,\mathrm{Ns/m^2}$ at $293\,\mathrm{K}$. The density of the air at inlet to the pipe:

$$\rho_1 = p_1/RT_1$$

$$= 800 \times 10^3/(287 \times 293)$$

$$= 9.51\,\mathrm{kg/m^3}$$

from which the Reynolds number (equation (2.40)) is

$$Re = 9.51 \times 5.53 \times 0.07 \times 10^6/18.08$$

$$= 203\,500$$

Using equation (2.43) the pressure loss is

$$\Delta p = 1.6 \times 10^3 \times 0.17^{1.85} \times 200/(0.07^5 \times (800 \times 10^3))$$

$$= 8972\,\mathrm{Pa}$$

Assuming $\lambda_L = 0.02$ and using equation (2.41) (since $Re > 10\,000$)

$$\Delta p = 0.02 \times 9.5135 \times 200 \times 5.525^2/(2 \times 0.07)$$

$$= 8297\,\mathrm{Pa}$$

from which it can be seen that in spite of some simplifying assumptions, equation (2.43) can be used with confidence. The pressure loss calculated using equation (2.43) is higher than that calculated using equation (2.41).

Example 2.6 Calculation of Reynolds number Re and gas friction factor λ_L

Given pipes of $D = 50$ and $100\,mm$ and gas velocities $v = 1$, 10, 20 and $40\,m/s$, calculate the Reynolds number and the corresponding gas friction factors λ_L and f_L, i.e. using the Blasius and Koo equations.

Reynolds number $Re = vD/v$. At $t = 20\,°C$, $v = 15.1 \times 10^{-6}\,m^2/s$. At $v = 1\,m/s$ and $d = 50\,mm$

$$Re = \frac{1 \times 0.05}{15.1} \times 10^6$$

$$= 3.31 \times 10^3$$

Friction factors: (a) Blasius

$$\lambda_L = 0.316/Re^{0.25}$$

$$= 0.04166$$

(b) Koo

$$f_L = (0.014 + 0.125)Re^{0.32}$$

$$= 0.0107$$

$$\lambda_L = 4f_L = 4 \times 0.0107 = 0.0429$$

Table 2.9 Calculation of friction factors λ_L and f_L using the Blasius and Koo equations

D(mm)	50	50	50	50	100	100	100	100
v(m/s)	1	10	20	40	1	10	20	40
$Re \times 10^{-3}$	3.31	33.1	66.2	132.00	6.62	66.2	132.00	264.00
λ_L (Blasius)	0.0417	0.0234	0.0197	0.0166	0.035	0.0197	0.0166	0.0139
f_L (Koo)	0.0107	0.0059	0.0049	0.0043	0.0089	0.0049	0.0043	0.0037
$4f_L$	0.0429	0.0235	0.0199	0.01071	0.0355	0.0199	0.0171	0.0148

Note that $\lambda_L = 4f_L$. Table 2.9 gives results calculated using the Blasius and Koo equations.

REFERENCES

1. (1975) *Atlas Copco Air Compendium*, Atlas Copco AB, Stockholm, Sweden, p. 38.
2. Kraus, M.N. (1980) *Pneumatic Conveying of Bulk Materials*, McGraw-Hill, New York, pp. 37–40.
3. Eastop, T.D. and McConkey, A. (1970) *Applied Thermodynamics for Engineering Technologists*, Longman, London, p. 70.
4. (1978) *Compressed Air*, Spirax Sarco Information Book IB 12, Spirax Sarco Ltd, p. 3.
5. (1978) *Compressed Air*, Spirax Sarco Information Booklet IB 12, Spirax Sarco Ltd, p. 5.
6. (1975) *Atlas Copco Air Compendium*, Atlas Copco AB, Stockholm, Sweden, p. 587.
7. (1975) *Atlas Copaco Air Compendium*, Atlas Copco AB, Stockholm, Sweden, p. 587.
8. Schlichting, H. (1960) *Boundary Layer Theory*, 4th edn, McGraw-Hill, New York.
9. Klinzing, G. E. (1981) *Gas Solid Transport*, McGraw-Hill, New York.
10. (1978) *Compressed Air*, Spirax Sarco Information Booklet IB 12, Spirax Sarco Ltd, p. 19.

3
Fluid and particle dynamics

3.1 INTRODUCTION

In pneumatic conveying, particles are generally in suspension in a turbulent gas stream. The question of drag on a single particle, and the effects of Reynolds number, particle shape and roughness, voidage, turbulence intensity and scale of turbulence, acceleration, etc. on drag are relevant to pneumatic conveying. These factors will be discussed in this chapter. Equations for calculating important properties such as drag coefficient, terminal velocity, minimum fluidization velocity, and the equation for flow through a packed bed are presented. The characteristics of a powder in terms of its fluidization behaviour are relevant to pneumatic conveying, and will also be discussed.

3.2 LAW OF CONTINUITY

In most cases air is used as the conveying medium. For safety conditions nitrogen or any other gas can be used. In these special cases closed loops (Section 1.6.4) are used in order to circulate these gases and only the losses will be supplemented. One of the major problems in pneumatic conveying is that of gas expansion. This means that gas density and gas velocity change downstream from the product intake until the end of the duct.

For the air alone situation, the air mass flow rate is constant for the total length provided that there is no leakage. The air mass flow rate is given by

$$\dot{Q} = \dot{V}\rho = Av\rho = \text{constant} \tag{3.1}$$

where

$$\rho = p/(RT) \tag{3.2}$$

and p stands for the local static pressure. R is the gas constant and T the absolute temperature (Section 2.3). The pressure is given by

$$p = p_{\text{o}} \pm \Delta p_{\text{g}} \tag{3.3}$$

p_{o} is barometric pressure and $\Delta p_{\text{g}} =$ gauge pressure. Values of the gas constant for air and nitrogen are

$$R = \begin{cases} 287.3 \text{ J/kg K} & \text{air} \\ 296.8 \text{ J/kg K} & \text{N}_2 \end{cases}$$

t is the ambient temperature in °C, i.e.

$$T = (273 + t) \text{ K} \tag{3.4}$$

3.3 DRAG ON A PARTICLE

3.3.1 The standard drag coefficient curve

Studies of the magnitude of drag force on spheres in steady motion in a fluid date back to Newton's experiments in 1710. In general the drag force F is expressed by

$$F = C_D \frac{\rho}{2} w^2 A^* \tag{3.5}$$

$$= C_D \frac{\rho}{2} (v_\varepsilon - c)^2 A^*$$

where w is the relative velocity between the gas and the solid, A^* the projected area normal to flow and C_D the drag coefficient.

For a spherical particle the cross-sectional area normal to flow, A^*, can be expressed in terms of its diameter d giving

$$F = C_D \frac{\rho}{2} w^2 \frac{\pi d^2}{4} \tag{3.6}$$

A simple dimensional analysis would show that C_D is a function of the particle Reynolds number ($Re_p = wd/v$), where v is the kinetic viscosity. For a spherical particle moving in an unbounded stationary fluid, the form of the relationship between C_D and Re_p is known as 'the standard drag coefficient curve' [1]. This is curve A in Fig. 3.1. The drag coefficient for a single particle in an unbounded fluid is denoted here as $C_{D\infty}$.

Referring to Fig. 3.1, the standard drag curve can be conveniently divided into four regions:

1. Stokes' law regime (creeping flow regime) with $Re_p < 2.0$

$$C_{D\infty} \simeq 24 Re_p^{-1} \tag{3.7}$$

2. Intermediate region, with $0.5 < Re_p < 500$, first studied by Allen [2],

$$C_{D\infty} = 18.5 Re_p^{-0.6} \tag{3.8}$$

3. Fully developed turbulence regime (Newton's law region), with $500 < Re_p < 2 \times 10^5$

$$C_{D\infty} \simeq 0.44 \tag{3.9}$$

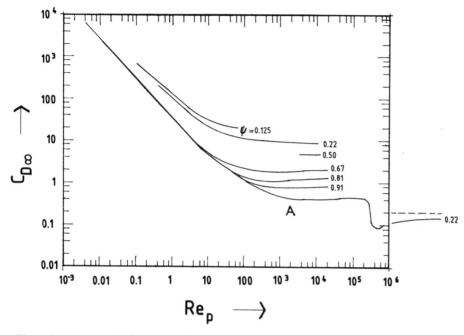

Figure 3.1 Drag coefficient curves for particles with different sphericity (after [10]).

4. Turbulent boundary layer region (or supercritical regime) with

$$Re_p \geqslant 2 \times 10^5$$
$$C_{D\infty} \simeq 0.1 \text{ increasing slowly with } Re_p$$

(3.10)

The onset of the supercritical regime is characterized by a sharp drop of drag coefficient from about 0.4 to 0.1. The Reynolds number at $C_{D\infty} = 0.3$ is conveniently defined as the critical Reynolds number. Few systematic studies have been reported on drag in the supercritical regime [3] although it is known that the magnitude of the critical Reynolds number is sensitive to the presence of free stream turbulence in the flowing fluid and is sensitive to the rate of acceleration of a particle in non-steady state flow.

A large number of theoretical and empirical equations other than equations (3.7) to (3.9) are available in the literature to represent the standard drag curve up to and including the Newton's law region. These have been reviewed and discussed by Boothroyd [4], Soo [5], LeClair, Hamielec and Pruppacher [6], and Clift and Gauvin [7]. The following equation proposed by Clift and Gauvin [8] is based on a modification of the earlier equation of Schiller and Nauman [9] and is applicable over the entire range of Re_p up to 10^5:

$$C_{D\infty} = (24/Re_p)(1 + 0.15Re_p^{0.687}) + 0.42/(1 + 4.25 \times 10^4 Re_p^{-1.16}) \quad (3.11)$$

Another equation which is applicable over the whole range of Reynolds number is the often used equation due to Kaskas [10]:

$$C_{D\infty} = 24/Re_p + 4/Re_p^{0.5} + 0.4 \tag{3.12}$$

Equation (3.11) fits the standard drag curve of Lapple and Shepherd with a maximum deviation of 4%. Equation (3.12) is simpler to use and deviates more from the standard drag curve at high Re_p. The use of either equation is recommended here.

In Section 3.4.2 equation (3.11) will be used to derive equations for calculating terminal falling velocity of a single particle.

3.3.2 Effect of shape on drag

For non-spherical particles the standard drag curve is no longer applicable. For creeping flow theoretical equations describing drag coefficient for various arbitrary shapes are available [11]. The shape of irregular particles is best defined by a 'shape factor'. A number of shape factors are in common use and these have been reviewed by Allen [12] and Zenz and Othmer [13]. For drag of a particle in a fluid, the most often used shape factor is the sphericity, ψ, defined by:

$$\psi = \frac{\text{surface area of sphere with same volume as particle}}{\text{surface area of particle}}$$

If d_v denotes the equivalent volume diameter of a particle (i.e. $V = \pi d_v^3/6$) and s is its area, then

$$\psi = \pi d_v^2/s \tag{3.13}$$

ψ has the value of 1 for a spherical particle and $0 < \psi < 1$ for non-spherical particles.

The specific surface diameter d_{vs} is the diameter of a sphere having the same ratio of surface area to volume as the particle. It can readily be shown that the ratio d_{vs}/d_v is equal to the sphericity ψ.

Values of ψ for some materials are given in Table 3.1 [14]. Drag coefficient as a function of Re_p for various values of ψ is presented in Fig. 3.1 [15]. Note that volume equivalent diameter is used here in the definition of Re_p. It should be stressed that the relation of $C_{D\infty}$ as a function of ψ is an approximate one. A single shape factor does not completely define the shape of a particle. Thus particles with the same sphericity may have different shapes and their $C_{D\infty}$ versus Re_p relationship will be different.

While the choice of sphericity is recommended here as an appropriate shape factor for use in the present applications, it should be pointed out that there are other possibilities [16].

Another method for estimating the effect of sphericity is through its effect on

Table 3.1 Data on sphericity ψ [14]

Material	ψ
Sand	0.534–0.861
Iron catalyst	0.578
Bituminous coal	0.625
Pulverized coal	0.696
Celite cylinders	0.861
Broken solids	0.63
Silica	0.554–0.628

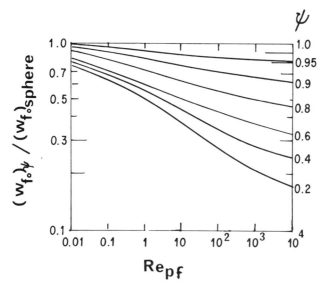

Figure 3.2 Effect of particle shape on terminal settling velocity. $Re_{pf} = \rho d w_f / \eta$, (after Govier and Aziz [15]).

free fall velocity. Figure 3.2 from Govier and Aziz [15] may be used to calculate the free fall velocity of a particle with a given sphericity from a knowledge of the free fall velocity of a spherical particle of the same volume equivalent diameter. Calculation of free fall velocity (or terminal velocity) is described in Section 3.4.2. Further discussion, pertaining to more recent investigations into particle shape analysis, is covered in Section 4.1.

3.3.3 Effect of fluid turbulence

The standard drag curve shown in Fig. 3.1 refers to the motion of a smooth sphere at constant velocity through an otherwise undisturbed and unbounded fluid. In pneumatic conveying, particles are entrained generally in a turbulent fluid. In this case the drag coefficient is dependent not only on the particle Reynolds number, but also the characteristics of the turbulence in the gas stream, and we can write

$$C_{D\infty} = f(Re_p, I_R, \lambda_t/d) \tag{3.14}$$

Where I_R is the relative turbulence intensity defined by $(v_y^2/w)^{1/2}$ and λ_t is the spatial macroscale. v_y is the fluctuating fluid velocity component in the direction of mean motion. Although there is ample experimental evidence that turbulence can change the drag coefficient markedly, the results reported in the literature are confusing. The literature falls into two categories:

1. Early wind tunnel measurements in fixed spheres with low $I_R (0 \leqslant I_R \leqslant 0.05)$ and high $Re_p (10^5 \leqslant Re_p \leqslant 10^6)$[17–20].
2. More recent measurements with freely moving spheres at lower Re_p and I_R up to 0.4[3, 21–23].

The work of Zarin [24] is intermediate between the above two groups in that the spheres are magnetically suspended in an air stream with $200 \leqslant Re_p \leqslant 5000$ and $0 \leqslant I_R \leqslant 0.13$.

There is no quantitative agreement among any of these authors, but qualitatively the critical Reynolds number decreases with increase in turbulence intensity, and drag is increased by the presence of turbulence at subcritical

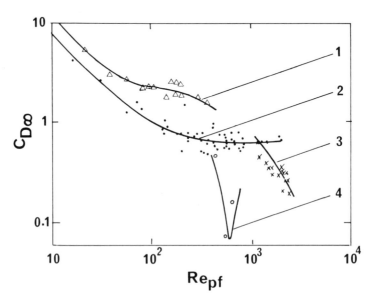

Figure 3.3 Comparison of typical results from different workers (after Uhlherr and Sinclair [22]). 1, $I_R = 0.4$ [22]; 2, $I_R = 0.1$ [22]; 3, $I_R = 0.1$ [21]; 4, $I_R = 0.4$ [21].

Reynolds number. The decrease in critical Reynolds number $(Re_p)_{crit}$ can be very marked. Torobin and Gauvin [21] reported $(Re_p)_{crit}$ down to 400 at $I_R = 0.4$ compared with 2×10^5 at $I_R = 0$ and they suggested the following empirical equation for correlating their results:

$$(Re_p)_{crit} I_R^2 = 45 \tag{3.15}$$

The effect of spatial macroscale on drag appears to be insignificant, particularly in the range of $(\lambda_t/d) > 1$ [23, 24].

An illustration of the conflicting results reported in the literature is illustrated in Fig. 3.3 which compares the measured $C_{D\infty}$ from different workers. It can be seen that considerable uncertainty exists in the estimation of $C_{D\infty}$ in a turbulent fluid. This will lead to uncertainty in predicting relative velocity between a particle and a gas in dilute phase pneumatic conveying.

3.3.4 Effect of voidage/solid concentration

Voidage is an important parameter in multiphase flow. Essentially voidage describes the volume between the particles in a given volume element or the volume of the pipe section occupied by the carrier gas alone. As such, a suspension with a voidage at almost one, will be extremely dilute. Voidage is thus defined by:

$$\varepsilon = \frac{\rho_p - \rho_m}{\rho_p - \rho} \tag{3.16}$$

A full discussion on voidage is provided in Section 4.11.

The standard drag coefficient curve shown in Fig. 3.1 refers to a single particle in an unbounded fluid with a voidage of one. It is generally recognized that drag increases with increase in particle concentration (i.e. decrease in voidage (Section 4.11)). A number of experimental and theoretical studies in drag for flow through an assemblage of fixed spheres of different geometry and different voidage has been reported in the literature [25–37]. Further, drag coefficient can also be inferred from liquid–solid fluidization and sedimentation measurements in which particles are mobile [33–37] and from measurements of pressure drop for flow through a packed bed [38, 39].

The reported experimental results show that drag coefficient of a particle in a fixed assemblage is generally larger than that in a mobile particle at the same voidage such as a fluidized or sedimenting bed [29, 32, 33].

For flow through a packed bed of spheres pressure drop is related to velocity by the Ergun equation [38]:

$$\frac{\Delta p}{\Delta Z} = 150 \frac{(1-\varepsilon)^2}{\varepsilon^3} \frac{\eta v}{(\psi d_v)^2} + 1.75 \frac{1-\varepsilon}{\varepsilon^3} \frac{\rho v^2}{\psi d_v} \tag{3.17}$$

Equation (3.17) can be expressed in terms of the drag coefficient of a particle in a packed bed, $C_{D\varepsilon}$, defined in terms of superficial gas velocity, v, i.e.

$$\text{Drag force} = F_\varepsilon = C_{D\varepsilon}\frac{\rho}{2}v^2 A^* \tag{3.18}$$

where v' is the superficial gas velocity. From equations (3.17) and (3.18) the following equation for drag coefficient of a particle in a packed bed can readily be derived:

$$C_{D\varepsilon} = \frac{200(1-\varepsilon)}{Re'_p\varepsilon^3} + \frac{7}{3\varepsilon^3} \tag{3.19}$$

where $Re'_p = vd/v$ based on superficial velocity.

Equation (3.19) may be used for quantitative determination of the effect of voidage on drag coefficient within a range of voidage up to about 0.6 [5]. Predictions from equation (3.19) are presented in Fig. 3.4. It should be cautioned that equation (3.19) should not be used at voidage higher than about 0.6.

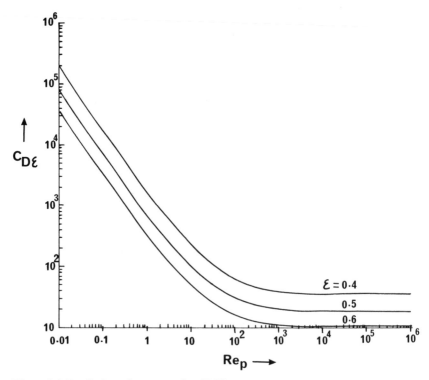

Figure 3.4 Predictions from equation (3.19).

Another source of guidance on the effect of voidage on drag is the theoretical solution of LeClair and Hamielec [32] for a fixed assemblage of equally spaced spheres in space. Experimental results for different forms of assemblage are given by Gunn and Malik [29].

For mobile particles, Wen and Yu [36] assumed that $(C_{D\varepsilon}/C_{D\infty})$ is dependent only on voidage. By correlating the results in fluidization and sedimentation empirically they proposed the following relationship for estimating the effect of voidage on drag coefficient for mobile particles:

$$C_{D\varepsilon} = \varepsilon^{-4.7} C_{D\infty} \qquad (3.20)$$

where $C_{D\varepsilon}$ is the drag coefficient on a single particle at voidage ε defined in equation (3.18) and $C_{D\infty}$ is the drag coefficient at infinite dilution (i.e. $\varepsilon = 1$). Using the Schiller–Naumann [9] equation for describing $C_{D\infty}$, Wen and Yu suggested that equation (3.20) is applicable to a particle Reynolds number up to 10^3, the limit of applicability of the Schiller–Naumann equation. It can readily be shown that if the Clift and Gauvin [8] equation (3.11) is used to describe $C_{D\infty}$, the range of applicability of equation (3.20) is extended to a much higher particle Reynolds number. In pneumatic conveying, drag on a mobile particle is more relevant than drag on a fixed particle. Equation (3.20) is useful in estimating particle velocities in pneumatic conveying [40, 41].

It should be pointed out that in deriving equation (3.20) the effect of fluid turbulence has not been considered. The interactive effects of turbulence and voidage on drag of a flowing particle are complex [4, 5, 42–48] and will not be treated here.

3.3.5 Effect of acceleration

When a particle is accelerating (or decelerating) in a fluid, it experiences drag forces which may be considerably different to those experienced in steady motion. The acceleration effect was originally explained in terms of the 'added mass' concept, derived from potential flow theory, in which the effect of particle acceleration on the fluid is assumed to be equivalent to a fixed mass of fluid accelerated with the particle [49]. Although this concept has some value for describing low Reynolds number motion, its use above the intermediate Reynolds number regime can be both inaccurate and misleading [7]. It is generally preferable to treat the acceleration effect in terms of an instantaneous total drag coefficient, C_{DA}, from experimental measurements or from theoretical treatments.

Our understanding of the effect of acceleration, except at very low Reynolds number [11] is, however, far from complete. No clear pattern emerges from published results. For accelerating motion, we can write

$$C_{DA} = F(Re_p, M_A, M_D, I_R, \rho_p/\rho) \qquad (3.21)$$

where

M_A = acceleration modulus, $(dc/dt)d/w^2$
M_D = displacement modules, x/d where x is distance moved by particle from rest
I_R = relative turbulence intensity

In addition to the factors on the right-hand side of equation (3.22), C_{DA} is also dependent on whether a particle is accelerating or decelerating.

The apparently conflicting results reported in the literature can be explained by the fact that not all the relevant factors have been considered. The confusion is compounded by the effect of acceleration in merely modifying the flow field around a particle and the effect in changing the flow regime by altering the critical Reynolds number. Thus Lunnon [49] reported increase of C_{DA} with acceleration of falling particles while Ingebo [50] found greatly reduced C_{DA} values for accelerating particles entrained in a gas stream. Painter [51] correlated his results for accelerating spheres by:

$$C_{DA} = 7.5 Re_p^{-0.233} M_A^{0.836} I_R^{-0.150} \qquad (3.22)$$

By contrast, Wang [52] correlated his results for decelerating spheres by

$$C_{DA} = 0.34 + 5.426 M_A^{0.313} I_R^{0.642} \qquad (3.23)$$

While there is evidence that the drag coefficient of an accelerating particle, C_{DA}, is in general higher than that predicted by the standard drag curve at the same Reynolds number, the overall picture is confusing. In the light of such confusion, calculations in pneumatic conveying are generally carried out with the assumption that acceleration has no effect on the drag coefficient [4, 41]. Comprehensive reviews of the effect of acceleration on drag are available elsewhere [7, 21].

3.3.6 Miscellaneous other effects

The drag on a particle is also affected by a number of other factors including roughness of surface, wall effect, rotation and orientation of the particle, and electrostatic effects. These will be considered briefly here.

(a) Roughness

The main effect of surface roughness is that it decreases the critical Reynolds number. However, in the presence of fluid turbulence, the effect of surface roughness is not clear [7].

(b) Particle rotation

Torobin and Gauvin [21] reviewed the effect of particle rotation on drag and concluded that at large Reynolds number, the effect is small. This is not consistent with the suggestion that for large ρ_p/ρ, rotational effects are insignificant [53].

(c) Wall effect

A considerable amount of literature is available on wall effect on particle drag [11]. In the Stokes law region, the following equations of Ladenburg [54] and Francis [55] can be used to estimate C_{DW}, the drag coefficient of a single particle in a tube of diameter D where wall effects are significant:

$$C_{DW}/C_{D\infty} = (1 + 2.4d/D)^2 \qquad \text{(Ladenburg's equation)} \qquad (3.24)$$

or

$$C_{DW}/C_{D\infty} = (1 - d/D)^{-4.5} \qquad \text{(Francis' equation)} \qquad (3.25)$$

In the intermediate Reynolds number regime $C_{DW}/C_{D\infty}$ is also a function of the particle Reynolds number [56–58]. In the turbulent regime Munroe's equation [59] obtained for $900 \leqslant Re_p \leqslant 11\,000$ can be used:

$$C_{DW}/C_{D\infty} = [1 - (d/D)^{1.5}]^{-2} \qquad (3.26)$$

In pneumatic conveying, wall interference effects are often not important compared with interference effects between neighbouring particles except for flow near a wall. Equations (3.24) to (3.26) refer to flow of particles in the axis of a tube and will be of little relevance when a particle flows near the wall of the tube.

(d) Electrostatic effect

The force on particles due to the electrostatic charge they carry is often important in pneumatic conveying, particularly when the particles are small and the conveying air is dry. The subject of electrodynamics of particles has been reviewed at great length by Soo [5]. There is some evidence that electrostatic charge may significantly increase pressure drop in pneumatic conveying [60, 61] although the mechanism through which the increase occurs is not entirely clear.

3.4 EQUATIONS FOR CALCULATION OF RELEVANT PROPERTIES

In Section 3.3 the question of drag of a single particle is discussed. This is used here to consider the calculation of properties relevant to pneumatic conveying.

3.4.1 Air velocity

Due to the compressibility of the flowing gas, it is preferable to calculate the local air velocity from the air mass flow rate equation (3.1), i.e.

$$v = \dot{Q}/(A\rho)$$

where

$$\rho = p/(RT) \qquad (3.27)$$

and

$$T = (273 + t) \qquad t \text{ in } °C \qquad (3.28)$$

3.4.2 Terminal velocity for a particle

(a) Spherical particles

The terminal velocity (or free fall velocity) of a single sphere can be estimated by equating drag and buoyancy forces with gravitational force giving,

$$C_{D\infty}\frac{\rho}{2}w_{fo}^2\frac{\pi d^2}{4} = (\rho_p - \rho)\frac{g\pi d^3}{6} \tag{3.29}$$

or

$$C_{D\infty} = \frac{4\rho d^3(\rho_p - \rho)g}{3\eta^2 Re_{pf}^2} = \frac{4d(\rho_p - \rho)}{3w_{fo}^2\rho}g \tag{3.30}$$

$$w_{fo} = \left(\frac{4}{3}\frac{d}{C_{D\infty}}\frac{\rho_p - \rho}{\rho}g\right)^{1/2} \tag{3.31}$$

Combining equation (3.30) with (3.11) yields the following general equation for estimating the terminal velocity of a single sphere:

$$Ga = 18Re_{pf}(1 + 0.15Re_{pf}^{0.687}) + 0.315Re_{pf}^2/(1 + 4.25 \times 10^4 Re_{pf}^{-1.16}) \tag{3.32}$$

where $Re_{pf} = \rho w_{fo}d/\eta$ and Ga, the Galileo number, is given by

$$Ga = \rho(\rho_p - \rho)gd^3/\eta^2 = \rho\Delta\rho gd^3/\eta^2$$

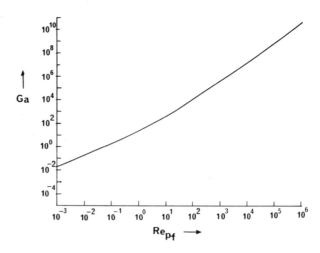

Figure 3.5 Graphical solution for equation (3.32).

Table 3.2 Terminal velocity of spheres of unit specific gravity in air at 20 °C and 1 atm

d (μm)	w_f (m/s)
0.2	1.25×10^{-6}
0.3	4.2×10^{-6}
0.5	10×10^{-6}
1.0	35×10^{-6}
2.0	128×10^{-6}
3.0	275×10^{-6}
5.0	780×10^{-6}
10	3.0×10^{-3}
20	12×10^{-3}
30	27×10^{-3}
50	72×10^{-3}
100	250×10^{-3}
200	750×10^{-3}
300	1.15
500	2.00
1000	3.85

where η represents the dynamic viscosity. A graphical solution for equation (3.32) is given in Fig. 3.5 from which the terminal velocity of different size spheres in atmospheric air is calculated and given in Table 3.2.

An alternative method to calculate w_{fo} is to combine one of the drag coefficient equations (i.e. equations (3.7) to (3.10)) with equation (3.31) to give equations (3.33) to (3.36). In the Stokes regime

$$w_{fo} = \frac{d^2(\rho_p - \rho)g}{18\eta} \tag{3.33}$$

$$Re_{pf} < 2.0$$

For the intermediate regime

$$w_{fo} = \frac{0.153g^{0.71}d^{1.14}(\rho_p - \rho)^{0.71}}{\rho^{0.29}\eta^{0.43}} \tag{3.34}$$

$$0.5 < Re_{pf} < 500$$

In Newton's regime

$$w_{fo} = 1.74\left(\frac{d(\rho_p - \rho)g}{\rho}\right)^{0.5}$$ (3.35)

$$500 < Re_{pf} < 2 \times 10^5$$

For the supercritical regime

$$w_{fo} = 3.65\left(\frac{d(\rho_p - \rho)g}{\rho}\right)^{0.5}$$ (3.36)

$$Re_{pf} > 2 \times 10^5$$

The calculation procedure involves using one of the above equations to obtain w_{fo} and to calculate Re_{pf} to check that the correct equation has been used as demonstrated in Section 3.4.2.1.

(b) Non-spherical particles

To estimate the free fall velocity of a non-spherical particle, we need to calculate the free fall velocity of a spherical particle with the same volume. Correction for shape effect can then be carried out in one of two ways:

(i) Using Fig. 3.2 to yield the ratio $(w_{fo})_\psi/(w_{fo})_1$, where

$(w_{fo})_\psi$ = free fall velocity of particle with sphericity of ψ
$(w_{fo})_1$ = free fall velocity of spherical particle of same volume.

(ii) Using the following empirical equation (3.37):

$$(w_{fo})_\psi/(w_{fo})_1 = 0.843 \log(\psi/0.065)$$ (3.37)

The use of both methods will be demonstrated in Section 3.4.2.1 to illustrate the uncertainties of estimating $w_{f,\psi}$.

3.4.2.1 Worked examples on free fall velocity

Calculate the terminal velocity in air (atmospheric pressure and 20 °C) of a particle with density 1300 kg/m³ with a volume equivalent diameter of 150 μm: (i) for a spherical shape particle; and (ii) for a particle with a shape factor of 0.8. At atmospheric pressure and 20 °C the density of air, $\rho = 1.2\,kg/m^3$ and the viscosity of air, $\eta = 1.78 \times 10^{-5}\,kg/(m\,s)$.

(a) Spherical particle

$$Ga = \rho(\rho_p - \rho)gd^3/\eta^2$$

$$= 1.2(1300 - 1.2) \times 9.8 \times (150 \times 10^{-6})^3/(1.78 \times 10^{-5})^2$$

$$= 163$$

From Fig. 3.5 or equation (3.32)

$$Re_{pf} = 6.0 = \rho w_{fo}/(d/\eta)$$

$$w_f = 6.0 \times 1.78 \times 10^{-5}/(1.2 \times 150 \times 10^{-6})$$

$$= 0.59 \text{ m/s}$$

Alternative method

Assume equation (3.33) is applicable (Stoke's regime); therefore

$$w_{fo} = \frac{(\rho_p - \rho)gd^2}{18\eta}$$

$$= \frac{(1300 - 1.2) \times 9.8 \times (150 \times 10^{-6})^2}{18 \times 1.78 \times 10^{-5}}$$

$$= 0.89 \text{ m/s}$$

Check Re_{pf}:

$$Re_{pf} = \frac{1.2 \times 0.89 \times 150 \times 10^{-6}}{1.78 \times 10^{-5}}$$

$$= 9.0$$

This is outside the range for equation (3.33) to be applicable.
Assume equation (3.34) is applicable (intermediate regime):

$$w_{fo} = \frac{0.153 \times 9.8^{0.71} \times (150 \times 10^{-6})^{1.14} \times (1300 - 1.2)^{0.71}}{1.2^{0.29} \times (1.78 \times 10^{-5})^{0.43}}$$

$$= 0.77 \text{ m/s}$$

Check Re_{pf}:

$$Re_{pf} = \frac{1.2 \times 0.77 \times 150 \times 10^{-6}}{1.78 \times 10^{-5}}$$

$$= 7.8$$

and is within the range of applicability of equation (3.34). Hence 0.77 m/s is acceptable.

Summary of w_{fo} calculations for spherical shape:

From equation (3.32)   0.59 m/s

From equation (3.34)   0.77 m/s

The difference is caused by the use of different empirical equations to fit the standard drag curve given in Fig. 3.1.

(b) Non-spherical particle

Using a value of $w_{fo} = 0.59$ m/s for the spherical particle, we shall illustrate below, two methods for calculating w_{fo} for a particle with the same volume equivalent diameter (150 μm) and a shape factor of $\psi = 0.8$.

From Fig. 3.2 for $\psi = 0.8$ and $Re_{pf} = 0.6$:

$$(w_{fo})_\psi/(w_{fo})_1 = 0.62$$
$$(w_{fo})_\psi = 0.62 \times 0.59$$
$$= 0.37 \text{ m s}^{-1}$$

From equation (3.37)

$$(w_{fo})_\psi = [0.843 \log (\psi/0.065)](w_{fo})_1$$
$$= [0.843 \log (0.8/0.065)] \times 0.59$$
$$= 0.54 \text{ m s}^{-1}$$

The above examples illustrate some of the uncertainties in estimating w_{fo}.

3.4.3 Pressure drop through a packed bed

A large number of equations are available for predicting pressure gradient for flow of a fluid through a bed of granular materials. Perhaps the most often used is the Ergun equation [38]:

$$\frac{\Delta p}{\Delta Z} = 150 \frac{(1-\varepsilon)^2}{\varepsilon^3} \frac{\eta v}{(\psi d_v)^2} + 1.75 \frac{1-\varepsilon}{\varepsilon^3} \frac{\rho v^2}{\psi d_v} \qquad (3.17)$$

In streamline flow the first term on the right-hand side of equation (3.17) predominates, giving

$$\frac{\Delta p}{\Delta Z} = 150 \frac{(1-\varepsilon)^2}{\varepsilon^3} \frac{\eta v}{(\psi d_v)^2} \qquad \text{for } \frac{\rho v(\psi d_v)}{\eta} < 20 \qquad (3.38)$$

In turbulent flow at high Reynolds number the second term on the right-hand side of equation (3.17) predominates, giving

$$\Delta p/\Delta Z = 1.75(1-\varepsilon)\rho v^2/\varepsilon^3(\psi d_v) \qquad \text{for } \rho v(\psi d_v)/\eta > 1000 \qquad (3.39)$$

Equation (3.17) is claimed to predict pressure drop to within $\pm 25\%$ for a randomly packed bed at a voidage of below about 0.6. At higher voidages the actual pressure drop can be significantly greater than that predicted by the Ergun equation.

For a bed of mixed-size and mixed-shape particles, a volume-surface mean diameter should be used in the Ergun equation as defined by,

$$\Psi \bar{d}_v = \left(\sum^{\text{all } i} [x_i/(\Psi_i d_{vi})] \right)^{-1} \tag{3.40}$$

where x_i = volume or weight fraction of particles with d_{vi} and sphericity Ψ_i.

If the particles of the different size fraction are similar in shape $\Psi_i = \bar{\Psi}$. In general

$$\Psi \bar{d}_v = \bar{\Psi} \left(\sum^{\text{all } i} (x_i/d_{vi}) \right)^{-1} \tag{3.41}$$

Equation (3.17) is written in the integrated form assuming constant fluid density along the entire packed bed. For low pressure drop, the equation can be applied using the density of the gas at the arithmetic average of the end pressure. When the pressure drop is large or the absolute pressure is low, the variation in gas density can be accounted for by writing the Ergun equation in differential form as

$$\frac{dp}{dZ} = K_1 \frac{G_f}{\rho} + K_2 \frac{G_f^2}{\rho} \tag{3.42}$$

where $G_f = \rho v$ and is a constant along the entire length of column

$$K_1 = 150(1-\varepsilon)^2 \eta/\varepsilon^3 (\Psi d_v)^2 \tag{3.43}$$

$$K_2 = 1.75(1-\varepsilon)/\varepsilon^3 \Psi d_v \tag{3.44}$$

Equation (3.42) can readily be integrated by expressing ρ in terms of pressure and assuming either isothermal or adiabatic conditions. For isothermal flow, for instance,

$$\frac{p_2^2 - p_1^2}{2\Delta Z} = \frac{K_1 G_f + K_2 G_f^2}{(RT/M)} M \tag{3.45}$$

For adiabatic flow, we have

$$p_2^{(\kappa-1)/\kappa} - p_1^{(\kappa-1)/\kappa} = \frac{\kappa+1}{\kappa} \frac{\Delta Z}{p_1^{(\kappa-1)/\kappa}} (K_1 G_f + K_2 G_f^2) \frac{RT_1}{M} \tag{3.46}$$

where

$$\kappa = C_p/C_V. \tag{3.47}$$

(a) A worked example for flow through a packed bed

Calculate the pressure gradient across a packed bed of particles with the
following size distribution at a superficial air velocity of 0.002 m/s.

With diameter smaller than d_v (μm)	Cumulative weight (%)
	0
20	10
40	40
60	75
105	92
150	100

Sphericity of particles = 0.8. Calculate mean particle size from equation (3.40):

Diameter range (μm)	d_{vi}	x_i	x_i/d_{vi} ($1/\mu$m)
20–40	30	1.0	0.00333
40–60	50	0.30	0.00600
60–80	70	0.35	0.00500
80–105	93	0.17	0.00183
105–150	128	0.08	0.00063
		$\Sigma(x_i/d_{vi}) =$	0.01679

$$\bar{d}_v = (\Sigma(x_i/d_i))^{-1} = 1/0.01679 = 60\ \mu\text{m}$$

Assume

$$\text{voidage of packed bed} = 0.35$$
$$\rho = 1.2\,\text{kg/m}^3$$
$$\eta = 1.78 \times 10^{-5}\,\text{kg/(m s)}$$

From equation (3.17)

$$\Delta p/\Delta Z = 150(1 - 0.35)^2 \times 1.78 \times 10^{-5} \times 0.002/[0.35^3(0.8 \times 60 \times 10^{-6})]^2$$
$$+ 1.75(1 - 0.35) \times 1.2 \times 0.002^2/(0.35^3 \times 0.8 \times 60 \times 10^{-6})$$
$$= 2.8\,\text{kPa/m}$$

3.4.4 Minimum fluidization velocity

When a gas is passed upwards through a stationary bed or granular material at increasing gas velocity, the pressure drop across the bed increases until it is sufficient to support the particles and the particles are said to be fluidized. The gas velocity at the onset of fluidization is defined here as the minimum fluidization velocity, v_{min}. If the bed voidage at the onset of fluidization, ε_{mf}, and the shape factor of the particles are known, the minimum fluidization velocity can be calculated by equating the right-hand side of the Ergun equation (3.17) with the apparent by weight of the particles, giving,

$$150\frac{(1-\varepsilon_{mf})^2}{\varepsilon_{mf}^3}\frac{\eta v_{min}}{(\bar{\psi}\bar{d}_v)^2} + 1.75\frac{(1-\varepsilon_{mf})}{\varepsilon_{mf}^3}\frac{\rho v_{min}^2}{\bar{\psi}\bar{d}_v} = (1-\varepsilon_{mf})(\rho_p - \rho)g \qquad (3.48)$$

Equation (3.48) permits the calculation of the minimum fluidization velocity v_{min} and can be further simplified as in equations (3.38) and (3.39) to give, for

$$\rho v_{min}\bar{\psi}\bar{d}_v/\eta < 20$$

$$v_{min} = \frac{\varepsilon_{mf}^3}{150(1-\varepsilon_{mf})}\frac{(\rho_p - \rho)g}{\eta}(\bar{\psi}\bar{d}_v)^2 \qquad (3.49)$$

and for

$$\rho v_{min}\bar{\psi}\bar{d}_v/\eta > 1000$$

$$v_{min}^2 = \frac{\varepsilon_{mf}^3}{1.75}\frac{(\rho_p - \rho)}{\rho}g\bar{\psi}\bar{d}_v \qquad (3.50)$$

Often data for ψ and ε_{mf} are not readily available. Wen and Yu [36] showed that for a large variety of systems,

$$14\psi\varepsilon_{mf}^3 = 1$$

and

$$(1-\varepsilon_{mf}) = 11\psi^2\varepsilon_{mf}^3$$

Equation (3.48) can then be simplified as

$$v_{min}d_v\rho/\eta = [33.7^2 + 0.0408d_v^3\rho(\rho_p - \rho)g/\eta^2]^{0.5} - 33.7 \qquad (3.51)$$

$$Re_{mf}' = [33.7^2 + 0.0408Ga']^{0.5} - 33.7 \qquad (3.52)$$

where Ga' and Re_{mf}' are defined in terms of the volume equivalent diameter (not specific surface equivalent diameter).

While a large number of equations are available in the literature for predicting

v_{min}, equation (3.52) is one of the most reliable and is claimed to predict v_{min} with a standard deviation of $\pm 34\%$ [36]. Its use is recommended here. Equation (3.52) is applicable to multi-size particles, provided the correct mean particle diameter described by equation (3.40) is used [62]. It is worth pointing out that equation (3.49) correctly predicts that the addition of a small amount of fines to a coarse material can significantly reduce the minimum fluidization velocity. Detailed discussion on the effect of size distribution on minimum fluidization velocity is available in the literature [63].

Often in design, a very reliable estimate of the minimum fluidization velocity is required. This can be obtained by experimental determination at a given condition and the result can be extrapolated to another operating condition (such as different temperature and pressure) using equation (3.49) or (3.50). The test rig required for the minimum velocity measurement has been described by Weber [64].

(a) A worked example on minimum fluidization velocity

Calculate the minimum fluidization velocity, v_{min}, for the silica alumina catalyst with volume-surface mean diameter of 75 μm and ψ of 0.8. Particle density is 1300 kg/m^3, $\varepsilon_{mf} = 0.35$, density and viscosity of air are 1.2 kg/m^3 and 1.78×10^{-5} kg/m/s respectively.

Solution 1.

Assume that $Re_{mf} < 20$, so that equation (3.49) applies:

$$V_{min} = \frac{(0.35)^3}{150(1-0.35)} \frac{(1300-1.2) \times 9.81}{1.78 \times 10^{-5}} (0.8 \times 75 \times 10^{-6})^2$$

$$= 1.1 \times 10^{-3} \text{ m/s}$$

Check

$$Re_{mf} = \frac{1.2 \times 1.1 \times 10^{-3} \times 60 \times 10^{-6}}{1.78 \times 10^{-5}}$$

$$= 4.4 \times 10^{-4} < 20$$

Solution 2.

v_{min} can be calculated directly from equation (3.48). Thus,

$$\frac{150(1-0.35)^2}{(0.35)^2} \frac{1.78 \times 10^{-5} v_{min}}{(0.8 \times 75 \times 10^{-6})^2} + \frac{1.75(1-0.35)}{(0.35)^3} \frac{1.2 v_{min}^2}{0.8 \times 75 \times 10^{-6}}$$

$$= (1-0.35)(1300-1.2)9.81$$

This is simplified to a quadratic equation which can be solved to give

$$v_{min} = 1.1 \times 10^{-3} \text{ m/s}$$

3.4.5 Relationship between v_{min} and w_{fo}

A number of workers have attempted to correlate v_{min} with w_{fo} [65–67] and this was reviewed by Richardson [68]. From equation (3.32) we have Re_{pf} as a function of Ga, while in equation (3.48) Re_{mf} can be expressed as a function of Ga and ε_{mf}. The two equations can be combined to yield

$$w_{fo}/v_{min} = f(Ga, \varepsilon_{mf}) \tag{3.53}$$

Figure 3.6 shows the relationship represented by equation (3.53) for various values of ε_{mf}. Measured ratio of w_{fo}/v_{min} varies from 9 to 90 and is in reasonable agreement with the prediction from equation (3.53). Fig. 3.6 may be useful to give approximate estimation of w_{fo} or v_{min} if experimental data for v_{min} or w_{fo} are available respectively. Alternatively, the following equations due to Bourgeois and Grenier [67] may be used for air–solid systems:

(a) For $10^2 < Ga < 4 \times 10^4$

$$w_{fo}/v_{min} = 135.7 - 45.0 \log Ga + 4.1 (\log Ga)^2 \tag{3.54}$$

(b) For $4 \times 10^4 < Ga < 8 \times 10^6$

$$w_{fo}/v_{min} = 26.6 - 2.3 \log Ga \tag{3.55}$$

(c) For $8 \times 10^6 < Ga$

$$w_{fo}/v_{min} = 10.8 \tag{3.56}$$

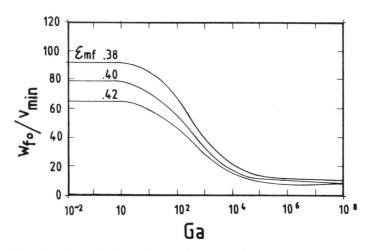

Figure 3.6 Ratio of terminal velocity to minimum fluidization velocity w_{fo}/v_{min} versus Galileo number $[\rho(\rho_p - \rho)gd^3/\eta^2]$ for various ε_{mf} (after Richardson [68]).

3.5 FLUIDIZATION CHARACTERISTICS OF POWDERS

In dense phase pneumatic conveying and in the feeding device of a pneumatic conveyor, the ease with which the material can be handled depends on the 'fluidization characteristics' of the powder. Materials are described loosely as 'fluidizable' or 'difficult to fluidize'. These properties are qualitatively assessed by: (i) the occurrence of severe channelling in a fluidized bed; (ii) whether bubbles are formed at a velocity immediately above the minimum fluidization velocity; and (iii) whether bubbles grow indefinitely with bed height and fluidization velocity (see Section 3.4.5).

Geldart [69, 70] attempted to quantify the fluidization properties of a powder and proposed four classes of solids, depending mainly on particle diameter and density and to a minor degree on gas density and viscosity. Geldart's classification is given in Fig. 3.7 and discussed below:

1. Group A powders are those where the bed expands considerably when the fluidization velocity is increased above the minimum fluidization velocity before gas bubbling commences. If v_{mb} is defined as the minimum fluid velocity at which bubbling occurs, group A powder is characterized by

$$v_{mb}/v_{min} > 1$$

Group A powder has been described as 'aeratable'. If the fluidizing gas is shut

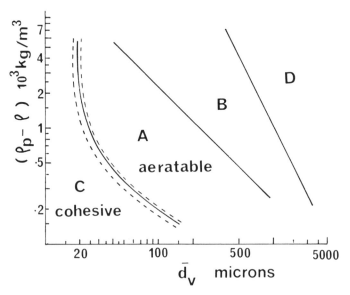

Figure 3.7 Fluidizing characteristics of powders (after Geldart [69]).

off suddenly in a fluidized bed of this type of powder, the bed collapses slowly (at rates of 3 to 6 mm/s). When the fluidization velocity is high enough to cause slugging the slugs are axisymmetric. For discharge from a hopper, group A solids have the tendency to 'flood' unless suitable precaution is taken.

2. Group B powders are those where bed expansion is small when the fluidization velocity is increased above the minimum fluidization velocity. Bubbles start to form in the bed at or at slightly above v_{min}, i.e.

$$v_{mb}/v_{min} \simeq 1$$

The bed of group B powders collapses very rapidly when the fluidization gas is turned off suddenly. With these powders, bubbles increase in size rapidly with bed height and fluidizing gas velocity. Group B powder has been termed 'sandy' as many sands are in this group.

3. Group C powders are the fine cohesive powders in which interparticle forces are comparable to or greater than the drag force exerted by the fluidizing gas. The interparticle forces could be caused by electrostatic charges or the presence of moisture or sticky material. Such powders are hard to fluidize and if fluidized in a small diameter column, the whole bed tends to rise *en bloc* with a void rising below it. This type of void is known as the square nose bubbles [71] as against the round nose bubbles and slugs. Stirring or vibration of the bed will be necessary to promote proper fluidization.

4. Group D particles are of large size and/or large density. The demarcation between group B and group D is diffuse. With group D powders, stable spouting can be maintained if the fluidizing gas is introduced through a centrally positioned hole. Thus group D particles have been referred to as 'spoutable powders' [69].

The fluidization properties of a powder can be quantitatively predicted from Fig. 3.7 due to Geldart. Alternatively the following criteria can also be employed to determine solid classification [72]. These criteria are purely in terms of particle fluid density difference and particle diameter.

Group C powders are those for which, when

$$(\rho_p - \rho) > 1000 \, \text{kg/m}^3$$
$$d < 20 \, \mu m$$

and when

$$(\rho_p - \rho) < 1000 \, \text{kg/m}^3$$
$$d < 20000/(\rho_p - \rho) \mu m$$

Group A powders are those which are not within group C but for which

$$d < 225000/(\rho_p - \rho) \mu m$$

Group B powders are those which are neither group A nor C powders but for which

$$d^2 < 10^9/(\rho_p - \rho)\mu m^2$$

Group D powders are those for which

$$d^2 > 10^9/(\rho_p - \rho)\mu m^2$$

The behaviour of the four classes of powder in pneumatic conveying, particularly dense phase conveying, has been discussed at length by Doig [72]. Thus group A powders can be conveyed as a long homogeneous dense phase plug with little problem of blockage as in cement for instance. Group B powders are usually free flowing and can be transported at solids to gas mass flow ratios of up to 100 [73]. Group D powders are generally conveyed at higher gas velocities and lower solid to gas mass ratios. Rapid change in voidage occurs at pipe bends and re-acceleration is slow as a result of the higher particle inertia and the smaller rate of change of drag force with decrease in porosity. Because of their cohesive nature, group C powders tend to build up in a conventional pneumatic conveying pipe. The continual build-up or scale formation can result in pipe blockages. It is thus recommended that with such cohesive materials, flexible conveying tubes should be used. The flexibility promotes the destruction of any build-up in the conveying pipe.

The relative merits of group A and group C powders in pulse phase pneumatic conveying versus bypass pneumatic conveying have also been discussed [74, 75] and are also discussed in Chapter 6. Although it is not yet possible to design pneumatic conveying systems from the mere knowledge of the class of a particular powder, Geldart's classification of powders has a significant application in the evolution of the quantitative design of pneumatic conveying systems.

REFERENCES

1. Lapple, C.E. and Shepherd, C.B. (1940) *Ind. Eng. Chem.*, **32**, 605–17.
2. Allen, H.S. (1900) *Phil. Mag.*, **5**, 50, 323.
3. Clamen, A. and Gauvin, W.H. (1969) *AIChE J.*, **15**, 110, 2, 184–9.
4. Boothroyd, R.G. (1971) *Flowing Gas-Solids Suspension*, Chapman and Hall, London.
5. Soo, S.L. (1967) *Fluid Dynamics of Multiphase Systems*, Blaisdell Publishing Co., Waltham, Mass.
6. LeClair, B.P., Hamielec, A.E. and Pruppacher, H.R. (1970) *J. Atmospheric Sci.*, **17**, 308–15.
7. Clift, R. and Gauvin, W.H. (1971) *Can. J. Chem. Eng.*, **49**, 439–48.
8. Clift, R. and Gauvin, W.H. (1970) *Proceedings of Chemeca 70*, Vol. 1, Butterworths, Melbourne, pp. 14–28.
9. Schiller, L. and Naumann, A. (1933) *Z. Ver Deu. Ing.*, **77**, 318–29.
10. Kaskas, A. (1960) *Diploma Research Thesis*, Lehrstuhl für Verfahrens Technik der T.U. Berlin.

11. Happel, J. and Brenner, H. (1965) *Low Reynolds Number Hydrodynamics*, Prentice Hall, Englewood Cliffs, New Jersey.
12. Allen, T. (1975) *Particle Size Measurement*, 2nd edn., Chapman and Hall, London.
13. Zenz, F.A. and Othmer, D.F. (1960) *Fluidization and Fluid Particle Systems*, Reinhold, New York.
14. Kunii, D. and Levenspiel, O. (1969) *Fluidization Engineering*, Wiley, New York.
15. Govier, G.W. and Aziz, K. (1972) *The Flow of Complex Mixtures in Pipes*, Van Nostrand Reinhold, New York.
16. Albertson, M.L. (1953) Effects of shape on the fall velocity of gravel particles, *Proc. 5th Iowa Hydraulics Conference*, Iowa.
17. Dryden, H.L. *et al.* (1936) Measurements of intensity and scale of wind tunnel turbulence and their relation to the critical Reynolds number of spheres, *N.A.C.A.T.R.*
18. Fage, A. (1930) The drag of circular cylinders and spheres at high values of Reynolds numbers, *Tech. Tep. Aero Research Comm.*, **1**, 172–84.
19. Horner, S. (1935) Versuche mit Kugeln betreffend Kennzahl, Turbulenz and Oberflachen beschaffenheit, *Luftfahrtforschung*, **12**, 42–54.
20. Platt, R.C. (1936) Turbulence factors of N.A.C.A. wind tunnels as determined by spheres tests, *N.A.C.A.T.R.*, 558.
21. Torobin, L.B. and Gauvin, W.H. (1959, 1960). Fundamental aspects of solids–gas flow: Parts I–V, *Can. J. Chem. Eng.* **37**, 189–99, 167–76, 224–36, **38**, 142–53, 189–99.
22. Uhlherr, P.H.T. and Sinclair, C.G. (1970) The effect of free-stream turbulence on the drag coefficient of spheres, *Proceedings of Chemeca 70*, Vol. 1, Butterworths, Melbourne, pp. 1–13.
23. Anderson, T.J. and Uhlherr, P.H.T. (1977) The influence of stream turbulence on the drag of freely entrained spheres. *Proc. 6th Australasian Hydraulics and Fluid Mechanics Conference*, Inst. Engrs Australia, pp. 541–5.
24. Zarin, N.A. (1970) Measurement of non-continuum and turbulence effects on subsonic sphere drag, *N.A.S.A.C.R.*, 1585.
25. Martin, J.J., McCabe, W.L. and Monrod, C.C. (1951) *Chem. Eng. Prog.*, **27**, 91–4.
26. Happel, J. and Epstein, N. (1954) *Ind. Eng. Chem.*, **46**, 1187–94.
27. Richardson, J.F. and Meikle, R.A. (1961) *Trans. Inst. Chem. Engrs*, **39**, 357–62.
28. Rowe, P.N. (1961) *Trans. Inst. Chem. Engrs*, **39**, 176–82.
29. Gunn, D.J. and Malik, A.A. (1966) *Trans. Inst. Chem. Engrs.*, **44**, 371–87.
30. Happle, J. (1958) *AIChE J.*, **4**, 197–201.
31. Kuwabara, S. (1959) *J. Phys. Soc. Japan*, **14**, 527.
32. LeClair, B.P. and Hamielec, A.E. (1968) *Ind. Eng. Chem. Fundamentals*, **7**, 542–9.
33. Davidson, J.F. and Harrison, D. (1961) *Fluidized particles*, Cambridge University Press, Cambridge.
34. Richardson, J.F. and Zaki, W.N. (1954) *Chem. Eng. Sci.*, **3**, 65–73.
35. Richardson, J.F. and Zaki, W.N. (1954) *Trans. Inst. Chem. Engrs*, **32**, 35–53.
36. Wen, C.Y. and Yu, Y.H. (1966) *Chem. Eng. Prog. Symposium Series*, **62**, No. 62, 100–11.
37. Vakhrushev, I.A. (1966) Drag coefficient of particles under hindered settling and in fluidized beds, *Khimicheskaya Promyshlennost*, **42**.
38. Ergun, S. (1952) *Chem. Eng. Prog.*, **48**, 89–94.
39. Leva, M. (1959) *Fluidization*, McGraw-Hill, New York.
40. Wen, C.Y. and Simons, H.P. (1959) *AIChE J.*, **5**, 263–7.
41. Yang, W.C. (1973), *Ind. Eng. Chem. Fundamentals*, **12**, 349–52.
42. Boothroyd, R.C. (1967) *Trans. Inst. Chem. Engrs*, **45**, 297–310.

43. Soo, S.L. (1962) *Ind. Eng. Chem. Fundamentals*, **1**, 33–7.
44. McCarthy, H.E. and Olson, J.H. (1968) *Ind. Eng. Chem. Fundamentals*, **7**, 471–83.
45. Baw, P.S.H. and Peskin, R.L. (1971) *J. basic. Eng. Trans. ASME*, 631–5.
46. Reddy, K.V.S. and Pei, D.C.T. (1969) *Ind. Eng. Chem. Fundamentals*, **8**, 490–7.
47. Nagarajan, M. and Murgatroyd, W. (1971) *Aerosol Sci.*, **2**, 15–22.
48. Fortier, A. and Chen, C.P. (1976) *J. de Mechanique*, **15**, 155–83.
49. Lunnon, R.G. (1926, 1928), *Proc. R. Soc.*, **110A**, 302, **118A**, 680.
50. Ingebo, R.D. (1956) *NACA Report*, TN 3762.
51. Painter, D.J. (1969) *M. Eng. Thesis*, McGill University.
52. Wang, C.C. (1969) *M. Eng. Thesis*, McGill University.
53. Owen, P.R. (1969) *J. Fluid Mech.*, **39**, 406–32.
54. Ladenburg, R. (1907) Uber den Einfluss von Wandon auf die Bewegung einer Kugel in einer reibenden Flussigkeit, *Ann. der Phys.*, **23**, 447–58.
55. Francis, A.W. (1933) *Physics*, **4**, 403–13.
56. Fidleris, V. and Whitmore, R.L. (1961) *Br. J. Appl. Phys.*, **12**, 490–4.
57. McNown, J.S., Lee, H.M., McPherson, M.B. and Engez, S.M. (1948) Influence of boundary proximity on the drag of spheres, *Proc. 7th Inst. Congress for App. Mech.*, **2**(1), 17–29.
58. Uhlherr, P.H.T. (1965) Fluid particle dynamics, *Ph.D. Thesis*, Monash University.
59. Munroe, H.S. (1888) *Trans. Am. Inst. Mining Metc. Engrs*, **17**, 637–47.
60. Richardson, J.F. and McLeman, N. (1960) *Trans. Inst. Chem. Engrs*, **38**, 257–66.
61. Yousfi, Y. and Gau, G. (1974) *Chem. Eng. Sci.*, **29**, 1947–53.
62. Reboux, P. (1954) *Phenomenes Fluidization*, Assoc. Francaise de Fluidization, Paris.
63. Rowe, P.N. and Nienow, A.W. (1975) *Chem. Eng. Sci.*, **30**, 1365–9.
64. Weber, M. (1974) *Stromungs-Fordertechnik*, Krausskopf-Verlag.
65. Pinchbeck, P.H. and Popper, F. (1956) *Chem. Eng. Sci.*, **6**, 57–64.
66. Goddard, K.A. and Richardson, J.F. (1969) *Chem. Eng. Sci.*, **24**, 363–7.
67. Bourgeois, P. and Grenier, P. (1968) *Can. J. Chem. Eng.*, **46**, 325–8.
68. Richardson, JF. (1971), in *Fluidization* (eds J.F. Davidson and D. Harrison), Academic Press, London.
69. Geldart, D. (1973) *Powder Technology*, **7**, 285–92.
70. Geldart, D. and Abrahamsen, A. R. (1978) *Powder Technology*, **19**, 133–6.
71. Thiel, W.J. and Potter, O. (1977) *Ind. Eng. Chem. Fundamentals*, **16**, 242–7.
72. Doig, I.D. (1975) *South African Mech. Eng.*, **25**, 394–403.
73. Muschelknautz, E. and Krambrock, W. (1969) *Chem. Ing. Tech.*, **41**, 1164–72.
74. Leung, L.S. (1977) *Proceedings of Pneumotransport 3*, BHRA Fluid Engineering, Cranfield, UK, pp. 272-4.
75. Flain, H.J. (1967) *Proceedings of Pneumotransport 3*, BHRA Fluid Engineering, Cranfield, UK, pp. 281.

4
Fundamentals

4.1 INTRODUCTION

Pneumatic transport involves the movement of millions of particles in a confined space. To begin the understanding of this form of transport a detailed analysis of the behaviour of a single particle is necessary. From this basic understanding we can develop the more complex systems involving many particles with their interactions with themselves and the confinement surface.

Most peoples' experience with single particle movement has to do with the settling phenomenon where particles move through a fluid at rest under the influence of gravity. While this process appears superficially to be well understood, there are many subtleties to be carefully considered. Kaye [1] in his recent book discusses many of these points, one being the clustering tendency of the particles in the settling process.

In pneumatic transport particles are moved by a conveying gas stream. Both the fluid and the particles are in motion. As the two velocities approach each other, the system becomes more and more like a single phase flow situation. In practice this situation rarely happens.

4.2 FORCES ACTING ON A SINGLE PARTICLE IN AN AIR STREAM

The basic particle dynamic equations (Chapter 3) have a number of different terms: drag force, pressure gradient interaction, acceleration of the apparent mass of the particle relative to the fluid, the Basset force accounting for the deviation of the flow pattern from steady flow, and external forces such as gravity and electrostatics. A number of researchers have addressed this dynamic equation [2, 3, 4, 5].

For pneumatic transport a more practical approach to the dynamic equation is to employ an all-encompassing frictional term. For a single particle analysis consider the drag and external forces as the dominant forces counterbalancing the accelerating force. One can write this

$$m_p \frac{dc}{dt} = \text{drag} - \text{external forces} \tag{4.1}$$

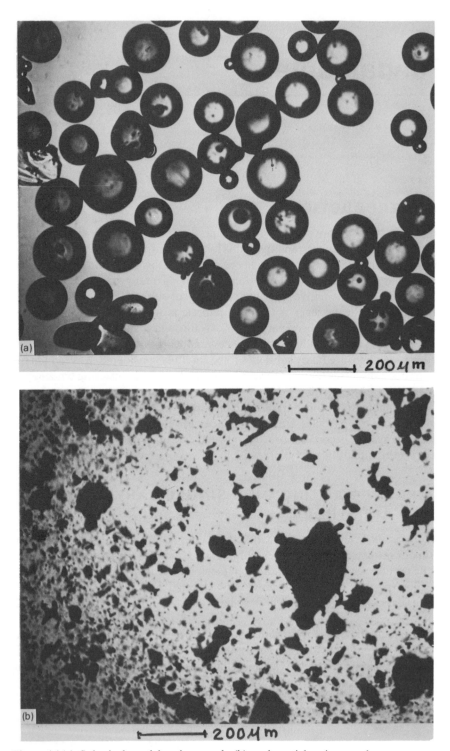

Figure 4.1 (a) Spherical particle micrograph; (b) coal particle micrograph.

The drag force (F_D) for the single particle can be written as

$$F_D = \tfrac{3}{4}m_p \frac{C_D \, \rho}{d \, \rho_p}(v_\varepsilon - c)^2 \tag{4.2}$$

and the external forces for gravity (F_g) and electrostatics (F_e) as

$$F_g = (m_p - m_f)g \tag{4.3}$$

$$F_e = E_x\!\left(\frac{q}{m_p}\right)m_p \tag{4.4}$$

In the above expressions a number of terms must be defined:

C_D = drag coefficient
m_p = mass of the solid particle diameter d
m_f = mass of displaced fluid of a diameter d
E_x = electric field
(q/m_p) = charge per unit mass

Examining these initial expressions for the forces on a single particle one finds the mass or diameter of the particle occurring more than once. The question then arises as to what is the particle diameter. Consider Fig. 4.1 for glass spheres and coal particles. For the spherical particles here represented as a monodispersed system, little doubt is left as to what particle diameter to employ. In the case of the coal sample one sees a variety of shapes and sizes. For an accurate description of the dynamic equations, the variables of size and shape must be addressed. An averaging method for size and shape and a measurement of the deviation to classify a distribution of size and shape are essential.

4.3 PARTICLE SIZE

Practically all material to be transported by pneumatic means has a distribution of both size and shape. Particles that are formed by an attrition or breaking process mostly can be represented by a logarithmic normal size distribution. For particles or droplets created by condensation a Gaussian distribution is valid. The log normal distribution can be written as

$$f_n(d) = \frac{1}{\log \sigma_g (2\pi)^{1/2}} \exp\!\left(-\frac{(\log d - \log d_g)^2}{2\log^2 \sigma_g}\right) \tag{4.5}$$

Fig. 4.2 shows a typical graphic representation of a coal sample following this distribution. The log geometric standard deviation, σ_g, gives a measure of the width of the distribution over the particle sizes d; the smaller the value of σ_g, the closer the size distribution approaches a monodispersed system.

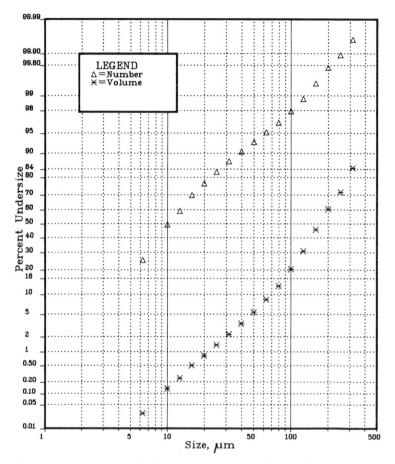

Figure 4.2 Particle size distribution of dispersed-32 mesh Pittsburgh seam coal.

For particles shown in Fig. 4.1(a) the question of diameter is easily documented as the diameter of the sphere. The particles shown in Fig. 4.1(b) represent problems in establishing what the diameter should be. Depending on the sizing method this diameter can vary. In using a sieving technique for sizing, the particles will align themselves to pass through the opening of the sieve. In settling, the particles are oriented to produce the minimum drag. Light scattering measurement techniques yield a volume average. Microscope technique can be handled manually or automatically and show the particles in an equilibrium state. Viewing the particles in Fig. 4.1(b) once again, the diameter can be classified by the longest chord through the particle. This latter designation is termed the Feret diameter. Automatic microscopic sizing is becoming more prevalent with high speed counting techniques where numerous particles can be sized in a short time, i.e. 100 000 particles in 20 minutes. The automatic sizer often takes the longest horizontal chord through the particle to represent the particle size. By sizing thousands of particles and assuming a random orientation of a dispersed non-agglomerated state of particles, a true average size in static equilibrium can be easily found.

One last point on agglomeration of particles is one that should also be addressed. The grouping of particles is a phenomenon that is well known. This agglomerate state is dependent upon the surface states of the various particles be they of one or many species. In reference to pneumatic transport we have a very perplexing situation as to the size of the particles in the actual transport line. The *in situ* state may but probably does not represent the state under which the actual sizing has taken place, be it by sieving or by the microscope. Be this as it may we must size the particles with the techniques on hand. Thus a certain limitation presents itself to us. Some investigators have used the dynamic equation to work out the effective particle diameter. While this approach may seem logical, this is no proof that the results are the true effective particle sizes. Experiments conducted *in situ* are essential to resolve the problem. In the field of settling, agglomerates or clusters have been observed. The concept of clusters or streamers in pneumatic transport has been postulated by a number of researchers [6, 7].

One of the most common bases for size analysis is the sieving method. Here a mass average size is obtained since the basic concept of separation is based on gravity. Light measuring and scattering techniques yield a volume average size since the principle of measurement is based on volume element. For a microscope a length average size is obtained. The length averages can be converted to any number of mean sizes. The most popular ones are

$$\text{length mean diameter} = \Sigma nd / \Sigma n$$

$$\text{surface mean diameter} = (\Sigma d^2 / \Sigma n)^{1/2}$$

$$\text{volume mean diameter} = (\Sigma nd^3 / \Sigma n)^{1/3}$$

$$\text{volume--surface mean diameter} = \Sigma nd^3 / \Sigma nd^2$$

$$\text{weight mean diameter} = \Sigma nd^4 / \Sigma nd^3$$

where n is the number of particles of a certain size. One of the most popular sizes in this designation is the volume--surface mean diameter which is related to the mass transferred over the surface area of the particle. This diameter is of importance in combustion. For a log normal distribution this volume--surface diameter can be written as

$$d_{\text{vsg}} = \exp\left(\ln d - 2.5 \ln^2 \sigma_{\text{g}}\right) \tag{4.6}$$

Table 4.1 has a listing of a few of these diameters determined for some common materials.

Table 4.1 Averaged diameters

Type	General formula
Length mean diameter	$d_1 = \sum nd / \sum n$
Surface mean diameter	$d_s = (\sum nd^2 / \sum n)^{1/2}$
Volume mean diameter	$d_v = (\sum nd^3 / \sum n)^{1/3}$
Volume–surface mean diameter	$d_{vs} = \sum nd^3 / \sum nd^2$
Weight mean diameter	$d_w = \sum nd^4 / \sum nd^3$
Log mean diameters	
length	$d_{lg} = \exp(\ln d_g + 0.5 \ln^2 \sigma_g)$
surface	$d_{sg} = \exp(\ln d_g + 1.0 \ln^2 \sigma_g)$
volume	$d_{vg} = \exp(\ln d_g + 1.5 \ln^2 \sigma_g)$
volume–surface	$d_{vsg} = \exp(\ln d_g - 2.5 \ln^2 \sigma_g)$
weight	$d_{wg} = \exp(\ln d_g + 5.0 \ln^2 \sigma_g)$

Note: $\ln d_g$ is the natural log geometric mean diameter and $\ln \sigma_g$ is the natural log geometric standard deviation.

In operating a pneumatic transport facility knowledge of the sizes of transported particles is thus essential in order to operate the system efficiently. Narrow cuts on the distribution tend to yield results that have greater predictability.

4.4 SHAPE

The property of shape should be equally treated as the property of size. Even though this is so, the problem of quantifying shape is very much more complex in comparison to quantifying size. Recent breakthroughs in the topic of shape indicate in the near future that we may have this parameter in a quantitative manner within our reach. The simplest concept of shape is a comparison of the particle shape with a sphere. The sphericity is termed as the ratio of the surface area of a sphere having the same volume as the particle in question divided by the surface area of the particle. The closer this ratio approaches 1.0 the more sphere-like the particle becomes. Heywood [8] did pioneering work in the field of shape analysis. He addressed particle shape by considering the overall dimensions (length, width, and height) of a particle in its most stable position. Some empirical parameters were also classified for use in formulae to obtain surface area and volume of a particle.

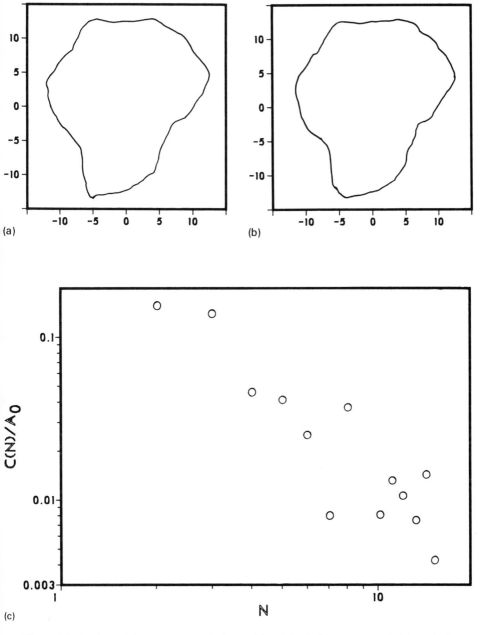

Figure 4.3 Coal particle reconstructed shape: (a) original; (b) regenerated; (c) analysis coefficients.

More recent analysis of shape has been spearheaded by Beddow and his co-workers [9, 10, 11]. Their approach has been to use a Fourier series analysis of the particle shape. They quantify the particle protrusions and indentations by a Fourier series obtaining a unique signature for each particle presented by the Fourier coefficients obtained. Examples of a few common materials as to shape are shown in Fig. 4.3. The coefficients for the analysis are also given.

Another avenue to represent particle shape has its roots in ancient Greece but has only been incorporated in recent times into modern technology by Mandelbrot [12]. The easiest way to explain the concept is to pose the question: What is the length of the coastline of Britain? If one has a map of Britain and a pair of dividers, one can step off finite increments around the map and obtain an estimate of the perimeter or coastline of Britain. Decreasing the divider step produces a more accurate value. Plotting the perimeter against the size of step on a logarithmic scale for a particle shape produces Fig. 4.4. The slope of the line obtained is called the fractal dimension of the shape, a term coined by Mandelbrot. This fractal dimension is related to the number of steps and the sizes of the steps. It is a measure of the ruggedness of the coastline or, as applied to a particle, the ruggedness of the particle or its shape. This technique of classification by fractal dimension has been applied by Kaye [13] and Flook [14] for the analysis of some common materials. Table 4.2 gives fractal dimensions for some materials. These fractal dimensions can be obtained manually or by use of modern image analysers. Such instruments can employ erode and dilate modes to obtain the fractal dimensions of multiparticle systems in a relatively short period of time. Since the fractal dimension can be obtained in a somewhat automatic fashion and represents one or two parameters only, this procedure for shape analysis appears to be more attuned to industrial applications.

Table 4.2 Some fractal dimensions

Shape	Fractal dimension measured
Flook [14]	
Circle	1.01
Koch Triadic Island	1.26
Koch Quadric Island	1.50
Carbon black aggregate	1.37
Simulated floc	1.47
Kaye [13]	
Atomized aluminum	1.09
20 μm rubber crumb	1.09
Barite crystal	1.08
Sponge iron	1.20
Meteorite	1.48
Purkinje cell	1.42

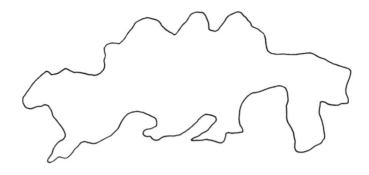

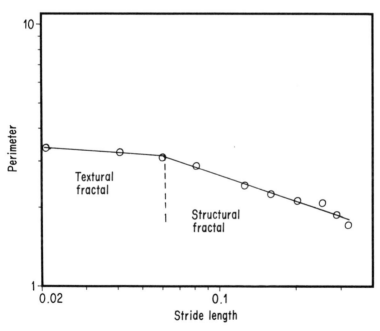

Figure 4.4 Typical Richardson plot of a particle: $\delta_t = 1.07$, textural fractal; $\delta_s = 1.33$, structural fractal. Reproduced by permission of Brian Kaye, Laurentian University. Spherical Particle Drag Coefficient Versus Particle Reynolds Number (Boothroyd (2)). Reproduced by permission of Taylor and Francis Ltd.

4.5 DYNAMIC EQUATIONS

The basic dynamic equation for a particle in pneumatic transport has been given in equation (4.1). The crucial terms of particle size and shape have been discussed in sections 4.3 and 4.4. The item of importance which will now receive further analysis is the drag term in which the drag coefficient appears. The drag coefficient and the relative velocity $(v_\varepsilon - c)$ are intimately associated such that various flow regimes need to be explored. The Reynolds number can be used to compare the inertial to viscous forces of the particle; Fig. 3.1 shows how this coefficient varies for a sphere over the flow regimes. Table 4.3 has a tabulation of these coefficients discussed in Section 3.3.1. If one does not have knowledge of the particle Reynolds number, McCabe and Smith [15] have suggested a convenient criterion to determine the drag coefficient dependent on the physical properties of g, ρ, ρ_p, m_f and d. The factor is

$$K = d\left(g\rho \frac{\rho_p - \rho}{\eta^2} \right)^{1/3} \tag{4.7}$$

One finds the following ranges to apply:

$$K < 3.3 \text{ Stokes}$$
$$3.3 < K < 43.6 \text{ intermediate}$$
$$43.6 < K < 2360 \text{ Newton}$$

With the basic information on size and drag coefficient one can begin to investigate the particle behaviour.

Table 4.3 Drag coefficients C_D

Flow regions	Re	C_D
Stokes	$Re_p < 2.0$	$24/Re_p$
Intermediate	$0.5 < Re_p < 500$	$18.5 Re_p^{-0.6}$
Newton's range	$500 < Re_p < 2 \times 10^5$	0.44
Turbulent boundary layer	$Re_p > 2 \times 10^5$	0.1
General C_D to $Re_p = 10^5$		$\dfrac{24}{Re_p}(1 + 0.15 Re_p^{0.687})$ $+ \dfrac{0.42}{(1 + 4.25 \times 10^4 Re_p^{-1.16})}$
General C_D to $Re_p = 10^5$		$\dfrac{24}{Re_p} + \dfrac{4}{Re_p^{0.5}} + 0.4$

4.6 TERMINAL VELOCITY

The simplest dynamics of a particle are when only a gravitational field is acting on the particle and a steady state is established. In Section 3.4.2 an analysis of the forces acting on the particle to give the terminal velocity is presented.

For the three regimes of flow the terminal velocity can be written in convenient forms as follows:

$$
w_{\text{fo}} = \begin{cases} \dfrac{d^2(\rho_p - \rho)}{18\eta}g = \dfrac{d^2\Delta\rho}{18\eta}g & \text{Stokes} \quad (4.8) \\[4mm] \dfrac{0.153g^{0.71}d^{1.14}(\rho_p - \rho)^{0.71}}{\rho^{0.29}\eta^{0.43}} & \text{intermediate} \quad (4.9) \\[4mm] \left(\dfrac{4}{3}\dfrac{d(\rho_p - \rho)}{C_D\eta}g\right)^{1/2} = \left(\dfrac{4d\Delta\rho}{3C_D\eta}g\right)^{1/2} & \text{Newton} \quad (4.10) \end{cases}
$$

It is worth noting that the additional external force of electrostatics may be considered in the analysis and as such a change in the terminal velocity will be experienced.

4.7 SINGLE PARTICLE ACCELERATION

The next level of complication is a system that is not in a steady state and is accelerating. For a system without gravitational and electric forces and when the fluid velocity is zero equation (4.1) is reduced to:

$$
m_p \frac{dc}{dt} = \frac{3}{4}m_p C_D \frac{\rho c^2}{\rho_p d} \tag{4.11}
$$

$$
\frac{dc}{dt} = \frac{3}{4}C_D \frac{\rho c^2}{\rho_p d} \tag{4.12}
$$

Establishing the flow regime sets the value of C_D and permits equation (4.12) to be solved for the particle velocity at different times. For the Stokes regime the time for the particle to reach 62.3% of its final velocity is called the relaxation time. The relaxation time for this case is given as

$$
\tau = \frac{d^2\rho_p}{18\eta} \tag{4.13}
$$

For the case when the fluid velocity is not zero one obtains

$$\frac{(v_\varepsilon - c)\alpha}{(v_\varepsilon - c)\omega} = \exp\left(-\frac{18\eta t}{d^2 \rho_p}\right) \tag{4.14}$$

where t is the acceleration time of a particle to attain a certain velocity.

4.8 CENTRIFUGAL FLOW

Not all flows encountered are those through pipelines. Once having transported the solids over a section of pipe most likely the solids must be collected. One of the most common collection devices is the cyclone separator. In these devices the particles are imparted a centrifugal force with the aim of collection. Full details pertaining to the design and selection of such collection devices are discussed in Chapter 10. Consider Fig. 4.5 for analysis of the centrifugal flow. The particle is located at a position R within a separator having an outer radius R_2 and an inner radius R_1. The radial particle velocity is termed c_R and the tangential particle velocity c_T. Thus

$$c_R = dR/dt \tag{4.15}$$

and

$$c_T = Rd\theta/dt \tag{4.16}$$

where θ is the angular position.

In order to apply Newton's second law to this motion the accelerations must be determined. For radial acceleration and tangential acceleration one has respectively

$$A_R = \frac{dc_R}{dt} = \frac{d^2 R}{dt^2} - k\left(\frac{d\theta}{dt}\right)^2 \tag{4.17}$$

$$A_T = \frac{dc_T}{dt} = \frac{Rd^2\theta}{dt^2} + \frac{2d\theta}{dt}\frac{dR}{dt} \tag{4.18}$$

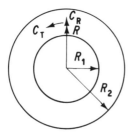

Figure 4.5 Velocities acting on a particle in a centrifugal field.

Multiplying the acceleration of the particle by the mass of the particle gives the force which acts on the particle. A drag resistance acts counter to this as

$$m_p \left(\frac{d^2 R}{dt^2} - \frac{R d\theta}{dt} \right)^2 - F_{DR} = 0 \tag{4.19}$$

$$m_p \left(\frac{R d^2 \theta}{dt^2} + \frac{2 dR \, d\theta}{dt \, dt} \right) - F_{DT} = 0 \tag{4.20}$$

The drag term can be given by equations in Table 4.3 for the general representation. The particle and gas are assumed to have little slip in the tangential direction ($F_{DT} \sim 0$) and the Stokes regime is assumed to be valid in the radial direction so $F_{DR} = 3 \pi \eta d c_R$. Under this assumption and combining equations (4.19) and (4.20) one obtains

$$\frac{d^2 r}{d\tau^2} + \frac{1}{T} \frac{dr}{d\tau} - \frac{1}{r^3} = 0 \tag{4.21}$$

using the dimensionless terms, $r = R/R_2$, $\tau = t c_{T2}/R_2$, and $T = m_p c_{T2}/3 \pi \eta d R_2$. This equation is nonlinear and can be integrated numerically for an exact solution. Under the premise that the second-order term can be eliminated one obtains the radial drift time between R_1 and R_2 as

$$t = \frac{9}{2} \frac{\eta}{\rho_p - \rho} \left(\frac{R_2}{v_{T2} d} \right)^2 \left(1 - \frac{R_1}{R_2} \right)^4 \tag{4.22}$$

Cyclone efficiencies calculated using the above assumption tend to overestimate the efficiencies of the unit. (More details pertaining to the design and selection of cyclones are covered in Chapter 10.)

4.9 SLIP VELOCITY IN A GRAVITATIONAL FIELD

For a single particle in a flowing fluid under the influence of gravity, the slip velocity defined as the difference between the fluid velocity and the particle velocity can be formulated from equation (4.1) without the acceleration term to yield

$$\frac{3}{4} m_p \frac{C_D \rho}{d \rho_p} (v_\varepsilon - c)^2 = (m_p - m_f) g \tag{4.23}$$

For the case of Stokes' law for the drag coefficients ($C_D = 24/Re_p$) one has the slip velocity as

$$v_\varepsilon - c = \frac{d^2 (\rho_p - \rho)}{18 \eta} g = \frac{d^2 \Delta \rho}{18 \eta} g \tag{4.24}$$

If one incorporates the electric force also into this analysis the slip velocity will increase due to the additional force on the particle.

4.10 MULTIPLE PARTICLE SYSTEMS

The topic of systems with multiple particles can be very complex. One could treat each particle–particle interaction along with all particle–wall interactions and arrive at a model that could predict the behaviour of pneumatic transport under a variety of conditions. The approach of taking these multiple interactions on an individual basis will not be treated here in detail. Later the format of these interactions will be considered briefly. A more pragmatic approach will be utilized to develop the multiparticle system along the lines of a single particle system. The equation for the particle and that for the transporting fluid will be considered singularly and together. For the particle one can write on a differential section

$$\Delta m_p \frac{dc}{dt} = d[\text{drag}] - d[\text{gravity}]_{\text{solid}} - d[\text{friction}]_{\text{solid}}$$

$$+ d[\text{pressure}]_{\text{solid}} - d[\text{electrostatic}] \tag{4.25}$$

Of note in comparison of equation (4.1) with the single particle equation is a term for friction. This frictional term represents the total effects of interparticle and particle–boundary bombardments. A similar type of equation can be written for the gas or fluid phase:

$$\Delta m_f \frac{dv}{dt} = d[\text{drag}] - d[\text{gravity}]_{\text{fluid}} - d[\text{friction}]_{\text{fluid}} + d[\text{pressure}]_{\text{fluid}} \tag{4.26}$$

The expressions for each of the differential forces must be supplied in order to complete the picture:

$$d[\text{drag}] = -\frac{3}{4} C_D \frac{\rho}{\Delta \rho} \frac{\Delta m_p}{d} (v_\varepsilon - c)^2 \tag{4.27}$$

Wen and Yu [16] have shown that for a multiparticle system the drag coefficient for a single particle should be related to voidage (ε) of the flow system. The method to account for this is to multiply the single particle drag by ($\varepsilon^{-4.7}$) (see equation 3.21). Another representation for the effect of drag coefficients for single and multiple particle systems is given in Section 6.4.2. It should be noted that this drag force acts in the opposite direction on the fluid phase. Therefore there is always equilibrium between these two main forces.

The differential force terms are given as:

$$d[\text{gravity}]_{\text{solid}} = g\Delta m_p \tag{4.28}$$

Equation (4.28) is valid for vertical flow; for horizontal flow, other practitioners have used a lift term for the particles which can be expressed as $\rho_p(1 - \varepsilon)gw_f/v$ according to Barth [19].

$$d[\text{friction}]_{\text{solid}} = \frac{\lambda_Z^* C^2 \Delta m_p}{2D} \tag{4.29}$$

$$d[\text{pressure}]_{\text{solid}} = \left(-\frac{\partial p}{\partial x}\right)\frac{\Delta m_p}{\rho_p} \tag{4.30}$$

The format for the solid frictional term follows the general frictional force in fluid mechanics. Special consideration is given to the slip velocity representation shown in this frictional term. Other representations involving only c can be written. The electrostatic force term can be expressed as:

$$d[\text{electrostatic}]_{\text{solid}} = E_x \frac{q}{m_p}(\Delta m_p) \tag{4.31}$$

For the fluid phase the differential terms are as follows:

$$d[\text{gravity}]_{\text{fluid}} = g\Delta m_f \tag{4.32}$$

and

$$d[\text{friction}]_{\text{fluid}} = 2f_L \frac{v_\varepsilon^2}{D}\Delta m_f \tag{4.33}$$

$$d[\text{pressure}]_{\text{fluid}} = \left(\frac{-\partial p}{\partial x}\right)\frac{\Delta m_f}{\rho} \tag{4.34}$$

Note that $\lambda_L = 4f_L$ where f_L is the Fanning friction factor.

Combining these terms results in the basic dynamic equations for the multiparticle analysis. Similar analysis can be performed on this set of equations as was done on the single particle. Flow conditions will determine whether the electrostatic and gravity terms must be included or not. For horizontal flow the gravity term is eliminated. In the steady state case both acceleration terms are zero, and summing the two equations should yield the very useful pressure drop equation for the gas–solid flow system. One is cautioned here that the flow has been assumed to be incompressible at this point. This assumption has been relaxed in the following discussion. The differential amounts of particles and fluid can be written in terms of the voidage (ε) of the system: for the particles

$$\Delta m_p = (1 - \varepsilon)\rho_p \Delta V \tag{4.35}$$

for the fluid

$$\Delta m_f = \varepsilon\rho\Delta V \tag{4.36}$$

The voidage term is a very important factor in all pneumatic transport. The measurement of this value is essential for understanding the flow behaviour of a pneumatic system. Inserting these expressions in the steady state analysis yields

$$-\frac{\Delta p}{\Delta L} = \rho \varepsilon g + \rho_p(1-\varepsilon)g + \lambda_Z^* \rho_p(1-\varepsilon)\frac{c^2}{2D} + 2f_L\frac{\rho \varepsilon v_\varepsilon^2}{D} \qquad (4.37)$$

For horizontal flow, the gravity term has been modifed into a lift term by some researchers. The present format incorporates this effect in the overall solids frictional term.

The first two terms of this equation are termed static contributions while the latter are the frictional ones. Generally the fluid static contribution can be ignored in preference to the solid static term. Table 4.4 has a listing of the two frictional terms for a specific flow test system. The relative percentages of each term can be noted. Equation (4.37) has been analysed by Yang [17] in reference to various particle size fractions of solids that are transported. Each size fraction contribution has a unique effect on the dilute phase system and summing over all size fractions would yield the final format. When electrostatic forces are present an additional term must be added to equation (4.37):

$$E_x\frac{q}{m_p}(1-\varepsilon)\rho_p = E_x\frac{q}{m_p}\rho^* \qquad (4.38)$$

It should be mentioned that a few other formulations exist to describe the overall energy loss sum in terms of the pressure drop [26]. Govier and Aziz [18] have used the mechanical energy balance to arrive at a somewhat similar representation. The hydrostatic term is the same, however, an additional factor due to the kinetic energy term is separated from the frictional term. Weber [19] has also presented his formulation in a similar manner.

4.11 VOIDAGE AND SLIP VELOCITY

The parameters of voidage and slip velocity are closely linked. Their measurements in pneumatic transport are essential to the modelling and understanding of gas–solid flow. In spite of their relative importance, there are very few cases in the literature where these two quantitites have been recorded. The reason for the absence of these data is due to the difficulty of obtaining accurate measurements of the voidage and slip velocity. The basic definition of voidage as derived by Wen [20] considered the number of particles in a given volume element.

Consider the element dL with a number of solid particles n as shown in Fig. 4.6. The volume of the pipe element is V and the volume of the enclosed solids is V_s. The voidage is then

$$\varepsilon = \frac{V - V_s}{V} = 1 - \frac{V_s}{V} \qquad (4.39)$$

Table 4.4 Individual contributions to the total pressure drop Δp due to gas friction f_L, solids friction λ_z^* and static head using Yang's solids frictional term for particle size 5 μm

Test	Conveying line solids mass flow rate, $\dot{G}$ (kg/h)	Related pressure drop to pipe length, $\Delta p/\Delta L$ (N/m³)							Gas mass flow rate, $\dot{Q}$ (kg/min)
		Horizontal			Gas	Vertical			
		Solid	Static	Total		Solid	Static	Total	
1	125.8	16.9	27.0	6.44	50.4	17.3	18.8	36.1	2.88
2	76.6	17.3	23.9	5.66	47.3	17.6	16.96	34.5	2.88
3	126.6	18.9	30.1	7.69	53.7	15.7	21.0	37.2	2.88
4	156.4	15.5	26.2	6.9	48.7	15.9	18.9	34.9	2.88

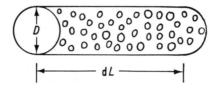

Figure 4.6 Volume element with a number of solid particles.

The sum of the enclosed particles is

$$V_s = nV_p = \frac{\dot{G}}{\rho_p c} dL \qquad (4.40)$$

Thus,

$$\varepsilon = 1 - \mu \frac{\rho}{\rho_p} \frac{v_\varepsilon}{c} = 1 - \frac{\rho^*}{\rho_p} \qquad (4.41)$$

with ρ^* as the apparent bulk density.

One sees from equation (4.41) that a knowledge of the mass flow ratio and velocities v_ε and c as well as the densities ρ and ρ_p will yield the voidage. Similarly knowing the voidage and mass flow ratio and density, the particle velocity can be found.

The gas transporting the solids must flow through the system of suspended particles and solids, thus causing an increase in the gas velocity over that for an empty tube. If v is the superficial gas velocity based on the tube diameter, then the actual fluid velocity between the particles, i.e. voidage, can be written as

$$v_\varepsilon = v/\varepsilon \qquad (4.42)$$

It should be noted that all the former equations were cast in the v_ε format.

The slip velocity has been mentioned previously as

$$w_s = v_\varepsilon - c = \frac{v}{\varepsilon} - c \qquad (4.43)$$

The slip velocity is the resultant velocity between the fluid and solid caused by the particle–particle and particle–wall interactions. Determination of this quantity brings us very close to exact modelling of pneumatic transport systems.

Faced with the dilemma of determining the voidage and particle velocity there are a few avenues one may pursue. For fine particles ($< 40\,\mu m$) one can assume that the particles and the gas velocities are approaching one another in dilute flow and their difference is given by the particle terminal velocity:

$$v - c \approx w_{fo} \qquad (4.44)$$

In 1954 Hinkle [21] wrote a classic thesis on pneumatic transport. His analysis has served as a basis for many later works in the field. From his basic data on particle velocity he developed an empirical correlation which has been widely used. Recently IGT [22] has modified his basic analysis to include a wider database and suggests the following equation for the particle velocity

$$c = v(1 - 0.68d^{0.92}\rho_p^{0.5}\rho^{-0.2}D^{-0.54}) \tag{4.45}$$

The significance of this equation lies in the fact that the particle velocity is only a function of the system parameters. Yang [27] has determined the various parts of the steady state dynamic equation of the particle, and so has obtained the particle velocity as

$$c = \frac{v}{\varepsilon} - w_{fo}\left(1 + \frac{\lambda_Z^* c^2}{2gD}\varepsilon^{4.7}\right)^{1/2} = v_\varepsilon - w_{fo}\left(1 + \frac{\lambda_Z^*}{2}F_r^{*2}\varepsilon^{4.7}\right)^{1/2} \tag{4.46}$$

It should be noted that he has chosen the particle velocity term c^2 instead of the slip velocity $(v_\varepsilon - c)^2$ in the frictional representation. The implicit nature of this equation necessitates numerical iteration for a solution. The frictional factor in this equation can be found from Table 4.5. Rizk has presented experimental data determined by the double solenoid method for particle/fluid velocities (Chapter 6).

The determination of the system voidage in the past had to rely on the inconvenient double solenoid valve set-up of measuring the weight of material trapped in a line. Recently dielectric and conductance meters operating *in situ*

Table 4.5 Solids friction factor for various models

Investigator	Solids friction factor, $\lambda_Z^*/4$
Stemerding [91]	0.003
Reddy and Pei [92]	$0.046c^{-1}$
Van Swaaij, Buurman and van Breugel [93]	$0.080c^{-1}$
Capes and Nakamura [94]	$0.048c^{-1.22}$
Konno and Saito [95]	$0.0285/gDc^{-1}$
Yang [96], vertical	$0.00315\dfrac{1-\varepsilon}{\varepsilon^3}\left(\dfrac{(1-\varepsilon)w_{fo}}{v_\varepsilon - c}\right)^{-0.979}$
Yang [97], horizontal	$0.0293\dfrac{1-\varepsilon}{\varepsilon^3}\left(\dfrac{(1-\varepsilon)v_\varepsilon}{(gD)^{1/2}}\right)^{-1.15}$
Stegmaier [98]	$0.52\mu^{-0.3}Fr^{-1}Fr^{*0.25}(d/D)^{-0.1}$

have been designed to monitor system voidage. Another improvement in measurement technology has been the ability to apply cross-correlation devices to flow arrangements. (Full details pertaining to these techniques are described in Chapter 13.)

Preliminary data taken by Mathur and Klinzing [23] indicate some rather unique behaviours of the slip velocity as the various flow regimes change in pneumatic transport. For a particular coal transport line the slip velocity was found to vary with mass loading ratio, $\mu = \dot{G}/\dot{Q}$. A maximum value is seen as the loading increases indicating a change in the flow regime and particle–particle–

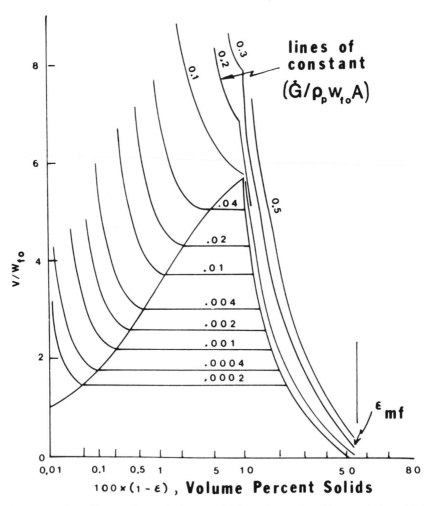

Figure 4.7 Phase diagram for vertical gas–solid flows. Reproduced by permission of John Matsen [24], Exxon Research and Engineering.

wall interactions. The behaviour can be fitted to the phase diagram approach suggested by Matsen [24]. In fact, using Matsen's theoretical diagram cross plots of the slip velocity can be found to be remarkably similar to experimental findings (Fig. 4.7).

From a physical viewpoint at dilute loading conditions the particles are free to move relatively unaffected by the other particles and the wall. By increasing the loading more particle collisions are seen and as such impede the movement and cause larger slip velocities. At high loadings the particles are more restricted by their neighbouring particles, and the solids and gas act more fluid-like to reduce the slip velocity.

The Matsen [27] model is discussed further in Section 5.2.2.4 with reference to the choking phenomenon.

4.12 FRICTIONAL REPRESENTATIONS

The expression for the pressure drop given by equation (4.37) has two frictional representations which come from the energy loss due to the conveying gas and due to the solid particles interacting with the wall and with other particles. The analysis assumes that these effects are summed linearly. In the majority of pneumatic transport systems the gas is found in the turbulent regime thus the basic friction factor found in single phase flow in pipes (Chapter 2) is employed to represent the energy loss for the transport gas. A number of different expressions could be used for this gas flow, however, the Koo equation is recommended [28]:

$$f_L = 0.0014 + 0.125Re^{-0.32} \tag{4.47a}$$

while the Blasius equation is another form

$$f_L = 0.079Re^{-0.25} \tag{4.47b}$$

where $f_L = \lambda_L/4$. The Reynolds number is calculated by use of the gas properties in the transport line.

The solid effect friction factor is given by λ_Z^*. The insertion of the appropriate value for this quantity is not a simple matter. A knowledge of the flow regime is essential to establish the correct value for λ_Z^*. The velocity factor associated with λ_Z^* has been stated as the slip velocity $(v_\varepsilon - c)^2$. Previously it was noted that Yang among other investigators has used the particle velocity factor c^2 instead of the slip velocity. A number of investigators have explored the solid friction factor term under a variety of conditions. Undoubtedly, the degree of variations in expressions is quite large. The flow condition dictates what format should be used for λ_Z^*. It is felt that the slip velocity usage is probably the most correct, however, this format has such a limited database that it would be foolhardy to ignore other forms. Table 4.5 has a listing of the various λ_Z^* expressions in the literature using the particle velocity format of c^2. These expressions are probably most valid for

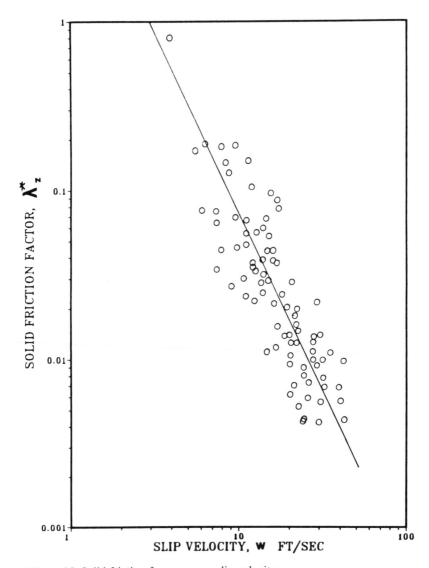

Figure 4.8 Solid friction factor versus slip velocity.

dilute phase transport; however, some of these formats agree with dense phase studies. Using the slip velocity format Mathur and Klinzing [23] have collected limited data for the value for λ_z^*. Figure 4.8 shows the results of this study. It should be noted that this study covered a wide range of flow conditions. Klinzing [25] and Mathur and Klinzing [23] have analysed numerous data sets covering the minimum pressure drop range and higher solid loading ranges to establish the λ_z^* term.

For dilute phase transport Weber [19] has recommended an expression for the solid friction factor that depends on the Froude number. One uses, for the solid contribution to the pressure drop, the form

$$\frac{\Delta p_z}{\Delta L} = \mu \lambda_z \frac{\rho}{2} v^2 \frac{1}{D} \tag{4.48}$$

$$\lambda_z = \lambda_z^* \frac{c}{v} + \frac{2\beta}{cv^{-1}Fr^2} \tag{4.49}$$

with $Fr = v/(Dg)^{1/2}$ and

$$\beta = w_f/v \tag{4.50}$$

$$\beta = 1 \quad \text{for vertical flow} \tag{4.51}$$

The term λ_z^* is obtained from Fig. 4.9 with $Fr_f = w_f/(Dg)^{1/2}$. Note that μ is the mass loading ratio. Rizk has shown the coefficients λ_z^* and β as a function of mass loading ratio and Froude number (Chapter 6).

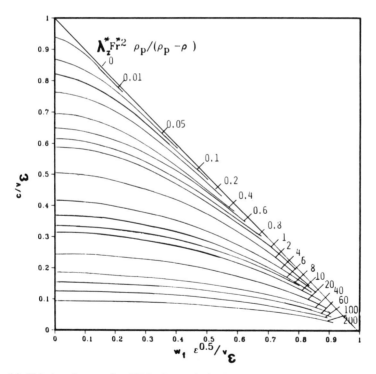

Figure 4.9 Frictional term for Weber's analysis [19]. Reproduced by permission of Krausskopf Verlag.

4.13 ACCELERATION AND DEVELOPMENT REGIONS

For any pneumatic transport system the particles must be injected into the gas stream and there exists a period over which the particles and gas are not at a steady state. Similar situations occur in single phase flow for entrances and exits to piping systems. Entrances and exits to bends also have deceleration and acceleration regions. To analyse unsteady operations with gases and solids the basic equations given by equations (4.25) and (4.26) must be considered. Equation (4.26) will be developed in more detail for analysis. Consider:

$$\frac{dc}{dt} = \frac{3}{4}\frac{C_D}{\varepsilon^{4.7}}\frac{\rho}{\rho_p - \rho}\frac{(v_\varepsilon - c)^2}{d} - g - \frac{\lambda_z^* c^2}{2D} - \frac{\partial p}{\partial x}\left(\frac{1}{\rho_p}\right)$$

(4.52)

The electrostatic term is eliminated here; however, it can be included in the acceleration analysis. The obvious treatment of equation (4.52) is to integrate the equation to establish the velocity of the particle with time. Before this is attempted it is wise to consider a few other points relevant to the process. Since the particle velocity with time is probably not useful, the acceleration term can be rewritten as $c\,dc/dL$. The next point to address is the correct representation of λ_z^*. The question is whether the steady state expression can be utilized in this unsteady development. Little information is available on this point. Also of concern in the analysis, is the voidage term which will obviously vary until the steady state is achieved. The expression relating the voidage to the solid flow and particle velocity should be employed here. It should also be noted that since the voidage varies so does v_ε since v/ε is equal to v_ε. This expression needs to be included in the final format. The pressure drop term has a multiplier of $1/\rho_p$ which decreases the significance of this factor such that it can generally be dropped with little consequence. Manipulating equation (4.52) into an integral form yields

$$\int_{L_1}^{L_2} dL = \int_{c_1}^{c_2} c\,dc\left(\frac{3}{4}\frac{C_D}{\varepsilon^{4.7}}\frac{\rho}{\rho_p - \rho}\frac{(v_\varepsilon - c)^2}{d} - g - \lambda_z^*\frac{c^2}{2D}\right)^{-1}$$

(4.53)

Investigations of the denominator of the integral should be performed to establish the character of the equation. For a horizontal condition the gravity term is often dropped. Weber's analysis does have a transport term for horizontal flow that cannot be eliminated.

Little experimental data have been taken on the acceleration and the associated development lengths in pneumatic transfer. Shimizu, Echigo and Hasigawa [29], Kerker [30] and Yousfi and Alia [31] have explored such experimental arrangements. In a recent work Enick and Klinzing [32] have compiled their findings to encounter a particle size to tube size effect on the development length. The development is given by the expression:

$$\frac{L}{D} = 0.527\left(\frac{D}{d}\right)^{-1.26}(1 + \mu)Re$$

(4.54)

4.14 PARTICLE DISTRIBUTION IN PNEUMATIC CONVEYING

In most of the modelling procedures little if anything is stated as to the condition of particle distribution within the conveying pipe. Generally it is assumed in vertical flow that one has a system with a homogeneously distributed number of particles across the tube. There are some data on specific systems which tend to contradict this, however, a closer examination of a few variables is essential before any generalizations can be made on the subject. The ratio of diameter of the particles to the diameter of the tube must be viewed carefully. The larger this ratio, the better the expected homogeneity. As the choking regime is approached, however, slug formation takes place, with a corresponding decrease in homogeneity.

One must also examine the direction of the flow system, whether vertical or horizontal. Some unique behaviour is seen for both conditions. Considering the vertical transfer system, observations that place a dominance of particles in the wall region can be subject to error, since it is generally difficult to view through a wall ladened particle system to establish the core condition unless spatial sampling or X-rays are employed. Additionally electrostatic forces tend to play a large role in particle adhesion to the tube wall.

Several investigators have observed the wall regions to be more concentrated with particles. Table 4.6 shows the systems studied by these investigators.

Zenker [33] also found for $238\,\mu$m particles the concentration of particles shifted to the centre of the tube. This would represent $d/D = 58 \times 10^{-4}$. Some investigators used X-rays on a vertical 'fast fluidization' column to explore the particle concentrations [34]. As the particle concentration increased, the wall region was found to be dominant in particles and actually a certain downflow resulted with increased loading. At low gas velocities, Capes and Nakamura [35] observed the wall region to have a dominance of particles and even have proposed an annular flow arrangement for these conditions. The ratio of d/D for their study ranged from 67 to 250×10^{-4}. From the observation of the various investigators, a possible pictorial sequence as shown in Fig. 4.10 can be proposed for a build-up of solids concentration. As the diameter of the particle to the diameter of the wall increases, less annularity is possible.

For the horizontal case a well documented sequence of flow developments with particles present has been shown by Wen and Simon [36]. See Fig. 4.11 for the

Table 4.6 High wall region particle concentrations

Investigators	Particle diameter, d (m)	Pipe diameter, D (m)	Diameter ratio, d/D
Soo *et al.* [99]	50×10^{-6}	0.13	3.85×10^{-4}
Arundel *et al.* [100]	15×10^{-6}	0.076	1.7×10^{-4}
Zenker [101]	42×10^{-6}	0.041	10.2×10^{-4}

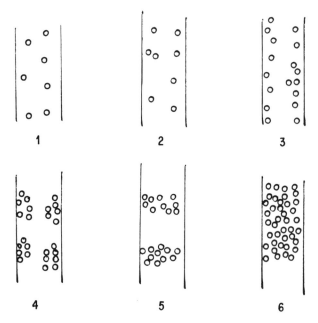

Figure 4.10 Distribution of particles with increased loading for vertical flow.

details. As seen, the lower pipe region suffers a build-up due to saltation of particles. This then degenerates into dune flow and eventually to slug flow.

4.15 COMPRESSIBILITY EFFECT NOT NEGLIGIBLE

In most of the analyses of gas–solid transport systems the assumption is generally made that since the transfer takes place over relatively short distances then the gas density is constant. Because of the interest in longer distance and higher pressure systems this non-compressibility assumption must be relaxed. Associated with the gas density changes is the equally important effect of gas velocity variability with transfer distane. The variation of the gas velocity produces with it a change in the solids velocity. The pressure drop over a section of pipe in general terms can be written as:

$$dp = \rho_p(1 - \varepsilon)gdl - \rho\varepsilon gdl + 2f_L \frac{\rho\varepsilon v_\varepsilon}{D}dl$$

$$+ \lambda_Z^* \rho_p \frac{1 - \varepsilon}{2D} c^2 dl + \varepsilon\rho v_\varepsilon dv_\varepsilon + (1 - \varepsilon)\rho_p cdl \tag{4.55}$$

The last two terms represent a modification in the incompressible case with both fluid and particle velocities changing with distance. The gas density ρ likewise varies with distance along with the voidage (ε) term.

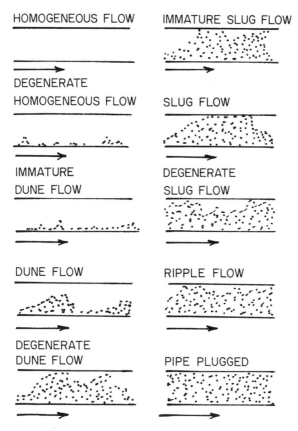

HOMOGENEOUS FLOW

DEGENERATE
HOMOGENEOUS FLOW

IMMATURE
DUNE FLOW

DUNE FLOW

DEGENERATE
DUNE FLOW

IMMATURE SLUG FLOW

SLUG FLOW

DEGENERATE
SLUG FLOW

RIPPLE FLOW

PIPE PLUGGED

Figure 4.11 Horizontal flow gas–solid flow patterns (Wen and Simon [36]). Reproduced by permission of AIChE.

In order to perform the integration of equation (4.55) to obtain the exit pressure of the system, the case of dilute phase transport will be considered. For the dilute phase where the law of continuity is applicable

$$\frac{\dot{Q}}{A} - \rho v_\varepsilon = C_1$$

and

$$\frac{\mathrm{d}\rho_f}{\rho_f} + \frac{\mathrm{d}v_\varepsilon}{v_\varepsilon} = 0 \tag{4.56}$$

In addition for the solid phase one can write

$$\rho_p c(1 - \varepsilon) = C_2 \tag{4.57}$$

where C_1 and C_2 are constants.

The analysis can be carried out under isothermal, isentropic or polytropic conditions. For the isothermal case one can use the ideal gas law for air as

$$\rho = \frac{p}{RT} \tag{4.58}$$

Exploring each term of equation (4.65) and noting for dilute phase transport

$$\varepsilon \simeq 1.0 \tag{4.59}$$

and that an expression relating the particle and fluid velocity such as

$$c = \alpha v_\varepsilon \tag{4.60}$$

From equations (4.55) and (4.56) one obtains for dilute gas–solid flow

$$\int_{p_1}^{p_2} dp = \frac{g(MW)C_2}{RTC_1\alpha} \int_{L_1}^{L_2} p\,dl + \frac{g(MW)}{RT} \int_{L_1}^{L_2} p\,dl + \frac{2f_L C_1^2 RT}{D(MW)} \int_{L_1}^{L_2} \frac{dl}{p}$$

$$+ \lambda_Z^* C_2 C_1 \frac{\alpha RT}{2(MW)} \int_{L_1}^{L_2} \frac{dl}{p} - \frac{C_1^2 RT}{(MW)} \int_{p_1}^{p_2} \frac{dp}{p_2} + \frac{C_1 C_2 \alpha RT}{(MW)} \int_{p_1}^{p_2} \frac{dp}{p_2} \tag{4.61}$$

where MW stands for the molecular weight of the gas. In order to carry out the integrations of the pressure terms with distance an arithmetic average in pressure is assumed. Thus

$$p_2 - p_1 = \frac{g(MW)C_2}{RTC_1\alpha} \left(\frac{p_1 + p_2}{2} \right) L + \frac{g(MW)}{RT} \left(\frac{p_1 + p_2}{2} \right) L$$

$$+ \frac{2f_{Lg}C_1^2 RT}{D(MW)} \frac{2L}{p_1 + p_2} + \lambda_Z^* C_1 C_2 \alpha \frac{RT}{2(MW)} \frac{2L}{p_1 + p_2}$$

$$+ \frac{C_1^2 RT}{(MW)} \left(\frac{1}{p_2} - \frac{1}{p_1} \right) + C_1 C_2 \frac{\alpha RT}{(MW)} \left(\frac{1}{p_2} - \frac{1}{p_1} \right) \tag{4.62}$$

Equation (4.62) can be solved numerically most easily for the value of p_2, the pressure at a distance L.

For the isentropic and polytropic cases the form of the pressure–density expression is

$$p\rho^{-\kappa} = \text{constant} \tag{4.63}$$

where $\kappa = C_p/C_V$ for the isentropic case. In analysing the dense phase system the expressions given in equations (4.56), (4.57) and (4.58) must be relaxed to include a voidage factor that can vary from the value of 1.0.

4.16 SPEED OF SOUND IN GAS–SOLID TRANSPORT

The presence of solids in gases can profoundly affect the speed of sound in a gas. This speed controls the rate at which pressure pulses are transmitted along a pipe. For heavy solids loading conditions the transmission of the pressure pulses can be significantly altered from the normal speed of sound in a pure gas. Weber [19] and Rudinger [37] addressed this speed change due to the presence of solids by applying basic principles of thermodynamics and continuity. Weber starts his analysis by considering the energy equation of a mixture of gas and solids as

$$dH + dZ + \varepsilon \rho v_\varepsilon dv_\varepsilon + (1 - \varepsilon)\rho_p c dc = dQ - dW \tag{4.64}$$

For the condition of no heat and work done, the horizontal case can be written as:

$$T dS + \frac{1}{\rho} dp - \varepsilon \rho v_\varepsilon dv_\varepsilon + \rho_p c dc = 0 \tag{4.65}$$

where the enthalpy term has been expanded for the gas.
Employing the continuity equation

$$\varepsilon \rho v_\varepsilon + (1 - \varepsilon)\rho_p c = \text{constant} \tag{4.66}$$

the base equation can be differentiated noting that the gas density is a function of the pressure and entropy. Thus

$$d(\varepsilon \rho v_\varepsilon + (1 - \varepsilon)\rho_p c) = \left(\frac{\partial \rho}{\partial p}\right)_s \varepsilon v_\varepsilon dp + \left(\frac{\partial \rho}{\partial S}\right)_p \varepsilon v_\varepsilon dS$$

$$+ \varepsilon \rho dv_\varepsilon + \rho v_\varepsilon d\varepsilon - (1 - \varepsilon)\rho_p dc - \rho_p c d\varepsilon \tag{4.67}$$

The definition of the speed of sound for a pure gas can be given as

$$\left(\frac{\partial p}{\partial \rho}\right)_s = a^2 \tag{4.68}$$

Employing the polytropic condition for changes in a gas

$$\frac{dp}{p} = n \frac{d\rho}{\rho} \tag{4.69}$$

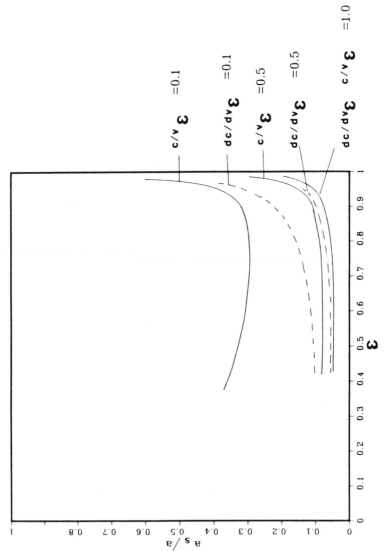

Figure 4.12 Sound velocity of solid–gas mixtures as a function of void fraction, velocity ratio and acceleration ratio of the phases (Weber [19]). Reproduced by permission of Krausskopf Verlag.

and another differential form for the continuity equation

$$\frac{\dot{Q}}{A} = \varepsilon v_\varepsilon \rho = \text{constant}$$

$$\frac{d\varepsilon}{\varepsilon} + \frac{dv_\varepsilon}{v_\varepsilon} + \frac{d\rho}{\rho} = 0 \tag{4.70}$$

The above expressions can be combined into a format given as

$$-\left(1 + \mu\frac{dc}{dv_\varepsilon}\right)\varepsilon\rho_f\frac{v_\varepsilon^2 dv_\varepsilon}{a^2} + \rho dv_\varepsilon\left(1 + \frac{1 - \varepsilon}{\varepsilon}\frac{v_\varepsilon}{c}\frac{dc}{dv_\varepsilon}\right) - v_\varepsilon\left[\frac{\rho T}{a^2} - \left(\frac{\partial\rho}{\partial S}\right)_p\right]dS = 0 \tag{4.71}$$

For the case of constant entropy $dS = 0$, terms 1 and 2 of equation (4.71) must be equal producing:

$$\frac{v_\varepsilon}{a} = \frac{a_s}{a} = \left(1 + \frac{1 - \varepsilon}{\varepsilon}\frac{v}{c}\frac{dc}{dv_\varepsilon}\right)^{1/2}\left[\left(1 + \mu\frac{dc}{dv_\varepsilon}\right)\varepsilon\right]^{-1/2} \tag{4.72}$$

where μ is the solids loading and a_s is the speed of sound in the gas–solid system. Figure 4.12 shows the behaviour of the speed of sound ratio with voidage at fixed dc/dv_ε values. A rapid drip in the value of the ratio is seen with a slight deviation of the voidage from 1.0.

4.17 GAS–SOLID FLOW WITH VARYING CROSS-SECTIONAL AREA

In gas–solid flow as in any gas flow, whereas the cross-sectional area of the pipe increases the velocity decreases and the pressure decreases. A series of pipe expansions in long distance pipelines is known as telescoping. This technique is used in order to deliver more solids over longer distances. The one danger in the system is for the velocity to become too low causing saltation to occur in horizontal flow and choking conditions in vertical transport. The energy losses experienced by the system for vertical flow have been studied by Jung [38,39] while Yamamato et al. [40] have explored the horizontal arrangement. Yamamato et al. studied the flow of 1.1 mm diameter spherical polyethylene beads with a variety of expansions and contractions for solids loadings to 5.0. They suggest for both contractions and expansion that the pressure loss across the pipe diameter change can be given as

$$\frac{\zeta}{\mu} = \frac{\Delta P \text{ additional due to solids}}{\rho v_\varepsilon^2 \mu/2} - \frac{\Delta P \text{ solids (steady state)}}{\rho v_\varepsilon^2 \mu/2} \tag{4.73}$$

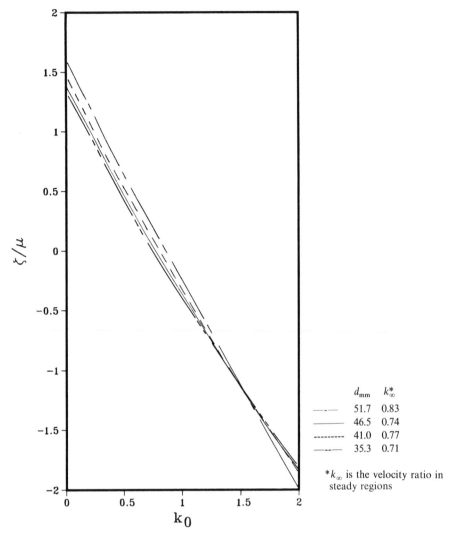

Figure 4.13 Additional pressure loss due to area change versus initial velocity ratio (Morimoto *et al.* [41]). Reproduced by permission of S. Morimoto.

where ζ/μ is found from Fig. 4.13. Figure 4.13 indicates how this former value varies with the initial velocity ratio of $c/v = k_0$. The initial velocity ratio is the ratio of particle to gas velocity just before the contraction or expansion. The same plot can be used for an expansion by using the modified initial velocity ratio as

$$\left(\frac{c}{v}\right)_{initial} = \left(\frac{c}{v}\right)_{upstream}\left(\frac{D_2}{D_1}\right)^2 \tag{4.74}$$

where D_2 is the downstream diameter and D_1 is the upstream diameter.

4.18 BRANCHING ARRANGEMENTS

As in any transport system, branching of lines is a must in the design of a delivery system which has versatility. Splitter valves are often used in conjunction with these arrangements. The appropriate selection of a splitter valve that minimizes erosion in gas–solid flows is essential for design. Branching can take a variety of forms. The angle at the branching point can vary from a small value to 90° abrupt changes. Line sizes can be equal or unequal for the branches. Morikawa and his co-workers [41, 42, 43] have explored the various arrangements for branching. The system studied by Morikawa *et al.* utilized a 50 mm diameter line with rather large polyethylene particles ($d = 3.4$ mm). Considering a Y-branch arrangement as shown in Fig. 4.14, pressure loss was measured as a function of loading to 8.0 and 2θ to 120°. The pressure loss is given as:

$$\frac{\Delta p_{total}}{\rho v_1^2/2} = \left(\frac{\dot{V}_2}{\dot{V}_1}\right)^2 - 1.59\left(\frac{\dot{V}_2}{\dot{V}_1}\right) + 0.97 + \mu_2\left[0.48\left(\frac{\dot{V}_2}{\dot{V}_1}\right)^2 + 0.09\right] \quad (4.75)$$

for $2\theta = 45°$, where $\dot{V}$ is volumetric air flow rate. For $2\theta = 90°$ the loss equation is:

$$\frac{\Delta p_{total}}{\rho v_1^2/2} = \left(\frac{\dot{V}_2}{\dot{V}_1}\right) - 1.21\left(\frac{\dot{V}_2}{\dot{V}_1}\right) + 0.93 + \mu_2\left[0.74\left(\frac{\dot{V}_2}{\dot{V}_1}\right)^2 + 0.06\right] \quad (4.76)$$

When the loading is zero, the equation is valid for air transport alone through the branch.

Another branching arrangement explored by Morikawa and coworkers [41] is the single and double T-branch. Again a 50 mm diameter line was employed with 1.43 mm polyethylene pellets with varying solid/gas loadings of 5.0. The loss coefficients were found to vary linearly with solids loading. The geometric arrangement of the T-branch is shown as in Fig. 4.15. The results show that a branching loss decreases as the solids conveyed in a pipeline increases.

$$\frac{p_0 - p_b}{\rho v_0^2/2} = 1.038 - 0.643n + 0.842n^2 + \alpha_b(n)\mu \quad (4.77)$$

and

$$\frac{p_0 - p_c}{\rho v_0^2/2} = -0.085 - 0.079n + 0.56n^2 + \alpha_c(n)\mu \quad (4.78)$$

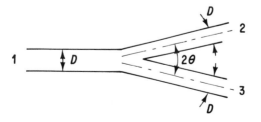

Figure 4.14 Configuration of a Y-branch.

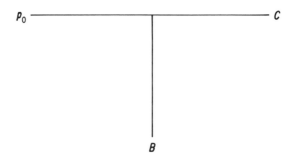

Figure 4.15 Configuration of a T-branch.

Table 4.7   Coefficient $\alpha = \phi(n)$ and air distribution ratio in branched pipe, i.e. ratio of average flow in branch pipe to main pipe

n	0	0.173	0.388	0.605	1
α_b	—	-0.015	-0.0189	-0.107	-0.0186
α_c	0.264	0.086	-0.010	—	—

with the coefficient α given as functions of n, the air distribution ratio of branched pipe (Table 4.7).

4.19 BEND ANALYSIS

Undoubtedly, the most common pipe or tubing fitting is the bend, be it a sharp 90° turn or a gradual sweep bend. It is clear that straight horizontal and vertical runs are luxuries few can afford in a plant situation where one wants to minimize transport distances.

In the past few years there has been a flurry of activity in trying to quantify the effect of two-phase, gas–solid flow in bends. All the system parameters come into play when gas–solid flows experience the centrifugal and secondary flows incited by bends. The bend geometry is an effective phase separator.

In order to assess the two-phase pressure losses in bends it is essential to have a clear understanding of the single-phase situation. Most notable among the studies on single-phase flow in bends is the work of Ito [43,44]. These comprehensive studies give design suggestions in order to predict pressure losses around bends. The most notable feature of the work is the careful experimentation taken to ensure that the precise effect of the bend was quantified. The pressure drop for fully developed turbulent flow is given as:

$$\Delta p = \left(\frac{0.029 + 0.304[Re(r_0/R_B)^2]^{-0.25}}{(R_B/r_0)^{1/2}} \right) \frac{L\rho\bar{v}^2}{2D} \qquad (4.79)$$

where L represents the length of the bend. The dimensionless Dean number $Re(r_0/R_B)^{1/2}$ is seen to play an important role in the analysis. Equation (4.79) is valid for a range of the parameter $Re(r_0/R_B)^2$ as:

$$300 > Re(r_0/R_B)^2 > 0.034 \qquad (4.80)$$

When the parameter falls below 0.034, the bend is truly sweeping and the straight pipe section pressure loss can be used for the bend.

When beginning to analyse gas–solid flows in pipe bends the easiest and most obvious approach is to assume that the equivalent length guidelines used for single-phase flows also apply to the two-phase conditions. For example for a 90° elbow of standard radius the equivalent length in pipe diameter terms is 32D. This sort of application can be made for all sorts of pipe connections.

One of the first investigators to address the bend problem for gas–solid flow was Schuchart [45]. Schuchart investigated a number of different bends, however, treating rather large particles, from 1–2 mm in diameter for volumetric concentrations to 5%. For the solid contribution to pressure loss he suggests:

$$\frac{\Delta p_{\text{bend}}}{\Delta p_Z} = 210 \left(\frac{2R_B}{D} \right)^{-1.15} \qquad (4.81)$$

The contribution due to the solids calculated in equation (4.81) must have a reference point for the pressure loss due to the solids only. This can be obtained from any previously mentioned pressure loss contribution due to the solids alone. One must remember that the total loss in the bend must be the sum of the loss due to the solids added to loss due to the gas. The latter loss can be found from Ito's expression for example. For the case of a sharp 90° bend another format is given:

$$\Delta p_{\text{bend}} = 12 \left(\frac{\rho_p}{\rho} \right)^{0.7} \left(\frac{\rho \bar{v}^2}{2} \right) \left(\frac{\Delta L_B}{D} \right) C_t \qquad (4.82)$$

where

$$\Delta L_B = \pi D/4 \qquad \text{for a 90° bend}$$

$$C_t = \frac{\text{solid volumetric flow rate}}{\text{total volumetric flow rate}}$$

Of late a number of investigators have explored pressure losses in bends for gas–solid systems. Table 4.8 has a tabulation of the parameters studied. Analysis of the data obtained was compared by a number of existing models, however, no concrete simplified approach could be obtained by making such an analysis. It was found that the design suggestion of equivalent lengths given by the single-phase flow underpredicted the data of Spronson *et al.* [46] and Mason and Smith [47]. The Schuchart model both under- and overpredicted the experimental work of Spronson depending on the ratio of D_B/D going from 6 to 24. The Mason

Table 4.8 Flow, particle and tube properties studied in investigations on bends

Investigators	Particle type	Particle size, d (μm)	Particle density, ρ_p (kg/m³)	Loading μ	Tube diameter, D (m)	Diameter ratio, D_B/D
Schuchart [45]	Glass	1500–3000	2610	0–20	0.034	—
	Plastic	2180	1140			
Spronson, Gray and Haynes [46]	Coal	12 800	1143	2.8–6.7	0.126	6.24
Mason and Smith [47]	Alumina	15	3990	0.4–4.8	0.051	20
Morikawa et al. [48]	Polyethylene	1100	923	0–8	0.04	

and Smith data were overpredicted by the Schuchart model having $D_B/D = 20$. Morikawa *et al.* [48] suggest the model for bend flow as

$$\frac{\Delta p_{B\ \text{solids}}}{\Delta p_{\text{st}\ \text{solids}}} = \frac{1.5 \times 10^4 D}{Fr(D_B/D)^{0.2}\Delta L} \qquad (4.83)$$

In comparing this model with Spronson's data the model mostly underpredicts the data. The same underprediction is also seen for the Mason and Smith data.

In an effort to analyse the effect of bends from a different perspective the acceleration length as previously discussed can be considered. This seems like a rational approach since the particles in a bend must first be decelerated then accelerated as the change in direction is experienced. Duckworth and Rose [49] recognized this principle first and the idea has been followed by a number of researchers. Thus equation (4.53) can possibly be used to calculate the pressure loss over a bend through the acceleration pressure loss.

Likewise the development length correlation as suggested by Enick and Klinzing [51] could also be used in the case of bends.

Using a 0.0254 m diameter line for the transport of fine coal 30% and 70% minus 20° mesh was studied by Mathur and Klinzing [52] in a large sweep bend ($D_B/D = 65$). The pressure loss was compared on the same format as used by Enick and Klinzing and Shimizu *et al.* [53]. Fig. 4.16 shows the results which are also compared with the Schuchart analysis. The use of the modified Reynolds number was successful in linearizing the results. Schuchart's equation was also successful in predicting the overpressure loss.

The concept of having a transport system employ long sweep bends has been questioned by several investigators. Using the data obtained on a Fuller Company rig, Marcus, Hilbert and Klinzing [54] analysed the data obtained on a system comparing long sweep bends and sharp 90° elbows. It was found that, for fine materials, the sharp elbow gave an overall pressure loss less than the long sweep bend. (Recent tests have shown that this is not the case for large particles.) This finding has important industrial significance. Apparently the sharp bend takes the abrupt losses quickly and then returns to a steady state while the long sweep carries any unsteady condition over a longer distance. The question of wear always arises in situations of this sort and good documentation on this topic is lacking. In high wear situations the employment of a T with one unit blocked off as a sharp bend is recommended. The particulate matter can then erode against itself in producing a packed portion of powder in the long leg of the T.

Bodner [50] has carried out an extensive study on the effect of bend configuration in dilute phase pneumatic transport. Overall the blinded T had the longest service outlasting the radius bend 15 times. Sand ($+ 210$ to $- 410\,\mu m$) and simulated zirconium and zirconium–sodium blends ($< 150\,\mu m$) were employed in aluminium pipes. The bend radius to tube diameter ranged from 8 to 24. Besides the bends of varying radius of curvature Fig. 4.17 shows the other varieties of bend that were tested. Their failure points are indicated in the Figure.

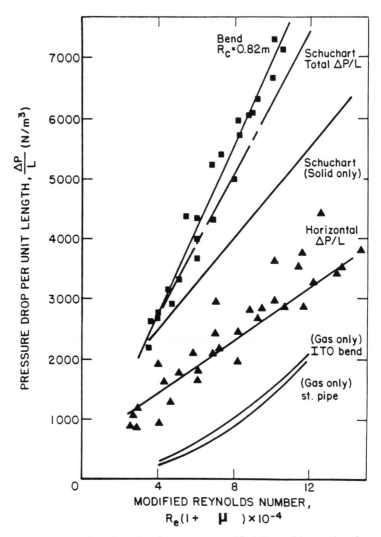

Figure 4.16 Pressure drop in a bend versus a modified Reynolds number for various models. Reproduced by permission of M.P. Mathur; US DOE, PETC.

The pressure drops were found not be significantly different for blinded tees as compared to radius bends.

4.20 DOWNWARD SLOPING PARTICLE FLOW

Most of the flows considered in design and the literature involve horizontal and vertical upflow situations. Invariably in the downward flow of solids, the gravity

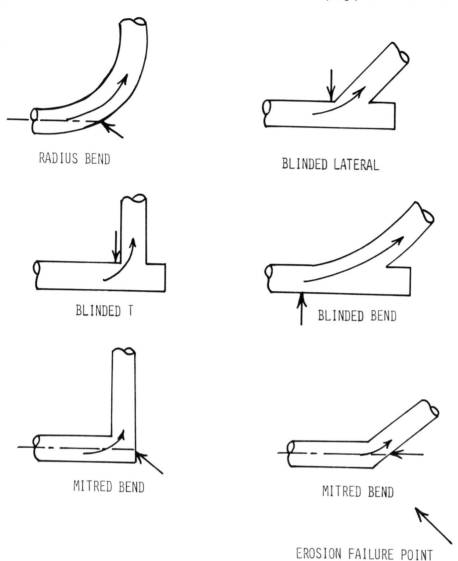

RADIUS BEND

BLINDED LATERAL

BLINDED T

BLINDED BEND

MITRED BEND

MITRED BEND

EROSION FAILURE POINT

Figure 4.17 Bend configuration tested in dilute phase solid transport loops (Bodner [50]). Reproduced by permission of the Powder Advisory Centre.

head is working for the designer. A number of researchers have attempted to analyse this downflow condition and in general have found existing theories and frictional representations are inadequate (Smeltzer *et al.* [55], Saroff *et al.* [58] and Tsuji and Morikawa [56]). In all of these works conclusions have been made that the system is in a state of acceleration and thus must be handled differently from the steady flow cases. In their study Tsuji and Morikawa [56] measured the

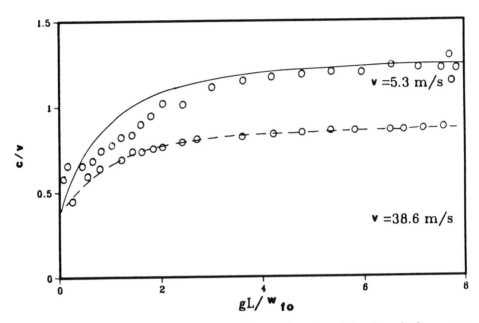

Figure 4.18 Ratio of particle to gas velocity as a function of the dimensionless group (gL/x_{fo}^2) (Tsuji and Morikawa [56]). Reproduced by permission of Chemie Ing. Techn.

particle velocity for the downward flow and discovered some unique relationships. Fig. 4.18 shows how the particle velocity behaves along the flow path. One sees that at high transport gas velocity, the particle velocity is below the transport gas velocity while the reverse occurs at larger distances with a smaller transport gas velocity. This indicates that the solid velocity overtakes the gas velocity due to the gravitation action. Fig. 4.19 gives a comparison between the upward and downward sloping flows for the particle velocity as a function of the gas velocity. A material property effect is more evident in downward sloping flows.

4.21 DENSE PHASE TRANSPORT

The use of the word dense is far from being precise. Canning and Thompson [57] have utilized the word in pneumatic conveying to mean solid particles flowing at a velocity less than their saltation velocity. Others have used the phase diagram to designate the region to the left of the minimum pressure drop curve as the dense phase region of flow. Since dense phase conveying involves low velocities, erosion and attrition of the particles is indeed low. Fig. 4.20 shows the possibilities that can occur in dense phase conveying from a homogeneous condition to a packed and bypass condition. The characteristics of the solids to be conveyed are even more important for dense phase than for dilute phase movement. Canning and

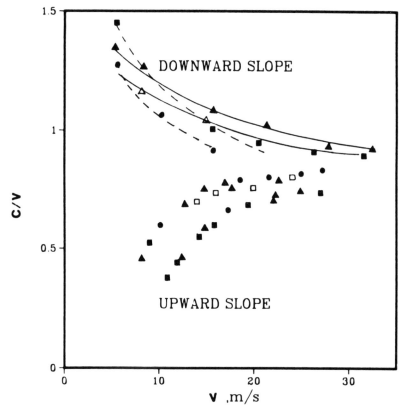

Figure 4.19 Ratio of particle to gas velocities versus the gas velocity for downward and upward sloping flows (Tsuji and Morikawa [56]). Reproduced by permission of Chemie Ing. Techn.

Thompson have emphasized the point and Lohrmann [59] has proved this point further.

The condition of fast fluidization which has been intensively studied by Yerushalmi and Cankert [60] and Weinstein [61] is often termed a vertical dense phase system of transport. By and large the dominant tests on dense phase pneumatic transport have been for horizontal movement. When considering vertical transport, the whole subject of choking and slug formation becomes evident. The particle size and tube size is critical in the analysis of the choking phenomenon (Chapter 5). For these conditions Dixon [62] has combined Yang's criteria and Geldart's powder classification to define slugging regimes and types. (Fig. 4.21). The equations for the division lines are given as

$$\frac{w_{fo}}{(gD)^{1/2}} < 0.5 \qquad Fr_f < 0.5 \qquad (4.84)$$

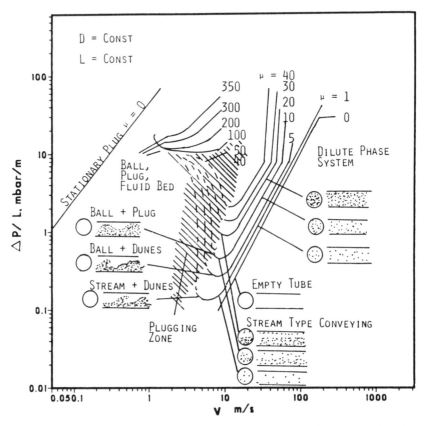

Figure 4.20 Phase diagram of pneumatic conveying for solids with particle size $200\,\mu m$ (Canning and Thompson [57]). Reproduced by permission of ASME.

for asymmetric slugs, and

$$\frac{w_{fo}}{(gD)^{1/2}} < 0.35 \qquad Fr_f < 0.35 \qquad (4.85)$$

for axisymmetric slugs.

It should be noted that the boundary for axisymmetric slugs is dependent on the tube diameter and can be made to shift one way or the other with changing tube diameters.

Thompson and Canning have assessed powder types with Geldart's classification as to the utility of transporting powders in dense phase flow. They suggest it is unwise to convey type C powder in the dense mode; however, pulsed systems can be employed. Group A powders are the best candidates for dense phase transport. The Warren Spring pulsed phase system has transported type A powders for

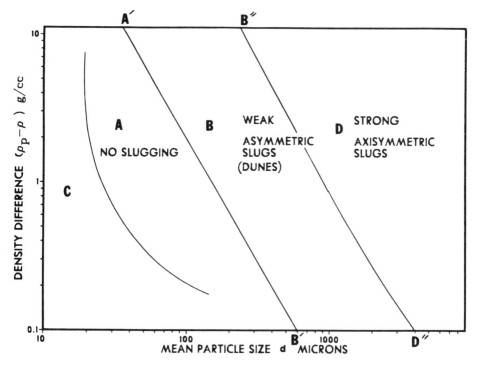

Figure 4.21 Geldart diagram with superimposed slugging behaviour as a function of pressure, 0.102 m (4″) diameter pipe (Canning and Thompson [57]). Reproduced by permission of ASME.

200 m. The Bühler–Miag Fluidstat or Waeschle Pneumosplit seem more appropriate for longer distances (Chapters 7 and 9). The powders of Group B are not good for potential dense phase applications. For the Group D powders only narrow size distribution materials have dense phase potential.

The question of the maximum loading possible in a dense phase system has been addressed by Dixon [62] who considered the condition to be where the relative velocity between the gas and the solids just equals the minimum fluidization velocity. He obtained the expression

$$\mu_{max} = \dot{G}/A\left(\rho v_{mf} + \frac{\varepsilon_{mf}}{1-\varepsilon_{mf}}\frac{\rho}{\rho_p}\frac{\dot{G}}{A}\right)^{-1} \tag{4.86}$$

The gas pressure is an intimate part of this as shown by the gas density factors. The maximum loading decreases with increasing pressure. If conveying lines are of substantial length, then the density of the gas will decrease with length. The limiting μ_{max} thus occurs near the solids entrance point.

A crucial factor in analysing any state of a pneumatic system is the pressure drop requirements. For a homogeneous dense system the approach taken previously with the appropriate solid friction factor can be applied. When one goes into the pulse dense region, the analysis of the pressure drop across the plugs is essential. A number of investigators have addressed this issue (Muschelknautz and Kram- brock [63], Konrad *et al.* [64] and Tsuji *et al.* [65]). These analyses are associated more closely with powder mechanics issues such as shear stresses and permeabilities.

For dense phase flow Stegmaier [98] has developed an expression for the solid friction for dense phase flow shown in Table 4.5.

4.22 ESTIMATION OF PRESSURE DROP IN SLUGGING DENSE PHASE CONVEYING

4.22.1 Analogy between slugging conveying and slugging fluidization

In a slugging dense phase conveying particles are transported upwards with the help of bubbles equal to the size of the tube known as slugs (Figure 4.22). This

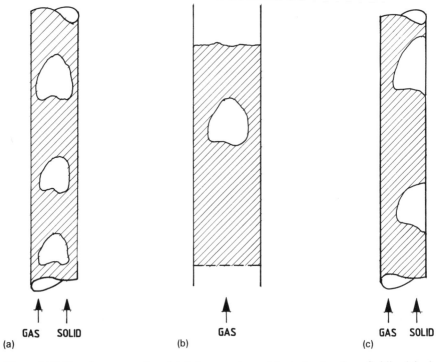

Figure 4.22 Slugging conveying: (a) full nose slugs; (b) single slug in a fluidized bed, $U_B = 0.35 \, (gD)^{1/2}$; (c) half nose slugs, $U_B = 0.35 \, (2gD)^{1/2}$.

mode of conveying is characterized by violent pressure fluctuation caused by the passage of the slugs through a tube.

Literature on slugging conveying is meagre but we can borrow from the extensive literature on slugging fluidization. The literature on a slugging fluidized bed has been reviewed by Hovmand and Davidson [66] and Thiel and Potter [67]. The information on slugging fluidization relevant to slugging conveying is summarized below:

(i) the rate of rise of a single slug (Fig. 4.22(b)) in a fluidized bed is given [68] by

$$v_B = 0.35(gD)^{1/2} \tag{4.87}$$

(ii) for continuously generated slugs at a fluidization velocity of v, the absolute velocity of rise of a slug is given by [68, 69] and v_0 the minimum slug velocity:

$$v_{Ba} = v - v_0 + 0.35(gD)^{1/2} \tag{4.88}$$

(iii) for some systems at high fluidization velocity (particularly for coarse particles) asymmetrical half nose slugs (Fig. 4.22(c)) are formed [70]. These behave as if they are moving in a tube of twice the actual diameter. Equation (4.88) becomes, for half nose slugs

$$v_{Ba} = v - v_0 \tag{4.89}$$

(iv) Bed expansion in a slugging fluidized bed can be described by [71]

$$Z_{max} - Z_0 = (v - v_0)/0.35(gD)^{1/2} \tag{4.90}$$

where

Z_{max} = maximum bed height of slugging bed
Z_0 = bed height at minimum fluidization

Equation (4.87) can be written in terms of voidage to give

$$(\varepsilon - \varepsilon_0)/(1 - \varepsilon) = (v - v_0)/0.35(gD)^{1/2} \tag{4.91}$$

where ε refers to the average voidage at Z_{max}.

Some of the above information on slugging fluidization is applicable to pneumatic conveying. Equation (4.90) for instance can be extended to pneumatic conveying [72] by assuming that the voidage in pneumatic conveying is the same as that in slugging conveying at the same slip velocity. In a fluidized bed, the slip velocity is (v/ε), thus equation (4.90) can be rearranged and written as

$$w_{sl} = v_0/\varepsilon + (\varepsilon - \varepsilon_0)0.35(gD)^{1/2}/[\varepsilon(1 - \varepsilon)] \tag{4.92}$$

In pneumatic conveying

$$w_{sl} = \frac{v}{\varepsilon} - \frac{c}{1-\varepsilon} \tag{4.93}$$

Comparing equations (4.92) and (4.93) gives, for the conveying case

$$\frac{v}{\varepsilon} - \frac{c}{1-\varepsilon} = \frac{v_0}{\varepsilon} + \frac{(\varepsilon - \varepsilon_0)0.35(gD)^{1/2}}{\varepsilon(1-\varepsilon)} \tag{4.94}$$

Equation (4.94) can be written in the more convenient form of

$$(1-\varepsilon)/(1-\varepsilon_0) = [c/(1-\varepsilon_0) + v_B](v + c - v_0 + v_B) \tag{4.95}$$

where v_B is given by equation (4.87) for a full nose slug and for a half nose slug, it is given by

$$v_B = 0.35(2gD)^{1/2} \tag{4.96}$$

4.22.2 Pressure drop estimation in slugging conveying

In slugging conveying the major component in making up the total pressure drop is due to gravity, i.e. $\rho_p(1-\varepsilon)gZ$. Ormiston [73] found good agreement (within 10%) between the measured pressure drop and that calculated from the weight of solids for vertical pneumatic conveying of sand for superficial fluid velocity up to 3.1 m/s and superficial solid velicity up to $0.12\,\mathrm{m\,s^{-1}}$.

Little information is available to predict frictional loss in slugging conveying. It is possible for low gas operating velocities (v slightly higher than w_f) that the wall frictional loss is negative as a result of solid downflow near the wall instead of upflow [74, 75]. For a voidage less 0.85, it is suggested that the frictional pressure drop may be neglected and

$$\Delta p = \rho_p(1-\varepsilon)g\Delta Z + \rho g\Delta Z + \frac{1}{A}[\dot{G}c + \dot{Q}v]_{Z_0}^{Z_1} \tag{4.97}$$

and ε is to be estimated from equation (4.95). This may be compared with the suggestion of Zenz and Othmer [76] that 'the pressure drop per unit length in slug flow be taken as 40–60% of the normal bulk density of solids'. For voidage greater than 0.85, equations which include the wall frictional loss for dilute phase flow, such as the Konno and Saito correlation is recommended.

It should be stressed that the above recommendations are tentative as available information is limited. For Geldart type A [77] material, the axisymmetrical bubble equation may be used in equation (4.95). For Geldart type B and type D solids, the use of equation (4.96) for half nose slug rather than equation (4.87) may be more appropriate.

4.23 ESTIMATION OF PRESSURE DROP IN NON-SLUGGING DENSE PHASE CONVEYING

Non-slugging dense phase flow, also known as fast fluidization [78], or a circulating fluidized bed [79], is characterized by: extreme turbulence; particles travelling in clusters and strands, which break up and reform continuously; extensive backmixing of solids; and a slip velocity an order of magnitude greater than the free fall velocity of the largest particles. The major application of this mode of flow is that of a gas–solid reactor. The advantages of using a recirculating fluidized bed (or fast fluidization) has been reviewed by Reh [80].

The definition of non-slugging dense phase conveying is not precise. As discussed in Section 5.4, the demarcations between dilute phase flow and non-slugging phase flow, and non-slugging and slugging dense phase flow, are diffuse. Volumetric solids concentration in non-slugging dense phase flow can be as high

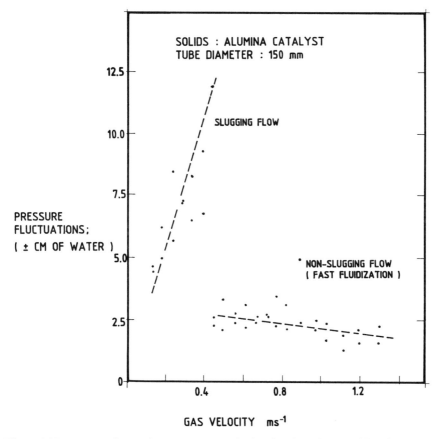

Figure 4.23 Pressure fluctuation versus gas velocity showing the transition from non-slugging flow to slugging flow.

as 25% before slugging dense phase flow sets in. A discontinuity in the magnitude of pressure fluctuations from high fluctuations in a slugging flow to much lower fluctuations in non-slugging flow has been reported [79] and is shown in Fig. 4.23. This may be developed as the criterion for transition from non-slugging flow to slugging flow.

Little information is available in the literature for predicting pressure drop in the non-slugging dense phase mode. The only plausible models available are those due to Nakamura and Capes [81, 82] and Yerushalmi and Cankurt [79]. Although neither of these models has been developed to a stage useful for *a priori* prediction of pressure drop, we shall discuss these briefly as they show two different analytical approaches.

4.23.1 Model of Yerushalmi and Cankurt

Yerushalmi and Cankurt [79] analysed their experimental pressure drop results in a 150 mm riser by assuming that all the particles are segregated in densely packed spherical clusters (Fig. 4.24). The system is taken to be that of low gas flow through uniformly dispersed clusters of diameter d_C and density $\rho_p(1 - \varepsilon_0)$ and

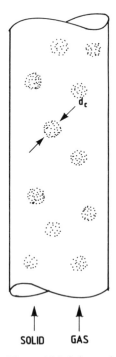

Figure 4.24 Schematic diagram showing clustering of particles.

voidage of gas outside clusters $\bar{\varepsilon}$. $\bar{\varepsilon}$ is related to the actual voidage by

$$1 - \varepsilon = (1 - \bar{\varepsilon})(1 - \varepsilon_0) \tag{4.98}$$

Let there be n clusters per unit volume in the tube. A balance in the clusters assuming negligible solids wall frictional loss yields

$$C_D \frac{\rho}{2} \left(\frac{v}{\varepsilon} - c \right)^2 A_C = \rho_p (1 - \varepsilon) g v_C \tag{4.99}$$

$$A_C = \pi d_C^2 / 4 \quad \text{and} \quad v_C = \pi d_C^3 / 6 \tag{4.100}$$

$$d_C = 0.75 \rho (v/\bar{\varepsilon} - v)^2 C_D / \rho_p (1 - \varepsilon_0) g \tag{4.101}$$

C_D, the drag coefficient acting on a single cluster at a voidage ε, is a function of the cluster Reynolds number and $\bar{\varepsilon}$. Yerushalmi and Cankurt [79] chose the Richardson–Zaki equation [83] to give

$$C_D = C_{D\infty} \bar{\varepsilon}^{-2n} \tag{4.102}$$

where $C_{D\infty}$ is the standard drag coefficient for a single particle in an infinite medium and is related to the cluster Reynolds number by the standard drag coefficient curve. n is the exponent in the Richardson–Zaki equation [83] given by

$$n = \begin{cases} 4.6 & \text{for} \quad 0 < Re_f < 0.2 \\ 4.4 \, Re_f^{-0.03} & \text{for} \quad 0.2 < Re_f < 1 \\ 4.4 \, Re_f^{-0.1} & \text{for} \quad 1 < Re_f < 500 \\ 2.4 & \text{for} \quad Re_f > 500 \end{cases}$$

Yerushalmi and Cankurt calculated ε from this pressure drop measurement in fully developed flow by neglecting friction loss

$$\frac{\Delta p}{\Delta Z} = \rho_p (1 - \bar{\varepsilon}) g$$

$\bar{\varepsilon}$ is obtained from equation (4.98). d_C is then calculated from equations (4.101) and (4.102). They correlated their results for alumina catalyst and Dicalite in a 150 mm riser by plotting d_C versus $1 - \varepsilon$. The result of their correlations is given in Fig. 4.25. Yerushalmi and Cankurt suggested that it is significant that all the calculated points lie on a curve, which 'lends credibility to the premise upon which it (the model) is based, especially to the assumption that gas–solid interactions are governed by the aggregation of the particles into densely packed clusters...'.

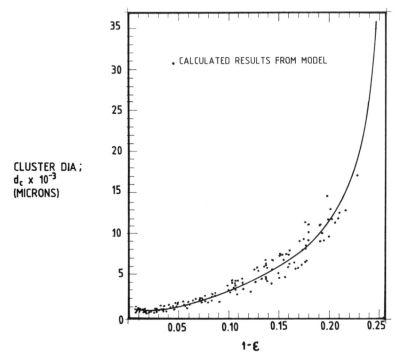

Figure 4.25 Cluster diameter versus voidage: ●, calculated results from model [79].

Although the correlation in Fig. 4.25 can be used for the calculation of Δp in the non-slugging dense phase flow, its use at this stage is not recommended as the general validity of such a correlation needs to be further verified. However, the correlation represents the only published method for estimating pressure drop in non-slugging dense phase flow. The procedure for using Fig. 4.25 for estimating Δp is as follows:

1. For the given c and v, assume a value of ε.
2. Calculate $\bar{\varepsilon}$ from equation (4.98).
3. Estimate d_C from equations (4.101), (4.102) and the standard drag curve.
4. Compare calculated d_C with correlated d_C from Fig. 4.25.
5. If the two d_C coincide, then the assumed value of ε is correct. Otherwise, repeat procedures (ii), (iii) and (iv) with a new assumed value of ε.
6. Calculate fully developed flow pressure drop by $\Delta p/\Delta Z = \rho_p/(1 - \bar{\varepsilon})g$.

4.23.2 Annular flow model of Nakamura and Capes

Nakamura and Capes [81] proposed two separate models for vertical pneumatic conveying: the uniform flow model and the annular flow model. The uniform flow

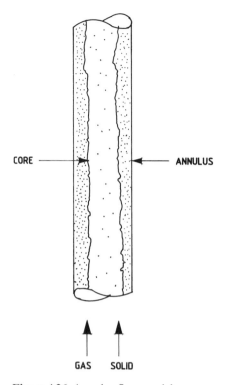

CORE ⟶ ⟵ ANNULUS

↑ ↑

GAS SOLID

Figure 4.26 Annular flow model.

model is applicable to high gas velocity ($\gg w_f$) at which lean phase flow occurs. The model is similar to that of Hinkle and others [85, 86, 87]. This will not be further discussed here.

In the annular flow model, particle flow is considered to occur in two regions, the core and the annulus as shown in Fig. 4.26. Particles flow upwards in the core and downwards in the annulus with an overall net upflow. The gas velocity, solid velocity and voidage in the two regions are different. As solid flow is downwards near the wall the annular flow model predicts negative wall friction, as has been reported by van Swaaij *et al.* [75]. The model describes approximately the physical situation in non-slugging dense phase flow in which particle recirculation is observed. The annular flow model is a more realistic model for describing non-slugging dense phase conveying than the model of Yerushalmi and Cankurt [79].

Nakamura and Capes [81] presented two sets of momentum equations, one for flow in the annulus and the other for the core. The equations contained many unknowns, e.g. voidage in the two regions, mass flow of solid and gas in the two regions, size of the core, shear stress across the core–annulus interface, as well as the wall shear stress. By neglecting the shear stress across the core–annulus interface and by assuming that flow in the riser is such that the pressure drop is minimized, equations were derived which were shown to give qualitative agreement with observations. Further support for the model is available from the recent experimental results of Bandrowski *et al.* [88]. Further refinement of the model and more experimental work will be necessary, however, before equations based on the model can be used directly for the prediction of pressure drop in non-slugging dense phase flow.

4.24 PLUG FLOWS

Low velocity conveying is becoming more and more popular in pneumatic transport systems in order to reduce pipe wear and breakage of the conveyed materials.

In many situations in horizontal flow plugs of solids build up and flow as integral parts separated by air gaps. This situation can also take place in vertical flow as well. Specific designs have used this concept and have introduced a secondary air flow to ensure equal spacings of the plugs. This procedure is rather effective in transporting cohesive materials as well as providing convenient flow of other less cohesive solids. The overall velocities associated with such flow are generally low when compared to high velocity dilute phase transport systems. The overall pressure losses for a plug flow system separated by an air gap is determined by finding the loss due to one plug and one air gap and multiplying this number by the number of units present in the pipelines. Weber [19] and Konrad *et al.* [64] have given a detailed analysis of the plugs from a force balance on a plug. The analyses and design equations of both investigators will be presented. The treatment of Weber will first be considered. Starting with a force balance one has:

$$-A(\mathrm{d}p) = [g(1-\varepsilon)\rho_\mathrm{p}A\mathrm{d}L]\sin\theta + \mu_\mathrm{w}[g(1-\varepsilon)\rho_\mathrm{p}A\mathrm{d}L]\cos\theta$$

$$+ \mu_\mathrm{w}(p_\mathrm{ws}\pi D\mathrm{d}L) + A\mathrm{d}\sigma_{yy} \tag{4.103}$$

where θ is the angle of inclination of the pipe, A the cross-sectional area, μ_w the coefficient of sliding friction, p_ws the pressure of the solids perpendicular to the wall ($=p_\mathrm{rad}$), and σ_{yy} is the principal stress in the y-direction.
The stresses in the solid can be related as

$$\lambda = \frac{(\sigma_{yy})_\mathrm{w}}{\sigma_{yy}} = \frac{p_\mathrm{rad}}{p_\mathrm{ax}} \tag{4.104}$$

The pressure loss of the gas through the plug can be given as

$$\frac{\mathrm{d}p(x)}{\mathrm{d}L} = \lambda_{\mathrm{Zp}}\frac{1-\varepsilon}{\varepsilon}\frac{\rho(x)}{2}(v-c)^2\frac{1}{d} \tag{4.105}$$

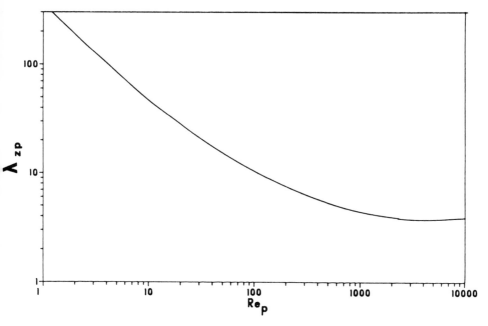

Figure 4.27 Weber's treatment of plug flow. Loss coefficient versus Reynolds number.

Weber [19] suggests Fig. 4.27 for the value of λ_{Zp}. Note that the slip velocity of the solid has been employed in equation (4.105). Considering (1) as the beginning of the plug and the isothermal condition

$$\rho = \frac{p}{p_1}\rho_1$$

equation (4.105) can be reduced and integrated to the form

$$P_{(x)} = (p_1^2 - 2K_1 x)^{1/2}$$

where

$$K_1 = \lambda_{Zp}\left(\frac{1-\varepsilon}{\varepsilon}\right)\frac{\rho_1}{2}(v-c)^2\frac{1}{d}p_1 \qquad (4.106)$$

In order to obtain the pressure drop from this expression the slip velocity must be known. Equation (4.103) can be simplified in terms of constants to read:

$$\frac{d\sigma_{yy}}{dx} + K_2\sigma_{yy} + K_3 - \frac{K_4}{1-K_5 x} = 0 \qquad (4.107)$$

with

$$K_2 = \lambda \mu_R \pi dp / A$$

$$K_3 = g \rho_p (1 - \varepsilon)(\sin \theta + \mu_R \cos \theta)$$

$$K_4 = \lambda_{z_p} \frac{1 - \varepsilon}{\varepsilon} \rho(v - c)^2 \frac{1}{2d}$$

$$K_5 = 2K_4 / p_1$$

Solving equation (4.107) yields

$$\sigma_{yy}(x) = \frac{K_3}{K_2} \{\exp[K_2(L - x)] - 1\} + \sigma_{yy2} \exp[K_2(L - x)]$$

$$- \frac{K_4}{K_2} \left(\frac{\exp[K_2(L - x)]}{1 - (K_5/p_1)} - \frac{1}{[1 - (K_5/p_1)x]^{1/2}} \right) \tag{4.108}$$

where σ_{yy} is the conveying pressure of the plug and σ_{yy2} is the pressure at the end of the plug (or system).

Weber has also treated the case of plug flow where a secondary air source is used to move the plugs. His suggested analysis of this case by a force balance is:

$$- dp A = \Delta G g \beta$$

where

$$\Delta G = \text{mass of solids in plug}$$

$$\beta = \sin \theta \, \mu_R \cos \theta$$

$$\theta = \text{angle of inclination}$$

Using the expression

$$\Delta G g = g \dot{G} dL / c \tag{4.109}$$

and

$$\mu = \dot{G} / \dot{Q} \tag{4.110}$$

then

$$- dp = \beta \mu \rho g \frac{1}{c/v} dL \tag{4.111}$$

Employing the ideal gas equation reduces the expression to

$$- \frac{dp}{p} = \frac{\beta g \mu}{RT} \frac{dL}{c/v} \tag{4.112}$$

Assuming a constant $\beta g \mu / RT(c/v)$ one obtains

$$p_1 = p_2 \exp\left(\frac{\beta \mu g L}{RTc/v}\right) \tag{4.113}$$

For horizontal flow $\beta = \mu_R$ and Weber assumes $\beta = 0.6$. This value depends upon the solid concentration and velocity. This latter expression can also be used to find the pressure loss across a single plug as well as equation (4.106).

Following the Weber analysis Konrad et al. [64] approached the subject of slugs in a similar, yet different manner. Konrad et al. have constructed a packed bed model to analyse the flow of plugs. This is based on the Ergun equation for flow through a stationary packed bed. The Ergun equation states that

$$\frac{\Delta p}{\Delta L} = 150 \frac{(1-\varepsilon)^2}{\varepsilon^3} \frac{\eta w}{d^2} + 1.75 \frac{1-\varepsilon}{\varepsilon^3} \rho \frac{w^2}{d} \tag{4.414}$$

Note the use of the slip velocity w. Consider a plug flow situation as shown in Fig. 4.28. The total pressure drop would be equal to the pressure drop from one plug multiplied by the number of plugs in the pipe plus the contribution due to one plug of air flowing through the pipe times the number of air plugs in the pipe. Konrad et al. did not always observe the distinct plug flow situation. Their observation showed the situation in Fig. 4.29. Here l_{ex} represents the length of extra material associated with the plug while l_g is the length of the stationary bed in the pipe.

From a material balance analysis considering n plugs of mass in the line

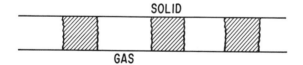

Figure 4.28 Plug flow situation.

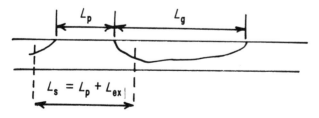

Figure 4.29 Observation of Konrad et al. [64] for plug flow situation.

of length ΔL one has the total plug length as $L_p = nl_p$ and the extra length as $L_{ex} = nl_{ex}$. Combining this information with equation (4.114) one produces:

$$\Delta p = \left(150\eta \frac{(1-\varepsilon)^2 w}{\varepsilon^3 d^2} + 1.75 \frac{\rho(1-\varepsilon)w^2}{\varepsilon^3 d} \right) \frac{\dot{G}\Delta L_T}{A\rho_B c} \tag{4.115}$$

In addition, the specific pressure losses required to move a plug were developed employing the field of solid mechanics. One can write a force balance as

$$\frac{dp}{dy} + \frac{d\sigma_{yy}}{dy} + \frac{4\tau_w}{D} + \rho_B g \sin \theta = 0 \tag{4.116}$$

where the last term is zero for horizontal flow; the shear stress at the wall τ_w assumes a Coulombic behaviour thus

$$\tau_w = \mu_w(\sigma_{rr})_w + C_w \tag{4.117}$$

where

$\mu_w = \tan \phi_w$

$\phi_w =$ angle of wall friction

$(\sigma_{rr})_w =$ principal radial stress

$C_w =$ particle–wall cohesion

For a passive failure

$$(\sigma_{rr})_w = K_w(\sigma_{yy})_w + (K_w + 1)c' \cos \phi \cos (\omega + \phi_w) + \rho_B g D/2 \tag{4.118}$$

where

$K_w =$ coefficient of internal friction at the wall $= \dfrac{1 \pm \sin \phi \cos (\omega \pm \phi_w)}{1 \pm \sin \phi \cos (\omega \pm \phi_w)}$

$(\sigma_{yy})_w =$ principal stress in the y-direction at the wall

$c' =$ interparticle cohesion

$\phi =$ angle of internal friction

$\psi = \dfrac{F' \pm C \cot \phi}{1 \pm \sin \phi}$

$\sin \omega = \dfrac{\sin \phi [\psi + c_w \cot \phi_w]}{1 - \sin \phi [\psi + c \cot \phi]}$

Thus

$$\tau_w = \mu_w K_w(\sigma_{yy})_w + \mu_w(K_w + 1)c' \cos \phi \cos (\omega + \phi_w) + C_w \tag{4.119}$$

Assuming $(\sigma_{yy})_w = \sigma_{yy}$ equation (4.115) can be integrated with the boundary conditions

$$\sigma_{yy} = B' \text{ (stress on back-end of plug at } y = 0)$$
$$\sigma_{yy} = F' \text{ (stress on front-end of plug at } y = h)$$

where h is the height of a single plug. Setting $F' = B'$ one obtains the pressure gradient

$$\frac{\Delta p}{L_p} = \rho_B g \sin \theta + \frac{4\mu_w K_w F'}{D} + \frac{4\mu_w (K_w + 1)c' \cos \phi \cos (\omega + \phi_w)}{D} + \frac{4C_w}{D} \quad (4.120)$$

For the horizontal case one can write

$$\frac{\Delta p}{L_p} = \frac{4\mu_w K_w F'}{D} + \frac{4\mu_w (K_w + 1)c' \cos \phi \cos (\omega - \phi_w)}{D} + 2\rho_B g \tan \phi_w + \frac{4C_w}{D} \quad (4.121)$$

The terms for the stresses F' and B' must be further developed. From a momentum analysis

$$F' = \rho_B \frac{dc^2}{1 - d} \quad (4.122)$$

and

$$d = \frac{1}{1 + c/0.542(gD)^{1/2}}$$

Oftentimes $F = B$. Also one should note that the factor c' is zero for cohesiveless powders. Such a simplification for a cohesiveless powder can reduce the complexity of equations (4.115) and (4.116). For a non-cohesive powder in horizontal flow the overall pressure drop in a pipe of length ΔL can be written as:

$$\frac{\Delta p}{L_p + L_{ex}} = \rho_B \mu_w \left[2g + \frac{2.168 K_w (gc)^{1/2}}{D^{1/2}} \left(\frac{1 - 2\dot{G}/\rho_B Ac}{1 - \dot{G}/\rho_B cA} \right) \right] \quad (4.124)$$

One can combine equations (4.115) and (4.116) for the packed bed model and the above equation (4.124) to eliminate Δp to solve a cubic equation for the particle velocity.

A procedure is recommended for calculating the pressure drop across a plug using the above equations. Given the mass flow of solids, the length of the tube and its area, the mean air density is assumed. Considering the roots of the cubic equation in the particle velocity the mass flow rate of the air is found that satisfies

$$\left(v + w - \frac{2\dot{G}}{\rho_B A} \right) + \frac{a}{bp} \left(v - v_\varepsilon - c - \frac{2\dot{G}}{\rho_B A} \right) > \frac{2\rho_B g \mu_w}{bp}$$

where

$$a = 150\frac{(1-\varepsilon)^2}{\varepsilon^2}\frac{\eta}{d}$$

$$b = 1.75\frac{(1-\varepsilon)}{\varepsilon^3}\frac{1}{d}$$

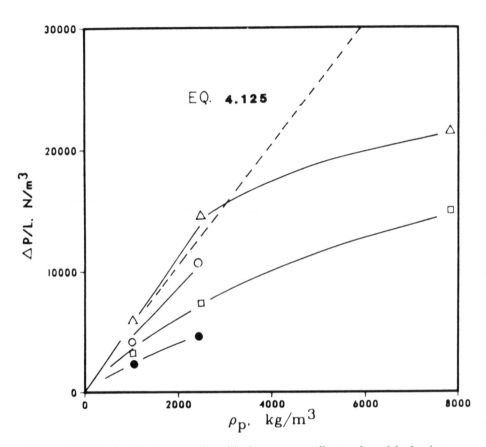

Figure 4.30 Relationship between the critical pressure gradient and particle density:

$\triangle\,D_p = 3\,\text{mm}$	$\bigcirc\,D_p = 1\,\text{mm}$	$\square\,D_p = 3\,\text{mm}$	$\bullet\,D_p = 1\,\text{mm}$
$D_t = 27\,\text{mm}$	$D_t = 27\,\text{mm}$	$D_{tt} = 50.8\,\text{mm}$	$D_t = 50.8\,\text{mm}$;

(Tsuji, Morikawa and Honda [65]). Reproduced by permission of International Powder Institute.

The cubic equation in c is solved and the root lying in the range of $(v + w) > c > \dot{G}/(\rho_B A)$ is taken. The particle velocity is inserted in the pressure drop equation (4.123) to determine this value. The mean gas density is then checked and revised and iterated if necessary.

Studies on stationary plugs and conveying of coarse particles with secondary injection were carried out by Tsuji, Morikawa and Honda [65, 89, 90]. In a horizontal pipe 27 and 50.8 mm diameter with particle diameters between 1 and 3 mm and densities of 1000–7800 kg/m³ they studied the pressure drop needed to blow off a stationary plug in horizontal flow. From a force balance they developed an expression for the pressure gradient causing the particles to move as

$$\frac{\Delta p}{\Delta L} = \frac{g\rho_p}{\sqrt{3}} \frac{1}{1 + (3/2)(C_D/n)\varepsilon/(1 - \varepsilon)} \tag{4.125}$$

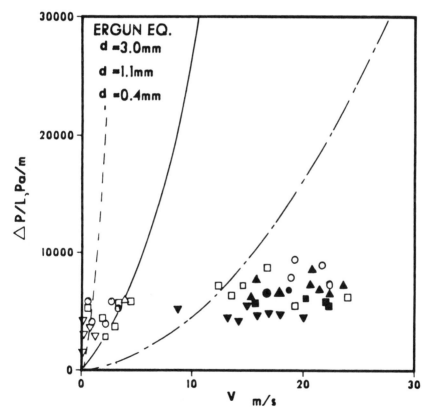

Figure 4.31 Pressure drop across a plug versus gas velocity (Tsuji and Morikawa [89]). Reproduced by permission of Pergamon Press Inc.

where

$$\frac{C_{\mathrm{D}}}{n} = \frac{24}{300}\left(\frac{1-\varepsilon}{\varepsilon}\right)$$

Fig. 4.30 shows that the data agree with the equation for the 27 mm diameter pipe except for large particle densities.

With secondary air injection they attempted to apply the equation of Ergun for

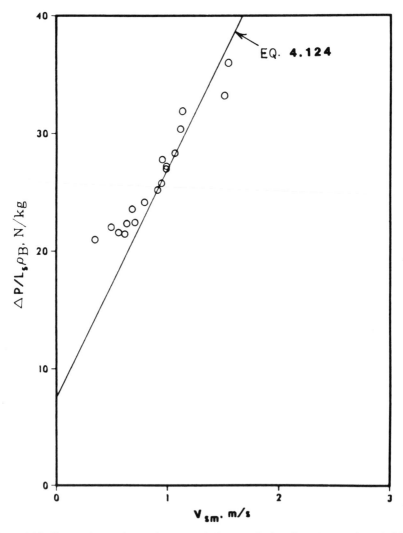

Figure 4.32 Comparison of experiment and theory of plug flow (Konrad *et al.* [64]). Reproduced by permission of BHRA Fluid Engr.

the pressure drop analysis without success for a 50 mm diameter pipe and 8 and 10 mm inner pipe studying 0.4, 1.1 and 3.0 mm diameter particles. The Ergun equation predicted larger pressure drops over the plug than experienced in the experiments. Fig. 4.31 depicts their findings. Konrad *et al.* were successful in predicting their findings on plug flow without a secondary assist using a solid shear stress balance for 4 mm diameter particles in a 47.3 mm diameter pipe for particle density of 920 kg/m^3 (Fig. 4.32).

4.25 WORKED EXAMPLES

Example 4.1

Consider the horizontal transport of solids having density 1340 kg/m^3 and average particle size 250 μm. The transport gas is air at atmospheric conditions. It is decided to use a 5 cm diameter copper pipe for transport. The solids flow rate is 1000 kg/h. Determine the energy loss to transport this solid at gas velocities of 10, 20 and 30 m/s.

As an example in this case the Konno and Saito solid friction equation will be employed. For horizontal flow

$$\frac{\Delta p}{L} = 2f_L \frac{\sigma \varepsilon v^2}{D} + \lambda_z^* \frac{\rho_p (1 - \varepsilon) c^2}{2D}$$

for $v = 10$ m/s

$$Re = \frac{0.05 \times 1.2 \times 10}{10^{-5}} = 60\,000$$

$$\frac{\Delta p}{L} = 2 \frac{0.0014 + 0.125\,Re^{-0.32}}{0.05} (1.2)(10)^2 \varepsilon$$

$$+ 4 \times 0.0285(9.8 \times .03)^{1/2} \frac{c \times 1340 \times (1 - \varepsilon)}{2 \times 0.05} c^2$$

For the particle velocity the Hinkle (IGT) correlation will be employed

$$c = v(1 - 0.68 d^{0.92} \rho_p^{0.5} \rho^{-0.2} D^{-0.54})$$
$$= 10(1 - 0.68(250 \times 10^{-6})^{0.92}(1340)^{0.5}(1.2)^{-0.2}(0.05)^{-0.54}$$
$$= 9.4 \text{ m/s}$$

and the voidage is

$$\varepsilon = 1 - \frac{1000}{(\pi/4)(0.05)^2 \times 9.4 \times 1340}$$
$$= 0.988$$

The loading for the condition is

$$L = \frac{1000/3600}{(\pi/4)(0.05)^2 \times 10 \times 1.2} = 11.69$$

Substituting these values into the pressure drop equation gives

$$\left(\frac{\Delta p}{L}\right)_{10 \text{ m/s}} = 141 \text{ N/m}^3$$

for the other cases

$$\left(\frac{\Delta p}{L}\right)_{20 \text{ m/s}} = 209 \text{ N/m}^3$$

$$\varepsilon = 0.994$$

Loading, μ, is calculated as

$$\mu = 5.84$$

$$c = 18.8 \text{ m/s}$$

$$\left(\frac{\Delta p}{L}\right)_{30 \text{ m/s}} = 311 \text{ N/m}^3$$

$$\varepsilon = 0.996$$

For $\mu = 3.89$

$$c = 28.2 \text{ m/s}$$

Example 4.2

For a heavy loaded gas–solid mixture the friction factor found by Mathur and Klinzing has been suggested. Consider the vertical flow of coal of 100 μm diameter at a rate of 10000 kg/h in a 0.05 m diameter pipe using nitrogen at atmosphere conditions. The solid density is 1280 kg/m^3. The gas velocity is 20 m/s. Determine each pressure drop contribution.

The pressure drop equation is given as

$$\frac{\Delta p}{L} = \rho_p(1-\varepsilon) + \rho(\varepsilon) + \frac{2f_L \rho \varepsilon v g^2}{D} + \lambda_z^* \frac{\rho_p(1-\varepsilon)}{2D}(v_\varepsilon - c)^2$$

for 20 m/s

$$Re = \frac{0.05 \times 1.2 \times 20}{10^{-5}} = 120\,000$$

using 15.15 m/s as the particle velocity from measurements:

$$\varepsilon = 1 - \frac{10000/3600}{(\pi/4)(0.05)^2 \times 15.15 \times 1280} = 0.967$$

Loading, $\mu = 26.6$

$$\frac{\lambda_Z^*}{4} = 0.395(v_\varepsilon - c)^{-1.65} \qquad \text{(Mathur and Klinzing)}$$

$$\frac{\Delta p_{total}}{L} = 582 \, \text{N/m}^3$$

Individual contributions

$$\rho_p(1 - \varepsilon) = 413 \, \text{N/m}^3$$

$$\rho(\varepsilon) = 11.4 \, \text{N/m}^3$$

$$2f_L \frac{\rho\varepsilon(v/\varepsilon)^2}{D} = 99.8 \, \text{N/m}^3$$

$$\lambda_Z^* \frac{\rho_p(1 - \varepsilon)(v_\varepsilon - c)^2}{2D} = 57.8 \, \text{N/m}^3$$

Note the large contribution due to the vertical lift.

Example 4.3

Consider the transfer of 0.0252 kg/s of 200 μm diameter coal particles by carbon dioxide at an average velocity of 6.1 m/s in a 0.0508 m ID pipe. Determine the pressure loss around a 90° bend having a 0.61 m radius of curvature. The gas is at 3441 kN/m² and 38 °C. Use the design suggestion and the Schuchart analysis to determine the pressure loss.

$$\rho = 38 \, \text{kg/m}^3$$

$$\text{length of bend} = (\pi/2)(0.61) = 0.958 \, \text{m}$$

Design suggestion

$$\Delta p = 2f_L \frac{\rho v_\varepsilon^2 L}{D} + \lambda_Z^* \rho_p \frac{(1 - \varepsilon)c^2 L}{2D}$$

assuming $v_\varepsilon \simeq c = 6.1 \, \text{m/s}$ and the Konno and Saito friction is

$$\frac{\lambda_Z^*}{4} = 0.0285(gD)^{1/2}/c = 0.0033$$

$$\varepsilon = 1 - \dot{G}/A(\rho_p)c = 0.998$$

$$f_L = 0.0028$$

$$Re = 11.8 \times 10^5$$

$$\Delta p = 149.3 + 11.1 = 160.4 \, \text{N/m}^2$$

for a 90° bend

$$\Delta p_{\text{bend}} = 20 \Delta p_{\text{straight}} = 3208 \, \text{N/m}^2$$

Schuchart analysis

$$\left(\frac{\Delta p_{\text{bend}}}{\Delta p_{\text{straight}}} \right)_{(\text{solids})} = 210 \left(\frac{2R_B}{D} \right)^{-1.15}$$

$$\Delta p_{\text{bend (solids)}} = 6.32 \Delta p_{\text{straight (solids)}}$$

$$= 6.32(11.1) = 70.1 \, \text{N/m}^2$$

One must add the Δp for the gas alone as it passes through the bend. A variety of expressions could be used for this such as Ito's analysis. Taking the design suggestion for single phase flow one would have

$$\Delta p_{\text{bend (gas)}} = 20(149.3) = 2986 \, \text{N/m}^2$$

adding the solids effect one finds

$$\Delta p_{\text{bend}} = 2986 + 70.1 = 3056 \, \text{N/m}^2$$

Example 4.4

Often the question arises as to which frictional representation should be used for a particular analysis. A comparison will be made between the Konno and Saito and the Yang expressions for vertical flow of a gas–solid system. Consider the case where the following conditions are specified:

$$\rho_p = 1340 \, \text{kg/m}^3$$

$$d = 250 \, \mu\text{m}$$

$$\dot{G} = 1000 \, \text{kg/h}$$

$$v = 30 \, \text{m/s}$$

$$\rho_p = 1.2 \, \text{kg/m}^3$$

Using Example 4.1 as a base the vertical contribution must be added to the expression for $\Delta p/Z$. Using the Hinkle (IGT) particle velocity representation one can write

$$\frac{\Delta p}{Z} = 311 \text{ N/m}^3 + \rho_p(1 - \varepsilon) + \rho\varepsilon$$

$$= 311 + 16.1 + 1.2 = 328 \text{ N/m}^3$$

For the Yang expression an iterative technique must be employed since the particle velocity is implicitly related.

$$c = v_\varepsilon - w_{f0}\left(1 + \frac{\lambda_Z^* c^2 \varepsilon^{4.7}}{2gD}\right)^{1/2}$$

$$\lambda_Z^* = 0.0126 \frac{1 - \varepsilon}{\varepsilon^3}\left((1 - \varepsilon)\frac{Re_f}{Re_p}\right)^{-0.979}$$

where

$$Re_{pf} = \frac{w_{f0}\rho d}{\eta} \qquad Re_p = \frac{c\rho d}{\eta}$$

A Newton–Raphson iterative technique was devised yielding the following results:

$$\left(\frac{\Delta p}{Z}\right)_{vert} = 315.3 \text{ N/m}^3$$

$$c = 29.9 \text{ m/s}$$

$$\varepsilon = 0.9965$$

Comparing the two one sees

$$\left(\frac{\Delta p}{Z}\right)_{(K-S)} = 328 \text{ N/m}^3$$

$$\left(\frac{\Delta p}{Z}\right)_{(Y)} = 315.3 \text{ N/m}^3$$

Example 4.5

Estimation on the acceleration length in a gas–solid system is to be made. In order to approach this the Enick and Klinzing model is suggested

$$\frac{L}{D} = 0.527\left(\frac{D}{d}\right)^{-1.26}(1 + \mu)Re$$

For a 7.5 cm diameter tube conveying 300 μm particles at a Reynolds number of 10^5 estimate the acceleration length as a function of loading. Employing the above expression one has

$$L = 0.527(0.075)\left(\frac{0.075}{300 \times 10^{-6}}\right)^{-1.26}(1 + \text{loading})10^5$$

$$= (0.0395)(9.5 \times 10^{-4})(1 + \text{loading})10^5$$

Thus

L(m)	Loading
4.12	0.1
7.5	1.0
22.5	5

Example 4.6

Solids are being transported for 300 m in a horizontal 2.5 cm diameter pipe. The exit pressure is atmospheric. The solids flow is 500 kg/h with a solids to gas ratio of 2.0. Determine the upstream pressure 300 m from the exit. The solids have a density of 1300 kg/m³ and a diameter of 150 μm. Do not ignore compressibility effects. From equation (4.62) one can write for the isothermal compressible flow

$$p_2 - p_1 = \frac{g(MW)C_2}{RTC_1\alpha}\left(\frac{p_1 - p_2}{2}\right)L + \frac{g(MW)}{RT}\left(\frac{p_1 + p_2}{2}\right)L$$

$$+ f_L\frac{C_1^2 RT}{D(MW)}\frac{2L}{p_1 - p_2} + \lambda_z^* C_1 C_2\alpha\frac{RT}{MW}\frac{2L}{p_1 + p_2}$$

$$+ C_1^2\frac{RT}{MW}\left(\frac{1}{p_2} - \frac{1}{p_1}\right) + C_1 C_2\frac{\alpha RT}{MW}\left(\frac{1}{p_2} - \frac{1}{p_1}\right)$$

This equation must be solved numerically. Assume the constant α is 0.90 for the equation

$$c = \alpha v$$

The other parameters for the system are

$$MW = 29 \qquad \text{for air}$$
$$T = (273 + 20)K$$
$$g = 9.8\,\text{m/s}^2$$
$$L = 300\,\text{m}$$

$$p_1 = 1.013 \times 10^5 \,\mathrm{N/m^2}$$

$$R = 83.12 \times 10^2 \,\mathrm{m^3\,N/m^2/kg\,mol\,K}$$

$$f_{\mathrm{L}} = 0.0014 + 0.125(Re)^{-0.32}$$

$$\lambda_z^* = 0.0285(gD/c)^{1/2} \qquad \text{(Konno–Saito model)}$$

$$C_1 = 1.2v_\varepsilon$$

$$\varepsilon = 1 - \frac{\dot{G}}{\rho_{\mathrm{p}} Ac} = 1 - \frac{500/3600}{1300(\pi/4)(0.025)^2 c}$$

$$\mu = \text{loading} = 1 = \frac{\dot{G}/3600}{v\rho(\pi/4)(0.025)^2} = \frac{500/3600}{v(1.2)(\pi/4)(0.025)^2}$$

$$v = 118 \,\mathrm{m/s}$$

$$c = 106 \,\mathrm{m/s}$$

$$\varepsilon = 0.9979$$

$$C_1 = 142$$

$$C_2 = \rho_{\mathrm{p}} c(1 - \varepsilon) = (1300)(106)(0.002) = 275.6$$

Inserting these values and iterating on the equation gives p_2 as $1.673 \times 10^5 \,\mathrm{N/m^2}$ or $167.3 \,\mathrm{kN/m^2}$.

Example 4.7

The particle velocity in pneumatic transport is the result of dynamic forces acting between the particles, fluid and pipe walls. Assess the particle velocity of two flow situations assuming that the particles behave as individual entities.

(a)

$$d = 500 \,\mu\mathrm{m}$$

$$v = 20 \,\mathrm{m/s}$$

$$\rho_{\mathrm{p}} = 2500 \,\mathrm{kg/m^3}$$

$$\rho = 1.2 \,\mathrm{kg/m^3}$$

$$D = 5 \,\mathrm{cm}$$

$$\dot{G} = 2000 \,\mathrm{kg/h}$$

Short of carrying out a detailed experimental evaluation of this system to find c, one must must rely on some empirical model. For this case the Hinkle format as modified by IGT is appropriate:

$$c = v(1 - 0.68d^{0.92}\rho_{\mathrm{p}}^{0.5}\rho^{-0.2}D^{-0.54}),$$

$$= 20[1 - 0.68(500 \times 10^{-6})^{0.92}(2500)^{0.5}(1.2)^{-0.2}(0.05)^{-0.54}]$$

$$= 16.97 \,\mathrm{m/s}$$

The loading for this situation is

$$\mu = \text{loading} = \frac{\dot{G}}{vA\rho} = \frac{2000/3600}{20(\pi/4)(0.05)^2(1.2)} = 11.8$$

This is bordering on the medium dense phase regime.

(b)

$$d = 25\,\mu\text{m}$$
$$v = 30\,\text{m/s}$$
$$\rho_p = 1000\,\text{kg/m}^3$$
$$\rho = 1.2\,\text{kg/m}^3$$
$$D = 7.5\,\text{cm}$$
$$\dot{G} = 3000\,\text{kg/h}$$

Since the particle size is less than $40\,\mu\text{m}$, it is most appropriate to employ

$$c = v - w_{\text{fo}}$$

To determine the terminal velocity the characterization parameter K must be first determined

$$K = d\left(\frac{g\rho(\rho_p - \rho)}{\eta^2}\right)^{1/3}$$

$$= 25 \times 10^{-6}\left(\frac{9.8 \times 1.2(1000 - 1.2)}{(10^{-5})^2}\right)^{1/3}$$

$$= 1.21$$

The Stokes regime is thus applicable so

$$w_{\text{fo}} = \frac{d^2 g \Delta\rho}{18\eta} = \frac{(25 \times 10^{-6})^2(9.8)(1000 - 1.2)}{18 \times 10^{-5}}$$

$$= 0.0340\,\text{m/s}$$

Thus

$$c = 30 - 0.034 = 29.79\,\text{m/s}$$

The loading in this case is

$$\mu = \frac{3000/3600}{30(\pi/4)(0.075)^2(1.2)} = 5.2$$

This loading remains in the relatively dilute phase.

Example 4.8

Consider the horizontal gas–solid flow of silica particles with an average diameter of 200 μm being transported by air at 30.5 m/s and STP. The relative humidity of the air is 80%. The solids loading is 2.0 in a 0.025 m ID plastic pipe. The air relative humidity is lowered to 40% and the pressure drop is found to increase by 25%. Determine the magnitude of the electrostatic contributions.

Since the loading is relatively low the Konno and Saito frictional representation will be employed:

$$\frac{\Delta p}{L} = \frac{2f_L \rho \varepsilon v_\varepsilon^2}{D} + \lambda_z^* \frac{\rho_p (1 - \varepsilon)c^2}{2D}$$

Using Hinkle (LGT) correlation for c:

$$
\begin{aligned}
c &= v(1 - 0.68d^{0.92}\rho_p^{0.5}\rho^{-0.2}D^{-0.54}) \\
&= 30.5[1 - 0.68(200 \times 10^{-6})^{0.92} \\
&\quad \times (3590)^{0.5}(1.2)^{-0.2}(0.0254)^{-0.54}] \\
&= 30.5[1 - 0.68(0.000395)(59.9)(0.964)(7.27)] \\
&= 0.887(30.5) = 27.1 \text{ m/s}
\end{aligned}
$$

$$\mu = \text{loading} = 2 - \frac{\dot{G}}{(\pi/4)(0.0254)^2(1.2)(30.5)} \qquad \dot{G} = 0.037 \text{ kg/s}$$

$$\varepsilon = 1 - \frac{\dot{G}}{Ac\rho_p} = 1 - \frac{0.037}{(0.000645)(27.1)(3590)} = 0.9994$$

$$v \sim c$$

$$f_L = 0.0014 + 0.125(Re)^{-0.32}$$

$$Re = \frac{(0.0254)(30.5)(1.2)}{(10^{-5})} = 92.9 \times 10^3$$

$$\frac{\lambda_z^*}{4} = 0.0285(gD)^{1/2}/c = 0.0285(9.8 \times 0.0254)^{1/2}/27.1 = 0.00052$$

$$\frac{\Delta p}{L} = \frac{2 \times 0.0046(1.2)(0.9994)(30.5)^2}{0.0254}$$

$$+ \frac{4(0.00052)(3590)(0.0006)(27.1)^2}{2 \times 0.0254}$$

$$\Delta p/L = 404 + 64.8$$

$$\Delta p/L = 469 \text{ N/m}^3$$

For a 25% increase in $\Delta p/L$ due to electrostatics

$$\Delta p/L = 1.25(469) = 586 \text{ N/m}^3$$

thus

$$\left(\frac{\Delta p}{L}\right)_{electro} = 586 - 469 = 117\,\text{N/m}^3$$

$$\left(\frac{\Delta p}{L}\right)_{electro} = \frac{E_x q}{m_p}(1 - \varepsilon)\rho_p = 117\,\text{N/m}^3$$

The electrostatic force can be given by equation (4.38):

$$E_x q = 117\frac{\pi}{6}\frac{(200 \times 10^{-6})^3(3590)}{(3590)(1 - 0.9994)}$$

$$= \frac{4.9 \times 10^{-10}}{6 \times 10^{-4}} = 8.2 \times 10^{-5}\,\text{N}$$

Now considering $q = 10^{-14}\,\text{C}$

$$E_x = 8.2 \times 10^9\,\text{N/C}$$

This increased pressure drop caused by the electrostatic forces also affects the particle velocity.

One can develop this effect of electrostatics on the particle velocity at equilibrium as

$$c = v_e - w_{f0}\left(\frac{\lambda_z^* c^2}{2gD} + \frac{E_x q}{gm_p}\right)^{1/2}\varepsilon^{2.35}$$

For these $200\,\mu\text{m}$ diameter particles the characterization factor K is

$$K = 200 \times 10^{-6}\left(\frac{9.8 \times 3590 \times 1.2}{(10^{-5})^2}\right)^{1/3} = 14.8$$

This gives the intermediate range for w_{f0}:

$$w_{f0} = \frac{0.154g^{0.11}d^{1.14}\rho_p^{0.71}}{\rho^{0.29}\eta^{0.43}}$$

$$= \frac{0.153(5.06)(6.06 \times 10^{-5})(334)}{(1.05)(0.0071)} = 1.47\,\text{m/s}$$

$$c = 30.5 - 14.7\left(\frac{2 \times 0.00052c^2}{(9.8)(0.0254)} + 5.54\right)^{1/2}(0.9994)^{2.35}$$

This must be solved by trial and error or numerically to give

$$c = 26.25\,\text{m/s}$$

Example 4.9

Using Weber's analysis for the velocity of sound in a gas–solid system, determine this velocity for the following conditions.

(a) $c/v_\varepsilon = 0.5$, $\varepsilon = 0.8$
(b) $c/v_\varepsilon = 0.5$, $\varepsilon = 0.9$
(c) $c/v_\varepsilon = 1$, $\varepsilon = 0.94$

Using Fig. 4.9

for case (a): $a_s/a = 0.09$

$$a = 335\ \text{m/s} \qquad \text{at STP for air}$$

therefore

$$a_s = 30.2\ \text{m/s}$$

for case (b): $a_s/a = 0.11$

$$a_s = 0.11 \times 335 = 36.9\ \text{m/s}$$

for case (c): $a_s/a = 0.1$

$$a_s = 33.5\ \text{m/s}$$

Thus one sees a sizable reduction in the velocity of sound in a two phase system over that of a single phase.

Example 4.10

Consider a Y expansion unit where the angle between the Y is 45°. All pipe diameters are the same and there is an equal split of volumetric flows. The upstream gas velocity is 20 m/s with a density of 1.2 kg/m³. The solid loading is 5.0. Find the pressure loss across the Y.

$$\frac{\Delta p_{total}}{\rho v^2/2} = \left(\frac{\dot{V}_2}{\dot{V}_1}\right)^2 - 1.59\left(\frac{\dot{V}_2}{\dot{V}_1}\right) + 0.97(\mu)_2\left[0.48\left(\frac{\dot{V}_2}{\dot{V}_1}\right)^2 + 0.09\right]$$
$$+ (\mu)_2\left[0.48\left(\frac{\dot{V}_2}{\dot{V}_1}\right)^2 + 0.09\right]$$

Therefore

$$\Delta p_{total} = (1.2)\frac{(20)^2}{2}[(2)^2 - 1.59(2) + 0.97 + 5(0.48(2)^2 + 0.09)]$$

$$= 2842\ \text{N/m}^2$$

Example 4.11

Using Yang's format for frictional representation determine the particle velocity of the system.

$$\frac{\lambda_Z^*}{4} = 0.00315 \frac{1-\varepsilon}{\varepsilon^3} \left(\frac{(1-\varepsilon)w_{f0}}{v_\varepsilon - c} \right)^{-0.979}$$

and for the particle velocity

$$c = v_\varepsilon - w_{f0} \left[\left(1 + 4 \frac{\lambda_Z^* c^2}{2gD} \right) \varepsilon^{4.7} \right]^{1/2}$$

In order to solve this implicit system assume a value for c first and then calculate ε and v_ε

$$\varepsilon = 1 - \frac{\dot{G}}{cA\rho_p}$$

$$v_\varepsilon = v/\varepsilon$$

With this information λ_Z^* can be found. Insert c, λ_Z^* and ε into the particle equation to see if agreement is achieved. For the iterative process let

$$F_1 = c - v_\varepsilon + w_{f0} \left[\left(1 + \frac{\lambda_Z^* c^2}{2gD} \right) \varepsilon^{4.7} \right]^{1/2}$$

and

$$\frac{dF_1}{dc} = 1 + \frac{1}{2} \left(1 + 4 \frac{\lambda_Z^* c^2}{2gD} \right)^{-1/2} \frac{2\lambda_Z^* c}{2gD} \varepsilon^{2.35}$$

For the new estimate of c one uses the Newton–Raphson procedure, thus

$$c_{new} = c_{old} - \frac{F_1}{dF_1/dc}$$

The calculations return to the beginning and iterate until $c_{new} - c_{old} < 0.001$.

Example 4.12

Dixon has developed an expression to predict the maximum loading for gas–solid flow. This expression is given as

$$\mu_{max} = \dot{G}/A \left(\mu v_{mf} + \frac{\varepsilon_{mf} \dot{G}/A \, \rho}{1 + \varepsilon_{mf} \rho_p} \right)^{-1}$$

For particles 250 μm in diameter and a density of 1500 kg/m^3 with gas density of 1.2 kg/m^3 and the solid flow rate of 100 kg/m^2, the value of μ_{max} can be determined.

For small particles

$$v_{mf} = \frac{d^2 g(\rho_p - \rho)}{1650 \eta}$$

$$= \frac{(250 \times 10^{-6})^2 (9.8)(1500 - 1.2)}{(1650)(10^{-5})} = 0.056 \text{ m/s}$$

The voidage at this condition can be found from Ergun's equation in the form

$$\frac{1.75}{\phi_s \varepsilon_{mf}^3} Re_p^2 + \frac{1.50(1 - \varepsilon_{mf})}{\phi_s \varepsilon_{mf}^3} Re_p^2 - K^3 = 0$$

where

$$Re_p = \frac{v_{min} d \rho}{\eta}$$

$$\phi_s = \text{sphericity}$$

$$K = d\left(\frac{g\rho(\rho_p - \rho)}{\eta^2}\right)$$

with $\phi_s = 1$

$$Re_p = 1.68$$

$$K = 13.9$$

Thus

$$\frac{4.94}{\varepsilon_{mf}^3} + \frac{423(1 - \varepsilon)}{\varepsilon_{mf}^3} - 2686 = 0$$

$$\varepsilon_{mf} = 0.44$$

Therefore

$$\mu_{max} = 100\left((1.2)(0.056) + \frac{(0.44)(100)}{(0.56)}\frac{(1.2)}{1500}\right)^{-1}$$

$$= 769$$

For a 0.05 m diameter pipe

$$\dot{G} = 100(\pi/4)(0.05)^2 = 0.196 \text{ kg/s}$$

REFERENCES

1. Kaye, B.H. (1981) *Direct Characterization of Fine Particles*, Wiley, New York.
2. Boothroyd, R.G. (1971) *Flowing Gas Solids Suspensions*, Chapman and Hall, London.
3. Tchen, C.M. (1947) Ph.D. Thesis, Delft, Martinus Nijhoff, The Hague.
4. Corrosin, S. and Lumley, J. (1956) *Appl. Sci. Res.*, **6A**, 114.
5. Soo, S.L. (1967) *Fluid Dynamics of Multiphase Systems*, Blaisdell, Waltham, Mass.
6. Grace, J.R. and Tuot, J. (1979) *Trans. Inst. Chem. Engrs*, **57**, 49.
7. Yousfi, Y. and Gau, G. (1974) *Chem. Eng. Sci.*, **29**, 1939.
8. Heywood, H.J. (1963) *Pharm. Pharmacol. Suppl.*, **15**, 56T.
9. Beddow, J.K., Lee. Y., Vetter, A.F. and Lenth, R. (1980) *Powder Technology*, **25**, 137.
10. Beddow, J.K., Philip, G.C., Vetter, A.F. and Nasta, M.D. (1977) *Powder Technology*, **18**, 19.
11. Beddow, J.K., Fong, S.T. and Vetter, A.F. (1979) *Powder Technology*, **22**, 17.
12. Mandelbrot, B.B. (1983) *The Fractal Geometry of Nature*, Freeman, New York.
13. Kaye, B.H. (1983) *Modern Methods of Fine Particle Characterization* (ed. J.K. Beddow), CRC Press, Cleveland.
14. Flook, A.G. (1978) *Powder Technology*, **21**, 295.
15. McCabe, W.L. and Smith, J.C. (1976) *Unit Operations of Chemical Engineering*, 3rd edn, McGraw-Hill, New York.
16. Wen, C.Y. and Yu, Y.H. (1966) *Chem. Eng. Prog. Symp.*, **62**, 100.
17. Yang, W.C. (1976) *Pneumotransport*, VI.
18. Govier, G.W. and Aziz, K. (1972) *The Flow of Complex Mixtures in Pipes*, van Nostrand Reinhold, New York.
19. Weber, M. (1973) *Stromungs-Fordertechnik*, Krausskopf Verlag.
20. Wen, C.Y. (1971) *Proc. Bulk Handling Conference*, Vol. I, University of Pittsburgh, Pittsburgh, PA.
21. Hinkle, B.L. (1953) *Ph.D. Thesis*, Georgia Institute of Technology, Atlanta, Ga.
22. (1978) Institute of Gas Technology, Dept. of Energy, Contract FE 2286–32, October.
23. Mathur, M.P. and Klinzing, G.E. (1983) AIChE Annual Meeting Washington, D.C., Nov.
24. Matsen, J. (1981) AIChE Annual Meeting Washington, D.C., Nov.
25. Klinzing, G.E. *Ind. Eng. Chem. Process Design Development*.
26. Konno, H. and Saito, S.J. (1969) *Chem. Eng. Japan*, **2**, 211.
27. Yang, W.C. (1976) *Int. Powder & Bulk Solids Handling*, Chicago, May.
28. Klinzing, G.E. (1981) *Gas Solid Transport*, McGraw-Hill, New York.
29. Shimizu, A., Echigo, R. and Hasigawa, S. (1978) *Int. J. Multiphase Flow*, **4**, 53.
30. Kerker, L. (1977) *Ph.D. Thesis*, Universität Karlsruhe.
31. Yousfi, K. and Alia, Y. (1981) *Second World Congress of Chem. Engr*, Montreal.
32. Enick, R. and Klinzing, G. E. (1985) *Proc. Fine Particle Soc.*, Miami.
33. Zenker, P. (1972) *Staub-Reinhalt, Luft* **32**, 1.
34. Weinstein, H. (1983) AIChE Annual Meeting Washington, D.C., Nov.
35. Capes, C.E. and Nakamura, K. (1973) *Can. J. Chem. Eng.*, **51**, 31.
36. Wen, C.Y. and Simon, H.P. (1959) *AIChE J.*, **5**, 263.
37. Rudinger, G. (1976) *Gas-Solid Suspensions*, VKI Lecture Series 90.
38. Jung, R. (1966–8) *BWK*, **118**, 377.

39. Jung, R. (1969) *VDI Forch. Heft,* 532.
40. Yamamoto, A. Takashima, M., Yamaguchi, T., Tanaka, S. and Morikawa, Y. (1977) *Bull. JSME,* **20**, 991.
41. Morimoto, T., Yamamoto, A., Nakao, T., Tanaka, S. and Morikawa, Y. (1977) *Bull. JSME,* **20**, 991.
42. Morikawa, Y., Kono, T. and Heramato, T. (1978) *Int. J. Multiphase Flow,* **4**, 397.
43. Ito, H. (1959) *Trans. ASME J. Basic Eng.,* **81D**, 123.
44. Ito, H. (1960) *Trans. ASME J. Basic Eng.,* **82D**, 131.
45. Schuchart, P. (1969) *Chem. Eng. Technol.,* **41**, 1251.
46. Spronson, J.C., Gray, N.A. and Haynes, J. (1972) *Pneumotransport 2,* Paper B2.
47. Mason, J.S. and Smith, B.V. (1973) *Pneumotransport 2,* Paper A2.
48. Morikawa, Y., Tsuji, Y., Matsui, K.J. and Hani, Y. (1970) *Int. J. Multiphase Flow,* **4**, 575.
49. Duckworth, R.A. and Rose, H.E. (1969) *The Engineer,* March 14, 392.
50. Bodner, S. (1982) *Pneumatech I,* Stratford, England.
51. Enick, R. and Klinzing, G.E. (1989) *Int. J. Multiphase Flow* (in press).
52. Mathur, M.P. and Klinzing, G.E. (1989) *J. Freight Pipelines* (in press).
53. Shimizu, A., Echigo, R. and Hasegawa, S. (1978) *Int. J. Multiphase Flow,* **4**, 53.
54. Marcus, R.D., Hilbert, J. and Klinzing, G.E. (1989) *J. Freight Pipelines* (in press).
55. Smeltzer, E.E., Eckhardt, D.A., Yang, W.C. and Skriba, M.C. (1979) Research Report 79-8E3-PWTRS-RI, Westinghouse Research.
56. Tsuji, Y. and Morikawa, Y. (1980) *Fordern und Heben,* **30**, No. 6, 515.
57. Canning, D.A. and Thompson, A.I. (1982) *Century II Conf. ASME Meeting,* San Francisco, CA, August.
58. Saroff, L., Gromicko, F.H., Johnson, G.E., Strakey, J.P. and Haynes, W.P. (1976) *69th Annual Meeting AIChE,* Chicago.
59. Lohrmann, P. (1983) *M.Sc. dissertation,* University of the Witwatersrand, Johannesburg, South Africa.
60. Yerushalmi, J. and Cankert, N.T. (1979) *Powder Technology,* **24**, 187.
61. Weinstein, H. (1983). *AIChE Meeting,* Washington, Nov.
62. Dixon, G. (1979) *Int. Conf. on Pneumatic Conveying,* Cafe Royal, London, Jan.
63. Muschelknautz, E. and Krambrock, W. (1969) *Chemie-Ing-Tech.,* **41**, 1164.
64. Konrad, K., Harrison, D., Nedderman, R.M. and Davidson, J.F. (1980) *Pneumatransport,* **5**, Paper E1, p. 225.
65. Tsuji, Y., Morikawa, Y. and Honda, H. (1979) *J. Powder & Bulk Solids Technology,* **3**, 30.
66. Hovmand, S. and Davidson, J.F. (1971) in *Fluidization* (eds J.F. Davidson and D. Harrison), Academic Press, London, pp. 193–260.
67. Thiel, W.J. and Potter, O.E. (1977) *Ind. Eng. Chem. Fundamentals,* **16**, 242–7.
68. Steward, P.S.B. and Davidson, J.F. (1967) *Powder Technology,* **1**, 61–80.
69. Nicklin, D.J., Wilkes, J.D. and Davidson, J.F. (1962), *Trans. Inst. Chem. Engrs,* **40**, 61–8.
70. Kehoe, P.W.K. and Davidson, J.F. (1971) *Inst. Chem. Engrs (London) Symp. Series,* **33**, 97–116.
71. Matsen, J.M., Hovmand, S. and Davidson, J.F. (1969) *Chem. Eng. Sci.,* **24**, 1743–54.
72. Matsen, J.M. (1973) *Powder Technology,* **7**, 93–6.
73. Ormiston, R.M. (1966), Slug flow in fluidized beds, *Ph.D. Thesis,* University of Cambridge.

74. Capes, C.E. and Nakamura, K. (1973) *Can. J. Chem. Eng.*, **51**, 31–8.
75. Van Swaaij, W.P.M., Buurman, C. and van Breugel, W.C. (1970) *Chem. Eng. Sci.*, **25**, 1818–20.
76. Zenz, F.A. and Othmer, D.F. (1960) *Fluidization and Fluid Particle Systems*, Reinhold, New York.
77. Geldart, D. (1973) *Powder Technology*, **7**, 285–92.
78. Yerushalmi, J., Turner, D.H. and Squires, A.M. (1976) *Ind. Eng. Chem. Process Design Development*, **15**, 47–52.
79. Yerushalmi, J. and Cankurt, N. (1979) *Powder Technology*, **24**, 187–205.
80. Reh, L. (1971) *Chem. Eng. Prog.*, **67**(2), 58–63.
81. Nakamura, K. and Capes, C.E. (1973) *Can. J. Chem. Eng.*, **51**, 39–46.
82. Nakamura, K. and Capes, C.E. (1976), in *Fluidization Technology*, Vol. 2, (eds D.L. Keairns *et al.*), Hemisphere Publishing Corporation, Washington, pp. 159–84.
83. Richardson, J.F. and Zaki, W.N. (1954) *Trans. Inst. Chem. Engrs*, **32**, 35–53.
84. Knowlton, T.M., Hirsan, I. and Leung, L.S. (1978), in *Fluidization*, (eds J.F. Davidson and D.L. Keairns) Cambridge University Press, Cambridge.
85. Hinkle, B.L. (1953) Acceleration of particles and pressure drops encountered in horizontal pneumatic conveying, *Ph.D. Thesis*, Georgia Institute of Technology.
86. Wen, C.Y. and Simons, H.P. (1959) *AIChE J.*, **6**, 263–8.
87. Yang, W.C. (1974), *AIChE J.*, **20**, 605–7.
88. Bandrowski, J., Kaczmarzyk, G., Nowk, W. and Sciazko, M. (1977) *Inz. Chem.*, **7**, 243–53, 499–507.
89. Tsuji, Y. and Morikawa, Y. (1982) *Int. J. Multiphase Flow*, **8**, 657.
90. Tsuji, Y. and Morikawa, Y. (1982) *Trans. ASME*, **104**.
91. Stemerding, S. (1962) *Chem. Eng. Sci.*, **17**, 599.
92. Reddy, K.V.S. and Pei, D.C.T. (1969) *I.E.C. Fund*, **8**, 490.
93. Van Swaaij, W.P.M., Buurman, C. and van Breugel, I.W. (1970) *Chem. Eng. Sci.*, **25**, 1818.
94. Capes, C.E. and Nakamura, K. (1973) *Can. J. Chem. Eng.*, **51**, 31.
95. Konno, H. and Saito, S.J. (1969) Chem. Eng. Japan, **2**, 211.
96. Yang, W.C. (1976) *Int. Powder & Bulk Solids Handling*, Chicago, May.
97. Yang, W.C. (1978) *AIChE J.*, **24**, 548.
98. Stegmaier, W. (1978) *Fordern and Heben*, **28**, 363.
99. Soo, S.L., Dimick, R.C. and Hohnstreiter, G.F. (1964) *IEC Fund*, **3**, 98.
100. Arundel, P.A., Bibb, S.D. and Boothroyd, R.G. (1970) *Powder Tech.*, **4**, 302.
101. Zenker, P. (1972) *Staub-Reinhalt, Luft*, **32**, 1.

5
Flow regimes in vertical and horizontal conveying

5.1 INTRODUCTION

The characteristics of *vertical* upflow pneumatic conveying can best be described qualitatively in terms of Zenz's [1] often quoted plot of pressure gradient versus gas velocity for different solid flow rates (Fig. 5.1).

Line AB in Fig. 5.1 refers to zero solid flow in the pipe and a family of curves of increasing solid flow rates is also presented in the figure. Referring to a fixed solid flow rate of $\dot{G}_1$, at a high gas velocity (point C say), the solid volumetric concentration is low (well below 1%) and the particles are apparently uniformly dispersed. This is known as lean phase or dilute phase flow. When the gas velocity is reduced at the same solid flow rate $\dot{G}_1$, solid concentration in the pipe increases and wall frictional loss decreases. Pressure gradient in fully developed vertical conveying is made up of two components, namely a wall frictional loss component and a gravitational component. As the gas velocity is reduced, frictional loss decreases while the gravitational component increases as a result of an increase in solid concentration. Along CD the decrease in frictional loss is significantly higher than the increase in the gravitational component. Thus the overall pressure gradient decreases with decrease in gas velocity along CD. As the gas velocity is further reduced, the gravitational component becomes more significant and the curve goes through a minimum at E. A further decrease in gas flow rate will lead to an increase in pressure gradient along EF as the gravitational component becomes predominant. Along EF the solid concentration is high and the flow mode here is loosely defined as dense phase flow. The solid particles are no longer uniformly dispersed. Two types of dense phase are possible depending on the characteristics of the gas–solid tube system. In one, particles are conveyed upwards by 'slugs' or 'bubbles' and this is defined here as slugging dense phase conveying (Fig 5.2).

In the other dense phase mode, clusters of particles appear and solids are conveyed upwards with considerable internal solid circulation. This is defined as dense phase conveying without slugging (Fig. 5.3) and is analogous to a recirculating fluidized bed, or a 'fast fluidized bed' [2]. Whether a system behaves as in slugging dense phase conveying or non-slugging dense phase conveying

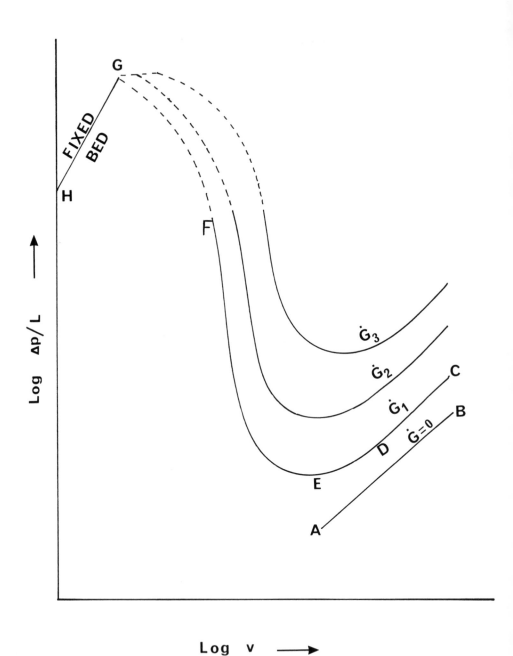

Figure 5.1 Flow characteristics in vertical pneumatic conveying (after Zenz [1]).

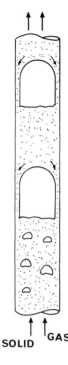

SOLID ↑ ↑GAS   **Figure 5.2** Slugging/bubbling dense phase conveying.

SOLID GAS   **Figure 5.3** Non-slugging dense phase conveying.

depends on the properties of the gas–solid tube system and will be considered in Section 5.2.

For the slugging conveying system, the transition from dilute phase flow to slugging conveying is a sharp one and this transition is known as 'choking'. For non-slugging dense phase conveying, the transition between dilute phase and

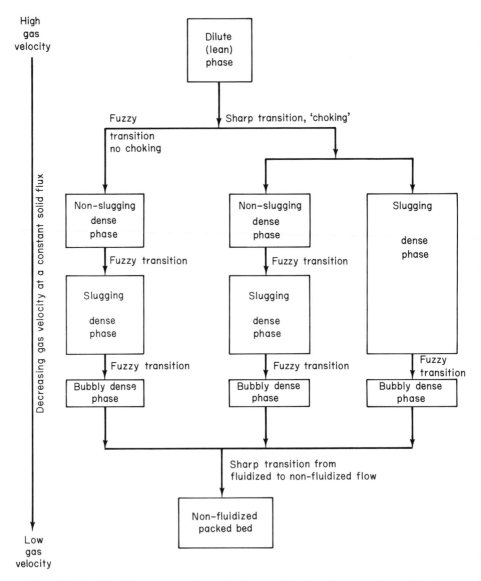

Figure 5.4 Possible flow patterns in vertical conveying showing two types of system: choking system (right-hand branch) and non-choking type system (left-hand branch).

dense phase conveying can be either sharp or diffuse. The flow chart in Fig. 5.4 shows the two possible classes of behaviour as the gas velocity is reduced from a high value at the same solid flow rate.

In general, fine particles in large tubes tend towards non-slugging dense phase flow, while choking is observed with coarse particles in small tubes. As shown in Fig. 5.4, when the gas velocity is further reduced in the non-slugging dense phase mode, slugging or bubbling dense phase conveying occurs although this transition from the non-slugging to the slugging/bubbling mode is also diffuse.

Returning to Fig. 5.1, as the gas velocity is further reduced beyond the point F, the relative velocity between gas and solid decreases until at F it is just sufficient to keep the particles in suspension. Further reduction of gas flow rate below F (along FG) results in packed bed flow or moving-bed flow in which solids move *en block* with little relative motion between particles and the solids are not entirely propelled by the gas. Point F in Fig. 5.1 represents the transition point from fluidized solid flow (where the solids are in suspension) to packed bed flow. This is a sharp transition and is indicated in Fig. 5.4. We shall define here a system that follows the left-hand branch of the chart in Fig. 5.4 as a 'non-choking system' while one that follows the right-hand branch as a 'choking system'.

In practice vertical pneumatic conveying is generally carried out in the dilute phase regime and much of the published work on vertical pneumatic conveying has been restricted to this regime. For operation in the dilute phase regime it is desirable to operate at as low an air flow rate as possible from energy requirements, pipe erosion and particle attrition considerations. Dense phase flow is less often used because of the erratic nature of the flow, the pressure fluctuations, high pressure drops and pipe line vibration. In a solid riser reactor, however, (in which the vertical pneumatic conveying tube acts as a gas–solid reactor) dense phase flow is sometimes preferred to give a high solid concentration in the tube. Moving-bed flow is generally to be avoided because of very high pressure drops and the problem of blockage.

In the design of a pneumatic conveying system, it is important to be able to predict the flow behaviour of a particular gas–solid system and to predict the transition velocities for various flow patterns and to predict particle segregation that may occur. These questions will be taken up in this chapter.

5.2 CHOKING VERSUS NON-CHOKING SYSTEM IN VERTICAL FLOW

5.2.1 The choking phenomenon

The phenomenon of choking in vertical pneumatic conveying has been described in detail by Zenz and Othmer [3]. At a high gas velocity particles are carried up the riser tube as an apparently evenly dispersed suspension in the so called dilute phase mode. If the air velocity is reduced gradually at the same mass flow rate of solid, the *in situ* solid concentration increases. A point will be reached when the uniformly dispersed suspension becomes unstable. The entire suspension collapses and particles are then transported up the riser in slugging flow (Fig. 5.2) or non-slugging dense phase flow (Fig. 5.3) at a higher average solid concentration. The point of choking is the sharp transition point from upflow of solids as a thin suspension (i.e. dilute phase flow) to slugging or non-slugging dense phase flow. The gas velocity at the choking point is the choking velocity at the particular solid flow rate. Similarly the choking transition can also be approached from the dense phase mode behaviour by gradually increasing the air velocity until a sharp transition to dilute phase conveying occurs.

It should be stressed that the choking transition is not the same as the transition or instability resulting from interaction between the characteristics of the blower and of the pneumatic conveying system [4]. With blowers characterized by reducing volumetric delivery at increasing delivery pressure, the transition from dilute phase flow to dense phase flow regime may be triggered off by a sudden increase in solid flow rate (or a sudden reduction of gas flow rate). This causes an increase of pressure drop in the conveying line and hence the blower delivery pressure. The blower volumetric delivery falls causing a further

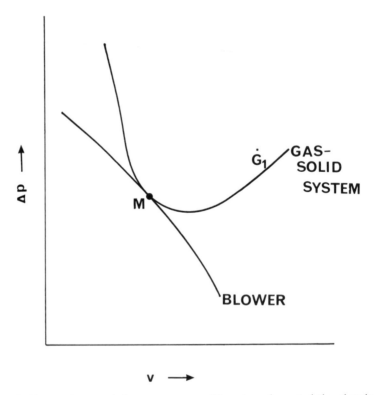

Figure 5.5 Blower characteristics versus gas–solid system characteristics showing tangential interception (after Bandrowski *et al.* [7]).

increase of pressure drop and so on. This instability may well lead eventually to choking depending on the characteristics of the blower and the operating conditions prior to the initial perturbation. Thus the onset of instability in this case occurs at a velocity somewhat higher than the choking gas velocity [5, 6]. Bandrowski *et al.* [7] defined choking for a gas–solid blower system where the blower characteristics curve and the system characteristics curve intercept tangentially to each other. Point M in Fig. 5.5 is defined as the choking point for the system at the solid flow rate $\dot{G}_1$. In this definition the choking flow rate is dependent on the characteristics of the blower. This definition will not be used here although the concept of defining a critical point at M in Fig. 5.5 has some merit in the design of pneumatic conveying systems [7].

The mechanism causing the 'choking phenomenon' is not entirely understood. Not all systems exhibit this phenomenon. In general fine powders in large diameter tubes are less likely to 'choke' than coarse particles in smaller diameter tubes. The quantitative prediction of whether a system exhibits the choking phenomenon will now be taken up.

5.2.2 Choking versus non-choking

A number of conflicting analyses on predicting whether a system could choke or otherwise is available in the literature [8, 10] and will be described and compared here.

5.2.2.1 Analysis of Yousfi and Gau [8]

In an analysis similar to that proposed by Molerus [11] for fluidization, Yousfi and Gau considered the stability of a uniform suspension of particles subject to a sinusoidal perturbation of gas velocity. The criterion for instability of the uniform suspension is when solid concentration increases with time and distance along the riser as a result of the imposed perturbation. Their analysis shows that for the uniform suspension to be stable, S (a constant) is given by

$$S = \varepsilon(1 - \varepsilon)Fr_{fd}^2 \tag{5.1}$$

where

$$Fr_{fd}^2 = w_{f0}^2/gd$$

The constant S is related to solid concentration at the onset of choking by

$$(1 - \varepsilon_c) = \left[1 - \left(1 - \frac{4S}{Fr_{fd}^2}\right)^{1/2}\right]^2 \tag{5.2}$$

Yousfi and Gau measured the choking voidage for a polystyrene system to give an experimental value of $S = 35$. Equation (5.2) has no solution for Froude number less than $2S^{1/2}$. Yousfi and Gau suggested that for $Fr_{fd}^2 < 4S$ the uniform solid suspension is stable, i.e. the system will not choke. For choking to occur

$$w_{f0}^2/gd = Fr_{fd}^2 > 4S > 140 \tag{5.3}$$

Yousfi and Gau claimed that the prediction is supported by their own experimental results on 20 μm and 55 μm catalysts which do not choke in practice in accordance with predictions from equation (5.3).

For choking systems, equation (5.2) can be used for predicting voidage at choking using $S = 35$. Good agreement between observed and predicted voidage was reported by Yousfi and Gau.

The analysis of Yousfi and Gau has two deficiencies, namely the assumption that drag force is not affected by change in voidage and that wall effects are not accounted for. As the analysis is for an unbounded fluid with no wall effects, it cannot predict the effect of pipe diameter on whether a system will choke. In practice, tube diameter is an important parameter—a gas–solid system may exhibit choking in a small tube but not in a large tube.

5.2.2.2 Analysis of Yang [9]

Yang [9] considered the stability of slugging conveying (as against the stability of a uniform suspension). Following an argument put forward by Harrison *et al.* [12] and de Koch [13] that a bubble in a fluidized bed becomes unstable when its velocity is the same as the terminal velocity of a single particle, Yang postulated that slugging conveying becomes unstable when the slug velocity ω_B, relative to the dense phase solids, is greater than w_{f0}, i.e.

$$w_b > w_{f0} \qquad \text{for no slugging} \tag{5.4}$$

The velocity of a slug w_b is given by [14]

$$w_b = 0.35 \, (gD)^{1/2} \tag{5.5}$$

where D is the tube diameter. Thus Yang's criterion becomes, from equations (5.4) and (5.5)

$$0.35 \, (gD)^{1/2} > w_{f0} \qquad \text{for no slugging (i.e. no choking)}$$

or

$$w_{f0}^2/gD = Fr_{fD}^2 > 0.12 \quad \text{for choking to occur} \tag{5.6}$$

In Yang's analysis the key parameter is the Froude number based on tube diameter, compared with the Froude number based on particle diameter in the analysis of Yousfi and Gau. Comparison of the two criteria is given in Fig. 5.6. It can be seen that both the criteria appear to represent the limited published data well.

A lot more experimental work is needed in the second and fourth quadrants of Fig. 5.6 to critically compare the two criteria.

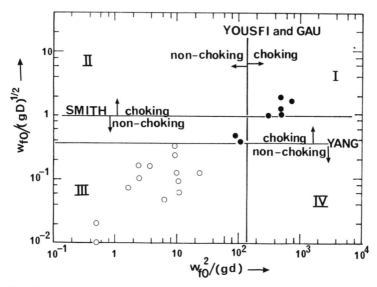

Figure 5.6 Comparison of experimental observations with prediction on demarcation between choking and non-choking systems: ○, observed non-choking systems; ●, observed choking systems (after Leung and Wiles [29]).

5.2.2.3 Analysis of Smith [10]

A third analysis dealing with choking versus non-choking systems is given by Smith [10, 15]. Using an earlier analysis of Slis *et al.* [16] on the velocity of propagation of a porosity wave, he showed that the wave velocity in vertical pneumatic conveying relative to the solid velocity is the same as that for a fluidized bed and is given by

$$v_\varepsilon = w_{f0}\varepsilon^n n(1 - \varepsilon)/\varepsilon \qquad (5.7)$$

where v_ε is the velocity of the porosity wave and n is the exponent in the Richardson–Zaki equation [17]. Equation (5.7) is derived using the Richardson–Zaki [17] equation relating voidage and relative velocity:

$$v/\varepsilon - c = w_{f0}\varepsilon^{(n-1)} \qquad (5.8)$$

The exponential n in equations (5.7) and (5.8) is a function of particle Reynolds number and (d/D) as given by Richardson and Zaki [17] (Chapter 4). Smith [10] postulated that bubbles cannot rise at a velocity higher than the wave propagation velocity v_ε. The bubble velocity is given by Davidson and Harrison [14] as,

$$w_b = 0.71 \, (gd_E)^{0.5} \qquad (5.9)$$

where w_b is the slug velocity and d_E the volume equivalent bubble diameter.

In vertical pneumatic conveying Smith suggested arbitrarily an effective bubble diameter in a riser tube so that equation (5.9) becomes

$$w_b = 0.41(gD)^{0.5} \tag{5.10}$$

where D is the tube diameter. For choking to occur (i.e. stable bubbles) according to Smith's postulate,

$$v_\varepsilon > w_b \tag{5.11}$$

Equations (5.7), (5.10) and (5.11) can be combined to yield

$$w_{f0}\varepsilon^{n-1}n(1-\varepsilon)/(gD)^{0.5} > 0.41 \tag{5.12}$$

for choking to occur. Equation (5.12) cannot, however, be used directly for the prediction of demarcation between choking and non-choking systems as ε is unknown. Taking the limiting case for a maximum value of $[\varepsilon^{(n-1)}(1-\varepsilon)]$ in equation (5.12) we have,

$$w_{f0}n([n-1]/n)^{n-1} - (1/n)]/(gD)^{0.5} > 0 \tag{5.13}$$

The range of n is from about 2.4 to 4.6 [17]. For $n = 2.4$ we have

$$Fr_{fD}^2 = w_{f0}^2/gD > 0.59 \quad \text{for choking to occur} \tag{5.14}$$

For $n = 4.6$ we have

$$Fr_{fD}^2 = w_{f0}^2/gD > 0.95 \quad \text{for choking to occur} \tag{5.15}$$

Equations (5.14) and (5.15) are similar in form to Yang's criterion given by equation (5.6)—although the bases of the analyses of Smith and of Yang are entirely different. Examination of the data in Fig. 5.6 suggests that Yang's equation is more consistent with observed results.

5.2.2.4 Analysis of Matsen [44]

The key point of Matsen's analysis is his observation of the implication of the slip velocity and voidage relationship in dense phase and in lean phase conveying. The slip velocity w is defined by

$$w = \frac{v}{\varepsilon} - \frac{c'}{1-\varepsilon} \tag{5.16}$$

In slugging dense phase conveying the slip velocity voidage equation can be obtained by extending a similar equation for a slugging fluidized bed to give

(Matsen *et al.*, 1969)

$$c' = \left(v - v_{min} - \frac{\varepsilon - \varepsilon_{mf}}{1 - \varepsilon} \right) \frac{1 - \varepsilon}{\varepsilon} \qquad (5.17)$$

Equation (5.17) has been shown to be applicable in the voidage range from about 0.5 to about 0.91 for slugging conveying.

In dilute phase conveying there is some evidence to suggest that voidage decreases with increase in slip velocity. One such empirical relationship is

$$w/w_{f0} = 10.8(1 - \varepsilon)^{0.293} \qquad \text{for } 0.9997 > \varepsilon > 0.91 \qquad (5.18)$$

A plot of gas superficial and solid superficial velocity with voidage as a parameter using equations (5.16) and (5.18) is shown in Fig. 5.7(a). When more than one voidage can occur at a given set of velocities, it can be shown that lines of steeper slope represent a condition in which solids flux (at constant gas flux) increases as voidage increases, a situation which is not stable to perturbations. In Fig. 5.7(b) only the stable operating lines are included in the flow regime diagram.

From Fig. 5.7(a), Matsen concluded that in the dilute phase regime for a system following equation (5.18), a limiting envelope formed by lines of constant voidage exists, i.e. curve ABC in Fig. 5.7(c). Thus dilute phase flow cannot exist to the left of curve ABC. In this region (i.e. left of ABC), slugging dense phase is applicable. Lines of constant voidage for slugging flow from equation (5.17) are included in the phase regime diagram in Fig. 5.7(c). It can readily be shown that curve ABC corresponds to $(\partial v / \partial \varepsilon)_{c'} = 0$.

Consider reducing gas velocity at a constant solids flux along line YBX in Fig. 5.7(c). In the region YB, dilute phase conveying occurs with a gradual decrease in voidage with decrease in velocity. At point B, transition to slugging conveying occurs with a stepwise change in voidage. Thus point B corresponds to the choking transition point. Further decrease in velocity along BX results in a gradual decrease in voidage in the slugging dense phase flow regime.

When the solids flux is high, Matsen showed that no stepwise change in voidage would occur, i.e. no choking. This is illustrated by considering gradual reduction in gas velocity along NAM in Fig. 5.7(c). Gradual decrease in voidage occurs throughout including at the transition point A from dilute phase to dense phase flow. Thus choking will not be observed for operation at this higher solids flux. Thus according to Matsen, all gas–solid systems may exhibit choking or non-choking behaviour depending on the solids flow rate.

5.2.2.5 *Choking versus non-choking—a summary*

In summary three criteria are available in the literature for predicting whether choking would occur in a system. The theoretical bases of the three criteria are different. Of the three predictions, Yang's analysis appears to be fairly consistent with experimental results, and equation (5.6) may be used for estimating if choking would occur in a particular system. The experimental evidence, however, is not conclusive and much further work is required.

For a choking system, the equation of Yousfi and Gau (equation (5.2)) and that of Smith (equation (5.12)) can be used for predicting the voidage at the onset of choking.

The analysis of Matsen [44] is the only one that recognizes the importance of solids flux. Recent work on 'fast fluidization' (loosely defined as vertical pneumatic conveying with very high solids flux) suggests that the behaviour of the system depends a great deal on solids flux. This is in support of Matsen's analysis. Matsen's approach is based on the empirically observed slip velocity voidage relationship for dilute phase flow. It has no mechanistic background. His approach also suffers from the uncertainty of the general validity of equation (5.18). Further work will be necessary to establish Matsen's approach on a firm basis.

It can be seen that there is still considerable uncertainty in the prediction of whether a given system will exhibit the choking transition. In the absence of further information, the use of Matsen's approach is tentatively recommended here for explaining the phenomenon as it appears to take into account most important parameters that may be relevant to choking. The equation of Yang (equation (5.6)) may be used for quantitative determination.

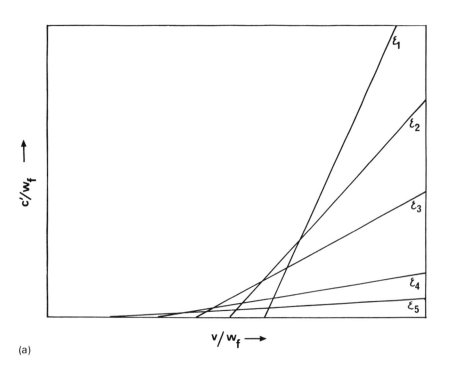

(a)

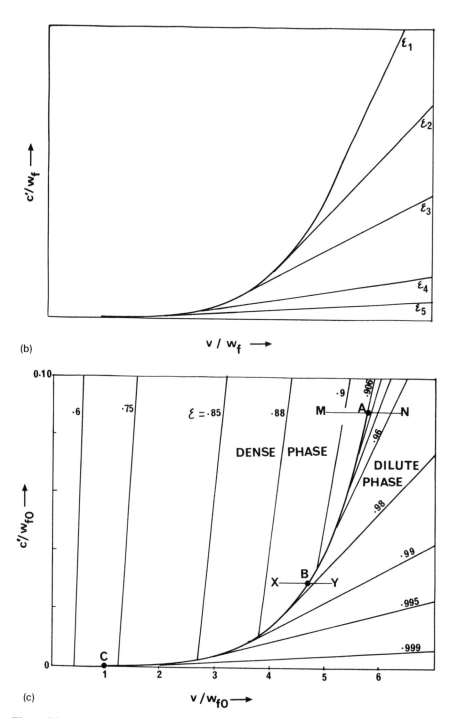

(b)

(c)

Figure 5.7 (a) Solution of equation (5.18) for various constant voidage; (b) stable solution of equation (5.18) for different constant voidage; (c) solutions for equation (5.18) for dilute phase and equation (5.17) for dense phase. (After Matsen [44].)

5.3 CHOKING SYSTEM IN VERTICAL FLOW

5.3.1 Prediction of choking velocity

The choking transition is the stepwise change from dilute phase conveying to dense phase conveying. The choking gas velocity, v_c, is the superficial gas velocity for a certain solids flow rate at which choking occurs; and the voidage at choking, ε_c, refers to the voidage of the dilute phase at the onset of choking. For systems that exhibit the choking phenomenon, prediction of the choking velocity is important as it sets the minimum gas velocity for operation in the dilute phase mode. In pneumatic conveying it is usually desirable to operate at as low an air flow rate as possible from energy requirements, pipe erosion and particle attrition considerations. In dilute phase conveying, the minimum conveying velocity may be set by the choking velocity in vertical conveying, by the analogous 'saltation' velocity in horizontal conveying, or by conditions to ensure self-cleaning after shutdown. This section is confined to the prediction of choking velocity in vertical pneumatic conveying.

Although the mechanism of choking is not properly understood, a large number of empirical equations are available in the literature for estimating choking velocity. Table 5.1 summarizes the correlations for predicting choking velocity. These have been reviewed by Doig and Roper [18] and more recently Punwani et al. [19], and Chong and Leung [45]. In particular Punwani et al. compare the various correlations by means of the root mean square relative deviation defined as

$$\left([1/(n-1)] \sum_{i=1}^{n} \{[(v_c)_{\text{calculated}} - (v_c)_{\text{measured}}]/(v_c)_{\text{measured}}\}^2 \right)^{1/2} \quad (5.19)$$

Table 5.1 Correlations for predicting choking velocity

---

1. *Barth [20]*

$$v_c^2/gD = K_1^2 \mu^{1/2}, \text{ where } v_c^2/gD = Fr_c^{*2} \quad (5.20)$$

2. *Gunther [21]*

$$K_2^2/(D/d)^{5/7} < Fr_c^{*2} < K_2^2/[(D/d)^{5/7}(1+\mu^{1/2})] + K_2^2\mu^{1/2} \quad (5.21)$$

3. *Zenz and Othmer [3]*

$$v_c^2/gd\rho_p^2 = \begin{cases} 0.04\,(\dot{G}/A\rho v_c)^{0.624}; & \dot{G}/A\rho v_c \leqslant 5 & (5.22a) \\ 0.029\,(\dot{G}/A\rho v_c)^{0.806}; & 5 < \dot{G}/A\rho v_c < 20 & (5.22b) \\ 0.015\,\dot{G}/A\rho v_c; & 20 < \dot{G}/A\rho v_c < 60 & (5.22c) \end{cases}$$

where ρ_p is in lb/ft^3

Table 5.1 (*contd.*)

4. *Doig and Roper [18]*

$$\log\left[v_{\mathrm{c}}/(gD)^{0.5}\right] = (w_{\mathrm{f0}} - 2)/28 + 0.25\log\mu \qquad (5.23\mathrm{a})$$

$$\text{for } 40 > w_{\mathrm{f0}} > 10$$

$$\log\left[v_{\mathrm{c}}/(gD)^{0.5}\right] = 0.03w_{\mathrm{f}} + 0.25\log\mu \qquad (5.23\mathrm{b})$$

$$\text{for } 10 > w_{\mathrm{f}} > 0.4$$

where w_{f0} is in ft/s

5. *Rose and Duckworth [22]*

$$v_{\mathrm{c}}/w_{\mathrm{f0}} = 3.2\,(\dot{G}/Av_{\mathrm{c}}\rho)^{0.2}(D/d)^{0.6}(\rho_{\mathrm{p}}/\rho)^{-0.7}(v_{\mathrm{c}}^2/gD)^{0.25} \qquad (5.24)$$

6. *Leung et al. [4]*

$$v_{\mathrm{c}} = 32.3\,c_{\mathrm{c}} + 0.97\,w_{\mathrm{f0}} \qquad (5.25\mathrm{a})$$

or

$$c'x_{\mathrm{if}} = 0.03\,x_{\mathrm{it}}[v_{\mathrm{c}}/(0.97 - w_{\mathrm{f0}i})] \qquad (5.25\mathrm{b})$$

$$\sum x_{\mathrm{if}} = \sum x_{\mathrm{it}} = 1 \qquad (5.25\mathrm{c})$$

for mixed size particles where x_{if} and x_{it} are the volume fractions of particle i in the feed and in the tube respectively with terminal velocity $w_{\mathrm{f0}i}$.

7. *Yousfi and Gau [8]*

$$v_{\mathrm{c}}/(gD)^{0.5}/Re_{\mathrm{pf}}^{0.06} = 32[\dot{G}/(A\rho v_{\mathrm{c}})]^{0.28} \qquad (5.26)$$

8. *Knowlton and Bachovchin [23]*

$$v_{\mathrm{c}}/(gD)^{0.5} = 9.07(\rho_{\mathrm{p}}/\rho_{\mathrm{f}})^{0.347}(\dot{G}d/A\eta)^{0.214}(d/D)^{0.25} \qquad (5.27)$$

9. *Yang [24]*

$$2gD(\varepsilon_{\mathrm{c}}^{-4.7} - 1)/(v_{\mathrm{c}} - w_{\mathrm{f0}})^2 = 0.01 \qquad (5.28\mathrm{a})$$

$$c' = (v_{\mathrm{c}} - w_{\mathrm{f0}})(1 - \varepsilon_{\mathrm{c}}) \qquad (5.28\mathrm{b})$$

10. *Punwani et al. [19]*

$$2gD(\varepsilon_{\mathrm{c}}^{-4.7} - 1)/(v_{\mathrm{c}} - w_{\mathrm{f0}})^2 = 0.074\rho^{0.77} \qquad (5.29)$$

For mixed size particles equation (5.28b) is to be replaced by

$$c'x_{\mathrm{if}} = (1 - \varepsilon_{\mathrm{c}})x_{\mathrm{it}}(v_{\mathrm{c}} - w_{\mathrm{f0}}) \qquad (5.30)$$

Table 5.2 Deviations between measured choking velocities and those calculated by various correlations (after Punwani *et al.* [19])

	Investigators					
	Low pressure data[a]			High pressure data		All data
Correlation source	Zenz	Lewis	Ormiston	Capes and Nakamura	Knowlton and Bachovchin	
	Relative deviation (%)					
Zenz and Othmer [3]	21	39	55	47	41[b]	41
Rose and Duckworth [22]	59	69	43	69	219[b]	140
Leung et al. [4]	20	39	27	18	67[c]	39
Yousfi and Gau [8]	27	14	12	68	31[b]	40
Knowlton and Bachovchin [23]	522	143	200	215	6[d]	257
Yang [24]	36	34	31	15	76[c]	44
Punwani et al. [19]	36	34	31	15	8[c]	25

[a] Yousfi and Gau [8] data not available for the present analysis.
[b] Based on the weighted average diameter of the feed size distribution $\sum x_{if} d_i$.
[c] Based on the weighted average diameter of the size distribution in the riser $\sum x_{it} d_i$.
[d] Based on surface-to-volume mean diameter $1/(\sum x_{if}/d_i)$.

where n is the number of experimental observations compared. Their evaluations of the various correlations are presented in Table 5.2. Detailed discussions of the published correlations will now follow.

5.3.1.1 Equations of Barth and Gunther

One of the earliest equations is that due to Barth [20] written in terms of the Froude number at choking versus solid–gas loading ratio, μ, and K_1 is a constant:

$$Fr_c^{*2} = v_c^2/gD = K_1^2 \mu^{1/2} \qquad (5.20)$$

The equation is derived to predict the velocity required to prevent saltation in horizontal conveying (Section 5.6) and was claimed to be useful also for predicting choking in vertical conveying. The constant K_1 in the equation depends on the characteristics of the solid particles and its value for wheat is available. Equation (5.20) is, however, of limited use as a general method of evaluating K_1 is not available.

Gunther [21] extended Barth's equation by an additional term to account for the behaviour of the system when μ is low. He suggested that the choking velocity should lie within the range of

$$K_2^2/(D/d)^{5/7} < Fr_c^{*2} < K_2^2/(D/d)^{5/7}(1 + \mu^{1/2}) + K_2^2\mu^{1/2} \qquad (5.21)$$

However, as a general method for evaluating K_2 in equation (5.21) is not available, Gunther's equation cannot be used to predict choking flow rate. For that reason perhaps, neither equation (5.20) nor equation (5.21) was evaluated by Punwani *et al.* [19] in their comparative study.

5.3.1.2 Equation of Zenz and Othmer

Zenz and Othmer [3] presented a graphical correlation of experimental results for choking and saltation of particles of uniform size. The correlation can be represented by equation (5.22) given in Table 5.1. The general applicability of equation (5.22) has been questioned [4, 25] as the parameters cannot be grouped dimensionlessly and the important relevant parameter of w_{f0}, the free fall velocity of a single particle, has not been included. For these reasons the use of equation (5.22) is not recommended here although there is fair agreement between its prediction and published measurements (Table 5.2).

5.3.1.3 Equation of Doig and Roper

Doig and Roper [18] recognized the importance of including w_{f0} and correlated the published results for choking and saltation up to 1960 by an extension of Barth's equation. Like the equation of Zenz and Othmer, their equation (equation (5.23) in Table 5.1) contains a parameter w_{f0} which was not grouped with other parameters to form a dimensionless group. Equation (5.23) was shown

[4] to give poor agreement with observed results and was not evaluated by Punwani *et al.* [19].

The use of the Doig–Roper equation for predicting choking velocity is not recommended here.

5.3.1.4 Equation of Rose and Duckworth

Rose and Duckworth [22] carried out a comprehensive dimensional analysis and correlated their own data in terms of a dimensionless equation (equation (5.24) in Table 5.1). Agreement between predictions from equation (5.24) with observed results is poor (Table 5.2) and the use of equation (5.24) is not recommended. More recently Duckworth [26] presented the following equation for predicting minimum transport velocity, v_{min}, for vertical pneumatic conveying:

$$v_{min}/w_{f0} = \mu^{0.3}\,\phi(d/D) \tag{5.31}$$

The function $\phi(d/D)$ is given in Fig. 5.8. Agreement between observed choking velocities with the predicted minimum transport velocity from equation (5.31) is poor. Thus the use of equation (5.24) or (5.31) for predicting choking flow rates is not recommended.

5.3.1.5 Equation of Leung et al.

Leung *et al.* [4] derived the following equation for calculating choking velocity by:

(a) assuming that the relative velocity between solid and gas is equal to w_{f0} at choking; and
(b) using an average value of 0.97 as the choking voidage:

$$v_c = 32.3\,(c_c) + 0.97\,w_{f0} \tag{5.25a}$$

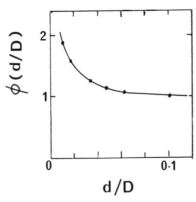

Figure 5.8 Function for equation (5.31) (after Duckworth [26]).

For mixed particle systems they suggested that equation (5.25a) can be written in the form

$$c'x_{if} = 0.03x_{it}(v_c/0.97 - w_{f0})_i \qquad (5.25b)$$

and

$$\sum x_{if} = \sum x_{it} = 1 \qquad (5.25c)$$

where

x_{if} = volume fraction of particles in **feed** with free fall velocity w_{f0i}
x_{it} = volume fraction of particles in **tube** with free fall velocity w_{f0i}

Equations (5.25b) and (5.25c) permit estimation of choking velocity for mixed size particles.

Table 5.2 shows that predictions from equation (5.25) are in good agreement with published results for tube size ranging from 25 mm to 75 mm. As the results on mixed sized particles are meagre, more work is required to ascertain the applicability of these equations for mixed size particles.

One major drawback of the equation of Leung *et al.* is that it does not account for the effect of tube size in choking.

5.3.1.6 Equation of Yousfi and Gau

Yousfi and Gau [8] correlated their own experimental results to yield a dimensionless equation for predicting choking velocity (5.26) in Table 5.1. As the equation's predictions are inconsistent with the careful experimental results of Capes and Nakamura [5] in an 80 mm tube (Table 5.2), its use is not recommended here.

5.3.1.7 Equation of Knowlton and Bachovchin

Knowlton and Bachovchin [23] studied choking in a 75 mm diameter tube at gas pressure up to 4700 kPa and presented an empirical equation (5.27) in Table 5.1 for correlating their results. Their equation contains a dubious particle Reynolds number based on the solid mass velocity relative to a stationary point. Equation (5.27), while predicting their own results well, gives poor prediction under different operating conditions (Table 5.2). For these reasons the use of equation (5.27) is not recommended. It should be pointed out that the experimental results of Knowlton and Bachovchin represent the only known high pressure choking data in the literature.

5.3.1.8 Equations of Yang

Yang [24] assumed that at choking the solid–wall friction factor λ_z is constant at 0.01 and that the relative velocity between gas and solid is equal to w_{f0}, the free fall velocity. From a force balance on the solids assuming $C_{D\varepsilon} = C_{D\infty}\varepsilon^{-4.7}$ (Chapter 3) he derived the following set of two equations which can be solved simultaneously to obtain the choking velocity and the choking voidage:

$$2gD(\varepsilon_c^{-4.7} - 1)/(v_c - w_{f0})^2 = 0.01 \tag{5.28a}$$

$$c' = (v_c - w_{f0})(1 - \varepsilon_c) \tag{5.28b}$$

Table 5.2 suggests that predictions from Yang's equations are in good agreement with published data in the literature. For particles of mixed size, w_{f0} in equation (5.28) may be replaced by a mean terminal velocity as follows:

$$\bar{w}_{f0} = \sum x_{if} w_{f0i} \tag{5.32}$$

It is not possible to assess the applicability of the extended equation for mixed size particles as insufficient experimental data are available. Note v_c, rather than v_c/ε_c, is used in equation (5.28) for convenience as an approximation, as voidage at choking is close to 1.

5.3.1.9 Equations of Punwani et al.

Punwani *et al.* [19] questioned the constant solid friction factor assumption of Yang and obtained an empirical relation for variation of the friction factor at choking with gas density based on the high pressure results of Knowlton and Bachovchin [23]. They then modified the Yang equation to allow for this variation to yield equation (5.29). Equation (5.29) can be combined with equation (5.28b) to predict choking voidage and choking velocity:

$$2gD(\varepsilon_c^{-4.7} - 1)/(v_c - w_{f0})^2 = 0.074\rho^{0.77} \tag{5.29}$$

where ρ is in lb/ft³. For mixed size particles Punwani *et al.* suggested that equation (5.28b) can be replaced by:

$$c'_c x_{if} = (1 - \varepsilon_c) x_{it}(v_c - w_{f0i}) \tag{5.30}$$

$$\sum x_{it} = \sum x_{if} = 1 \tag{5.25c}$$

Table 5.2, taken from Punwani *et al.*, shows that their own correlation (5.29) gives the least deviation between measured and predicted choking velocities. The superficial velocity, v_c, instead of v_c/ε_c is used in equations (5.29) and (5.30) for convenience as for equation (5.28) since voidage is close to 1.

5.3.1.10 Selection of choking velocity correlations

In summary a large number of correlations is available in the literature. These are all empirical in nature. The more reliable ones appear to be those due to Punwani *et al.*, Leung *et al.* and Yang [19, 4, 24] and the use of these three equations is recommended. All three correlations can be used for uniform size as well as mixed size particles. Comparison between predictions and experimental observation suggests that the choking velocity can be predicted to within about $\pm 50\%$. Thus a safety factor of 1.5 should be applied to the calculated choking velocity in setting the minimum transport velocity in vertical pneumatic conveying in the dilute phase flow mode. It should be cautioned, however, that all the experimental results have been obtained in tubes smaller than 80 mm diameter with a significant amount of results obtained in tubes smaller than 40 mm diameter. The applicability of these empirical equations to large tubes is uncertain. Further, the results on mixed size particles are meagre. The reliability of these three correlations for mixed size particles is therefore unknown. The effect of proximity of pipe bends on choking velocity in a vertical tube has yet to be studied systematically. Recently Chong and Leung [45] suggested the use of different equations for different systems. There is a need for more theoretical work aimed at understanding the phenomenon of choking and more experimental work aimed at extending the range of applicability of the empirical equations.

5.3.2 Transition from dense phase conveying to packed bed conveying

In dense phase conveying, particles are in suspension (i.e. fluidized). The relative velocity (or slip velocity) between gas and solid is necessarily higher than that corresponding to minimum fluidization, for the particles to be in suspension. If the gas velocity is reduced at a fixed solid flow rate a stage will eventually be reached when the slip velocity is insufficient to support the particles in suspension. Transition from dense phase fluidized solids flow (or bubbly dense phase flow) to packed-bed flow (or moving-bed flow) occurs when the slip velocity reaches a critical value equal to that at minimum fluidization. The equation for predicting the transition from dense phase flow (fluidized solids flow) to packed-bed flow may be derived by equating the slip velocity at vertical pneumatic conveying with the slip velocity at minimum fluidization [27]. At this transition the voidage in the riser tube is equal to the voidage at minimum fluidization, ε_{mf}, giving

$$\frac{v}{\varepsilon_{mf}} - \frac{\dot{G}}{\rho_p(1-\varepsilon_{mf})A} = \frac{v_{min}}{\varepsilon_{mf}} \tag{5.33}$$

Equation (5.33) relates the gas and solid velocities at the transition from fluidized solid flow to packed bed flow. Taking an average voidage of 0.45 for ε_{mf}, equation (5.33) can be simplified to the following dimensionless form for predicting this transition:

$$0.55(v/v_{min}) - 0.45(c'/v_{min}) = 0.55 \tag{5.34}$$

Equation (5.34) will be used for the development of a quantitative flow regime diagram in Section 5.3.3.

5.3.3 A quantitative flow regime diagram in vertical flow

For gas–solid systems in which the choking transition occurs, the equations presented in Sections 5.3.1 and 5.3.2 can be used to develop a quantitative flow regime diagram [28, 29]. Such a flow regime diagram is presented in Fig. 5.9 for a sand–air system showing regions of packed bed, dense phase and dilute phase flow. Figure 5.9 permits the quantitative estimation of flow regime for the system considered. In the figure, Yang's equation (5.28) was used to demarcate between dilute phase flow and slugging flow. Either of the other two recommended choking velocity equations (5.25) or (5.29) may also be used.

In pneumatic conveying it is often useful to express the solids to gas loading ratio μ as a parameter. Equation (5.34) for transition from fluidized bed flow to non-fluidized packed-bed flow can be written as:

$$\mu = 1.22 \, (\rho_p/\rho)(1 - v_{min}/v) \qquad (5.35)$$

Expressing v_{min}/v as $(v_{min}/w_{fo})(w_{fo}/v)$ and writing $w_{fo}/v_{min} = f(Ga)$, as given in equations (3.54)–(3.56), we have

$$\mu = 1.22(\rho_p/\rho)[1 - (w_{fo}/v)/f(Ga)] \qquad (5.36)$$

For the dilute phase to dense phase flow (i.e. choking) transition, Yang's equations (5.28a) and (5.28b) can also be expressed in the form

$$\mu = f[(\rho_p/\rho),(w_{fo}/v),(w_{fo}^2/gd)] \qquad (5.37)$$

For a given system, the Galileo number is known. Equations (5.36) and (5.37)

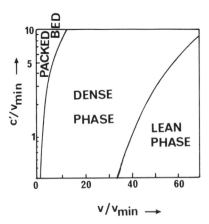

Figure 5.9 A quantitative flow regime diagram for vertical conveying for air–solid system (after Leung *et al.* [28, 29]) in 0.1 m diameter tube: $\rho_p = 2500 \, \text{kg/m}^3$, $\rho = 1.38 \, \text{kg/m}^3$, $v_{min} = 0.24 \, \text{m/s}$, $w_{fo} = 3.35 \, \text{m/s}$.

define the demarcation between non-fluidized flow and fluidized (dense phase) flow and between dense phase flow and dilute phase flow respectively. A quantitative flow regime diagram is presented in a plot of mass flow ratio μ versus dimensionless gas velocity v/w_{f0} in Fig. 5.10 for a sand–air system with different tube diameters.

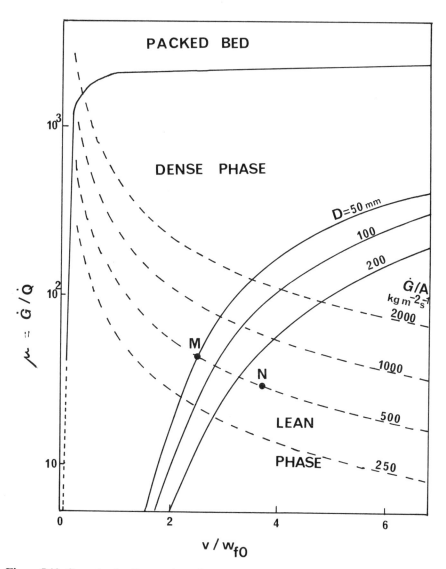

Figure 5.10 Quantitative flow regime diagram for vertical pneumatic conveying. (Data used in calculation: $v_{min} = 0.24$ m/s, $w_{f0} = 3.4$ m/s, $\rho_p = 2500$ kg/m^3, $\rho = 1.38$ kg/m^3 with tube diameters of 50, 100 and 200 mm). (After Leung *et al.* [29].)

The diagram is useful in defining the range of loading ratios for a given flow pattern. The maximum loading ratio possible for dilute phase flow and dense phase slugging can also be obtained from the diagram. Constant solid flux lines have been included in Fig. 5.10; for a given solid flux the diagram can be used in specifying the operating gas flow rate. For a tube diameter of 50 mm and a solid flux $G_s = 500 \, kg/m^2s$ shown in Fig. 5.10, the minimum gas velocity required to attain dilute phase flow is represented by point M in the figure. An appropriate safety factor of 1.5, say, may be applied to the gas flow rate to give a recommended gas flow rate corresponding to point N in the figure.

The existence of a maximum loading ratio limit for slugging dense phase flow for a given system as shown in Fig. 5.10, was first pointed out by Dixon [30] who showed how the maximum ratio varies quantitatively with powder properties, conveying air pressure and solid mass flux.

5.4 NON-CHOKING SYSTEM IN VERTICAL FLOW

In Section 5.2.2 equations for predicting whether a system will exhibit the 'choking transition' are presented. In general fine particles in large diameter tubes tend not to choke. This section pertains to non-choking systems. In a non-choking system, the four possible flow patterns as the gas velocity is reduced at a fixed solid flow rate are given in Fig. 5.4 as:

(a) dilute (lean) phase flow;
(b) non-slugging dense phase flow;
(c) slugging dense phase flow and bubbly dense phase flow;
(d) non-fluidized packed-bed flow.

The transition from dilute phase flow to non-slugging dense phase flow is diffuse. When gas velocity is reduced at a given solids flow rate in dilute phase mode, the solid concentration increases in the tube. The gas–solid system becomes less and less homogeneous, indicated by the presence of clusters and strands of particles. The system has the appearance of turbulence with intense solid mixing, with break-up and formation of clusters continuously. This is defined here as non-slugging dense phase flow. The onset of non-slugging dense phase flow is difficult to define exactly and no published equation is available to predict the fuzzy transition point. From the knowledge that the slip velocity in this flow mode may be substantially higher than the free fall velocity of a single particle, we can deduce that this transition gas velocity will be significantly higher than that calculated using the choking velocity equations discussed in Section 5.3.1.

The phenomenon of non-slugging dense phase conveying is analogous to the 'turbulent regime' of fluidization reported by Kehoe and Davidson [31]. They observed, as the velocity of gas flow through a fluidized bed of fine powder was raised, the breakdown of the slugging regime into 'a state of continuous coalescence—virtually a channelling state with tongues of fluid darting in zig-zag fashion through the bed'. The bed has the appearance of turbulence and is known as the turbulent regime. The turbulent regime of fluidization refers to zero transport of solids. If solids are introduced into the bottom of the fluidized bed and withdrawn from the top, as in pneumatic conveying, we have the recirculating fluidized bed operating in the turbulent regime. This recirculating fluidized bed has been termed 'fast fluidization' [2] and has commercial applications as a chemical reactor [32].

The 'non-slugging dense phase mode' defined here is similar to the so called fast fluidization. Thus the knowledge on non-slugging dense phase mode can be obtained from the recent studies on fast fluidization [2, 32, 33]. While little generalized quantitative information is available, the following characteristics of non-slugging dense phase flow can be established:

(a) Pressure gradient in the tube decreases with increase in gas velocity at a constant solid flow rate.
(b) Pressure gradient increases with solid feed rate at a given gas velocity.
(c) Slip velocities are high and can be an order of magnitude above the free fall velocity. There is some evidence that the higher the gas velocity, the higher the slip velocity.
(d) Solid volumetric concentrations as high as 25% have been observed before slugging flow sets in.
(e) The transition from dilute phase flow to non-slugging dense phase conveying is diffuse.
(f) The transition from non-slugging dense phase conveying to bubbling (or slugging) dense phase conveying is also diffuse.
(g) At a low gas velocity within this regime, it is possible to have solid downflow near the wall of the pipe although the net solid flow is upwards. This gives rise to the possibility of 'negative wall friction', i.e. the frictional pressure drop is negative.

Thus to summarize for non-choking systems, quantitative prediction of the two transition velocities from dilute phase flow to non-slugging dense phase flow and from non-slugging dense phase flow to slugging (bubbling) dense phase flow is not possible. Finally the transition from bubbly dense phase flow to packed-bed flow in this non-choking system is identical to that for the choking system. Equation (5.34) can therefore be used to predict this transition.

5.5 PARTICLE SEGREGATION IN VERTICAL PNEUMATIC TRANSPORT

When mixed-size or mixed-property particles are transported pneumatically, the *in situ* composition of the mixture in the pipe can often be significantly different from that of the feed or delivered mixture. This difference arises as a result of differences in velocity of particles of different size and properties. An estimate of the *in situ* composition (or the degree of segregation) is often important in relation to pressure drop estimation and more importantly in relation to riser reactor design (where a riser tube serves as a chemical reactor).

Segregation in vertical pneumatic conveying has been studied by a number of workers [4, 34, 35–37] and reviewed by Yang [37]. At very high gas velocity, the degree of segregation is negligible. Segregation becomes progressively more pronounced as the gas velocity is reduced. While little information is available to predict segregation in dense phase pneumatic conveying some equations are available for predicting segregation in dilute phase flow. The equations of Leung *et al.* [4] and of Yang [37] will be reported here as they can deal with multicomponent systems and appear to give good agreement with observation. The analyses of Muschelknautz [35] and of Nakamura and Capes [34] are more fundamental and complex but are restricted to binary systems.

5.5.1 Equations for predicting segregation

Segregation in a pneumatic conveying tube is caused by the non-uniformity in particle velocities for particles of different size and properties. A simple model is to assume slip velocity of each class of particle is equal to its free fall velocity, i.e. [4]

$$v - c_i = w_{f0i} \qquad (5.38)$$

The continuity equation for component i is given by

$$\dot{G}x_{if} = x_{it}c_i(1 - \varepsilon)\rho_{pi} \qquad (5.39)$$

where x_{if} is the mass fraction of component i in the feed mixture and x_{it} the *in situ* volume fraction of i in the pipe. From equations (5.38) and (5.39) the *in situ* composition in the tube and the degree of segregation can be calculated [4].

The segregation tendency calculated from the above simple model is greater than that observed in practice, especially at low gas velocity. Equation (5.39) does not take into consideration the interaction between particles and the effect of wall friction. Both these factors are taken into consideration in Yang's model. Allowing for voidage and wall effects, solid velocity is given by [37].

$$c_i = v - w_{fi}[(1 + \lambda_z^* c_i^2 / 2gD)\varepsilon^{4.7}]^{1/2} \qquad (5.40)$$

λ_z^* in equation (5.40) is a weighted average solid friction factor. w_{fi} in the equation is a modified terminal velocity of particle i to include the effects of 'interactions between different components'. Methods for calculating λ_z^* and w_{fi} were given by Yang. They can be used in conjunction with equations (5.39) and (5.40) to calculate the *in situ* concentration in the tube and hence the degree of segregation. Good agreement between predictions and observed segregation of binary mixture was reported by Yang. No multicomponent mixture segregation measurement has been reported in the literature and the validity of Yang's equations for multicomponent systems is therefore not known.

5.6 SALTATION IN HORIZONTAL CONVEYING

5.6.1 Theoretical considerations

The mechanism of saltation is complex and theoretical predictions of saltation velocity from first principles have yet to be developed. The complexity is compounded by: (i) the different definitions of saltation; (ii) different possible mechanisms depending on the size of a particle relative to the thickness of the laminar sublayer and buffer layer at the wall of a pipe; and (iii) the uncertain effects of solid concentration in the gas stream. In this section, we shall discuss a number of mechanisms of saltation.

For transport of a single particle in a gas stream in a horizontal pipe, four major threshold velocities have been defined by Zenz [38]:

(a) The minimum velocity required to transport a single particle by rolling, sliding or bouncing along the bottom of the pipe.

(b) The minimum velocity required to transport an injected particle without saltation and without obviously rolling and bouncing.

(c) The minimum velocity required to pick up a particle from rest in the bottom of a pipe and transport it in suspension.

(d) The minimum velocity required to pick up a particle from rest in a layer of particles and transport it in suspension.

The magnitude of these threshold velocities increases in that order, and Zenz's measurements show that the critical velocity (d) above, may be up to 2 to 2.5 times critical velocity (a) above. Note that the above definitions refer to a flowing gas stream with zero solid concentration, i.e. the case of infinite dilution. Similar definitions can be obtained for finite solid loadings in the gas. Most theoretical treatments consider the situations depicted in cases (c) and (d)—the velocity required to pick up a particle from rest.

Bagnold [39] considered the lifting of a particle as a result of flow of a gas over a flat surface. He suggested that a particle may be dislodged as a result of shear stress in the horizontal direction. Thomas [41] suggested that the forces relevant to saltation are gravity and lift force. The lift force is caused by 'the mean velocity gradient across the particles and by instantaneous velocity differences accompanying turbulent fluctuations'. He defined two types of situation depending on whether a particle is inside the laminar sublayer or not. Matsumoto *et al.* [40] suggested that particles are kept in suspension by bouncing motion.

All the theoretical analyses require a detailed description of the fluid velocity profile near the wall. For zero solid concentration in the gas phase, the universal velocity profile for turbulent flow may be used as an approximation. However, the real fluid velocity profile with finite and uneven solid concentration at a velocity slightly above the saltation velocity can be very different from the universal profile. To predict saltation velocity theoretically, a description of the velocity profile in the vicinity of the saltation point with particle flow is necessary.

Progress in theoretical prediction will have to await further information on such a velocity profile. Recent measurements by Tsuji and Morikawa [43] using a laser Doppler velocimeter (see Chapter 13) of the gas velocity profile in a 30 mm diameter pipe with 200 μm particles indicate that the gas velocity profile is flattened by the presence of the particles. They observed that the levels of turbulence were affected by the size of particles being transported. The larger particles increased the intensity of turbulence while the smaller ones decreased the intensity markedly. Further, the slip velocity was found to decrease with increase in loading. Further experimental work in this direction may lead to a better understanding of the mechanism of saltation.

Although the mechanism of saltation is not well understood, a number of empirical equations are available in the literature to predict the saltation gas velocity. These will be reviewed in the following section.

5.6.2 Saltation velocity correlations

Prediction of saltation velocity is important as it sets the minimum gas velocity for horizontal conveying. Scott [46] considered that 'the greatest difficulty facing the designer is the choice of an acceptable gas velocity. If the minimum transport saltation velocity for a given material in a particular system is known, a reasonable prediction can be made for that material in other systems. However, the choice of an acceptable minimum velocity for a new material must at present be based on experiments or on the designer's experience'.

A large number of correlations is available for estimating saltation velocity and have been reviewed by Leung and Jones [38]. They short-listed three equations for possible applications. They are those due to Rizk [39], Masumoto et al. [40] and Thomas [41, 42]. These equations will be described in detail below:

5.6.2.1   Equation of Rizk [39]

The Rizk equation states

$$\mu = \frac{1}{10^{\delta}} \left(\frac{v_s}{gD} \right)^{\kappa} \tag{5.41}$$

where

$$\delta = 1.44d + 1.96$$

$$\kappa = 1.1d + 2.5$$

and d (mm) is particle diameter (Chapter 6). The velocity v_s is the gas velocity at the saltation point.

5.6.2.2   Equation of Matsumoto et al. [40]

The equation of Matsumoto et al. is empirical and given by:

$$\mu = \alpha(\rho_p/\rho)^a [w_{fo}/10(gD)^{1/2}]^b [v_s/10(gD)^{1/2}]^c \tag{5.42}$$

where

$$\alpha = 1.11 \quad a = 0.55 \quad b = -2.3 \quad c = 3.0$$

5.6.2.3 Equation of Thomas [41, 42]

Thomas correlated minimum transport velocity through the friction velocity v_s^* defined by

$$v_s^* = (\Delta p D/4 L \rho_m) \tag{5.43}$$

where

$\Delta p/L$ = frictional pressure gradient for gas–solid mixture
ρ_m = density of gas–solid mixture

Thomas proposed two separate correlations depending on whether a particle is larger or smaller than the laminar sublayer. The method for estimating saltation velocity requires a prior knowledge of ρ_m and $(\Delta p/L)$. Leung and Jones [38] suggested that as a first approximation, the gas density, ρ and friction pressure drop due to gas alone may be used. The steps in calculating saltation velocity are as follows:

(a) Calculate friction velocity v_{s0}^* at infinite dilution by

$$\frac{w_{f0}}{v_{s0}^*} = 4.9 \left(\frac{d v_{s0}^* \rho}{\eta} \right) \left(\frac{D v_{s0}^* \rho}{\eta} \right)^{-0.6} \left(\frac{\rho_p - \rho}{\rho} \right)^{0.23} \tag{5.44}$$

(b) Equation (5.44) is applicable to particles larger than the laminar sublayer, i.e. for

$$d > 5\eta/(v_{s0}^* \rho) \tag{5.45}$$

Check that the condition given in (5.45) is satisfied from v_{s0}^* calculated from (5.44).
(c) If equation (5.45) is not satisfied, use equation (5.46) below to calculate v_{s0}^*:

$$w_{f0}/v_{s0}^* = 0.01(d v_{s0}^* \rho/\eta)^{2.71} \tag{5.46}$$

(d) Calculate the friction velocity at saltation v_s^* and the saltation velocity v_s from equations (5.47) and (5.48) via an iteration procedure:

$$v_s^*/v_{s0}^* = 1 + 2.8 (w_{f0}/v_{s0}^*)(1 - \varepsilon_s)^{0.5} \tag{5.47}$$

where

$$\varepsilon_s = \text{voidage at saltation}$$
$$v_s/v_s^* = 5 \log (\rho v_s D/\eta) - 3.90 \tag{5.48}$$

The iteration procedure is

1. Assume $v_{s0}^* = v_s^*$.
2. Calculate v_s from (5.48).
3. From v_s and solid flow, calculate ε_s by assuming a solid to gas velocity ratio of 0.5, i.e.

$$\varepsilon_s = 2\mu\rho\,(\rho_p + 2\mu\rho) \qquad\qquad (5.49)$$

where μ is the solid to gas loading ratio.
4. Recalculate v_s^* and v_s from equations (5.47) and (5.48).

A solid to gas velocity ratio of 0.5 is taken here for equation (5.49) as the calculated saltation velocity is not sensitive to the value of this ratio. Equation

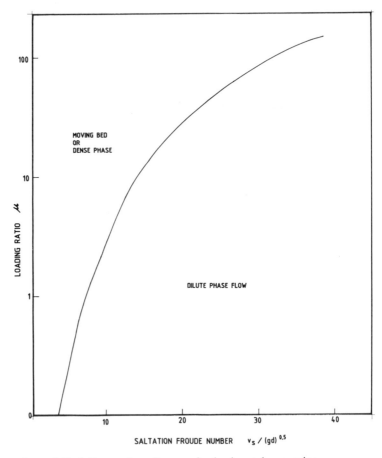

Figure 5.11 A flow regime diagram for horizontal conveying.

(5.48) relating gas velocity and friction velocity is taken from turbulent single phase flow in a pipe. In using the equation, it is implied that the presence of solid does not change the gas velocity profile.

5.6.2.4 A summary

Leung and Jones [38] showed that the above saltation velocity equations give reasonable agreement with published saltation measurements with a root mean square relative deviation (RMSRD) of less than 60%. The equation of Thomas (RMSRD = 44%) was recommended as it appears to have a sound theoretical base.

The equations of Rizk (RMSRD = 60%) and of Matsumoto *et al.* (RMSRD = 53%) are simpler to use and are particularly useful for extrapolation. Their use was also recommended.

5.6.3 A quantitative flow regime diagram for horizontal flow

Using the saltation velocity equation in Section 5.6.2 of Matsumoto *et al.* a quantitative flow regime diagram can be constructed for horizontal pneumatic conveying. We shall define operation at a gas velocity greater than the saltation velocity as dilute phase. Below the saltation velocity, operation will be in either dense phase flow or in extrusion flow. A flow regime diagram based on equation (5.4.2) is presented in Fig. 5.11 for the conveying of sand with a particle Froude number of 40 ($(w_{fo}/gd)^{0.5} = 40$) and a density ratio of 2000 ($\rho_f/\rho = 2000$). Such a diagram may be used in conjunction with the flow regime diagram for vertical conveying (Fig. 5.11) to determine flow patterns in different parts of a pneumatic conveying system and to set minimum operating gas velocity.

REFERENCES

1. Zenz, F.A. (1949) *Ind. Eng. Chem.*, **41**, 2801–6.
2. Yerushalmi, J., Turner, D.H. and Squires, A.M. (1976) *Ind. Eng. Chem. Process Design Development*, **15**, 47–52.
3. Zenz, F.A. and Othmer, D.F. (1960) *Fluidization and Fluid Particle Systems*, Reinhold Publishing, New York.
4. Leung, L.S., Wiles, R.J. and Nicklin, D.J. (1971) *Ind. Eng. Chem. Process Design Development*, **10**, 183–9.
5. Capes, C.E. and Nakamura, K. (1973) *Can. J. Chem. Eng.*, **51**, 31–8.
6. Ormiston, R.M. (1966), Slug flow in fluidized beds, *Ph.D. Thesis*, University of Cambridge.
7. Bandrowski, J., Kaczmarzyk, G., Malczyk, R. and Raczek, J. (1978) Aerodynamics of vertical pneumatic transport of granular materials part III, *Inzynieria Chemiczna*, **8**, 779–95.
8. Yousfi, Y. and Gau, G. (1974) *Chem. Eng. Sci.*, **29**, 1939–46.
9. Yang, W.C. (1977) *Proceedings Pneumotransport 3*, BHRA Fluid Engineering, Cranfield, E5-49-E5-55.
10. Smith, T.N. (1978) *Chem. Eng. Sci.*, **33**, 745–9.

11. Molerus, O. (1967) *Chem. Eng. Technol.*, **39**, 341–8.
12. Harrison, D., Davidson, J.F. and de Koch, J.W. (1961) *Trans. Inst. Chem. Engrs*, **39**, 202–12.
13. de Koch, J.W. (1961) Aggregative fluidization, *Ph.D. Thesis*, University of Cambridge.
14. Davidson, J.F. and Harrison, D. (1963) *Fluidized Particles*, Cambridge University Press, Cambridge.
15. Smith, T.N. (1977) *Proceedings of Chemeca 77*, Institution of Chemical Engineers, Australia, pp. 328–32.
16. Slis, P.L., Willemse, Th.W. and Kramers, H. (1959) *Appl. Sci. Res.*, **A8**, 209–19.
17. Richardson, J.F. and Zaki, W.N. (1954) *Trans. Inst. Chem. Engrs*, **32**, 35–53.
18. Doig, I.D. and Roper, G.H. (1963a), *Aust. Chem. Eng.*, **4**, No. 4, 9–19.
19. Punwani, D.V., Modi, M.V. and Tarman, P.B. (1976) A generalized correlation for estimating choking velocity in vertical solids transport, *Proc. Inst. Powder and Bulk Solids Handling and Processing Conference*, Powder Advisory Center, Chicago.
20. Barth, W. (1954) *Chem.-Ing.-Tech.*, **20**, No. 1, 29–32.
21. Gunther, W. (1957) *Dissertation*, Technische Hochschule Karlsruhe.
22. Rose, H.E. and Duckworth, R.A. (1969) *Engineer*, **227**, 392–6, 430–3, 478–83.
23. Knowlton, T.M. and Bachovchin, C.M. (1976) in *Fluidization Technology*, Vol. 2 (eds D.L. Keairns *et al.*), Hemisphere Publishing Corporation, Washington, pp. 253–82.
24. Yang, W.C. (1975), *AIChE J.*, **21**, 1013–5.
25. Leva, M. (1959) *Fluidization*, McGraw-Hill, New York, pp. 135–47.
26. Duckworth, R.A. (1977), in *Pneumatic Conveying of Solids* (ed. L.S. Leung), University of Queensland, pp. 39–74.
27. Leung, L.S., Wiles, R.J. and Nicklin, D.J. (1969) *Trans. Inst. Chem. Engrs*, **47**, 271–8.
28. Leung, L.S., Wiles, R.J. and Nicklin, D.J. (1972), *Proceedings of Pneumotransport 1*, BHRA Fluid Engineering, Cranfield, B93–104.
29. Leung, L.S. and Wiles, R.J. (1976), *Ind. Eng. Chem. Process Design and Development*, **15**, 552–7.
30. Dixon, G. (1979) The impact of powder properties on dense phase flow, paper presented at *International Conference on Pneumatic Conveying*, Powder Advisory Centre, London.
31. Kehoe, P.W.K. and Davidson, J.F. (1971), *Inst. Chem. Engr (London) Symp. Series*, **33**, 97–116.
32. Reh, L. (1971) *Chem. Eng. Prog.*, **67**(2), 58–63.
33. Cankurt, N.T. and Yerushalmi, J. (1978) in *Fluidization* (eds J.F. Davidson and D.L. Keairns), Cambridge University Press, Cambridge, pp. 387–393.
34. Nakamura, K. and Capes, C.E. (1976) in *Fluidization Technology*, Vol. 2 (eds D.L. Keairns *et al.*), Hemisphere Publishing Corporation, Washington, pp. 159–184.
35. Muschelknautz, E. (1959), *VDI Forsch.*, **476**, 32–5.
36. Hair, A.R. and Smith, K.L. (1972) *Mech. Chem. Eng. Trans., Inst. of Engineers, Australia*, MC8, **1**, 19–23.
37. Yang, W.C. (1978) *Proceedings of Pneumotransport 4*, BHRA Fluid Engineering, Cranfield, B21–31.
38. Leung, L.S. and Jones, P.J. (1978) *Proceedings of Pneumotransport 4*, BHRA Fluid Engineering, Cranfield, paper C1.
39. Rizk, F. (1973) *Proceedings of Pneumotransport 3*, BHRA Fluid Engineering, Cranfield, paper D4.
40. Matsumoto, S., Harada, S., Saito, S. and Maeda, S. J. (1975) *Chem. Eng.*, Japan, 7, 425.

41. Thomas, D.G. (1961) *AIChE J.*, **7**, 432.
42. Thomas, D.G. (1962) *AIChE J.*, **8**, 373.
43. Tsuji, Y. and Morikawa, Y. (1982) *J. Fluid Mech.*, **120**, 385.
44. Matsen, J.M. (1982) *Powder Technology*, **32**, 21.
45. Chong, Y.O. and Leung, L.S. (1985) *Powder Technology*, **47**, 43.
46. Scott, A.M. (1977) *Proceedings 4th International Powder Technology and Bulk Solids Conference*, Harrogate, pp. 10–14.

6

Principles of pneumatic conveying

6.1 INTRODUCTION—PUTTING IT ALL TOGETHER

In the preceding chapters the more fundamental facets of gas–solid suspensions have been discussed in terms of the findings of a large number of researchers. In Chapter 2, the issues pertaining to the flow of the gas alone were discussed whilst in Chapters 3, 4 and 5 issues relating to single and multiple particle dynamics, flow in vertical and horizontal pipes, particle characterization and the like were discussed.

In this chapter, the various principles enunciated thus far will be correlated in an attempt to obtain some simple equations to assist with the design of pneumatic conveying systems operating in the dilute phase.

Whereas adequate cross references will be made to the relevant sections in the preceding five chapters, those readers seeking a quick understanding of the design procedures need only consult Chapter 1. Those readers who wish to gain a deeper insight into the more microscopic aspects of gas–solid suspension flow, are advised to consult all the previous chapters.

6.2 THE STATE DIAGRAM REVISITED

In Section 1.8.1 the basic characteristics of the state diagram [1] were described. A closer look at the state diagram [2] reveals that it is a most useful method for obtaining important information relating to pneumatic conveying system design.

6.2.1 Modes of pneumatic conveying

In Chapter 1 the definitions of dilute and dense phase conveying were proposed. In addition, the concept of dilute and dense phase flow situations occurring under conditions of stable and unstable flow was also alluded to.

For fine particle suspensions (Section 1.9.3) five identifiable flow patterns have been observed. These observations have been made by either keeping the conveying gas velocity constant whilst increasing the solids feed rate, or keeping the solids feed rate constant whilst decreasing the conveying velocity.

In Fig. 6.1 a model of the flow phases is depicted as the concentration of solids is increased. From the description alongside each flow pattern it can be seen that

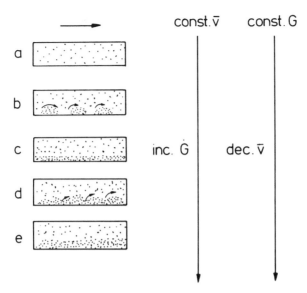

Figure 6.1 Flow phases for fine particle suspensions: (a) fully suspended, stable; (b) surging, unstable; (c) saltation point – stationary bed, stable; (d) moving bed, very unstable; (e) stationary bed, stable.

each flow description is preceded by a comment on whether the flow is stable or unstable. The stability or otherwise of the flow is believed to be a more effective means of describing the flow in a gas–solid suspension.

In fine particle suspensions, flow stability oscillates from being very stable to extremely unstable conditions. Of particular importance, is the formation of so called moving or stationary beds. It will be noted that conditions (c) and (e) in Fig. 6.1 are described as being stable in the presence of a stationary bed. Condition (d), however, depicts that situation in which 'explosions' are observed due to erratic duning. Condition (d) is synonomous with the observation of severe pressure surges in the conveying system.

6.2.2 The general state diagram and the normalized state diagram

The flow patterns described in Fig. 6.1 are easily located on a general state diagram. In Fig. 6.2(a) the pressure drop per unit length of conveying pipe is shown as a function of the conveying gas velocity. The conditions (a)–(e) as described in Fig. 6.1 are depicted in Fig. 6.2. Further the state $\dot{G}_0$ refers to the air alone situations, whilst states $\dot{G}_1$ to $\dot{G}_5$ are conditions in which the solids mass flow rate is increased. The similarity of the shape of the gas–solids flow curves to the air alone curve to the right of condition (c) should be noted.

Condition (c) on each trace is referred to as the pressure minimum point, and in coarse particle suspensions corresponds to the saltation point at which particles start dropping out of suspension.

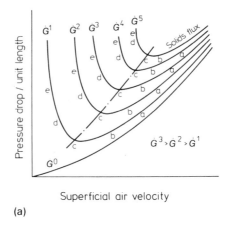

(a)

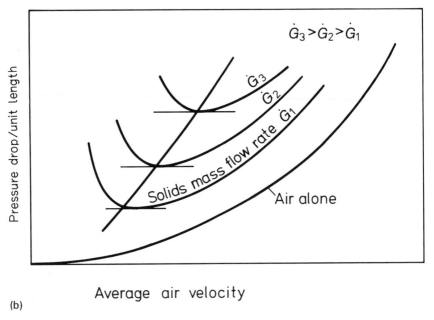

(b)

Figure 6.2 (a) The general state diagram; (b) state diagram showing pressure minimum.

Data for the so called pressure minimum curve are obtained by constructing a tangent at each minimum point on the curve of constant solids feed rate. In Fig. 6.2(b) the pressure minimum curve is shown as that line passing through these minima. It should be noted that the pressure minimum line always has a positive slope, a fact often neglected when trying to uprate a system. As such, should a user wish to increase the discharge capacity of an existing installation,

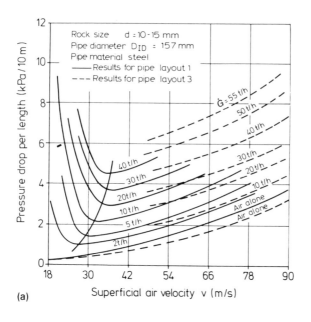

(a)

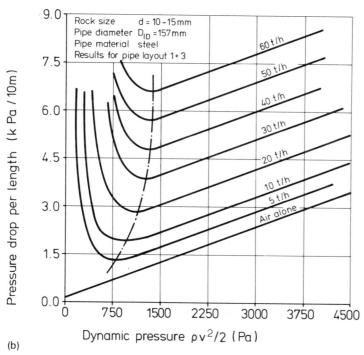

(b)

Figure 6.3 (a) State diagram for large particles; (b) the normalized state diagram for large particles.

the consequences of merely increasing the solids feed rate without adjusting the conveying gas flow rate could be disastrous.

Whilst convention has dictated that the state diagram is constructed by plotting the log of the pressure gradient against the log of the conveying gas velocity, this technique does lead to certain problems. In particular, the fact that the abscissa only reflects a velocity condition, presents problems in terms of how representative this condition is in terms of the actual conveying conditions in a system. The state diagram as depicted in Fig. 6.2(a) is thus very much dependent upon the location in a system where the observations were made. As such, by only considering the velocity, it is possible that a slightly distorted version of the state diagram might be obtained.

One way to rectify this situation is to normalize the state diagram by modifying the abscissa to represent a dynamic pressure term $(\rho v^2/2)$. By including a density term, it is possible to obtain a state diagram which is truly representative of all flow conditions in a system.

The significance of the normalizing procedures is illustrated in Fig. 6.3(a) and 6.3(b). In Fig. 6.3(a), observations obtained from two locations on a test facility [12], specially designed to investigate the pneumatic transport of large rocks, are depicted. Two test sections were selected to obtain information required to plot the state diagram. It can be seen that by plotting the results in the conventional format, two sets of curves (one for each test section) are obtained for the state diagram. As such, it is difficult to decide which set of conditions can be used to obtain the fundamental conveying parameters for large rocks.

The same observations used to obtain Fig. 6.3(a) are now plotted in Fig. 6.3(b) with the dynamic pressure term as the abscissa. All points fall on one set of curves, thereby eliminating any doubt as to which condition should be used for the determination of such parameters as the saltation velocity, minimum pressure, etc.. Thus, the inclusion of the density term with the velocity term helps define the exact conditions which prevail in the conveying system. Clearly, the density term and the velocity term are representative of those conditions occurring in the region of the system where the pressure gradient is being monitored.

6.2.3 The dimensionless state diagram

A useful method of confirming the reliability of experimental data points, is to construct a so called dimensionless state diagram. The diagram (Fig. 6.4) is constructed by plotting the mass flow ratio (μ) against the Froude number (Fr) in a log–log plot.

In Fig. 6.4 it can be seen that a series of parallel straight lines is obtained. The spacing between these lines is proportional to the change in solids feed rate. Any experimental points which fall too far off the straight line should be thoroughly investigated to ascertain their reliability.

6.2.4 General phase diagram for fine particles

To reinforce the notion of fine particle and coarse particle suspensions [3], Fig. 6.5 has been constructed depicting general trends obtained from visual

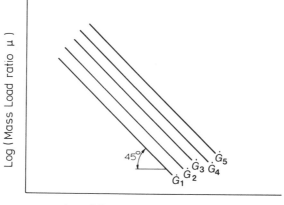

Figure 6.4 The dimensionless state diagram.

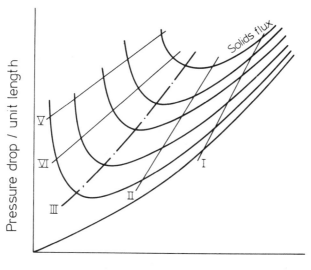

Figure 6.5 The general phase diagram for fine particles.

observations recorded for fine particle suspensions flowing in a horizontal pipe. In particular, referring to Fig. 6.1, all points corresponding to the flow pattern (a) are joined by line I, those corresponding to (b) are joined by line II, etc. . Line III corresponds to the pressure minimum trace. It should be noted that these lines all slope towards the pressure minimum.

Of particular significance however, is the fact that the saltation velocity for fine particles (line II, Fig. 6.5) takes place before the pressure minimum is attained.

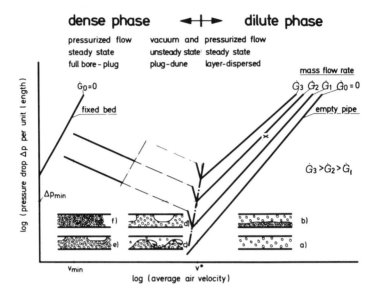

(a)

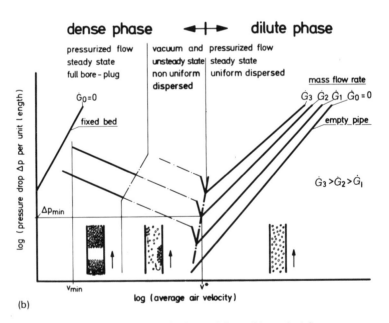

(b)

Figure 6.6 State diagrams: (a) horizontal flow; (b) vertical flow.

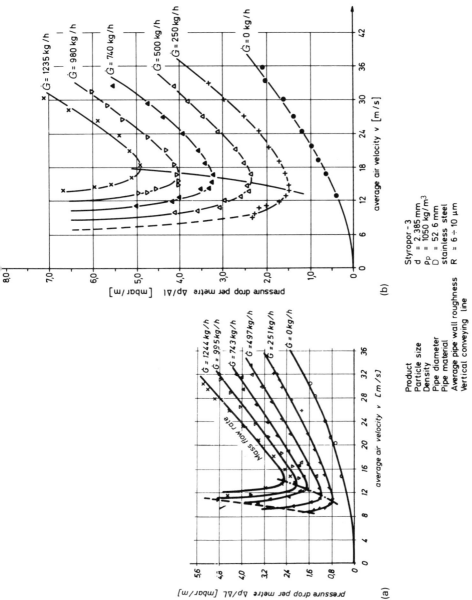

Figure 6.7 State diagrams for Styropor 3: (a) horizontal flow; (b) vertical flow.

(a)

pressure drop per metre Δp/ΔL [mbar/m]

average air velocity v [m/s]

Mass flow rate

Ġ = 1244 kg/h
Ġ = 995 kg/h
Ġ = 743 kg/h
Ġ = 497 kg/h
Ġ = 251 kg/h
Ġ = 0 kg/h

(b)

pressure drop per metre Δp/Δl [mbar/m]

average air velocity v [m/s]

Ġ = 1235 kg/h
Ġ = 980 kg/h
Ġ = 740 kg/h
Ġ = 500 kg/h
Ġ = 250 kg/h
Ġ = 0 kg/h

Product   Styropor – 3
Particle size   d   = 2.385 mm
Density p_P = 1050 kg/m³
Pipe diameter   D   = 52.6 mm
Pipe material   stainless steel
Average pipe wall roughness R   = 6÷10 μm
Vertical conveying line

This observation is at variance with that noted for coarse particle suspensions in which the pressure minimum coincides with the saltation velocity. The onset of saltation in fine particle suspensions is believed to be very significant and must be taken into account when designing dilute phase pneumatic conveying systems.

6.2.5 Diagram of state

When plotting the parameters used to construct Figs 6.1 and 6.5 on a log–log basis, the so called diagram of state (Fig. 6.6) is obtained. Figure 6.6(a) indicates the conditions which prevail in a horizontal pipe. The dilute and dense phase flow situations are shown to be right and left of the pressure minimum curve respectively. For conditions prevailing in a vertical pipe, Fig. 6.6(b) demonstrates the transition between dilute and dense phase.

The corresponding diagrams obtained from actual measurements performed on Styropor 3 (supplied by BASF AG) are shown in Figs 6.7(a) and 6.7(b). The Styropor has a particle size $d = 2.385$ mm, density $\rho = 1050$ kg/m^3. Tests were conducted in a conveying line with diameter $D = 52.6$ mm.

Results obtained from tests conducted on malt and fly ash in a horizontal $D = 100$ mm pipe [2] are shown in Figs 6.8 and 6.9 respectively. In Fig. 6.9, the various regions of stable and unstable flow as per Fig. 6.5 are also shown. These

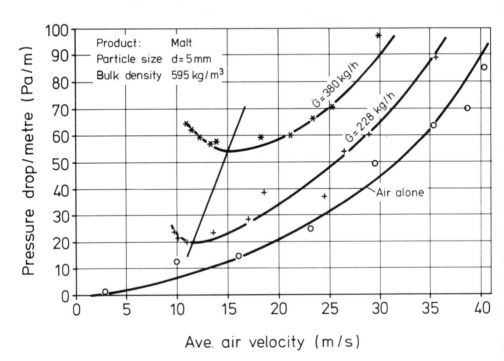

Figure 6.8 State diagram for malt.

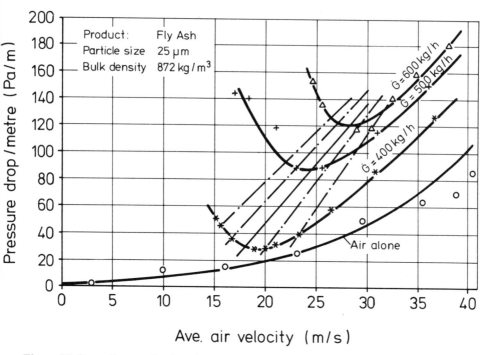

Figure 6.9 State diagram for fly ash.

regions were identified from visual observations recorded using a transparent section of conveying pipe.

It should be noted that other state diagrams have been proposed by Matsen, an example of which can be found in Fig. 4.6.

6.2.6 The dimensionless pressure minimum curve

In light of the above, the determination of the pressure minimum curve is seen to be most important. If the conditions of mass flow ratio (μ) and Froude number (Fr) prevailing at the pressure minimum conditions for each flow rate are plotted in a log–log format, Fig. 6.10 is obtained. In Fig. 6.10(a), the horizontal flow condition is depicted, whilst the vertical flow situation is shown in Fig. 6.10(b). From Fig. 6.10(b), an equation relating the conditions prevailing at the pressure minimum, can be approximated by

$$\mu = (1/10^\delta)\, Fr^\chi \tag{6.1}$$

The exponents δ, χ depend on the equivalent particle size and the pipe material, where:

$$\delta = 1.44d + 1.96 \tag{6.2}$$

$$\chi = 1.1d + 2.5 \tag{6.3}$$

and d is in mm.

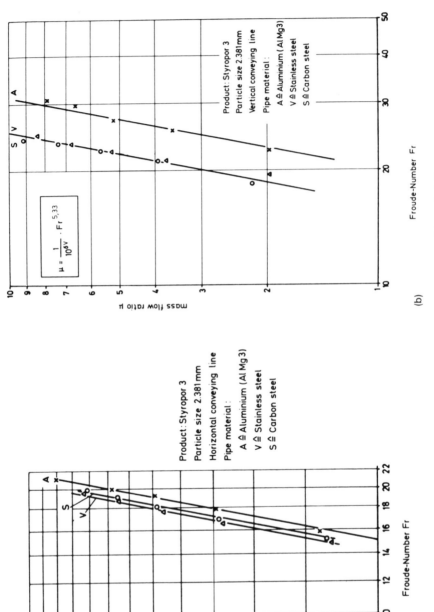

Figure 6.10 Mass flow ratio μ versus Froude number Fr: (a) horizontal flow; (b) vertical flow.

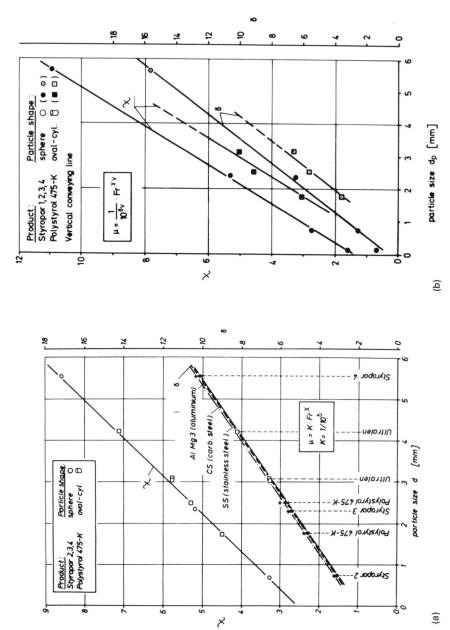

Figure 6.11 χ and δ versus d: (a) horizontal flow; (b) vertical flow.

(a)

(b)

The relationship is shown graphically in Figs 6.11(a) and (b), in which the exponents χ and δ have been plotted against the particle size d.

These curves allow the saltation velocity to be estimated for plastic materials with a density of about $1000\,\text{kg/m}^3$. Various relationships have been published for estimating the saltation velocity in horizontal pneumatic conveying systems and have been compared by Leung *et al.* [4], and covered in Section 5.6.

6.2.7 Verification of *μ–Fr* relationship

The mass load ratio has been plotted against Froude number in Fig. 6.12 with solid mass flow rate and pipe diameter ($D = 50$–$400\,\text{mm}$) as parameters. The values plotted represent results obtained by Siegel [5] and Rizk [6].

The average pressure-minimum curve for Polystyrol (BASF AG) with a particle size $d = 1$–$2.5\,\text{mm}$ in carbon steel pipes can be approximately defined by

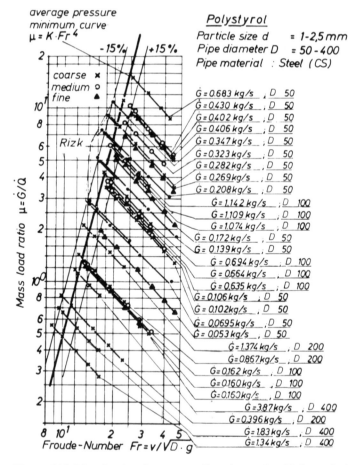

Figure 6.12 Mass load ratio μ versus Froude number Fr for polystyrol particles.

the equation $\mu = K Fr^4$. The deviation is $\pm 15\%$, expressed in terms of the Froude number. This confirms that the dimensionless numbers μ and Fr are the same in large plants as they are in small.

6.2.8 The relationship between the performance characteristics of the prime mover and product flow characteristics

The incorrect selection of the prime mover can have serious repercussions on the performance of a pneumatic conveying system. An awareness of the characteristics of the prime mover is essential in order to facilitate trouble free operation. The relationship between the performance characteristics of the prime mover and the flow characteristics of the product have a direct bearing on whether the system will block or not. As such this relationship has a direct bearing on the pressure minimum curve.

The choice of a prime mover suitable for pneumatic conveying applications is wide, and many are designed for specific applications. Manufacturers facilitate the choice by publishing tables listing pressure heads, gas flow rates, speeds and power consumptions under normal temperature conditions.

Characteristics for three types of prime movers are shown in Fig. 6.13 (I radial-flow fan, II rotary blower, and III positive-displacement rotary compressor). The ordinate in this diagram represents the total pressure drop (p) in the system; and the abscissa, the volumetric air flow rate ($\dot{V}$) at the blower intake.

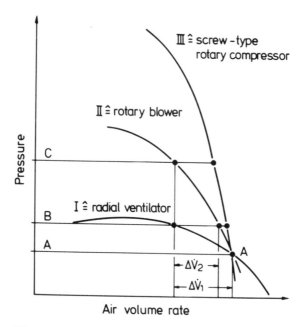

Figure 6.13 Prime mover characteristics.

Attention is drawn to two important operating points on these characteristics:

(a) The pressure drop when there are no solids in the pipe.
(b) The pressure drop when the solids are being conveyed.

The point A on the blower characteristic (I, II and III in Fig. 6.13) represents the pressure drop in the empty conveyor line. Since the slope is negative, the flow rate becomes less as the pressure drop increases. Thus the flow rate at the level B is less than that at A and greater than that at C; and the reduction in flow rate $\Delta \dot{V}_1$ brought about by raising the pressure drop from A to C is greater than that effected by raising the pressure drop from B to C, i.e. $\Delta \dot{V}_2$. It can also be seen from the curve that an increase in slope entails less reduction in the rate of air flow. In other words, pneumatic systems of high stability have characteristics with a steep slope.

Blower and product flow characteristics in the form of pressure drop/air flow curves are shown in Fig. 6.14. The point A at which the two blower characteristics

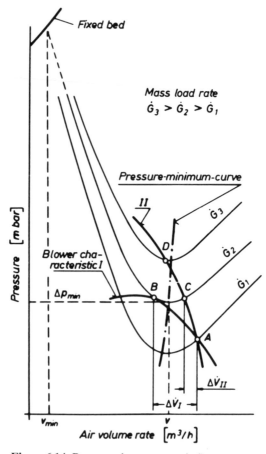

Figure 6.14 Pressure drop versus air flow rate.

(I and II) coincide should be the operating point in a conveying system. Since an increase in the solids mass flow rate is bound to raise the system's resistance, it will cause point A to shift either to B on curve I or to point C on curve II. Hence an increase in pressure drop is accompanied by a reduction in the air flow rate by an amount $\Delta \dot{V}$. In the particular case shown in Fig. 6.14, the reduction in air flow $\Delta \dot{V}_{\mathrm{I}}$ (on curve I) is decidedly greater than $\Delta \dot{V}_{\mathrm{II}}$ (on curve II).

The new operating point B on curve I is to the left of the pressure-minimum curve. In other words, it is located in the unstable zone of high pressure fluctuations and, in addition, lies on the apex of the blower characteristic. Point B represents the maximum possible mass flow rate $\dot{G}_2$ that can be achieved with blower characteristic I, and the risk of sedimentation and plugging at this point is very high. The slightest disturbance in conveying would suffice to cause blockage of the entire system.

Operation on the blower characteristic II is quite different. At point C, there is sufficient pressure in reserve to cope with any fluctuations in the feeder. Blower characteristic II allows the mass flow rate to be raised to the level of the $\dot{G}_3$ curve, i.e. to point D, which is in the vicinity of the pressure-minimum curve.

6.3 METHODS FOR SCALING-UP

By virtue of their inherent advantages, pneumatic conveying systems are attracting attention from more and more branches of industry. In view of the high costs incurred in practical trials, more reliance has to be placed on models for an accurate prediction of performance.

The results of model studies can be scaled up by applying the principle of similarity, which in this particular case can be regarded from three aspects: geometric, dynamic and flow similarity.

6.3.1 Geometric similarity

The principle of similarity can be applied in this case if the following conditions are valid:

1. The ratio of the pipe diameter to the particle diameter is constant, i.e.

$$D/d = \text{constant}. \tag{6.4}$$

2. The pipes are of similar quality and have inner walls of similar roughness.
3. The pipes are of similar geometry and the particles of similar shape.

6.3.2 Dynamic similarity

The theory of similarity can be applied in this case if the forces and their ratios (dimensionless numbers) that act on an element of volume in the gas–solids mixture in the gas stream are identical in both systems.

(a) Reynolds number

Reynolds number = inertial force/viscous force

Formula:

$$Re = vD/v = \text{constant} \tag{6.5}$$

Dimensional analysis:

$$Re = \frac{m}{s} m \bigg/ \frac{m^2}{s} = 1$$

where v is the velocity of air and D is the pipe diameter.

(b) Froude number

Froude number = inertia force/gravitational force

Formula:

$$Fr = v/(Dg)^{1/2} \tag{6.6}$$

Dimensional analysis:

$$Fr = (m/s)/(m.m/s^2)^{1/2} = 1$$

Important factors in model studies are the air velocity v, the particle velocity c, the terminal settling velocity w_f, and the following dimensionless Froude numbers propounded by Barth [7]:

$$Fr = v/(Dg)^{1/2} = \text{constant} \tag{6.7}$$

$$Fr^* = c/(Dg)^{1/2} = \text{constant with particle velocity} \tag{6.8}$$

$$Fr_f = w_f/(Dg)^{1/2} = \text{constant with settling velocity} \tag{6.9}$$

where D is the characteristic dimension for the pipe and g is the acceleration due to gravity. The following Froude number ratios are also of importance:

$$Fr^*/Fr = c/v = \text{constant} \tag{6.10}$$

$$Fr_f/Fr = w_f/v = \text{constant} \tag{6.11}$$

$$Fr_f/Fr^* = w_f/c = \text{constant} \tag{6.12}$$

6.3.3 Flow similarity

Mass load ratio $\mu = \dfrac{\text{solids mass flow rate}}{\text{gas mass flow rate}} = \text{constant}$

Formula:

$$\mu = \dot{G}/\dot{Q} = \text{constant} \tag{6.13}$$

Dimensional analysis:
$$\mu = (kg/s)/(kg/s) = 1$$

Solid mass concentration $= \dfrac{\text{conveying bulk density}}{\text{gas density in the pipe}} = \text{constant}$

Formula:
$$\mu^* = \rho^*/\rho = \text{constant} \tag{6.14}$$

Dimensional analysis:
$$\mu^* = (kg/m^3)/(kg/m^3) = 1$$

These conditions for similarity cannot be fulfilled all at once. The condition $D/d = \text{constant}$, hardly ever applies, because the diameter of the particles in the model is usually the same as that in the scaled-up plant, whereas the pipe diameters necessarily differ. Even if D/d were a constant, the aerodynamic forces in the two systems would comply with different aerodynamic laws to an extent depending on the magnitude of the scaled-up factor. Thus the following applies for particles of a given size:

$$Re_p < 1 \quad : \qquad F_D \sim (v - c)d \qquad \text{Stokes' law}$$
$$Re_p > 10^3: \qquad F_D \sim (v - c)^2 d^2 \qquad \text{Newton's law}$$

where F_D is the aerodynamic force, $(v - c)$ is the slip between gas and solids, and d is the particle size.

The pipe material and the quality of the inner wall surface must be the same in both cases, because the action of the particles on the pipe wall greatly influences the performance. Since the Reynolds number in pneumatic conveying is quite high, $(Re > 10^3)$, the effect of viscosity is small compared to that of the inertia force and can be neglected.

6.4 USE OF THEORETICAL MODELS AND DEFINITIONS

6.4.1 Compilation of power balance

A theoretical approach involving the investigation of each individual mechanism that takes place during the conveyance of solid particles is almost impossible, because the interactions between particles cannot be eliminated. Since two-phase flow processes are very complicated, macrocharacteristic studies have been resorted to for the case of gas–solids suspensions in ducts.

Figure 6.15 shows an element of pipe of length ΔS and diameter D through which a mixture of gas and bulk solids is flowing. If there are no losses, the total power at point 1 will be equal to that at point 2 for the case of steady-state flow.

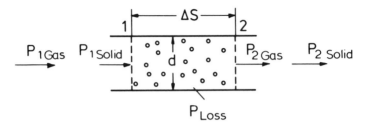

Figure 6.15 Power balance for an element of volume.

Thus,

$$P_{1\ gas} + P_{1\ solids} = P_{2\ gas} + P_{2\ solids} + P_{losses} \qquad (6.15)$$

If there are no losses,

$$(P_1 - P_2)_{gas} = (P_2 - P_1)_{solids} \qquad (6.16)$$

The difference $(P_1 - P_2)_{gas}$ represents the power required for conveying the solids, i.e.

$$P_{gas} = \Delta p_Z \dot{V} = \Delta p_Z A v = F_D v \qquad (6.17)$$

where Δp_Z is the pressure drop caused by transportation of the solids. Equation (6.17) relates the blower output $\dot{V}$ to the aerodynamic force F_D acting on the solid particles and the gas velocity v in the empty pipe.

The expression $(P_2 - P_1)_{solids}$ in equation (6.16) represents the sum of the power consumed in acceleration, friction and impact and the power required to keep the solids suspended in a horizontal duct (a term that embraces the effect of gravity). Thus for steady-state flow,

$$P_{solids} = (F_{impact} + F_{friction})c + (F_{impact} + F_{friction})(v - c) + F_g w_f \qquad (6.18)$$

It should be noted that it is difficult to separate the friction and impact terms thus these terms are combined in the following format:

$$P_{solids} = F_Z(c) + F_Z(v - c) + F_G w_f \qquad (6.18a)$$

Substituting equations (6.17) and (6.18a) in equation (6.16) gives

$$F_D v = F_Z v + F_G w_f \qquad (6.19)$$

6.4.2 Aerodynamic force or drag

Drag is the force brought about by the relative motion between the stream of gas and the solids flowing in it. The solid particles lose kinetic energy as a result of impact and friction, and further energy is required to keep them suspended in the gas stream. All this lost energy is replenished from the kinetic energy in the gas stream.

The resistance to motion offered by a cloud of particles flowing through a gas stream is given by

$$F_D = C_D n A_p \frac{\rho}{2} (v - c)^2 \tag{6.20}$$

(refer to equation (3.5) for a single particle)
where n is the number of particles, and A_p is the projected area in the gas stream. This transforms to [9]

$$F_D = \frac{C_D}{C_{Df}} \Delta M g \left(\frac{v - c}{w_f} \right)^2 \tag{6.21}$$

where C_{Df} is the drag coefficient for a single particle in free fall, and ΔM is the mass of particles in the control volume. For laminar flow,

$$F_D = \frac{C_D}{C_{Df}} \Delta M g \left(\frac{v - c}{w_f} \right) \tag{6.22}$$

Another expression for C_D has been given by Wen and Yu and is found in equation (3.21).

The general equation for drag is

$$F_D = \frac{C_D}{C_{Df}} \Delta M g \left(\frac{v - c}{w_f} \right)^{2 - x} \tag{6.23}$$

where $0 < x < 1$. The drag coefficient or resistance factor C_D is defined by

$$C_D = \alpha / Re_p^x \tag{6.24}$$

$$Re_p = (v - c) d\rho / \eta \tag{6.25}$$

For turbulent flow, i.e. $x = 0$ or $625 < Re_p < 3 \times 10^5$,

$$C_D = 0.44 = \text{constant}$$

For laminar flow, i.e. $x = 1$ or $Re_p \sim 5$,

$$C_D = 24 / Re_p$$

In the transition zone, $5 < Re_p < 625$, C_D lies between 50 and 0.45.

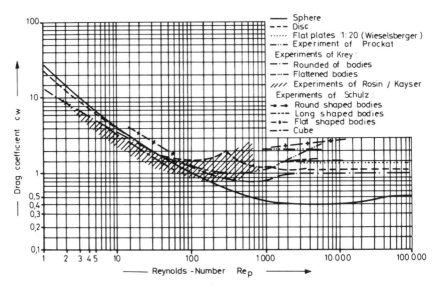

Figure 6.16 Drag coefficients for bodies of various shapes as a function of Reynolds number.

The entire range of flow is defined by the Kaskas [8] empirical equation:

$$C_D = 24/Re_p + 4/Re_p^{1/2} + 0.4 \tag{6.26}$$

Chapter 3 considers the drag coefficient in more detail. Fig. 6.16 shows the relationship between drag coefficients for bodies of different shapes and Reynolds number.

6.4.3 Forces of impact and friction

It follows from equation (6.19) that the various components of force can be studied separately. All forces restricting the motion of the particles, i.e. impact and friction, are included in the term F_Z.

If τ_Z is the shear stress acting on a length L of the pipe wall,

$$F_Z = \tau_Z D \pi L \tag{6.27}$$

and

$$\tau_Z = 0.25 \Delta p_Z D / \Delta L \tag{6.28}$$

The pressure drop caused by impact and friction is given by

$$\Delta p_Z^* = \lambda_Z^* \Delta M \frac{c^2}{2} \frac{1}{AD} \tag{6.29}$$

where λ_Z^* is the coefficient of impact and friction, $\Delta M c^2/2$ is the kinetic energy of the solids, and A and D are the cross-sectional area of the pipe and the diameter respectively.

Equations (6.30) and (6.31) follow from equation (6.29):

$$\Delta p_Z^* = \frac{\lambda_Z^* \mu^* c^2 \rho}{2} \frac{\Delta L}{D} \tag{6.30}$$

$$\Delta p_Z^* = \frac{\lambda_Z^* \rho^* c^2}{2} \frac{\Delta L}{D} \tag{6.31}$$

The following equations for the shear stress can be obtained by combining equations (6.28) and (6.30):

$$\tau_Z = \tfrac{1}{8} \lambda_Z^* \mu^* c^2 \rho \tag{6.32}$$

$$\tau_Z = \tfrac{1}{8} \lambda_Z^* \rho^* c^2 \tag{6.33}$$

The impact and friction force is obtained by substituting equations (6.29) and (6.28) in equation (6.27) (or equation (6.32) or (6.33) in equation (6.26)):

$$F_Z = \lambda_Z^* \frac{\Delta M}{2D} c^2 \tag{6.34}$$

6.4.4 Effect of gravity in a horizontal pipe

The effect of gravity has been explained by a theoretical model [9] and describes the many forces that contribute towards lifting the particles in a direction at right angles to the streamlines: the impact forces, the pressure forces resulting from unsymmetrical flow around the particles in the vicinity of the pipe wall, and the transverse forces caused by turbulence and rotation. If the transverse or upward velocity is u, the relative velocity is $(u - w_f)$. The energy consumed in lifting and conveying a particle suspended between two streamlines is obtained from the source described by equation (6.17). Figures 6.17 and 6.18 are schematic interpretations of particle trajectory and loss of height respectively.

Barth [7] pointed out that a horizontal component of energy is involved in lifting or suspending a particle, because the path ΔS followed by a particle in rising through a height of ΔZ in an interval of time Δt is governed by the air and particle velocities v and c and the settling velocity w_f.

It was shown in the model study that the specific work done in horizontal conveyance is given by,

$$W_G = \rho^* g \Delta L \frac{w_f}{v} \tag{6.35}$$

$$= \rho^* g \Delta L \beta \tag{6.36}$$

$$= \Delta M_g \Delta Z$$

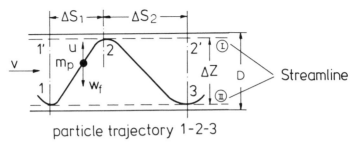

particle trajectory 1-2-3

Figure 6.17 Schematic interpretation of a particle trajectory between two streamlines.

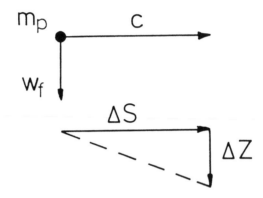

Figure 6.18 Schematic interpretation of loss of height in a horizontal line.

6.4.5 Power balance

Equation (6.19) describes the various contributions to the power. A dimensionless relationship is obtained by substituting the expressions in equations (6.21) and (6.34) for F_D and F_Z:

$$\frac{C_D}{C_{Df}}\left(\frac{v-c}{w_f}\right)^2 = 0.5\lambda_Z^* Fr^{*2} + \beta \tag{6.37}$$

6.5 ADDITIONAL PRESSURE DROP FACTOR (λ_z)

The additional pressure drop due to the presence of the solids is given as:

$$\Delta p_z = \mu\lambda_z\frac{\rho}{2}v^2\frac{\Delta L}{D} \tag{6.38}$$

The additional pressure drop factor λ_z can be obtained by equating equations (6.31), (6.36) and (6.38):

$$\lambda_z = \lambda_z^* \frac{c}{v} + 2 \frac{\beta}{(c/v)Fr^2} \qquad (6.39)$$

Using the balance between the drag and frictional forces of the solids the settling velocity w_f can be obtained from equations (6.37) and (6.39), i.e.

$$w_f = \left(\frac{C_D}{C_{Df}} (v-c)^2 \frac{2c/v}{\lambda_z Fr^{*2}} \right)^{0.5} \qquad (6.40)$$

The following assumption was made in the event that the settling velocity of a particle in a cloud differs from that of an individual isolated particle:

$$w_f = K w_{f0} \qquad (6.41)$$

If $C_D/C_{Df} \simeq 1$, the following expression applies to the factor K, which describes this difference in settling rates:

$$K = \left[\left(\frac{v-c}{w_{f0}} \right) \frac{2c/v}{\lambda_z Fr^{*2}} \right]^{0.5} \qquad (6.42)$$

Both terms on the right-hand side of equation (6.39) consist of dimensionless factors that can be used in similarity studies (cf. Section 6.4), i.e. the impact and friction factor λ_z^*, the velocity ratios c/v and $\beta = w_f/v$, and the Froude number.

At high velocities, i.e. very short residence times and low values of ΔZ, the ratio $\Delta Z/\Delta S = w_f/v = \beta$ becomes very small. Hence, the second term on the right-hand side of equation (6.39) is negligible, particularly since the square of the Froude number is in the denominator. Thus impact and friction are mainly responsible for the pressure drop $\lambda_z = \lambda_z^* c/v$. At low velocities, at which individual particles can no longer hover, ΔZ becomes zero and thus β as well. In this case, therefore, friction is mainly responsible for the pressure drop.

The effect of friction and impact λ_z^* and gravity β has been demonstrated by Bohnet [10] in a diagram in which λ_z is shown as a function of the Foude number for both coarse and fine materials (Fig. 6.19). The decreased effect of friction at low Froude numbers can be ascribed to the much lower particle velocity. It has been observed that the flow rate of the segregated layer in horizontal ducts is always lower than that of the particles in the gas stream flowing above it, especially if the products are fine. In this case, Bohnet [10] suggests the following modified equation for the pressure drop coefficient. In the presence of a moving bed the total additional pressure drop due to the solids is

$$\lambda_z = \frac{\mu_1}{\mu} \left(\frac{c}{v} \right)_{air} \lambda_z^* + 2 \frac{\mu_2}{\mu} \frac{\beta}{(c/v)_{bed} Fr^2} \qquad (6.43)$$

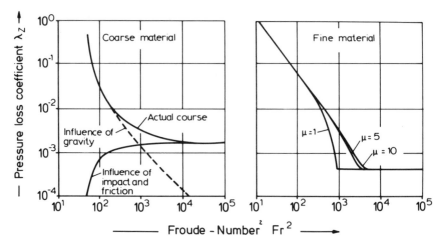

Figure 6.19 Pressure loss coefficient as a function of the square of the Froude number.

Equation (6.43) requires more information on the velocity ratio c/v and the distribution of the mass load ratios μ_1 and μ_2.

μ_1 is the mass load ratio in the suspended region of the flow (dilute phase), and μ_2 is the mass load ratio of the moving bed (dense phase). In this situation, two gas–solid flow modes (dilute phase and dense phase) coexist. Also, in this case, the velocity ratio c/v of each phase will be different.

The most important factor that has to be determined for the design of pneumatic systems is λ_Z.

6.6 PRESSURE DROP

Considerable theoretical and experimental work has been devoted to predicting the pressure drop in a gas–solid mixture in pipes, but a reliable general correlation has not yet been developed. The results of much scientific effort have allowed the pressure drop to be calculated for a given mass flow rate under optimum operating conditions. The power input to the blower is calculated from the total pressure drop in the system and the air flow rate according to the following equation:

$$P = \Delta p \dot{V} / \eta_{\mathrm{B}} \qquad (6.44)$$

where η_B is the efficiency ($0.5 < \eta_B < 0.7$). This pressure can be resolved into the following components:

$$\Delta p = \Delta p_{\text{transport}} + \Delta p_{\text{separator}} + \Delta p_{\text{valves}} \qquad (6.45)$$

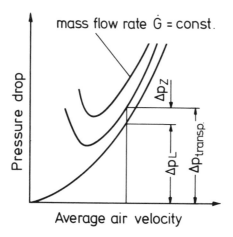

Figure 6.20 Graphical description of pressure drop increments: pressure drop versus average air velocity.

The pressure drop $\Delta p_{\text{transport}}$ is the sum of Δp_L for the clean air or liquid, Δp_A for accelerating the solids, Δp_Z^* for friction and impact, Δp_G for raising and suspending the particles, and Δp_B for the pipe bends, i.e.

$$\Delta p_{\text{transport}} = \Delta p_L + \Delta p_A + (\Delta p_Z^* + \Delta p_G)_{\text{horizontal}} \qquad (6.46)$$
$$+ (\Delta p_Z^* + \Delta p_G)_{\text{vertical}} + \Delta p_B$$

In steady-state flow,

$$\Delta p_A = 0. \qquad (6.47)$$

Fig. 6.20 shows pressure drop as a function of average air velocity.

6.6.1 Horizontal conveyance

$$\Delta p_{\text{transport}} = \Delta p_L + \Delta p_Z^* + \Delta p_G \qquad (6.48)$$
$$= \Delta p_L + \Delta p_{Z\,(\text{horizontal})} \qquad (6.49)$$

The Prandtl [11] pressure drop equation for the flow of clean air is as follows:

$$\Delta p_L = \lambda_L \frac{\rho}{2} v^2 \frac{\Delta L}{D} \qquad (6.50)$$

where λ_L is the resistance coefficient for air in pipes. λ_L is not a constant (see Example 2.7.5); it depends on the flow of gas and is thus a function of Reynolds number. It can be calculated for Reynolds numbers of up to $Re = 8 \times 10^4$ with the aid of the Blasius equation:

$$\lambda_L = 0.316/Re^{0.25} \tag{6.51}$$

In equation (6.38), λ_Z is an integral pressure loss coefficient.

6.6.2 Vertical conveyance

An analogous procedure applies to the vertical line, i.e.

$$\Delta p_{transport} = \Delta p_L + \Delta p_{Z \text{ (vertical)}} \tag{6.52}$$

and

$$\Delta p_{Z \text{ (vertical)}} = \Delta p_Z^* + \Delta p_G \tag{6.53}$$

$$\mu\lambda_{Z \text{ (vertical)}}\frac{\rho}{2}v^2\frac{\Delta Z}{D} = \lambda_Z^*\frac{\rho^*}{2}c^2\frac{\Delta Z}{D} + \rho^* g\Delta Z \tag{6.54}$$

where ΔZ is the height raised.

The pressure drop coefficient for vertical conveyor lines is given by,

$$\lambda_Z = \lambda_Z^*\frac{c}{v} + \frac{2}{(c/v)Fr^2} \tag{6.55}$$

In order to avoid error, attention is drawn to the fact that equation (6.39) for the horizontal line differs from equation (6.55) for the vertical line, as is shown below:

$$\lambda_{Z \text{ (horizontal)}} = \lambda_Z^* \text{ (horizontal)} \left(\frac{c}{v}\right)_{\text{(horizontal)}} + \frac{2\beta}{(c/v)Fr^2_{\text{(horizontal)}}}$$

$$\lambda_{Z \text{ (vertical)}} = \lambda_Z^* \text{ (vertical)} \left(\frac{c}{v}\right)_{\text{(vertical)}} + \frac{2}{(c/v)\,Fr^2_{\text{(vertical)}}}$$

Note that for the vertical line $\beta = 1$.

6.6.3 Compressibility of air

A major factor to be considered in the design of pneumatic systems is the compressibility of air. For short conveying distances, i.e. for relatively low pressure drops, it can be ignored, i.e. air can be treated as an incompressible fluid. However, at high pressures, air expansion is of great importance. Chapter 4 contains the basic formulation of compressible flow considerations.

The velocity v of the gas is compared to that of the solids c in an incompressible and a compressible medium in Figs 6.21(a) and (b). The pressure drops for clean air and for the mixture along the lengths of the pipe are shown in Fig. 6.21(c). If the pressure drop is high, i.e. if the pneumatic transport line is long, allowance must be made for expansion of the gas. The system undergoes a change of state.

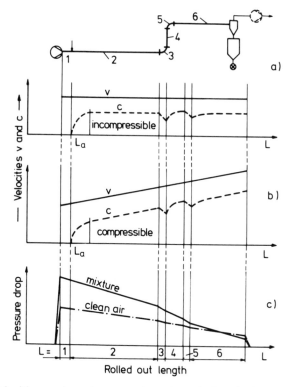

Figure 6.21 Velocities v and c and pressure drop along the length of a pneumatic conveyor line; for (a) incompressible and (b) compressible medium.

There are different variations and constraints that must be taken into consideration. Isothermal and polytropic expansion apply for pneumatic conveying.

(a) Isothermal expansion

For isothermal expansion:

$$p_1 v_1 = pv = \text{constant} \tag{6.56}$$

and

$$p_1/\rho_1 = p/\rho = \text{constant} \tag{6.57}$$

for

$$\rho = p/RT \qquad \rho_1 = p_1/RT \tag{6.58}$$

where R is the gas constant and T the absolute temperature. The velocity and gas density at any point are given by

$$v = v_1 p_1/p \tag{6.59}$$

$$\rho = \rho_1 p/p_1 \tag{6.60}$$

(b) Polytropic expansion

For polytropic expansion ($\kappa = 1.3$, see Chapter 2):

$$p_1 v_1^\kappa = p v^\kappa = \text{constant} \tag{6.61}$$

and

$$p_1/\rho_1^\kappa = p_2/\rho_2^\kappa = \text{constant} \tag{6.62}$$

The velocity and gas density are:

$$v = v_1 (p_1/p)^{1/\kappa} \tag{6.63}$$

and

$$\rho = \rho_1 (p/p_1)^{1/\kappa} \tag{6.64}$$

6.6.4 Pressure drop in a gas–solid mixture

Equation (6.50) can be written as follows:

$$dp = \lambda \frac{\rho}{2} v^2 \frac{dL}{D} \tag{6.65}$$

The coefficient for a gas–solid mixture is

$$\lambda = \lambda_L + \lambda_Z \mu \tag{6.66}$$

The pressure at the solids intake for positive and negative pressure displacement is obtained by integrating equation (6.65).

(a) Isothermal state

$$p_1 = \left(p_0^2 \pm \frac{\lambda}{D} \rho_0 v_0^2 \Delta L p_0 \right)^{0.5} \tag{6.67}$$

where + refers to a positive pressure system and − refers to a vacuum system.

(b) Polytropic state

$$p_1 = \left[p_0^{(1+n)/n} + \frac{\lambda}{2D} \rho_0 v_0^2 \Delta L p_0^{(1+n)/n} \left(\frac{1+n}{n} \right) \right]^{n/(n+1)} \tag{6.68}$$

6.6.5 Pressure drop due to acceleration

$$dp\, A = \dot{G}\, dc \tag{6.69}$$

The pressure drop for the isothermal and polytropic states is obtained by integration, i.e.

$$\Delta p_A = \begin{cases} \mu v_0 \rho_0 c & \text{vacuum system} & (6.70) \\ \mu v_1 \rho_1 c & \text{pressure system} & (6.71) \end{cases}$$

6.6.6 Pressure drop due to height ΔZ

$$dp = \rho^* g \, dZ \tag{6.72}$$

Integrating between $Z = Z_1$ and $Z = Z_0$ for both vacuum and pressure systems gives the following relationships:

(a) Isothermal state

$$p_1 = p_0 \exp \pm \left(\frac{v}{c}\right)_0 \rho_0 \frac{1}{p_0} g \Delta Z \mu \tag{6.73}$$

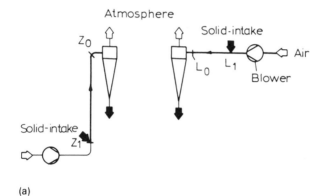

(a)

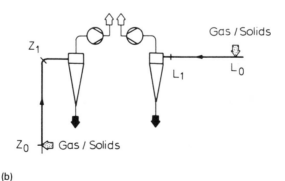

(b)

Figure 6.22 Marginal conditions for calculations: (a) positive pressure displacement; (b) negative pressure displacement.

(b) Polytropic state

$$p_1 = \frac{1}{p_0^{1/(\kappa+1)}} \left[p_0 \pm \mu \left(\frac{v}{c} \right)_0 \rho_0 g \Delta Z \frac{\kappa - 1}{\kappa} \right]^{\kappa/(\kappa+1)} \tag{6.74}$$

6.6.7 Boundary conditions for calculations

The following conditions apply:

(a) p_0, ρ_0 and v_0 are gas states at the terminal point of a section L_0 or Z_0 in the systems (Fig. 6.22(a)) or at the commencement of a system (Fig. 6.22(b)) at atmospheric conditions.

(b) p_1, ρ_1 and v_1 are gas states at the commencement of a section L_1 or Z_1 (Fig. 6.22(a)) or at the terminal point of the pipeline (Fig. 6.22(b)).

6.6.8 Comprehensive pressure drop equation

In terms of all the components which together constitute the pressure loss for a system, the following equation can be written:

$$\Delta p = \Delta p_{\text{transport}} + \Delta p_{\text{separator}} + \Delta p_{\text{valves}} \tag{6.45}$$

where

$$\Delta p_{\text{transport}} = \Delta p_L + \Delta p_A + (\Delta p_Z^* + \Delta p_G)_{\text{horizontal}} \tag{6.45a}$$

$$+ (\Delta p_Z^* + \Delta p_G)_{\text{vertical}} + \Delta p_B$$

$$= \Delta p_L + \Delta p_A + \Delta p_{Z \text{ (horizontal)}}$$

$$+ (\Delta p_{Z \text{ (vertical)}}^* + \Delta p_{G \text{ (vertical)}} + \Delta p_B \tag{6.45b}$$

$$= \lambda_L \frac{\rho}{2} v^2 \frac{\Delta L}{D} + \mu \rho v c + \mu \lambda_Z \frac{\rho}{2} v^2 \frac{\Delta L}{D}$$

$$+ \lambda_Z^* \frac{\rho^*}{2} c^2 \frac{\Delta Z}{D} + \rho^* g \Delta Z + 210 \left| \frac{2R_B}{D} \right|^{-1.15} \Delta p_Z \tag{6.45c}$$

A detailed expression for all the pressure loss factors in a total system is provided in a worked example (Example 14.4). In the example certain simplifying assumptions are made.

6.7 SOME IMPORTANT FUNCTIONAL RELATIONSHIPS

6.7.1 Introduction

In order to fully appreciate the influence of the various parameters described above, some experimental evidence will be used to illustrate the interrelationship between some of these parameters.

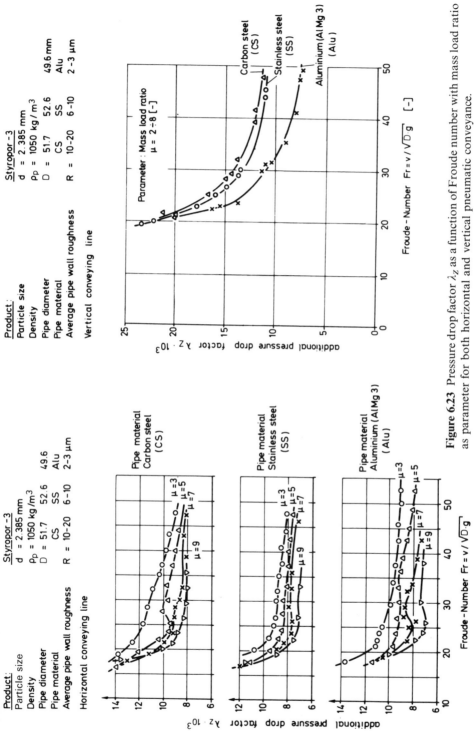

Figure 6.23 Pressure drop factor λ_Z as a function of Froude number with mass load ratio as parameter for both horizontal and vertical pneumatic conveyance.

6.7.2 Relationship of λ_z to *Fr* and μ

The pressure drop coefficient λ_z is shown as a function of Froude number *Fr* with mass load ratio μ and pipe material as parameters in Figs 6.23(a), (b). The range of Froude numbers represented is very wide (15–50). It can be clearly seen that λ_z decreases with an increase in Froude number *Fr*. It would appear that the main factors that affect the pressure drop coefficient in vertical lines are gravity, i.e. the increase in potential energy, and the pipe material.

6.7.3 Interpretation of λ_z^* and β

An interpretation of the main factors λ_z^* and β in equation (6.39) is demonstrated in Figs. 6.24 and 6.25. In Fig. 6.24, the impact and friction factor is plotted against the mass load ratio. This factor decreases with increase in μ, i.e. the interaction of the particles diminishes at higher mass load ratios. The influence of gravity is demonstrated in Fig. 6.25, where the velocity ratios β and β_0 are plotted against

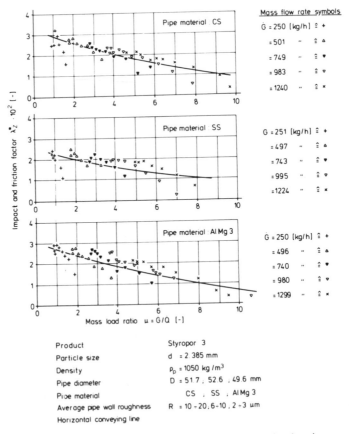

Figure 6.24 Impact and friction factor versus mass load ratio.

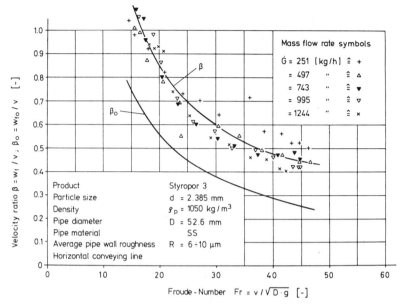

Figure 6.25 Velocity ratio versus Froude number.

the Froude number. In this case one sees that β is higher than β_0; this is due to the cloud effect.

6.7.4 Solid/gas velocity ratio c/v

In Figs 6.26(a), (b), the solids/gas velocity ratio c/v is shown as a function of particle size d for horizontal and vertical pipelines. These were determined experimentally by use of a double solenoid valve technique.

6.7.5 The determination of particle velocity (c) and voidage (ε)

A method suggested by Rizk [9] facilitates the estimation of the particle velocity (c) and the voidage (ε) for dilute phase suspensions. The method relies on the assumption that for such dilute suspensions there is little change in the particle velocity and the voidage during the conveying process.

The analysis leads to an important statement about the relationship between the mass load ratio (μ) and the mass concentration (μ^*) is defined as:

$$\mu^* = \rho^*/\rho \qquad (6.75)$$

Also, the following expressions are relevant to the discussion:

$$\text{Solid mass flow rate, } \dot{G} = A\rho^*c \qquad \text{(kg/s)}$$
$$\text{Gas mass flow rate, } \dot{Q} = A\rho v \qquad \text{(kg/s)}$$

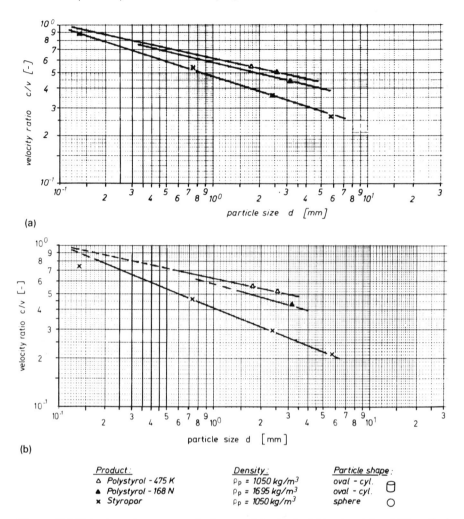

Figure 6.26 Velocity ratio versus equivalent particle size for (a) horizontal and (b) vertical conveying lines.

Now the mass load ratio (μ):

$$\mu = \frac{\dot{G}}{\dot{Q}} = \frac{\rho^* c}{\rho \, v} = \mu^* \frac{c}{v} \tag{6.76}$$

The relationship between μ^* and μ is shown in Fig. 6.27. In Fig. 6.27, the region applicable to pneumatic conveying lies in a narrow band in the second half of the quadrant ($45° \leqslant \phi \leqslant 90°$). The limiting value of $\phi = 45°$ represents the case when

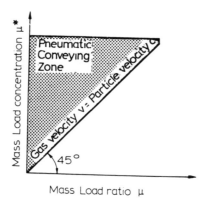

Figure 6.27 Conceptual relationship between μ^* and μ.

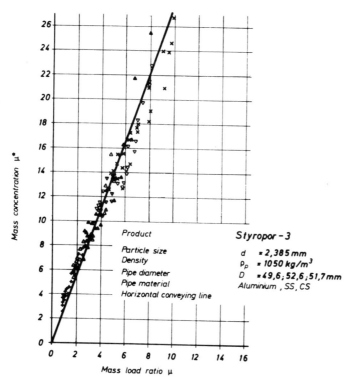

Figure 6.28 Measured relationship between μ^* and μ.

$\mu = \mu^*$ which implies that $c = v$ and hence no slip between the particles and the conveying gas takes place.

The ratio of the velocities c/v diminishes as the angle ϕ increases from $45°$ towards $90°$. At high gas velocities and for fine particles $\phi \geqslant 45°$.

The voidage can now be estimated from the definition proposed in equation (4.41), where the concentration μ^* or the apparent density ρ^* is to be measured.

Various techniques for effecting such measurements are presented in Chapter 13. In particular, the measurement of the solids velocity c is important. Techniques for measuring the solids mass concentration include the trapping of the solids flow at defined conditions in a pipe section fitted with quick acting shut-off valves. Results from such investigations [9] are shown in Fig. 6.28. From Fig. 6.28 a linear relationship between the mass concentration μ^* and the mass load ratio μ is evident. Using equation (6.76), it is possible to construct a set of curves indicating the relationship between the velocity ratio c/v and the gas velocity v (Fig. 6.29).

From Fig. 6.29, it can be seen that for the different mass flow rates, the ratio c/v remains constant until the pressure minimum is attained. The higher the solids mass flux, the earlier the solids drop out of the suspension, i.e. at high solid mass flow rates, saltation occurs at higher gas velocities.

6.7.6 Sequence to be followed to obtain the impact and friction factor λ_z^*

(a) Impact and friction factor out of the balance of energy equation in a volume

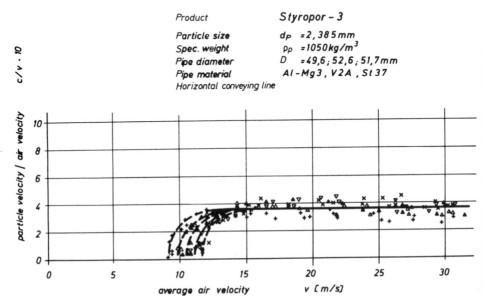

Figure 6.29 Relationship between c/v and v.

element

$$\lambda_z^* = \left(\lambda_z - \frac{2\beta}{(c/v)Fr^2}\right)\frac{v}{c}$$ (6.77)

(b) Impact and friction factor out of the balance of power on a particle cloud

$$\lambda_z^* = \left[\frac{C_D}{C_{Df}}\left(\frac{v-c}{w_f}\right)^2 - \beta\right]\frac{2}{Fr^{*2}}$$ (6.78)

Equating (a) and (b) one obtains

$$\lambda_z\frac{v}{c} - \frac{2\beta}{(c/v)Fr^2}\frac{v}{c} = \frac{C_D}{C_{Df}}\left(\frac{v-c}{w_f}\right)^2\frac{2}{Fr^{*2}} - \frac{2\beta}{Fr^{*2}}$$ (6.79)

Hence

$$\lambda_z\frac{v}{c} - \frac{2\beta}{(c^2/v^2)(v^2/Dg)} = 2\frac{C_D}{C_{Df}}\left(\frac{v-c}{w_f}\right)^2\frac{Dg}{c^2} - \frac{2\beta Dg}{c^2}$$

i.e.

$$\lambda_z\frac{v}{c} = 2\frac{C_D}{C_{Df}}\left(\frac{v-c}{w_f}\right)^2\frac{Dg}{c^2}$$ (6.80)

Out of this equation one obtains the settling velocity of a particle in a cloud:

$$w_f = \left[\frac{C_D}{C_{Df}}(v-c)^2\frac{2c/v}{\lambda_z c^2/Dg}\right]^{0.5}$$ (6.81)

with $Fr^{*2} = c^2/Dg$

$$w_f = \left[\frac{C_D}{C_{Df}}(v-c)^2\frac{2c/v}{\lambda_z Fr^{*2}}\right]^{0.5}$$ (6.82)

Assuming that the settling velocity of a particle in a cloud differs from that of an isolated particle, the next assumption was made:

$$w_f = K w_{f0}$$ (6.83)

A further assumption was made for the drag coefficients C_D and C_{Df}. Considering C_D and C_{Df} in a range where they are independent of the Reynolds number Re_p, (Fig. 3.1), their ratio C_D/C_{Df} is equal to one.

Now one can easily calculate the factor K in the general form,

$$K = \left[\frac{C_D}{C_{Df}}\left(\frac{v-c}{w_{f0}}\right)^2\frac{2c/v}{\lambda_z Fr^{*2}}\right]^{0.5}$$ (6.84)

for $C_D/C_{Df} = 1$

$$K = \left[\left(\frac{v-c}{w_{f0}} \right)^2 \frac{2c/v}{\lambda_z Fr^{*2}} \right]^{0.5}$$

(6.85)

From equation (6.85), to obtain the correction factor K, it is necessary to obtain from experimental tests carried out on the actual product and pipe material, the specific values of the solids velocity (c) and the additional pressure drop factor (λ_z).

Further, the gas velocity v can be calculated from equation (3.1), the settling velocity w_{f0} from equation (3.32) and the Reynolds number for the particle Re_p from:

$$Re_p = (v-c)d/v$$

(6.86)

In order to obtain the drag coefficient of the particle in an unbounded fluid ($C_{D\infty}$) equation (3.12) due to Kaskas is recommended.

With the above information, it is now possible to calculate the correction factor K. Using the value of K obtained from above, the cloud settling velocity w_f can be obtained. (It should be noted that w_f is, by virtue of the above discussions, obtained from experimental data.)

In order to calculate the impact and friction factor λ_Z^*, the velocity ratio $\beta = w_f/v$ (equation (4.55b)) must be calculated. Further, the Froude number (Fr) can be obtained from equation (4.55a). using equation (6.77), λ_Z^* can be calculated.

6.8 SEQUENCE TO BE FOLLOWED TO OBTAIN THE SYSTEM PRESSURE LOSS (Δp)

In order to illustrate the effectiveness of the various equations presented in this chapter, a typical conveying situation will be discussed and the method of determining the system pressure loss will be described.

Example 6.1

A producer of plastic raw materials has changed the formulation of one of its products. The original product was conveyed at a mass load ratio $\mu = 4.5$ to 5. The company wishes to employ the existing piping system with a total length of 75 m with an included vertical lift of 15 m. The pipeline has an internal diameter of $D = 110$ mm and includes two bends. It is required to convey the new product at a rate of $\dot{G} = 5$ t/h. Using the information below, check whether the product can be conveyed and whether an existing positive displacement blower can be used.

Solution

Required to convey a plastic material:

$$\dot{G} = 5 \text{ t/h}$$

$$\Delta L = 75\,\text{m (including 15 m vertical)}$$
$$\Delta Z = 15\,\text{m}$$

Given an existing pipe line, with two bends:

$$D = 110\,\text{mm}$$
$$\rho_p = 1\,000\,\text{kg/m}^3$$
$$d = 1.9\,\text{mm}$$

Step 1

From a series of laboratory tests the performance characteristics of the material were determined. The pressure minimum curve (μ against Fr) and the additional pressure drop curve (λ_z against Fr) with varying solids loading are presented in Figs 6.10(a),(b) and 6.23(a),(b) respectively.

(a) At a mass load ratio $\mu = 4.5$ from Fig. 6.10(a):

$$Fr_{min} = 24$$

(b) Air mass flow rate is obtained from equation (6.13):

$$\dot{Q} = \dot{G}/\mu = 5000/4.5 = 1111.11\,\text{kg/h}$$

(c) Volumetric air flow rate from equation (3.1):

$$\dot{V}_0 = \dot{Q}/\rho_0 = 1111.11/1.2 = 926\,\text{m}^3/\text{h}$$

where the ambient air density $\rho_0 = 1.2\,\text{kg/m}^3$ (Table 2.1), and the cross sectional area of the conveying pipe

$$A = \pi D^2/4 = \pi(0.11)^2/4 = 95 \times 10^{-4}\,\text{m}^2$$

Note that the use of the ambient air density implies the design of a vacuum system where the inlet is at atmospheric conditions (0).

(d) The initial air velocity

$$v_0 = \dot{V}/(A \times 3600) = 926/(95 \times 10^{-4} \times 3600)$$
$$= 27.1\,\text{m/s}$$

from which the Froude number can be calculated using equation (6.6):

$$Fr_0 = v_0/(Dg)^{1/2} = 27.1/[(0.11)(9.806)]^{1/2}$$
$$= 26.1$$

Note that in order to ascertain whether the conveying process can take place, the Froude number (Fr_0) obtained above, must be compared with the minimum Froude number (Fr_{min}) obtained from the experimental tests. In this case

$$Fr_{min} = 24 \qquad Fr_0 = 26.1.$$

Thus $Fr_0 > Fr_{min}$ which implies that the conveying air is sufficient to effect transportation.

(e) The velocity ratio c/v can be obtained from Figs 6.26(a), (b). At a particle diameter $d = 1.9$ mm, for horizontal flow $c/v = 0.4$.

(f) Particle velocity

$$c = (0.4)(v_0) = (0.4)(27.1)$$
$$= 10.84 \text{ m/s}$$

Step 2 Calculation of pressure drop
(Note: the expansion of the conveying gas will be neglected—low solids loading ratio).

(a) Reynolds number is obtained from equation (6.6):

$$Re = v_0 D/v = (27.1)(0.11)/(15.1 \times 10^{-6})$$
$$= 19.74 \times 10^4$$

where $v = 15.1 \times 10^{-6}$ m²/s (Table 2.6).

(b) Air friction factor λ_L is obtained from equation (2.44):

$$\lambda_L = 0.316/Re^{0.25} = 0.316/(19.74 \times 10^4)^{0.25}$$
$$= 0.015$$

(c) Pressure drop for air alone is obtained from equation (6.50):

$$\Delta p_L = \lambda_L \frac{\rho}{2} v^2 \frac{\Delta L}{D}$$

$$= (0.015)\left(\frac{12}{2}\right)(27.1)^2 \left(\frac{75}{0.11}\right)$$

$$= 4507 \text{ Pa}$$

(d) Pressure drop due to acceleration of solids is obtained from equation (6.70):

$$\Delta p_A = \mu v_0 \rho_0 c$$
$$= (4.5)(27.1)(1.2)(10.84)$$
$$= 1586 \text{ Pa}$$

(e) Additional pressure drop due to the solids in the horizontal line is obtained from equation (6.65). Neglecting the gas expansion one can write equation (6.65):

$$\Delta p_Z = \mu \lambda_Z \frac{\rho_0}{2} v_0^2 \frac{\Delta L}{D}$$

where $\lambda_Z = 3 \times 10^{-3}$ is obtained from experimental observations as shown in Fig. 6.23.

$$\Delta p_Z = (4.5)(3 \times 10^{-3})\left(\frac{1.2}{2}\right)(27.1)^2\left(\frac{75}{0.11}\right)$$

$$= 4056 \text{ Pa}$$

(f) Pressure drop due to elevation of solids is obtained from equation (6.72):

$$\Delta p_G = \rho^* g \Delta Z$$

where

$$\rho^* = \rho^* \frac{\rho}{\rho} = \mu^* \rho = \mu \frac{v}{c} \rho$$

$$\rho^* = \frac{\mu \rho}{c/v}$$

$$\Delta p_G = \frac{\mu \rho}{c/v} g \Delta Z$$

$$= \frac{(4.5)(9.806)(15)}{(0.4)}$$

$$= 1986 \text{ Pa}$$

(g) Pressure drop due to the bends is obtained from equation (4.91):

$$\frac{\Delta p_{\text{bend}}}{\Delta p_Z} = 210\left(\frac{2R_B}{D}\right)^{-1.15}$$

Assume that the bend radius is $R_B = 5D = 550$ mm. Now $\Delta p_Z = 4056$ Pa from (e) above for a pipe line 75 m long. The equivalent straight length of pipe for the bend

$$\Delta L_{\text{eq}} = 2\pi R_B/4 \qquad \text{(for a 90° bend)}$$

$$= \frac{2\pi(0.55)}{4} = 0.864 \text{ m}$$

Thus

$$\Delta p_{Z(\text{bend})} = \frac{4056}{75} \times 0.864 = 46.72 \text{ Pa}$$

Thus

$$\Delta p_{bend} = (46.72)(210)\left(\frac{2 \times 0.55}{0.11}\right)^{-1.15}$$

$$= 694.5 \,\text{Pa}$$

Now since there are two bends in the system

$$\Delta p_{bend} = 2 \times 694.5 = 1389 \,\text{Pa}$$

(h) Total pressure loss is found by adding all the components of the pressure losses:

$$\Delta p = 4507 + 1586 + 1986 + 1389 + 4056$$

$$= 13.52 \,\text{kPa}$$

(i) To calculate the terminal velocity of the air it is necessary to determine the density of the air at the exit of the system.

$$\text{Atmospheric pressure, } p_0 = p_{atm} = 1 \times 10^5 \,\text{Pa}$$

$$\text{Absolute exit pressure, } p_1 = p_0 - \Delta p$$

$$= 1 \times 10^5 - 0.1352 \times 10^5$$

$$= 0.865 \times 10^5 \,\text{Pa}$$

Density of air at exit (equation (6.58) and Section 2.5)

$$\rho_1 = p_1/RT_1$$

Taking $t_1 = 20\,°C$, $T_1 = (273.15 + 20) = 293.2 \,\text{K}$

$$\rho_1 = \frac{0.865 \times 10^5}{(287)(293.2)}$$

$$= 1.03 \,\text{kg/m}^3$$

Terminal velocity of air using equation (3.1):

$$\dot{V}_1 = \dot{Q}/\rho_1 = 1111.11/1.03$$

$$= 1078.7 \,\text{m}^3/\text{h}$$

$$v_1 = \dot{V}_1/(A \times 3600) = 31.5 \,\text{m/s}$$

(j) Average air velocity

$$\bar{v} = (v_0 + v_1)/2 = (27.1 + 31.5)/2$$
$$= 29.3 \text{ m/s}$$

(k) Pressure loss correction factor. Since the total pressure loss has been based on the inlet air velocity it is expedient to correct the pressure loss data to take into account the average air velocity.

$$\text{Correction factor, } \alpha = (\bar{v}/v_0)^2 = (29.3/27.1))^2$$
$$= 1.169$$

(Note: the correction factor is based on the velocity squared, since $\Delta p \propto v^2$.) The corrected system pressure loss:

$$\Delta p_{\text{correct}} = \Delta p \alpha = 13.52 \times 1.169$$
$$= 15.8 \text{ kPa}$$

(l) Corrected absolute exit pressure:

$$p_{1 \text{ correct}} = 1 \times 10^5 - 0.158 \times 10^5$$
$$= 0.842 \times 10^5 \text{ Pa}$$

(m) Corrected exist air density:

$$\rho_{1 \text{ correct}} = \frac{0.842 \times 10^5}{(237)(293.2)} = 1.0 \text{ kg/m}^3$$

From which

$$\dot{V}_{1 \text{ correct}} = 1111.11 \text{ m}^3/\text{h}$$

(n) Power consumption is obtained from equation (2.36) and taking the efficiency of the blower $\eta_B = 0.5$,

$$p = \Delta p \dot{V}/\eta_B$$
$$= \frac{0.158 \times 10^5 \times 1111.11}{(3600)(0.5)}$$
$$= 9.75 \text{ kW}$$

Step 3

To establish whether the existing blower will be adequate for the new application operating in a positive pressure mode as distinct from a vacuum mode, a quick check is possible. It is assumed that the total pressure drop is the same for both modes:

(a) Assume pressure at the solids feed point:

$$p_1 = p_0 + \Delta p$$
$$= 1 \times 10^5 + 0.158 \times 10^5$$
$$= 1.158 \times 10^5 \text{ Pa}$$

(b) Air density at solids feed point:

$$\rho_1 = p_1/RT$$

Firstly the temperature due to compression must be considered using equation (2.23):

$$T_1 = T_0\left(\frac{p_1}{p_0}\right)^{(\kappa-1)/\kappa}$$
$$= (293.2)\left(\frac{1.158 \times 10^5}{1 \times 10^5}\right)^{(1.4-1)/1.4}$$
$$= 305.5 \text{ K}$$

Hence

$$t_1 = 32.3\,°C$$
$$\rho_1 = \frac{1.158 \times 10^5}{(287)(305.5)}$$
$$= 1.32 \text{ kg/m}^3$$

(c) Air velocity at solids feed point:

$$v_1 = \dot{Q}(\rho_1 \times A \times 3600)$$
$$= 1111.11/(1.32 \times 95 \times 10^{-4} \times 3600)$$
$$= 24.61 \text{ m/s}$$

(d) Froude number at solids feed point:

$$Fr_1 = v_1/(gD)^{1/2}$$
$$= 24.61/[(9.806)(0.11)]^{1/2}$$
$$= 23.69$$

Comparing the Froude number at inlet Fr_1 to the minimum Froude number from tests Fr_{min} it can be seen that

$$Fr_1 < Fr_{min}$$

This indicates that the system operating in the positive pressure mode lies on the left-hand side of the pressure-minimum curve (Figs 6.17(a), (b)) in an unstable flow regime.

In order to operate in a safer flow regime the mass load ratio (μ) must be decreased by increasing the air flow rate at the blower.

Clearly, for a total system design, other contributions to the total pressure loss must also be taken into account. Such aspects as pressure loss across the feeder and the air–solids separation device etc. must be accounted for.

REFERENCES

1. Zenz, F.A. and Othmer, D.F. (1962) *Fluidisation and Fluid Particle Systems*, Reinhold, New York.
2. Meyers, S., Marcus, R.D. and Rizk, F. (1985) The state diagram for fine particle gas/solid suspensions, *Bulk Solids Handling*, Trans. Tech. Publications, August.
3. Boothroyd, R.G. (1971) *Flowing Gas–Solids Suspensions*, Chapman and Hall, London, pp. 129.
4. Leung, L.S. *et al.* (1978) *Proceedings of Pneumotransport 4*, BHRA Fluid Engineering, Cranfield.
5. Siegel, W. *VDI-Forsch.* **538** (1970).
6. Rizk, F. *Diss.* 1973. Univ. Karlsruhe.
7. Barth W, *VDI 92* (1950) 5; *CIT* **30** (1958) 3; *CIT* **32** (1960) 3; Mitt. VGB (1960) 79; *CIT* **35** (1963) 3.
8. Kaskas A, *Diplomarbeit*, TU Berlin, 1964.
9. Rizk F, BHRA Fluid Engn. 1976, *Pneumotransport, 3*; BHRA Fluid Engn. 1980, *Pneumotransport 5*; Transmatic 1981 Univ. Karlsruhe.
10. Bohnet, M. (1965) *VDI Forsch. 507* (1983) *CIT*, **55**, 7.
11. Prandtl, L. (1965) *Stromungslehre*, 6. Auflage Friedrich Vieweg, Braunschweig.
12. Mohlmann, H. (1985) *Ph.D. Thesis*, Faculty of Engineering, University of Witwatersrand, Johannesburg, September.

7

Feeding of pneumatic conveying systems

7.1 INTRODUCTION AND OVERALL DESIGN PHILOSOPHY

Essential to the effective operation of a pneumatic conveying system is the efficient feeding of the solids into the pipeline. Feeding devices perform a variety of functions, including a sealing function, in which the conveying gas is essentially sealed from a storage hopper holding the product to be conveyed. Further, these devices might be required to accurately control the solids feed rate into the pipeline for process control features as in chemical plants or in dosing operations.

In this chapter a variety of feeding devices both common and specialized, will be discussed in terms of their applications, design, limitations and suitability in relation to material characteristics. Where possible, design and selection criteria are provided as well as the adaptation of certain devices to meet specialist applications.

At the outset it must be pointed out that in most pneumatic conveying applications the single component which contributes to the largest pressure losses is normally the feeding device. As such, uppermost in the designer's mind should always be an attempt to minimize the losses associated with such devices.

In essence, all pneumatic conveying feeding devices normally involve the introduction of solids in an almost stationary mode into a fast moving gas stream, which is under pressure or vacuum. The rapid change in momentum of particles, coupled with a large amount of gas–solid turbulence in the feeding area are two predominant factors which account for the large pressure losses in feeding devices.

It can be said, that perhaps the one area which requires the most urgent attention from designers and researchers is in the reduction of the losses in the feeding zone. Already there is some evidence of attempts being made to streamline the flow and to produce suitable transition pieces between the feeder and the conveying pipe.

7.2 CLASSIFICATION OF FEEDING SYSTEMS

7.2.1 Pressure characteristics

Unlike pneumatic conveying systems in which classification is normally based on the mass flow ratio (μ), it is pertinent to classify feeding systems based on a pressure limitation. The pressure limitation is normally a function of the physical construction of the feeder, coupled with the methods of sealing.

In terms of commercially available feeding devices it is convenient to classify feeders in three pressure ranges:

(a) Low pressure – maximum 100 kPa (LP).
(b) Medium pressure – maximum 300 kPa (MP).
(c) High pressure – maximum 1000 kPa (HP).

7.2.2 Classification in terms of system requirements

The final classification of a feeding system is dictated by the needs of the system or process for which the pneumatic conveyer is being designed. In all cases it is necessary to determine whether the process requires continuous feeding or whether batch feeding is acceptable.

7.3 FEEDER SELECTION CRITERIA

In the selection of a suitable feeding device, it is also necessary to take into consideration the factors discussed above as well as a number of additional criteria. An attempt has been made to identify the salient features which ultimately assist the designer to select the most appropriate feeding system:

(a) Product characteristics: particle size, cohesive, friable, free flowing, is degradation of concern? required to operate at elevated temperatures? etc.
(b) Physical layout: does the plant layout restrict the amount of head room available?
(c) Cost: is the system being designed for a short or long term project?
(d) Continuous or batch operation.
(e) System conveying pressure.
(f) Accurate feeding control: is there a demand for fine solids feed control as in some chemical, packing or colour dosing operations?

Answers to all the above criteria are essential in order to select the most appropriate feeder. In terms of a checklist Table 7.1 indicates those areas in which feeders are suitable.

7.4 LOW PRESSURE FEEDING DEVICES

In terms of the classification of feeding devices, low pressure feeders include the feeders for application in a pressure range from vacuum to a maximum pressure

Table 7.1 Feeder selection criteria

| | Broad feeder | Classification | Special |
Criteria	Rotary	Stationary	features
1. Product			
Friable	−	+	
Free flowing		−	
Cohesive	−	+	
Large particles			+
High temperature			+
Corrosive			+
Toxic			+
Abrasive			+
2. System			
Head room limitations	+	−	
3. Process			
Continuous or batch	+	+	
Fine feed control	+	−	

Notes: 1.This is only a broad classification. In certain situations, combination of feeder
types provides a more suitable solution.
2. − = unsuitable
+ = suitable
3. Special features column indicates that selection must take into consideration the
unusual characteristics of the product.

of the order of 100 kPa (1 bar). In this section characteristics of these low pressure
feeders will be discussed.

7.4.1 The Venturi feeder

Perhaps the simplest form (from a mechanical point of view) of all feeders for
pneumatic conveying systems, is the Venturi feeder. Having once been the most
popular type of feeder, improved design and construction techniques have
resulted in a new breed of these feeders.

The Venturi feeder consists of an air entraining nozzle, so arranged that the
high air velocity through the nozzle creates a region of negative pressure in which
the material is entrained.

These feeders are restricted to short distances and relatively low material flow
rates. There are numerous specialized applications including the transport of
bottle tops, friable and degradable products such as potato crisps and a larger

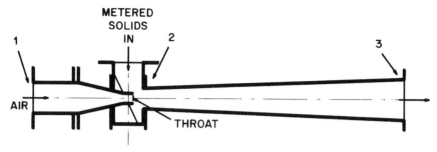

Figure 7.1 Layout of a typical Venturi feeder.

application in the transport of agricultural products (maize, wheat, barley, etc.).

Whereas much work has been done [1] on jet pumps and ejectors for a large number of applications, most of this work has limited application in the field of gas–solids suspensions. Recently [2] a comprehensive paper outlining the design procedures for a Venturi feeder has been presented. A more simplified approach [3] has been presented by Dixon on the design of Venturi feeders. The Venturi feeder shown in Fig. 7.1 consists of a convergent and divergent cone connected by a short parallel throat section. Dixon's approach is based on incompressible fluid flow theory and thus is only suitable with very low pressure conveying systems (typically 0.15 bar and less).

According to Bernoulli the following equation can be written:

$$p_{dyn1} + p_{stat1} = p_{dyn2} + p_{stat2} = p_{dyn3} + p_{stat3} = p_{tot} \tag{7.1}$$

where p_{dyn} is the velocity pressure and p_{stat} is the static pressure. In practice even with air flowing alone, irrecoverable pressure losses will occur and:

$$p_{stat3} - p_{stat2} = (1 - K_1)(p_{dyn2} - p_{dyn3})$$

or

$$p_{dyn2} = p_{dyn3} + (p_{stat3} - p_{stat2})/(1 - K_1) \tag{7.2}$$

where K_1 is a loss factor for a taper enlargement. The loss factor varies with the angle of the enlargement but with air alone is typically 0.1 for a 6° or 7° included angle. The feed Venturi differs from a simple Venturi by the addition of a feed hole in the wall of the throat. The pressure of this opening introduces additional losses because of the discontinuity of the throat surface, and because of the admission of air and/or material at this point.

For convenience, Dixon [3] makes allowances for this loss in the factor K_1. On this basis the factor K_1 is increased to a value of 0.2 to allow for these effects. Similarly Dixon writes an equation of the following form for the contraction:

$$p_{stat1} - p_{stat2} = (1 + K_2)(p_{dyn2} - p_{dyn1}) \tag{7.3}$$

where K_2 is the loss factor for tapered contractions and lies between 0.04 and 0.06 for included angles less than 45°. At an included angle of 25° a typical loss factor of $K_2 = 0.05$. On the basis of the discussions for K_1 it must be noted that there is no need for correcting K_2.

Venturi calculations start with the downstream static pressure p_{stat3}. This is the conveying pressure head calculated using the Dixon method as proposed in Chapter 12. Since p_{dyn3} is known to be the downstream conveying velocity pressure and p_{stat2} is the desired static pressure at the Venturi throat, it is possible to calculate p_{dyn2} by assuming a value of $K_1 = 0.2$. Having determined p_{dyn2}, it is then possible to calculate p_{stat1} and the overall pressure drop across the feed Venturi.

The method described above is only suitable for mass flow ratios of the order of $\mu = 1$ and conveying pressures of the order of 0.15 bar. If high solids loadings are used or if the Venturi back pressure is significantly greater than 0.15 bar, then the Venturi recovery cone design becomes critical. Full details pertaining to such a design are given in [2].

Example 7.1

Design a feed Venturi for a fan system which is to convey a plastic powder at a rate of $\dot{G} = 1.5$ tonnes per hour. Preliminary calculations have shown that:

(a) Using a $D = 75$ mm diameter conveying pipe and an airflow rate $\dot{V} = 400$ standard cubic metres per hour, a conveying pressure of 550 millibars is required.

(b) Using a $D = 150$ mm diameter pipe and an airflow $\dot{V} = 1400$ standard cubic metres per hour, a conveying pressure of 130 millibars is required (which includes an allowance for cyclone pressure drop). A mass flow ratio of $\mu = 0.9$ is applicable for this system.

Solution

Select the 150 mm conveying pipe for the following reasons:

(a) It satisfies the criteria that the solids loading (μ) should be less than 1.
(b) It satisfies the criteria that the conveying pressure should be 0.15 bar or less.
(c) That the pressure is suitable for a fan system and the solids/air loading $\mu = 0.9$ kg/h of solids per kg/h of air is suitable for a fan system also.

Diameter of Venturi upstream connection, $D_a = 0.15$ m
Diameter of Venturi downstream connection, $D_\omega = 0.15$ m

Air flow at discharge, $\dot{V}_\omega = \dfrac{1400}{1.13 \times 3600} = 0.344 \text{ m}^3/\text{s}$

Air velocity at discharge, $v_\omega = 19.46$ m/s ($v_\omega = \dot{V}_\omega/A$)
Static pressure at discharge, $p_{stat3} = 13 \text{ kN/m}^3$ (130 mbar)
Assume a static pressure at Venturi throat, $p_{stat2} = -0.075 \text{ kN/m}^2$

Velocity pressure, p_{dyn}. To convert an air velocity v (m/s) to an equivalent pressure (kN/m²), the following formula can be used for air at atmospheric pressure and 15 °C:

$$p_{dyn} = \frac{\rho v^2}{2} \, N/m^2$$

$$= \left(\frac{v}{40.42}\right)^2 kN/m^2$$

where

$$\rho = \frac{1.0325 \times 10^5}{(287)(288)}$$

$$= 1.25 \, kg/m^3$$

p_{dyn} should be corrected for changes in air density at each point but this is neglected in this simple example.

Starting at the Venturi discharge we can work back to find the velocity pressure at the throat:

$$p_{dyn2} = p_{dyn3} + (p_{stat3} - p_{stat2})/(1 - K_1)$$

$$= \left(\frac{19.46}{40.42}\right)^2 + \frac{[13 - (-0.075)]}{(1 - 0.2)}$$

$$= 0.23 + 13.075/0.8$$

$$p_{stat2} = 16.57 \, kN/m^2$$

Throat velocity, $v_{th} = 40.42(16.57)^{1/2}$

$$= 164.53 \, m/s$$

Area of Venturi throat, $A_{th} = \dfrac{1400}{164.53 + 3600}$

$$= 2.36 \times 10^{-3} \, m^2$$

Throat diameter, $D_{th} = (4/\pi \times 2.36 \times 10^{-3})^{1/2}$

$$= 0.055 \, m$$

Finally the static pressure at inlet to the Venturi can be calculated using

$$p_{stat1} = p_{stat2} + (1 + K_2)(p_{dyn2} - p_{dyn1})$$

Now $p_{dyn1} = p_{dyn3}$ for the same diameter pipe at inlet and outlet. Hence,

$$p_{dyn1} = 0.23 \, kN/m^2$$

$$p_{stat1} = -0.075 + (1 + 0.05)(16.57 - 0.23)$$

$$= 17.08 \, kN/m^2$$

Since the velocity pressures at inlet and outlet are essentially the same, the overall loss is given by the difference in static pressure $p_{stat1} - p_{stat3}$:

$$\text{Venturi loss} = 17.08 - 13$$
$$= 4.08 \, kN/m^2 \, (40.8 \, mbar)$$

Note that nearly 25% of the fan power is being used at the Venturi to create a vacuum for solids entrainment.

7.4.2 Negative pressure feeding devices

7.4.2.1 Vacuum nozzles

One area in which little research work has been done is in the design of nozzles for feeding of vacuum conveying systems. There is limited documentation on these feeders, and it would appear that most designers rely on a process of 'suck it and see' to obtain the best solution for a particular application.

Essentially, nozzles for vacuum applications should be designed to enable effective operation in a variety of uncontrolled situations. The design criteria must take into consideration situations in which the nozzle could be completely immersed in a large pile of solids, or where the nozzle is required to lift the remaining portion of material left in a ship's hold.

Classical work of Cramp and Priestly in 1924 [4] was studied in detail by Vogel in 1979 [5]. In terms of the work [5] a nozzle constant K_n was determined as follows:

$$K_n = \dot{G} A_n v \tag{7.4}$$

where $\dot{G}$ is the solids mass flow rate (t/h), v is nozzle superficial gas velocity (cm/s) and A_n the nozzle area (mm²). By continuity and assuming adiabatic conditions, this can be rewritten as:

$$\dot{G}_s = K_n \left(1 - \frac{p_n - p_1}{p_n} \right) v \tag{7.5}$$

where $\dot{G}_s$ is the mass flux, p_1 is the absolute pressure at any station in the riser, p_n is the absolute pressure at the nozzle, and v is superficial gas velocity in the riser. It was found [4] that the value of K_n remained nearly constant for each of nine configurations in nozzle design investigated.

From equation (7.5) it is apparent that in order to maximize $\dot{G}_s$ for a riser the value of K_n must be maximized. For a vacuum system, the maximum vacuum and the maximum superficial gas velocity obtainable are also limiting factors in maximizing the mass flux $\dot{G}_s$.

The nozzle configurations considered in the study [4] are shown in Fig. 7.2(a).

The horizontally configured nozzle (No. 9) in Fig. 7.2(a) yielded the most superior performance.

In a recent study [6] the work done by Cramp and Priestley was verified in an experimental situation designed to investigate the vacuum conveying of large lumps of coal. In this study [6] various peripheral aids were also evaluated in terms of their effectiveness. In particular, the use of an auxiliary air supply to aid solids entrainment, and the use of a bolt on type vibrator were found to have varying effects on nozzle efficiency.

The study [6] is concluded by noting:

(a) The nozzle cross section should be the same as the conveying line cross section.

(b) Auxiliary air entrainment increases nozzle efficiency for fine materials in terms of improving the fluidization characteristics at the entrance to the nozzle.

(c) In the case of coarse or granular particles, auxiliary air entrainment decreases nozzle efficiency.

(d) In certain cases the use of an externally fixed vibrator will result in a net improvement of nozzle efficiency.

The use of a double tube nozzle (Fig. 7.2(b)) is advocated by several commercial organizations. Such a nozzle permits the entrainment of air through the outer tube. There is much contention on the exact arrangement of the inner tube with respect to the outer tube. In a study on nozzle geometry [7] it was concluded that for materials which flow readily under the influence of gravity:

(a) By changing the geometry of the nozzle, such that the inner tube protrudes from the outer tube, a more efficient nozzle design is achieved.

(b) The optimum angle between the inner and outer tubes is such that the material flows into the nozzle under gravity but that an overfeeding situation is avoided, thereby preventing any pipe blockages.

In Fig. 7.2(c), a typical flexible vacuum conveying system is shown in which a nozzle is fixed to a flexible conveying pipe.

7.4.2.2 Stationary vacuum feeding devices

The nozzle configurations discussed in the previous section provide for flexibility and as such are well suited to 'vacuum cleaning' operations. Such operations would include the cleaning of spillage in factories and chemical plants, the cleaning of boilers, and the vacuum or loading of rail trucks, road vehicles and ships holds.

There are a number of applications in which there is a demand for stationary feeding devices. Such applications include the vacuum conveying of material from storage silos, open bins and stock piles. In all these cases, the design of the feeding system must make provision for an adjustable gas inlet. Such an arrangement facilitates the adjustment of the gas–solids loading to prevent pipe blockages. The gas inlet is adjusted by means of a sliding plate or collar so

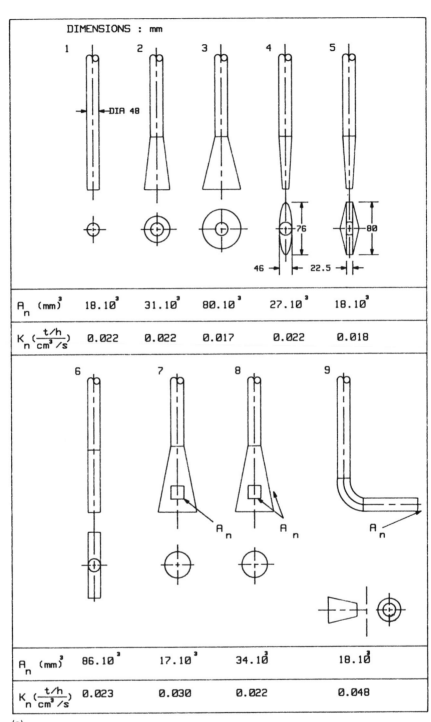

DIMENSIONS : mm

	1	2	3	4	5
A_n (mm^3)	18.10^3	31.10^3	80.10^3	27.10^3	18.10^3
$K_n (\frac{t/h}{cm^3/s})$	0.022	0.022	0.017	0.022	0.018

	6	7	8	9
A_n (mm^3)	86.10^3	17.10^3	34.10^3	18.10^3
$K_n (\frac{t/h}{cm^3/s})$	0.023	0.030	0.022	0.048

(a)

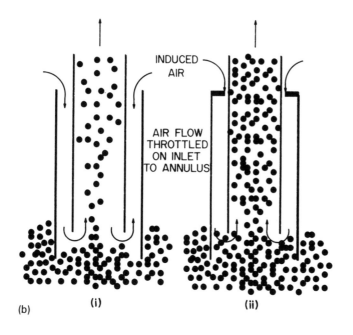

INDUCED AIR

AIR FLOW THROTTLED ON INLET TO ANNULUS

(b)

(i)

(ii)

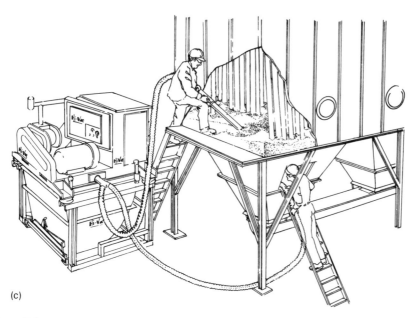

(c)

Figure 7.2 (a) Various vacuum nozzle configurations; (b) vacuum nozzle with adjustable geometry; (c) typical flexible vacuum conveying system (Hi-Vac, NFE International, Bensenville, Illinois, USA).

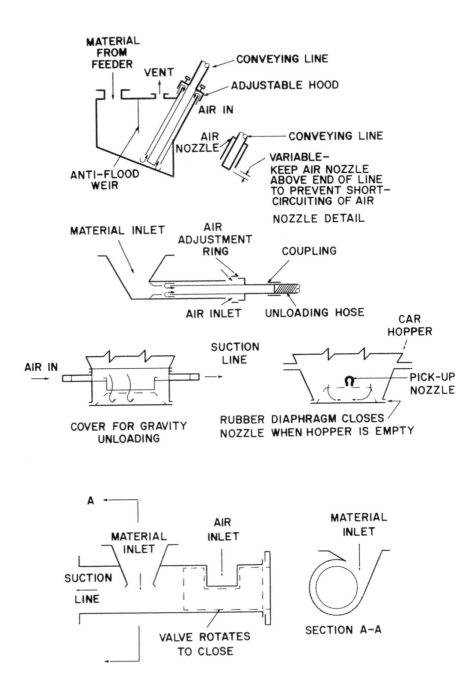

Figure 7.3 Stationary vacuum feeding devices.

arranged as to facilitate the fine adjustment of the amount of gas entering into the system in the vicinity of the feeding device.

In Fig. 7.3, a number of stationary feeding devices are depicted.

7.4.3 Rotary airlocks

7.4.3.1 Introduction and description

Perhaps the most widely used of all pneumatic conveying feeding devices is the rotary airlock (or rotary valve) (Fig. 7.4). As the name implies, the device provides both a pressure seal and acts as a feeding device. The valve is available in a variety of configurations, all conforming to a basic design consisting of a moving rotor and a stationary casing.

The rotor consists of segmented pockets which collect materials from an opening in the casing and deliver the material into the conveying gas stream.

The casing is constructed to accept some form of material feed hopper and also some form of transition piece to couple the valve to the conveying pipe. Depending upon construction, the casing can also be fitted with a vent pipe, purge air pipes and some mechanism to adjust clearance between blade tips and the casing.

7.4.3.2 Leakage through a rotary airlock

All rotary airlocks, irrespective of their construction or make, will leak. However, depending upon the construction, leakage rates can be minimized.

There are basically three categories of leakage which are associated with rotary airlocks (Fig. 7.5):

(a) Carry over leakage—due to the return of empty pockets.
(b) Labyrinth leakage—due to losses through shaft seals in the casing.
(c) Clearance leakage—due to the clearance between the rotor tips and the casing.

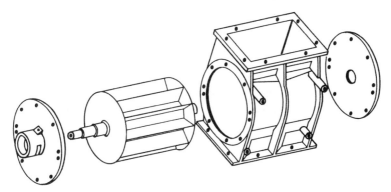

Figure 7.4 Typical arrangement of a drop through rotary airlock (Waeschle Maschinenfabrik GmbH, Ravensburg, West Germany).

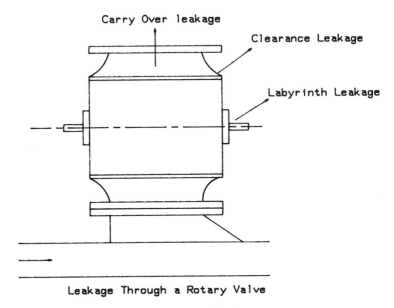

Carry Over leakage

Clearance Leakage

Labyrinth Leakage

Leakage Through a Rotary Valve

Figure 7.5 Leakage paths in a rotary airlock.

Essentially, carry over leakage in which the gas trapped at a high pressure has to be vented due to the returning pocket, is a fact of life and little can be done to avoid this source of gas loss. Labyrinth leakage can be totally eliminated by the use of good shaft seals, whilst clearance leakage can be minimized by reducing the gap between the rotor tips (both top and side) and the casing.

The amount of leakage which takes place in a rotary airlock is also dependent upon the operating pressure of the system. Both carry over leakage and the clearance leakage increase with increased operating pressure. Assuming that there is no labyrinth leakage, the total leakage through a rotary valve is given by:

$$\dot{V}_T^* = \dot{V}_c^* + \dot{V}_p^* \qquad (7.6)$$

where $\dot{V}_c^*$ is the clearance leakage and $\dot{V}_p^*$ is the carry over leakage.

The clearance leakage [8] is estimated by assuming that the pressure differential across the valve is converted into a velocity head in the valve clearance. If a contraction coefficient of 0.6 is assumed,

$$\dot{V}_c^* = 0.6kA(2\Delta p/\rho_a)^{1/2}(\text{m}^3/\text{s}) \qquad (7.7)$$

where k is a correction factor to allow for gas expansion, A is the leakage area (m^2), Δp is the pressure differential across the valve (Pa), and ρ_a is the higher pressure air density.

Also, for the carry over leakage:

$$\dot{V}_{p}^{*} = \frac{\pi}{4}D_{V}^{2}L_{V}v_{s} \tag{7.8}$$

where D_V is the rotor diameter (m), L_V is the length of the rotor (m), and v_s is the speed of the rotation of the valve.

Example 7.2

In order to illustrate the use of equations (7.7) and (7.8), an example is taken from Dixon [8].

A rotary airlock has a diameter of 300 mm and a length of 300 mm. The valve rotates at a speed of $v_s = 20$ rev/min and feeds materials into a conveying line against a pressure of 0.6 bar gauge (60 kPa). Estimate the air leakage for an open rotor, with rotor tips and side clearance of 0.2 mm.

Solution

Conveying pressure = 1.6×10^5 N/m²
Pressure drop value = 0.6×10^5 N/m².

For a nozzle k can be determined theoretically from formulae for frictionless adiabatic flow. Typical values for nozzle flow:

p_α/p_ω	k
1.2	0.9
1.5	0.8
1.9	0.7

where p_α is the static pressure below the rotary valve and p_ω is the static pressure above the rotary valve.

Assume that in the case of the rotary airlock, the k values will be further reduced by 0.2. In this case $p_\alpha/p_\omega = 1.6$.
Extrapolating

$$k = 0.78 - 0.2 = 0.58$$

Now rotor leakage area:

$$A = 2(0.3)(0.2)(10^{-3}) + 2(0.3)(0.2)(10^{-3})$$
$$= 2.4 \times 10^{-4}\,\text{m}^2$$

where the rotor has open sides. From equation (7.7) clearance leakage:

$$\dot{V}_{c}^{*} = (0.6)(0.58)(2.4)(10^{-4})[2(0.6)(10^{5})/1.96]^{1/2}$$
$$= 1.24\,\text{m}^3/\text{min}$$

where

$$\rho = 1.225 \, \text{kg/m}^3 \text{ for air at } 15\,^\circ\text{C}$$

$$\rho_\alpha = 1.225(1.6) = 1.96 \, \text{kg/m}^3 \text{ (at higher pressure)}$$

Also, for a valve speed $v_s = 20$ rev/min, from equation (7.8) the carry over leakage:

$$\dot{V}^*_\text{p} = \frac{\pi}{4}(0.3)^2 (0.3)(20)$$

$$= 0.4 \, \text{m}^3/\text{min}$$

Thus, the total leakage:

$$\dot{V}^*_\text{T} = \dot{V}^*_\text{c} + \dot{V}^*_\text{p} = 1.64 \, \text{m}^3/\text{min at } 1.6 \text{ bar}$$

$$\dot{V}^*_\text{t} = 2.62 \, \text{m}^3/\text{min free air.}$$

The results obtained from these calculations are comparable with extensive experimental studies [9], carried out on a range of valve sizes. Results from these studies are shown in Fig. 7.6. (The results for the pressure ratio of 1.6 and the 300 mm valve must be viewed in terms of the fact that the clearance and the valve speed are only 0.13 mm and 15 rev/min as opposed to 0.2 mm and 20 rev/min in the example above).

In certain situations, the air leakage through a valve (in particular the carry over leakage) can create severe hold-up problems in the storage hopper located above the valve. Excess fluidization and arching are synonymous with the air leakage from rotary airlocks.

In order to obviate some of these problems, a venting facility designed either into the valve or the hopper can be arranged (Fig. 7.7). The vent pipe located on the valve casing should normally be fed into a filter sock so as to avoid excessive dust leakage at the valve. The hopper vent usually incorporates a pipe leading to a filter located on top of the hopper.

7.4.3.3 Feeding efficiency of a rotary airlock

Essentially, a rotary airlock in a positive displacement device, and as such the quantity of material which is fed, is, up to a point, proportional to the speed of rotation. The limit of proportionality is reached at a critical speed above which there is a certain amount of carry over of material due to insufficient time for any one pocket to discharge completely.

The volumetric efficiency of a valve is not the same for all materials and it is found in practice that the speed at which the maximum feed rate occurs depends solely on the characteristics of the material being handled (Fig. 7.8). Thus, for each material there is a 'critical rotor speed' [10] which is found to depend on the

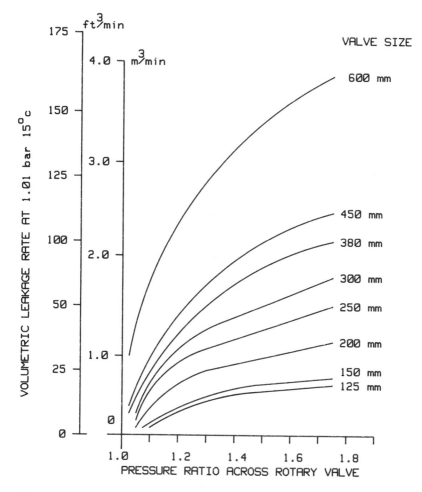

Figure 7.6 Typical air leakage values for a rotary airlock [9].

rotor pocket filling process. Typical feeding efficiency characteristics for a rotary airlock feeding a range of materials are shown in Fig. 7.9(a). A typical selection chart for rotary airlocks with 100% efficiency is shown in Fig. 7.9(b).

7.4.3.4 Valve configurations

Over the years a number of versions of rotary airlocks have been developed for a variety of applications. The selection of a suitable rotary airlock is a function of both the material characteristics and the system requirements. There is a basic

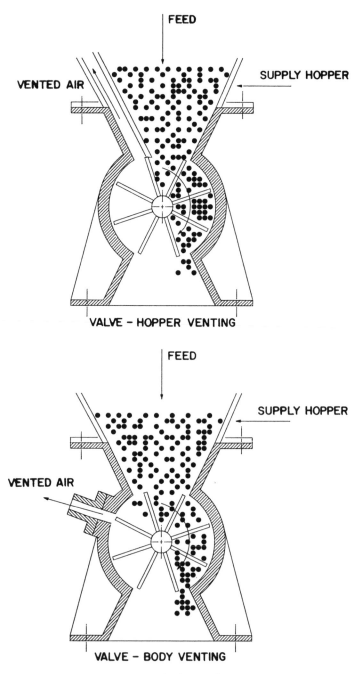

Figure 7.7 Rotary airlock fitted with venting arrangement.

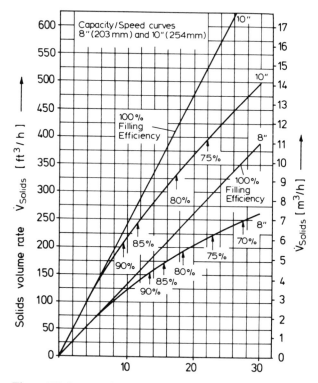

Figure 7.8 Rotary airlock feeding efficiency.

range of rotary airlocks which include:

(a) Horizontal rotor—drop through.
(b) Horizontal rotor—blow through.
(c) Vertical rotor—blow through.

The essential difference between the drop through configuration and the blow through configuration lies in the method of connecting the valve to the conveying pipe. In the case of the drop through valve the material is dropped into a transitional element known as the 'feeding tee' which links the valve to the pipeline.

The design of the feeding tee is a subject of much debate. To date only a limited amount of data is available on the design of an efficient transition piece. A typical arrangement is shown in Fig. 7.10 and Fig. 7.11. In addition to the transition arrangement, a nozzle (see equation (7.15)) is included on the clean gas side in an attempt to entrain the solids into the flowing gas stream.

The blow through configuration (Fig. 7.12) is designed to include a facility to connect the conveying pipe directly to the valve casing. In such valves, the gas stream passes through the pockets, thereby ensuring complete removal of all material. These valves are well suited to 'sticky materials'. Further, since there is no need for a feeding tee, such valves generally occupy less head room.

The vertical rotor arrangement (Fig. 7.13) was specifically designed to meet the requirements of a valve capable of handling large particles. In an extremely abrasive environment these valves can feed waste mine material up to 80 mm in size for backfilling of mines.

7.4.3.5 *Rotor configurations*

Perhaps the greatest variation in rotary airlock design occurs in the type of rotor configuration available. Rotors are manufactured to suit a wide range of

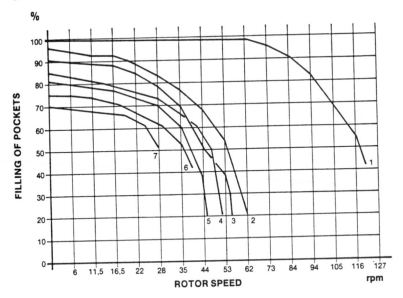

CURVE	MATERIAL	BULK DENSITY
1	CEREAL (CORN, MEALIES) EASY FLOWING AND ROLLING	0,75 t /m³
2	CRYSTALLIZED SUGAR, SALT, ETC.	0,8 - 0,9 t /m³
3	CEMENT	1,5 t /m³
4	LIME	0,5 t /m³
5	DUST (GRINDING)	0,4 t /m³
6	WOOD SHAVINGS NOT BIGGER THAN 2 x 2 x 30 mm	0,25 t /m³
7	SAW DUST	0,1 t /m³

(a)

Figure 7.9 (a) Volumetric feeding efficiency of a rotary airlock (AMD Services, South Africa).

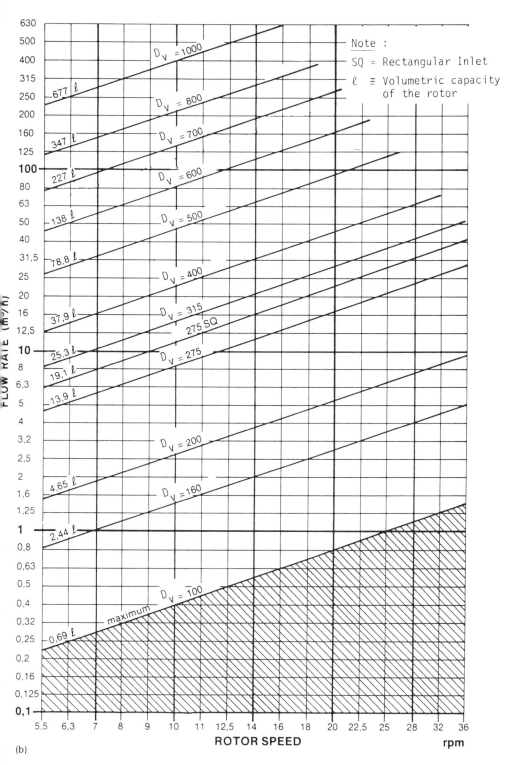

Figure 7.9 (b) Selection chart for rotary airlocks—100% filled pockets (AMD Services, South Africa).

(b)

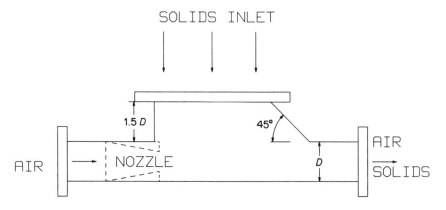

Figure 7.10 Arrangement of feeding tee and nozzle.

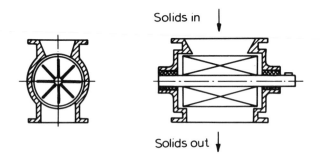

Figure 7.11 Drop through rotary airlock.

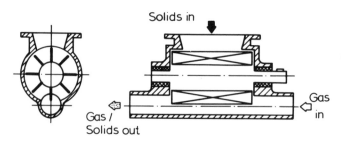

Figure 7.12 Blow through rotary airlock.

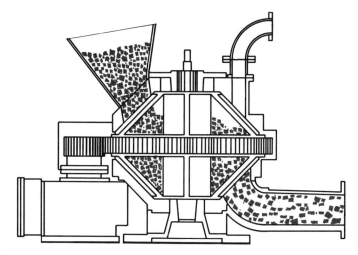

Figure 7.13 Vertical rotor configuration (Maschinenfabrik Karl Brieden & Co., Bochum, West Germany).

materials and applications and include: flexible tips, rigid tips, reinforced blades, shaped pockets, etc. (Fig. 7.14).

7.4.3.6 Casing configurations

In addition to providing a suitably robust body for the fixing of the storage hopper and the pipe work, the casing plays an important role in providing a mechanism for adjusting and minimizing clearance leakage, the provision of suitable mating surfaces for the rotor and such features as vent pipes, purge air devices and in the case of hot materials, cooling coils to protect the mechanical components. In addition specialist facilities such as pelican beaks are provided to assist with the flow of granular materials. (Fig. 7.15).

7.4.3.7 Valve arrangements

There are certain applications which require the arrangement of rotary valves in either series vertical or series horizontal mode. The series vertical arrangement (Fig. 7.16) is often used in applications where additional sealing capacity is required. Also, by fitting independent variable speed drives to each valve, it is possible to vary the mass flow of solids and the frequency at which the solids are introduced into the conveying pipe. The top valve (Fig. 7.16) is used for solids mass flow control, whilst the bottom valve can be rotated at a higher speed thereby 'smoothing' out the pressure surges which normally occur as discreet pockets of material are dumped into the pipeline.

Extensive tests [11] have been conducted on a series of vertical arrangements. Results on fine powder materials have shown that a substantial reduction in system pressure loss is achieved by increasing the frequency at which the solids

VALVE CLEARANCE ADJUSTMENT

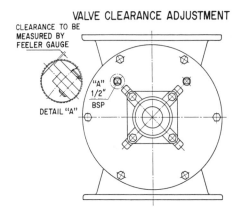

IMPELLER WITH HARD TIPS   IMPELLER WITH FLEXIBLE & ADJUSTIBLE TIPS

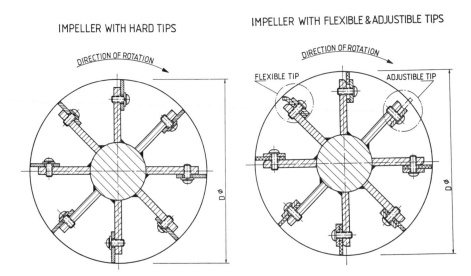

Figure 7.14 Various rotor arrangements (Pneutech Pty Ltd, South Africa).

are introduced into the system (Fig. 7.17). Savings of the order of 30% [11] can be achieved by smoothing the flow.

The series horizontal arrangement (Fig. 7.18) is particularly well suited to chemical dosing systems in which a discrete amount of various products is required to be transferred to a mixing process. In this case, rotary airlocks of the drop out type are arranged on a single conveying pipe. In such an arrangement it is suggested that only drop out and not blow through valves are used. With blow through valves, a situation occurs where product from an upstream valve will be passed through the blades of a downstream valve, thereby creating a potential wear problem.

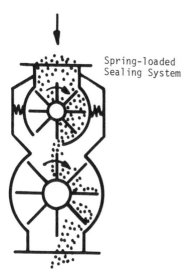

Spring-loaded
Sealing System

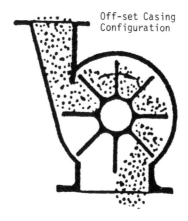

Off-set Casing
Configuration

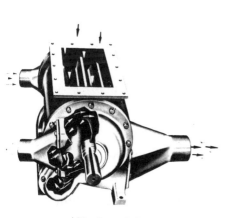

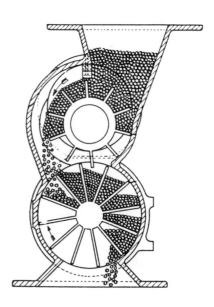

'Air Swept' Feeder
(CEA - Carter Day Co, Minneapolis, USA)

Figure 7.15 Various casing configurations.

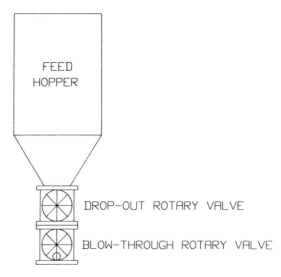

Figure 7.16 Rotary airlocks arranged in series vertical mode.

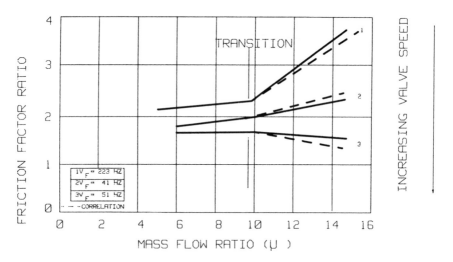

Figure 7.17 Influence of feeding frequency of system performance.

7.4.4 Combined negative pressure/positive pressure system

A novel method of combining the features of a Venturi nozzle and a blow vessel (see Section 7.6 for detailed discussion on blow vessel) is the so called Cyclonaire system [12] (Fig. 7.19). This system provides for the vacuum lifting and conveying of a product in one unit. An important feature of this system is the fact

Figure 7.18 Rotary airlocks arranged in series horizontal mode (Johannes Moller Hamburg GmbH & Co., Hamburg, West Germany).

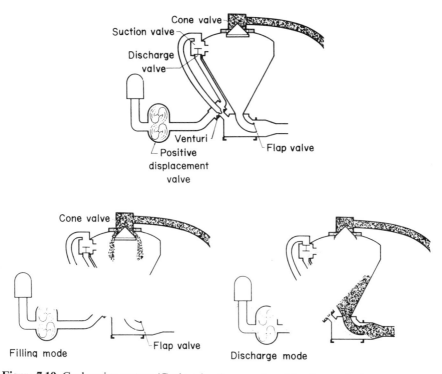

Figure 7.19 Cyclonaire system (Cyclonaire Corporation, Henderson, Nebraska, USA).

that since the vacuum is created by the Venturi, the risk of contaminating the blower with fine particles is eliminated.

The system operates by means of a series of valves and a volume controller which regulates the filling operation and ensures that the vessel is filled to an optimum level. The discharge cycle is initiated by a switchover of valves which diverts the airflow from the Venturi nozzle to pressurize the vessel and to provide air to effect positive pressure conveying.

There are a number of applications of the Cyclonaire including static installations for inplant handling, off loading rail cars and installations in which the units are mounted on board road tankers.

7.5 MEDIUM PRESSURE FEEDING SYSTEMS

Medium pressure feeding systems are normally designed to operate at pressures not exceeding 300 kPa (3 bar). Many of these feeding devices are ostensibly used in the cement industry and have resulted in the parallel development of a number of compressors with an upper pressure limit, specially designed to be linked with the range of medium pressure feeders.

7.5.1 The fluid–solids pump

Fluid–solids pump technology dates back to the early 1900's when Alfonso Kinyon [13] was awarded a patent for his design. Since then, a large number of manufacturers have produced several variations of fluid solids pumps to meet a variety of applications.

Essentially, most designs include a specially machined screw which continuously feeds material into the high pressure conveying gas. Several screw arrangements have been designed to ensure a high pressure seal so as to minimize air leakage through the feeder. The more popular arrangement includes a screw with a differential pitch profile so arranged as to compress the material to form a positive and continuous seal.

In addition to the screw profile, some pumps include a weighted non-return flap valve to provide an additional sealing arrangement, whilst there is one pump which is arranged to discharge the material vertically up. The vertical discharge arrangement uses the material mass to act as an additional seal.

Fluid–solids pumps provide a continuous feed and have a low profile which makes them ideally suited to a number of retrofit applications. The low profile arrangement also allows for lower construction costs in new installations. Gas is normally supplied into a mixing chamber so arranged as to ensure complete efficient mixing with the product.

A wide range of fluid–solids pumps are available to transport materials at rates of 280 m³/h over distances in excess of 500 m. Most systems are designed to handle fine fluidizable material, but there are systems in operation which can handle pulverized fuel with particle sizes up to 6 mm. Figs 7.20(a) and (b) show typical pumps.

In addition to those pumps providing an in-line discharge configuration, other variations include: side discharge, single start thread rotor in a double start thread stator, vertical discharge and a pump arranged to extrude the material by introducing just sufficient air to keep the material in a fluidized state.

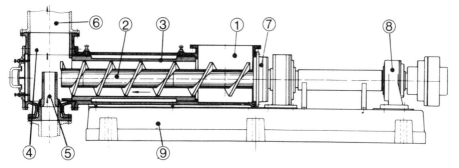

1. Inlet housing
2. Conveyor screw
3. Housing bush
4. Mixer head
5. Jet
6. Conveyor pipeline
7. Labyrinth stuffing box
8. Bearing block
9. Base plate

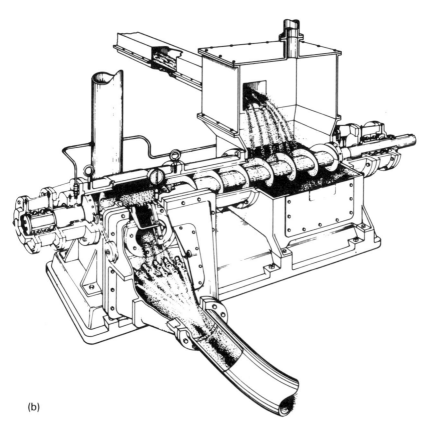

(b)

Figure 7.20 Fluid–solid pumps: (a) Johannes Moller Hamburg GmbH & Co., Hamburg, West Germany; (b) Fuller Company/GATX, Bethlehem, Pennsylvania, USA.

7.5.2 The Mono powder pump

The Mono powder pump (Fig. 7.21) is another variation of the fluid–solids pump. It consists of a metallic rotor revolving in a stator of resilient material. The pump conforms to the conventional Mono design with the addition of a pre-fluidizing air inlet located at the base of the powder inlet. A second air inlet (main fluidizing air) is located just downstream of the stator–rotor assembly. This main fluidizing inlet is located such that the powder on discharge from the rotor is effectively mixed with conveying air.

The radial cross section of the rotor is circular and is, at all points, eccentric to the axis; the centres of the sections lie along a helix and the axis of the helix forms the axis of the rotor. The pitch of the stator is twice that of the rotor and the two engage in such a fashion that the rotor section travels back and forth across the stator passage. The rotor maintains a constant line of seal between the intake and discharge ends of the pump. The seal is continuously moving at a uniform velocity through the stator and constantly recreating itself at the inlet. This has the effect of producing a positive and uniform rate of displacement which smoothly generates the flow of powder discharged through the long length of pipeline. In short the Mono powder pump is described as a progressive cavity pump.

The very nature of the seal maintained by the rotor–stator geometry implies that even when not in operation the pump acts as an effective stop valve. Since there are no return air pockets, as there are with other types of pumps, the pump also eliminates disruptions to powder flow encouraging uniform discharge. Another major advantage stemming from the positive displacement characteristics of the pump, is its ability to act as a metering or proportioning pump.

In a series of tests [14] the Mono powder pump was found to be an efficient, robust device capable of pumping a fine fluidizable powder. For the fly ash tests reported, the pump was found to have considerable potential. Tests in which an attempt was made to convey granular sodium sulphate through the same system indicated that the pump in its present form is not capable of handling materials which conform to the Geldart group B or group D materials (Chapter 4).

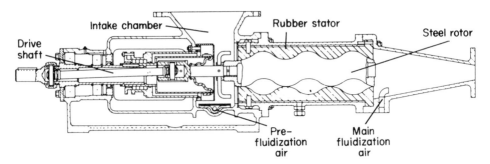

Figure 7.21 The Mono powder pump (Mono Pumps, South Africa).

For a relatively low powered pump (maximum motor power to drive the pump absorbed during tests [14] was of the order of 2.0 kW), the Mono powder pump provides a low profile continuous feeder. From visual observations made through a sight glass in the conveying pipe [14], it was clear that the pump is capable of delivering a high concentration continuous slug of material.

Tests indicated that a variation of main fluidizing air resulted in no change in solids mass of flow rate obtained from the pump until the pipe friction exceeded the fluidizing effect, as such a critical amount of main fluidizing air is required to be injected into the conveying line to ensure continuous movement of the dense slug.

Observations on the variation of both initial fluidizing air and pump speed indicate that a fine control on the discharge rate is obtainable from the pump. Results [14] indicated that the control was such that the Mono powder pump could be seen to be an effective positive displacement pump providing for accurate dosing of materials in pneumatic conveying systems.

In the fly ash tests [14] mass flow ratios $\mu = 20$ were obtained from trials conducted on a pipeline $D = 50$ mm diameter and a total length $L = 130$ m. Over a distance $L = 12$ m using the same pipe diameter, mass flow ratios of the order of $\mu = 200$ were obtained. The solids flow rate varied from $\dot{G} = 2.1$ t/h ($\mu = 20$) to $\dot{G} = 4.1$ t/h ($\mu = 200$).

Typical results obtained from the fly ash investigations are shown in Fig. 7.22.

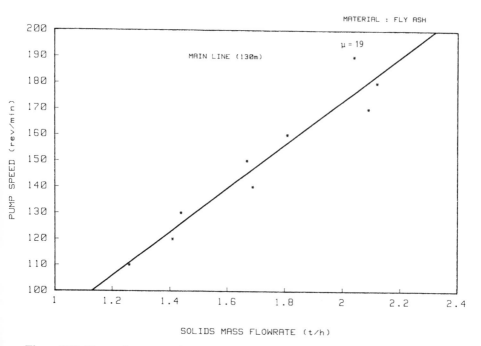

Figure 7.22 The performance of a Mono powder pump conveying fly ash.

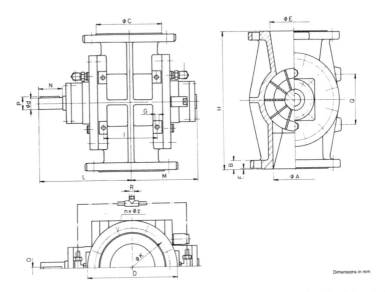

Dimensions in mm

Figure 7.23 The Waeschle high pressure rotary valve (Waeschle Maschinenfabrick GmbH, Ravensburg, West Germany).

7.5.3 The Waeschle high pressure rotary valve

In a new development, Waeschle of West Germany, have refined the design of rotary airlocks (Section 7.4.3) to accommodate differential pressures of up to $\Delta p = 300$ kPa (Fig. 7.23).

This development is significant inasmuch as it is now possible to use some of the special features of a rotary airlock in medium pressure systems. The added advantage of such a valve is the relatively low power required to rotate the rotor.

7.5.4 Vertical lift pump (air lift)

As the name implies, the vertical lift pump is a device designed to transport fine fluidizable materials vertically upwards. Conveying capacities up to 800 tonnes per hour can be achieved over vertical lifts of the order of 100 metres.

These pumps have no moving parts and their operation is based on a pressure balance between the gas supply pressure and the static head due to the gas–solids mixture (Fig. 7.24).

Most systems have a specially designed air entrainment nozzle located at the mouth of the vertical conveying pipe. This nozzle facilitates the entrainment of the solids into the conveying pipe, whilst some of the gas is bled off to provide an aeration effect in the feeding zone.

The pumps occupy a relatively small area and have the unique characteristic of having all the material being returned to the feeding container in the case of a power failure. The vertical arrangement thus facilitates easy start up.

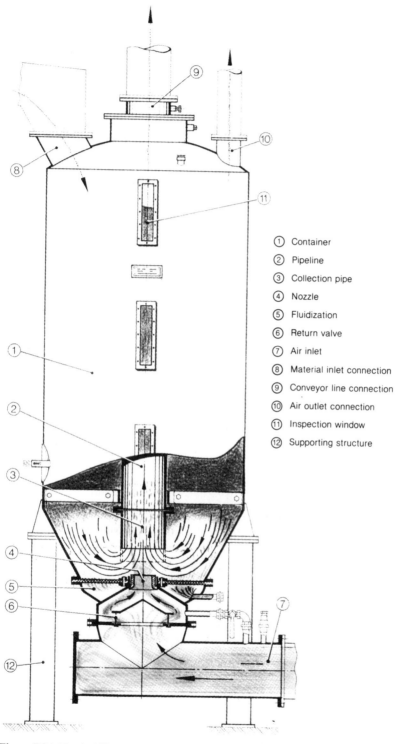

1. Container
2. Pipeline
3. Collection pipe
4. Nozzle
5. Fluidization
6. Return valve
7. Air inlet
8. Material inlet connection
9. Conveyor line connection
10. Air outlet connection
11. Inspection window
12. Supporting structure

Figure 7.24 Vertical lift pump (Johannes Moller Hamburg GmbH & Co., Hamburg, West Germany).

The performance of vertical lift pumps has been analysed by Weber [15]. Weber's analysis is based on the following assumptions and characteristics of the vertical lift pump.

(a) The system is open to atmosphere.
(b) Incompressible flow is assumed—these systems normally operate at low pressures and with relatively short pipe lines.
(c) Dilute phase operating conditions.
(d) They are essentially self-regulating systems.
(e) When the pressure drop across the conveying pipeline is less than the pressure drop across the bed of material in the vessel, the conveying process begins.
(f) Material is fed continuously (by another conveyor) into the tank.
(g) The operation of such systems is normally confined to fine fluidizable (Geldart group A) materials.
(h) The size of the vessel is related to the vertical conveying distance.
(i) Pressure drop across the system:

$$\Delta p = \Delta p_{\mathrm{L}} + \Delta p_{\mathrm{A}} + \Delta p_{\mathrm{IF}} + \Delta p_{\mathrm{G}} \tag{7.9}$$

where Δp_{L} is the pressure drop due to air alone, Δp_{A} is the acceleration pressure drop, Δp_{IF} is the pressure drop due to impact and friction, and Δp_{G} is the pressure drop due to gravity.

Full details pertaining to each parameter in equation (7.9) above are discussed in Section 6.6. Also, $\Delta p_{\mathrm{bed}} > \Delta p_{\mathrm{system}}$.

(j) Use is made of a low pressure blower to keep the mass flow ratio (μ) low.
(k) Air velocity

$$v = \frac{4\,\dot{G}}{\pi \rho \mu D^2} \tag{7.10}$$

The product velocity c is calculated using the expressions derived in Chapter 6. The procedure is to use equation (7.9) to calculate the pressure drop for different pipe sizes and different mass flow ratios to determine a pressure minimum.

(l) The minimum power is obtained from:

$$P_{\mathrm{min}} = \frac{[\Delta p_{\mathrm{min}} + (\rho/2)v^2]\,\dot{V}}{\eta_{\mathrm{B}}} \tag{7.11}$$

where η_{B} is the blower efficiency and $50\% \leqslant \eta_{\mathrm{B}} \leqslant 70\%$. Taking into account the additional pressure losses due to the filter, etc:

$$P_{\mathrm{min}} = \frac{\Delta p_{\mathrm{min}} + \Delta p_{\mathrm{dyn}} + \Delta p_{\mathrm{valves}}}{\eta_{\mathrm{B}}}\,\dot{V}$$

$$= \frac{\Delta p_{\mathrm{min}} + \rho v^2/2 + \Delta p_{\mathrm{V}}}{\eta_{\mathrm{B}}}\,\dot{V} \tag{7.12}$$

Example 7.3. Vertical lift pump

It is required to design a vertical lift pump [15] to conform to the following specifications:

Material	Sand
Material flow rate	$\dot{G} = 3000 \text{ kg/h}$
Material density	$\rho_p = 2410 \text{ kg/m}^3$
Particle size	$d = 1 \text{ mm}$
Vertical lift	$Z = 15 \text{ m}$
Mass flow ratio	$\mu = 10$
Air alone friction loss	$\lambda_L = 0.02$
Pressure drop factor due to pressure of solids	$\lambda_z = 0.007$
Air density	$\rho = 1.23 \text{ kg/m}^3$
Blower efficiency	$\eta_B = 70\%$.

The first step is to calculate the settling velocity for a single particle (Chapter 5 and equation (6.41), see also worked example in Chapter 12):

$$w_{f0} = 6.7 \text{ m/s}$$

The air velocity v is calculated:

$$v = \frac{4}{\pi} \frac{\dot{G}}{\rho} \frac{1}{\mu D^2}$$

$$= \frac{4(3000)}{\pi(3600)(1.23)(10)D^2} = 0.0863 \frac{1}{D^2}$$

The particle velocity is obtained from:

$$c = v - w_{f0}$$

$$= v - 6.7$$

The total pressure loss, taking an additional pressure loss $\Delta p_V = 1000$ Pa for filter and valves is given by:

$$\Delta p = 0.02 \left(\frac{15}{2}\right) 1.23 \frac{v^2}{D} + (10)(1.23)(9.81)(15)\frac{v}{c}$$

$$+ 10(0.007)\left(\frac{15}{2}\right)(1.23)\left(\frac{vc}{D}\right) + (1.23)(10) vc + 1000$$

$$= 0.1845 \frac{v^2}{D} + 1810 \frac{v}{c} + 0.646 \frac{vc}{D} + 12.3 vc + 1000$$

Table 7.2

Symbol	Units	Formula					
D	m		0.06	0.07	0.08	0.09	0.1
v	m/s	$0.0863/D^2$	23.97	17.6	13.5	10.6	8.6
c	m/s	$v - 6.7$	17.3	10.9	6.8	3.9	1.9
Δp_L	N/m^2	$0.1845\,v^2/D$	1767	818	419	233	137
Δp_G	N/m^2	$1810\,v/c$	2512	2921	3597	4976	8091
Δp_{IF}	N/m^2	$0.646\,vc/D$	4457	1773	739	302	108
Δp_A	N/m^2	$12.3\,vc$	5094	2364	1125	518	205
Δp_V	N/m^2	1000	1000	1000	1000	1000	1000
Δp	N/m^2	$\sum \Delta p_i$	14830	8876	6880	6929	8541
Δp_{dyn}	N/m^2	$\rho v^2/2$	353	190	112	70	46
P_{min}	kW	Equation (7.12)	1.47	0.877	0.677	0.673	0.930

Using the expression for v,c and Δp for varying pipe diameters, Table 7.2 can be constructed. The results from Table 7.2 are plotted in Fig. 7.25 below.

From Table 7.2 and Fig. 7.25 it can be seen that the friction and acceleration pressure losses decrease with increasing pipe diameter. Thus, lowering the velocity increases the gravitational pressure drop Δp_G (where G stands for solids gravity).

Because of the increase in Δp_G and the corresponding decrease in the other pressure loss terms, the minimum system pressure loss Δp occurs at a pipe diameter $D = 80$ mm. Note further, that the power consumption P_{min} is close to the minimum for the $D = 80$ mm pipe.

In Fig. 7.25, it can be seen that increasing the mass flow ratio (μ) results in an increase in the system pressure loss Δp for smaller pipe diameters. Further, the power consumption (P) decreases with increasing mass flow ratio (μ). At low values of mass flow ratio (μ) the power consumption (P) increases due to the higher volumetric gas flow rate ($\dot{V}$).

7.5.5 Double gate lock feeding device

Gate lock feeding devices have been designed to feed large particles or materials of an abrasive nature which are unsuited to a rotary feeder (Fig. 7.26). Essentially the feeder provides for a batching operation in which two flap type valves facilitate the introduction of the material into a high pressure conveying stream. A pressure balancing arrangement is provided to facilitate the opening of the flap valves under zero pressure gradient.

Another feature included in some systems is the provision of a second valve on the feed side which shuts off the material flow, thereby preventing the flap valve from having to close against a material flow.

By virtue of the intermittent operation, these valves will cause a certain amount of pressure surging as the material is introduced into the conveying stream.

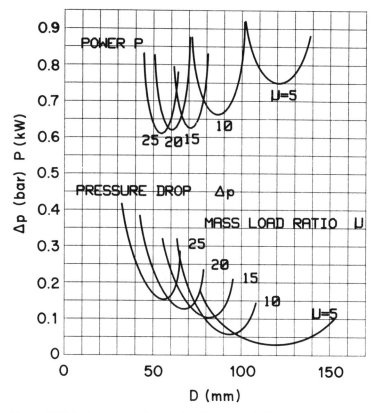

Figure 7.25 Performance of a vertical lift pump [15].

7.6 HIGH PRESSURE FEEDING DEVICES

The recent surge in interest in 'dense phase' conveying and long distance pneumatic transportation systems has resulted in the development of a range of purposefully designed feeding systems. Common to all such high pressure feeding devices is the 'blow vessel' designed to meet both the requirements as a material feeder and the relevant design codes for pressure vessels.

In this section, in addition to the various aspects pertaining to the design, operation and selection of blow vessels, various specialized systems including low velocity and plug conveying systems will be discussed.

7.6.1 Description of blow vessel

Blow vessels are essentially conical bottomed pressure vessels fitted with the necessary valves and fittings to suit the particular feeding requirements.

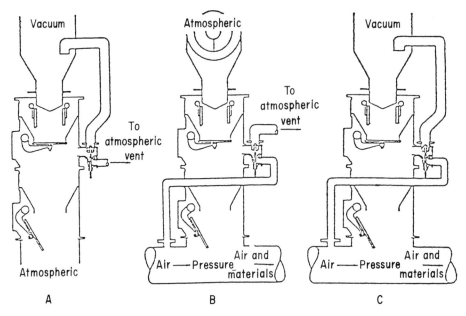

Figure 7.26 Double gate lock feeding system (Fuller Company/GATX, Bethlehem, Pennsylvania, USA).

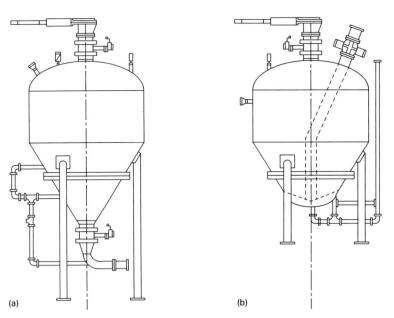

Figure 7.27 (a) Bottom discharge blow vessel; (b) top discharge blow vessel.

There are two basic blow vessel configurations: top discharge and bottom discharge (Figs 7.27(a), (b)).

The top discharge blow vessel relies on the efficient fluidization and entrainment of the material into the discharge pipe. These systems, although once extremely popular, are now only used in situations where space requirements are limited, or where a top discharge configuration is more suitable to the whole transportation system.

Much work [16] has been done on the positioning of the mouth of the discharge with respect to the fluidization pad, to suit a range of materials. It has been found [16] that these systems can be 'tuned' to optimize conveying efficiencies.

The bottom discharge blow vessel configuration appears to be more widely used and it is evident that most manufacturers are basing their designs on such an arrangement.

7.6.2 Blow vessel operation

It is common practice to design a blow vessel for fully automatic operation. By virtue of the availability of high pressure compressed air for conveying, the use of pneumatically actuated valves is favoured. Typically, the operating sequence for a fully automated blow vessel is as follows (Fig. 7.28). On initiation of the cycle all valves are closed:

(a) Vent valve (A) is opened to depressurize the vessel.

(b) After a short time delay material feed valve (B) is opened and the filling process is initiated.

(c) The material flows into the vessel until such time as the high level indicator (HL) is activated.

(d) The high level (HL) indicator activates a signal to close valves (A) and (B).

(e) After a time delay, the air supply valve (C) is opened to supply air to the vessel.

(f) Air is fed into the vessel until a pre-set pressure is attained in the vessel.

(g) A pressure switch (PS) is activated which in turn sends a signal to open the discharge valve (D). (Note the air supply is maintained open throughout the conveying cycle.)

(h) Material is conveyed until a low pressure signal is detected on the pressure switch indicating that all material has been transported.

(i) Normally the air supply is maintained for a short while to ensure that any material which might be left in the pipe is transported to the receiving station.

(j) The cycle is then re-initiated.

Some systems do not use a low pressure signal as the indicator for the end of the conveying cycle. Instead, use is made of a low level signal in the vessel. Normally in such systems, the discharge valve is located directly onto the flange of the blow vessel and provision is made for a feeding tee arrangement. This arrangement will facilitate the cleaning out operation as described in (i) above.

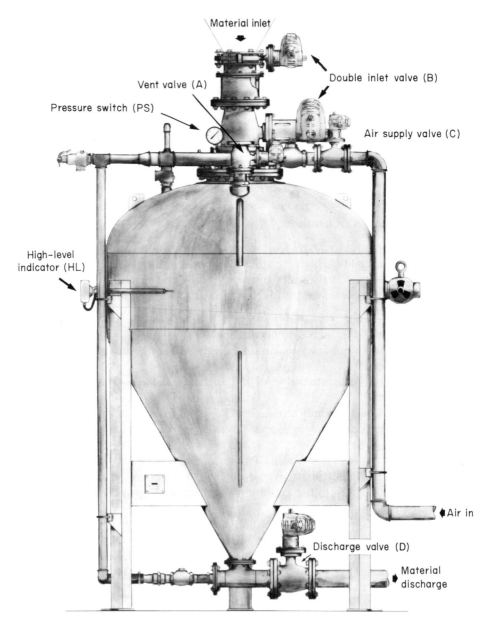

Figure 7.28 Fully automatic bottom discharge blow vessel (Bulk Pneumatic Handling, Randburg, South Africa).

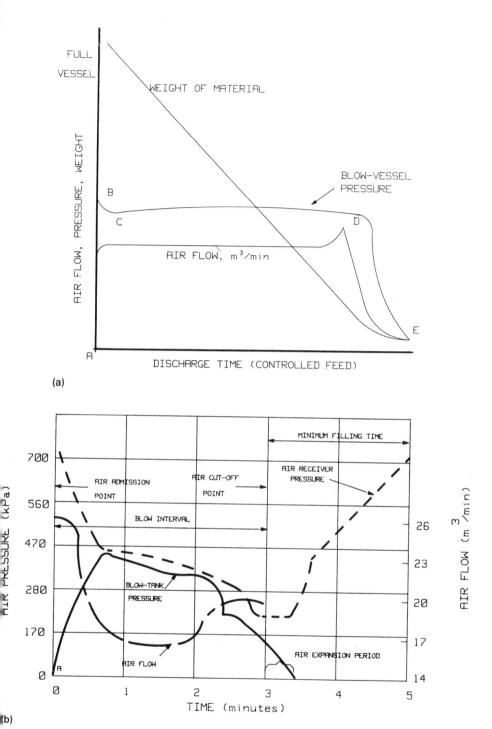

Figure 7.29 Pressure–time traces for a blow vessel: (a) with discharge valve; (b) without a discharge valve.

The automatic process described above implies the use of a discharge valve. There are, however, some systems which are designed without the inclusion of such a discharge valve.

7.6.3 Discharge characteristics of a blow vessel

In terms of the operation of a blow vessel, it is customary to obtain a pressure–time trace from which the maximum discharge capacity of the conveying system can be derived. A typical pressure–time trace obtained for a bottom discharge blow vessel is shown in Fig. 7.29(a) above. This trace is obtained from a bottom discharge blow vessel, fitted with a discharge valve. The vessel is pressurized prior to the opening of the discharge valve. From the trace the following observations can be made:

A–B   Represents the vessel pressurizing cycle.

B   Represents the initial vessel pressurization p_i.

B–C   Represents the drop in pressure as a result of the opening of the discharge valve.

C   Represents the average conveying pressure—a pressure which is attained by the gas–solids flowing in the conveying pipe.

C–D   Represents the conveying cycle and is the time taken for discharging the bulk of the product.

D–E   Is the clean out time in which the last remaining material is transported through the pipeline.

C–E   Is the total discharge time.

It can be seen that the sequence D–E represents a rapid depressurization of the vessel. This depressurization together with the small amount of material can result in a violent surge of high velocity solids in a dilute concentration. An awareness of this surge characteristic is necessary for the selection of an adequately sized air solids separation system on the receiving end (Chapter 10).

By introducing a low level detector at the bottom of the vessel, the D–E sequence is replaced by a depressurization time.

In Fig. 7.29(b) a pressure–time trace for a blow vessel without pre-pressurization is shown. Comparing Figs 7.29(a) and 7.29(b) it can be seen that in the latter case, a less well defined trace is obtained. Figure 7.29(b) is obtained by filling the vessel and supplying air to the vessel. The material forms its own natural resistance to the air flow and will cause a pressure build up in the vessel until conveying takes place.

The question as to whether a system is initiated with a pre-pressurizing cycle or not, depends on a number of factors *inter alia* material properties and manufacturers preference.

There is no doubt group B materials which tend to 'flood' from a blow vessel are best handled without a pre-pressurizing cycle. Such products tend to go into instantaneous pipe blockage when discharged from a blow vessel under pressure. There are other techniques of controlling the flow of group B materials from a blow vessel. Such techniques are discussed in Section 7.6.

With group A materials it is generally accepted that pre-pressurization provides a more efficient conveying situation. With such products the imposition of an initial vessel pressure tends to assist with the extrusion of the material in a 'dense' slug.

The maximum discharge capacity of a blow vessel [17] is constrained by the volume of the vessel and the total cycle time:

$$\dot{G}_B^* = \rho_B V_B / t_T \qquad (7.13)$$

where

$\dot{G}_B^*$ = the discharge rate
V_B = the volume of the vessel
t_T = the total discharge time
ρ_B = bulk density of material

Now

$$t_T = t_F + t_p + t_D \qquad (7.14)$$

where

t_F = the filling time (material)
t_p = the pressurizing time
t_D = the discharge time

For a single blow vessel it is desirable to minimize both t_F and t_p by ensuring that both the material inlet valve and the air supply arrangement are adequately designed.

7.6.4 Factors influencing blow vessel performance

Apart from the fact that blow vessels must be designed and constructed according to a recognized design code, there are three basic design parameters which can influence blow vessel performance: (a) cone angle; (b) vessel volume; and (c) vessel pressure.

The increased use of blow vessels for feeding materials with 'bad' flow properties necessitates the selection of a suitable cone angle. Vessels with incorrectly designed cone angles will result in either 'ratholing' or 'bridging' problems (Fig. 7.30).

Ratholing results in the formation of a blow hole through the material mass and, once formed, it is not possible to transport any more material. Bridging problems result in the product forming a barrier across the outlet of the vessel which prevents any further material flow.

The selection of a suitable cone angle could be aided by the use of the classical silo or hopper design criteria. However, these design criteria do not take into consideration that the product is under pressure and in certain situations, gas also percolates through the material. At present, much of the cone angle selection criteria are based on empirical data obtained from experience.

Some blow vessels are fitted with internal discharge aids which take the form of

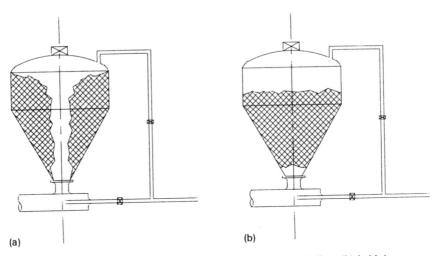

Figure 7.30 Discharge problems from a blow vessel, (a) ratholing; (b) bridging.

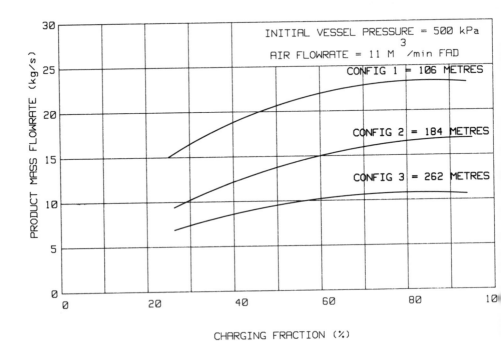

Figure 7.31 Influence of filling fraction on blow vessel performance.

vibrators, inflatable bags, sonic nozzles and various forms of mechanical agitators.

Vessel volumetric capacity is an important factor influencing blow vessel performance. In the case of products which are fluidizable and have reasonable flow characteristics, it is desirable to build the vessel as large as possible. A large capacity blow vessel ensures that the t_D component (equation (7.14)) on the total time t_T is large in comparison to the pressurization and clean out times.

Work done [18] on 'large capacity' blow vessels conveying cement and fly ash has demonstrated an overall improvement in conveying efficiency when compared to the performance of smaller capacity vessels.

From Fig. 7.31 it can be seen that for Geldart group A products such as cement and fly ash, an improved conveying efficiency is obtained by using a 'large' blow vessel. Fig. 7.31 has been obtained by carrying out tests [18] on a large volume blow vessel in which varying volumes of material were added. The filling fraction is thus defined as the ratio of the volume of material introduced into the vessel, to the actual volumetric capacity of the blow vessel itself. As such a filling fraction of 70% indicates that 70% of the volume of the vessel is filled with material.

For materials which have 'bad' flow characteristics or which have such free

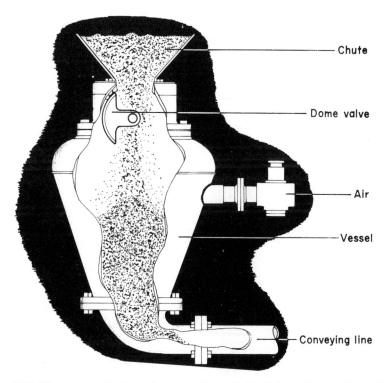

Figure 7.32 Blow vessel designed for materials with 'bad' flow characteristics (Simon Macawber SA Ltd, South Africa).

flowing characteristics that they tend to 'flood' the conveying line, it is advisable to use small capacity blow vessels. In such cases, the volume of the vessel is selected such that on discharge the conveying pipe cannot be overfilled and hence the risk of blocking is minimized (it is also possible to introduce solids flow control devices at the exit from the blow vessel—this is discussed in Section 7.6.5.2).

Essentially, small capacity blow vessels are designed on the basis of conveying material as a series of discrete plugs rather than as a continuous stream (Fig. 7.32). As such, the capacity of the vessel is selected such that on discharge a plug is formed which is just long enough to prevent blocking. Typically, systems to transport lumps of coal, various types of foundry sand and a range of granular abrasive materials employ the principle of a small blow vessel.

Blow vessel discharge capacities can be markedly influenced with a variation of the initial pressurization (Fig. 7.33). At the outset it should be pointed out that it

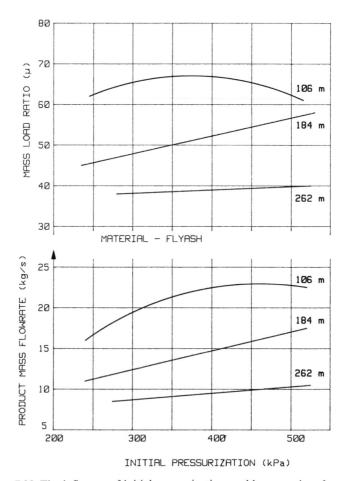

Figure 7.33 The influence of initial pressurization on blow vessel performance.

is sound practice to design a blow vessel for high operating pressures, albeit that initially it might only be required to be operated at a lower pressure. There is a relatively small cost differential between a vessel constructed to operate say 400 kPa (4 bar) and one constructed to operate at 700 kPa (7 bar).

The added pressure capacity could provide the user with an opportunity of extending either the capacity or the length of the conveying line without the need to purchase a second blow vessel.

Recent studies [19] and [20] have shown that substantial benefits can be obtained with the imposition of high initial vessel pressures. It is interesting to note that whilst an increase in discharge capacity can be obtained with certain fine fluidizable products, the average conveying pressure does not increase in the same proportion. As such, a large increase in initial vessel pressurization usually results in a relatively small increase in the average conveying pressure.

7.6.5 Blow vessel configuration

Within the range of bottom discharge blow vessel systems, there is a variety of vessel configurations to suit a number of materials and applications.

7.6.5.1 Continuous discharge

In order to obtain a continuous discharge from a blow vessel system, a minimum of two vessels are required. Continuous discharge can be obtained by placing one vessel on top of another, or else by arranging the vessels in the so called tandem mode.

In the first configuration (Fig. 7.34(a)), provision is made for the vessels to be interconnected with a pressure balancing pipe to avoid opening of the material feed valves against a pressure differential. In Fig. 7.34(a), valve A is opened to provide a balanced pressure across valve B. After a short time delay valve B is opened and the material is fed into vessel 1. Once vessel 1 is full, valves A and B are closed whilst valve C is opened after a time delay. A further time delay is provided before valve D is opened, thereby depositing material into vessel 2. The material is thus conveyed continuously out of vessel 2 without any loss in system pressure. The tandem blow vessel arrangement (Fig. 7.34(b)) provides for two separate blow vessels connected to a common controller. Whilst vessel 1 is in the discharge mode, vessel 2 is in the filling mode and vice versa. In certain situations [21] up to four vessels are connected to a single conveying line.

7.6.5.2 Solids flow control

The advent of long distance pneumatic conveying systems [20] has necessitated the development of solids flow control devices at the discharge of blow vessels. Also, many free flowing products which tend to flood the conveying pipe require some form of controlled feeding to inhibit pipe blockages. Thus there is a range of solids flow control devices and systems which are successfully operating in a variety of industries. In all the systems the amount of solids entering into the line is discretely monitored to ensure that at all times, the conveying pressure is carefully controlled within specified limits. These systems thus ensure optimum conveying conditions at all times, whilst controlling the solids flow to inhibit pipe blockage. In some systems, a further refinement includes a control on the gas flow entering the system.

(a) Cone dosing system

The cone dosing arrangement (Fig. 7.35) consists of a conical valve fitted via a long stem to an actuator located on top of the blow vessel. The movement of the stem is controlled by the actuator and both the frequency and the amplitude of the valve are regulated. The proportional and differential control is pneumatically regulated in terms of a pressure sensor connected to the conveying pipe.

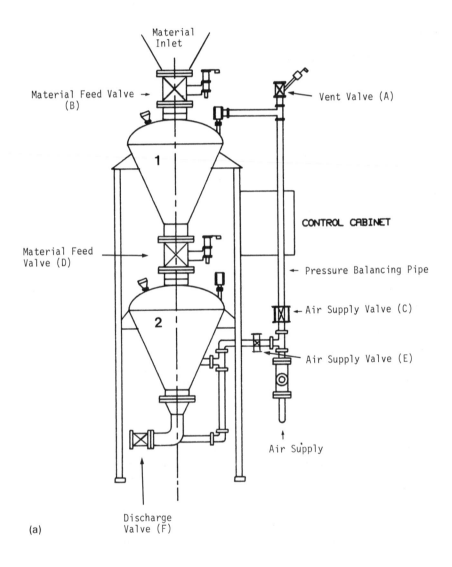

(a)

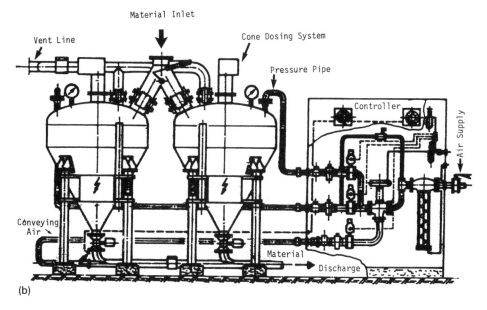

Figure 7.34 (a) Arrangement of a vertical tandem blow vessel system; (b) arrangement of a horizontal tandem blow vessel (Klockner-Becorit Industrietechnik GmbH, Hunxe, West Germany).

In addition to providing some form of solids flow control from the discharge of the blow vessel, the movement of the stem also provides for an effective discharging aid which is suitable for non free flowing products. It has been found [20] that many products which tend to adhere to the walls of the blow vessel are loosened by virtue of the movement of the stem. In some situations [21] a series of rakes have been attached to the stem of the control valve. These rakes have been useful in promoting the flow of materials out of the blow vessel.

An additional feature of the control system is the ability to select any system operating pressure. Pre-selection by means of a dial ensures the continuous control of a sufficient quantity of product resulting in the conveying system operating at optimum conditions at all times.

(b) Rotary valve system

Solids flow control can be accurately monitored by fitting a suitably designed rotary valve (to withstand the high static pressures) to the bottom of the blow vessel (Fig. 7.36). The valve is fitted with a DC variable speed drive connected to a controller. The variation speed of the valve provides the necessary solids flow control. The employment of a double rotary valve arrangement is described in Section 7.4.3.7 in conjunction with the blow vessel and can provide additional benefits in the form of eliminating pressure surges [11].

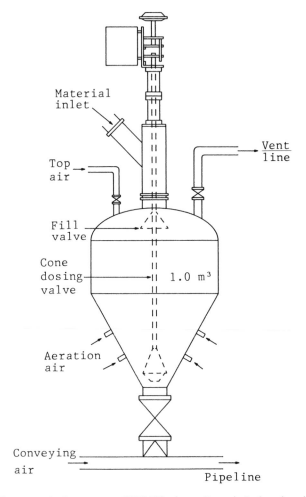

Figure 7.35 The cone dosing system (KBI Klockner–Becorit Industrietechnik GmbH, West Germany).

(c) Flap type controller

The fitting of a flap type valve actuated by a quarter turn pneumatic actuator has been applied in several areas of blow vessel technology (Fig. 7.37). Variations on the type of valves used and the fitting of a vibrator to the valve shaft to assist material flow are available.

The movement of the valve and the amount to which the valve is opened is controlled from a signal obtained from the system conveying pressure.

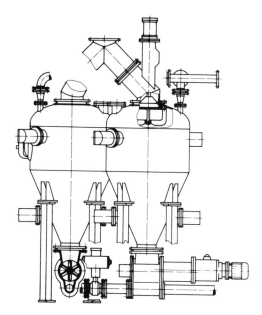

Figure 7.36 Rotary valve solids flow control (Maschinenfabrik Karl Brieden & Co., Bochum, West Germany).

(d) Modulode system

The modulode feeder (Fig. 7.38) consists of a disk valve located in a housing which is fitted to the bottom of the vessel. The vertical movement of the valve is controlled by a diaphragm which obtains its control air from the conveying gas. The conveying gas is passed through a variable orifice (butterfly valve), thereby causing a pressure differential which is used to actuate the diaphragm valve.

The diaphragm valve lowers the disk and permits material to flow into the conveying pipe. The material in turn creates a back pressure which reduces the differential across the orifice. The reduction in differential is sensed by the diaphragm, resulting in a regulation of material introduced into the conveying stream. The continuous movement of the disc valve ensures a regulated solids flow control and inhibits any pipe blockages.

7.6.5.3 Gas supply configurations

An important factor in blow vessel design is the method of introducing gas into the vessel. There are a number of variations of conveying gas supply arrangements, and many of the techniques employed [18] have resulted in a substantial improvement in the discharge capacity of a blow vessel system.

The supply arrangements are selected on the basis of the characteristics of the material to be conveyed. In many situations, whilst one arrangement might suit a

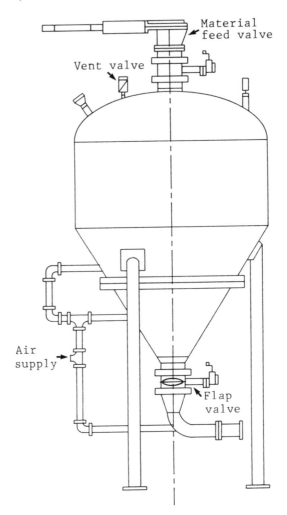

Figure 7.37 Flap type solids flow control.

particular material, the same arrangement could result in severe blockages in the conveying line when conveying another material.

Experience has also shown how, with careful design providing a number of variable orifice control valves, it is possible to 'tune' the system (Fig. 7.39). The variation in the gas flow into the various ports located in the blow vessel can lead to a more improved transportation system. The provision of these valves has proved to be a bonus to the plant commissioning engineer. In terms of the more commonly available commercial blow vessels, the following gas supply configur-

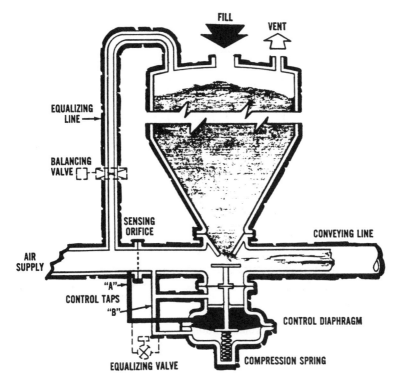

Figure 7.38 The Modulode system (Fuller Company/GATX, Bethlehem, Pennsylvania, USA).

ations are possible:

(a) Supply to top of vessel.
(b) Supply to an aeration cone.
(c) Supply to an entrainment nozzle.
(d) Supply to a ring Venturi.

In terms of each configuration, the following features are of importance:

Configuration 1

The position of the inlet pipe is arranged such that the gas supply is always on top of the material.

Configuration 2

In several systems it is customary to include an aeration cone to fluidize the material at the exit of the blow vessel.

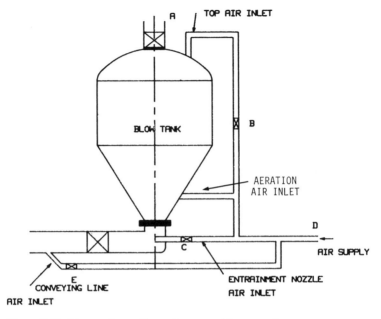

Figure 7.39 Air supply configurations to a blow vessel.

Configuration 3

The entrainment nozzle has been found to be a most useful device. The nozzle position is variable, making it possible to provide a flow inhibitor as well as a high velocity gas jet for effective entrainment of the solids.

Configuration 4

The ring Venturi is normally located just downstream of the discharge valve. The prime function of this device is to further dilute the flow to prevent pipe blockages. It is customary to balance the gas flow such that enough gas is available to keep the vessel pressurised.

Combination of configurations

In many situations a combination of the configurations provides the most effective arrangement. As such, for example, by supplying gas to inlets 1 and 3 it is possible to create a gravity flow situation by balancing the pressures across the materials.

Evidence of the influence of the gas supply configuration in terms of the ultimate discharge rate obtainable from a blow vessel is shown in Fig. 7.40. By introducing the air to the top of the vessel and through a centre nozzle, a substantial improvement in discharge rate was obtained [22].

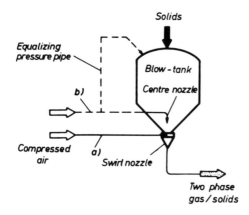

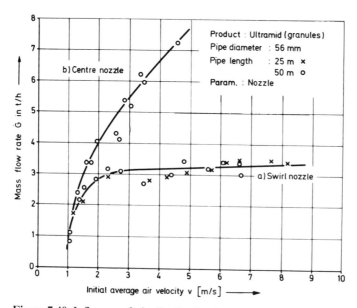

Figure 7.40 Influence of air distribution into a blow vessel.

7.6.5.4 Mass flow nozzles

In addition to the various gas inlet configurations discussed above, it is sometimes expedient to control the flow of gas into one or more inlets to the blow vessel. The insertion of a nozzle can assist with the performance of a blow vessel by providing a means in which the quantity of gas entering, say, the top of the vessel, can be greater than that flowing through the entrainment nozzle.

In tests carried out on gold slime [20], and more recent studies on fly ash [23], optimum conditions were obtained by introducing the conveying air at

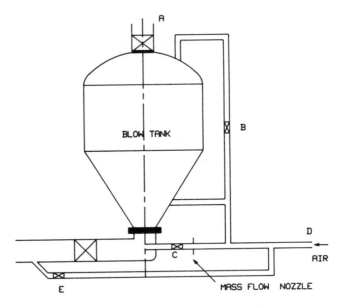

Figure 7.41 Blow vessel fitted with a sonic nozzle.

the top and the bottom of the blow vessel with a slight increase in pressure through the top inlet. Conveying conditions were further optimized by including a sonic nozzle in the air supply to the conveying pipe (Fig. 7.41).

The prime function of the nozzle was to prevent all the air going down the conveying pipe and thereby ensuring that a proportion of the air would enter into the top of the vessel.

The inclusion of sonic nozzles in other applications provide for effective gas mass flow control. Sonic nozzles are used in situations where it is desirable to 'split' the air flow from a compressor, the control of gas into a feeding tee for a dilute phase system, etc.

Mass flow nozzles can be designed according to the equations produced by Govier and Aziz [24]:

$$\frac{\dot{Q}}{A_n} = \left(\frac{2\kappa p_0}{(\kappa - 1)V_0}(0.5283)^{2/\kappa} - (0.5283)^{(\kappa + 1)/\kappa} \right)^{1/2} \tag{7.15}$$

where

$\dot{Q}$ = mass flow of air (kg/s)
A_n = area of nozzle (m^2)
κ = 1.4 for air
p_0 = upstream pressure (Pa)
V_0 = upstream specific volume air (m^3/kg)

Another technique of sizing mass flow nozzles is recommended by Dixon [25]. In addition to ensuring that the compressor is of adequate size, the conditions for the operation of a mass flow nozzle in a conveying system are as follows:

(a) For a constant mass flow of air, the absolute conveying pressure on the downstream side of the nozzle, or orifice, must never be greater than 0.528 of the lowest possible (absolute) pressure in the air receiver system, i.e. during the peak demand period.

(b) The initial pressure ratio p_2/p_1 which has a value of 0.528 for air and nitrogen has a different value for other gases.

(c) Provided the ratio of the downstream absolute pressure to the upstream absolute pressure is always less than 0.528, then the mass flow rate of air essentially independent of the down stream pressure can be obtained from the equation:

$$\dot{Q} = KC_N D^2 (p_1 \rho_1)^{1/2}\, \text{kg/s} \tag{7.16}$$

where

$K = 0.54$ for air and nitrogen
$C_N = 0.97$ for a well shaped Laval nozzle
$\quad = 0.7$ for sharp edged orifice
$p_1 = $ absolute upstream pressure
$\rho_1 = $ actual density at upstream conditions

Example 7.4

Size a nozzle throat and a sharp edged orifice to deliver 0.2 kg/s of air from an upstream pressure of 4 bar (gauge). What is the highest downstream pressure which will still result in 0.2 kg/s of air being delivered? Assume that atmospheric pressure $p_0 = 1.013$ bar, and that the air is at 15 °C.

Solution

Absolute upstream pressure, $p_1 = 4 + 1.013 = 5.013$ bar
$\qquad\qquad = 5.013 \times 10^5\, \text{N/m}^2$
Actual upstream air density, $\rho_1 = p_1/RT_1$

where

$$T_1 = 273.15 + 15 = 288.15\, \text{K}$$
$$\rho_1 = \frac{5.013 \times 105}{(287)(288.15)} = 6.06\, \text{kg/m}^3$$
$$(p_1\rho_1)^{1/2} = (5.013 \times 10^5 \times 6.06)^{1/2}$$
$$= 1.744 \times 10^3\, \text{kg/ms}$$

$$D^2 = \frac{0.2}{0.54 C_D (p_1 \rho_1)^{1/2}}$$

$$= \frac{0.2 \times 10^6}{0.54 \times 1.744 \times 10^3 \times C_D} \,\mathrm{mm}^2$$

$$D = \left(\frac{200}{0.54 \times 1.744 \times C_D} \right)^{0.5}$$

For a nozzle coefficient, $C_N = 0.97$; $D = 14.8\,\mathrm{mm}$.
For a sharp edged orifice, $C_N = 0.7$; $D = 17.4\,\mathrm{mm}$.
Highest downstream pressure which will result in 0.2 kg/s being delivered is given by:

$$p_2 = 0.528\, p_1 = 0.528 \times 5.013$$

$$= 2.647\,\mathrm{bar}$$

7.6.6 Low velocity and plug conveying systems

7.6.6.1 Introduction

An important development in pneumatic conveying technology has been the advent of low velocity and plug conveying systems. Essentially these systems provide a solution to the problems of conveying delicate granular and friable materials and products such as plastic granules which form 'streamers' in high velocity conveying systems. There are a number of commercial systems which have been designed to provide low velocity conveying. Most of these systems transport the product as a series of discrete plugs. All these systems have special peripheral devices to promote the flow regime required.

Whilst there is evidence of substantial benefits ([22] and [23]) which can be accrued from these systems, judicious selection of the correct system 'suitable for a particular product' is required.

By virtue of the low velocity characteristics, these systems are also well suited for the transportation of highly abrasive products. The low velocity ensures a limited amount of wear in system components.

A further additional feature of these systems is the fact that many of them use a limited amount of conveying gas. The smaller gas requirements permit the use of smaller gas–solids separation devices at the end of the process. This results in the saving on capital outlay for such gas–solids separation systems.

Many different arrangements are promoted by competing manufacturers, but the systems can be classified into three major groups. Most systems utilize some form of air injection or rejection to fluidize the material and prevent wedging between particles. Some provision is usually made to break up excessively long plugs, but plug development is not directly controlled. In contrast, plug forming systems create short, stable plugs at the feed point. Finally, defensive systems destroy plugs on formation and usually operate in the strand or dune phases.

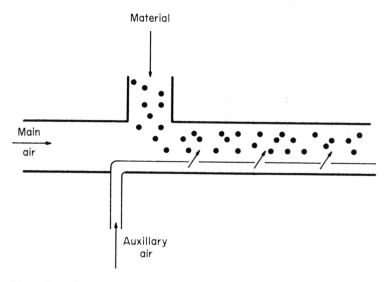

Figure 7.42 Gattys system.

7.6.6.2 Fluidization/turbulence systems

(a) Gattys

Auxiliary air is injected from a sub-pipe mounted inside the main conveying line as shown in Fig. 7.42. An increased auxiliary air flow rate [28] has been found to increase plug velocity and reduce the level of the stationary bed. However, its use is limited to well behaved materials as the supply of air is not controlled. For instance, if a plug formed, auxiliary air would not be forced into the plug to break it up. Also, air cushions between plugs would be able to leak away, enabling excessively long plugs to form. Finally, the continuous addition of auxiliary air increases the air velocity and quickly takes the material away from the optimum conveying range. However, this early system spurred the development of other low velocity solutions.

(b) Fluidstat/Turboflow

The Fluidstat arrangement was initially developed by Muschelknautz [33] and incorporates a series of bypass pipes open to the conveying line approximately every half metre, as shown in Fig. 7.43. Substantial energy savings have been reported in conveying fine materials over various distances [26]. Suitable materials must exhibit good air retention properties and under normal conveying conditions the bypass lines serve to maintain fluidization of the material. In this way, the conveying velocity can usually be dramatically decreased before material settles out and increases the pressure drop. Interestingly, no advantage

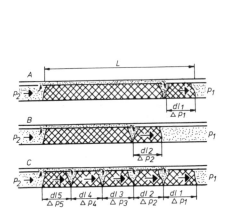

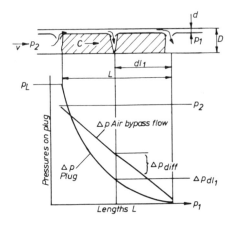

FLUIDSTAT conveying pipe; material is split up into individual slugs; conveying process in the conveying pipe.

Pressure curve for FLUIDSTAT conveying; pressures on individual slugs, for conveying pipe with bypass.

Figure 7.43 Fluidstat system (Buhler Brothers Ltd, Uzwil, Switzerland).

is revealed when conveying bakery flour; this material is so fine and light that it fluidizes readily without help, and the bypass lines merely increase drag.

With reference to plug formation, the fluidized state of the material would usually separate the individual particles and keep the pressure drop approximately proportional to plug length. However, if a solid plug does form (e.g. starting after a long delay), the blockage will be 'chipped' away from its front end by conveying air which is forced through the bypass. This ensures the overall reliability of the system; however, a precondition is that the pressure drop across a bypass pipe is greater than that across a plug of equal length. Thus the system must be carefully sized for each particular requirement. It is stated [26] that the increased cost of the conveying pipe is compensated by a lower compressed air consumption.

Another variation of the bypass conveying system is the so called turbulence booster (Fig. 7.44). The hardware for such a system is similar to that employed in the conventional bypass system. However, according to the designers the system operates on the principle of regeneration of turbulence in the conveying pipe.

The system is essentially a low velocity system and substantial savings in energy have been realized by converting conventional systems to include the special piping arrangement.

(c) Trace-air/dynamic-air

As shown in Fig. 7.45, the trace-air method utilizes a series of boosters incorporating a pressure regulator and a check valve. The material is essentially extruded out of the blow vessel and air is only added where necessary to prevent

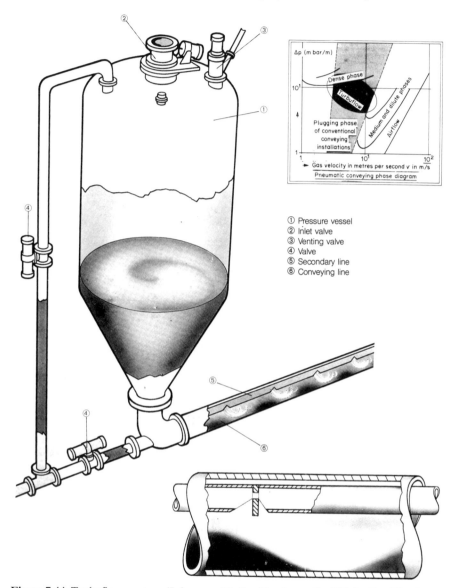

Figure 7.44 Turbuflow system (Johannes Moller Hamburg GmbH & Co., Hamburg, West Germany).

a blockage. The spacing between boosters is typically 3–13 m and depends on the material's properties and the desired reliability. The system can be rapidly 'tuned' to achieve the desired performance by adjusting the pressure regulators.

However, each booster is relatively expensive, and this creates a complicated trade-off situation between booster spacing, air consumption and plant reliabi-

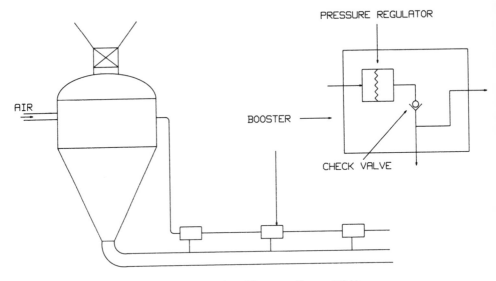

Figure 7.45 Trace air system (Semco Inc., Houston, Texas, USA).

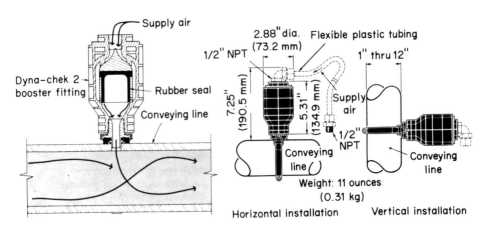

Figure 7.46 Dynamic air system (Dynamic air conveying systems, St Paul, Minnesota, USA).

lity. For instance, very fine materials like titanium dioxide would require booster spacings every half metre, or sufficient air to ensure dilute phase conveying, to ensure 100% reliability. Therefore, a typical system would seldom operate at the optimum condition.

The dynamic air system (Fig. 7.46) is very similar except that volume (rather than pressure) is controlled at each booster, and the check valve is incorporated at the injection point.

7.6.6.3 *Plug forming systems*

(a) The pulsed conveyor

The pulsed conveyor, developed by Warren Spring Laboratories in the UK [30] has been widely used for fine powders which are generally not free flowing.

The basic arrangement of the pulse conveyor includes a bottom discharge blow vessel fitted with an 'air knife' located just downstream of the discharge valve (Fig. 7.47). The air knife is supplied with compressed gas and its operation is controlled by a variable setting timer. Both the frequency of operation of the air knife and the time allowed for the gas to pass through the air knife can be adjusted to suit a particular product.

The gas is injected by the air knife into the flowing solid stream. When the gas supply to the knife is 'on', the gas pulse splits the powder mass, stops the flow of material from the vessel and pushes the severed 'plug' a short distance along the conveying pipe. The conveying process consists of a series of material plugs interspaced by a gas gap. The system relies on a plug forming characteristic of the material and is suited to products with a cohesive nature. The most serious limitation of this type of system is the absence of any method of easily removing a blockage once it has formed. Therefore the system is more suitable for intermittent conveying.

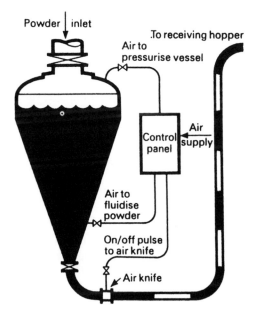

Figure 7.47 Arrangement of pulse phase system (Sturtevant Engineering Ltd, United Kingdom).

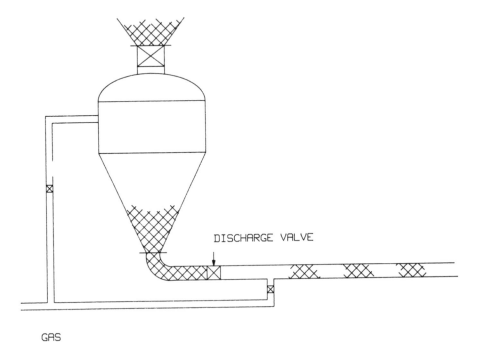

DISCHARGE VALVE

GAS

Figure 7.48 Intermittent solids feed system.

(b) Intermittent solids feed conveyor

For granular materials the cyclic operation of a specially produced solids flow control valve, permits the introduction of the solids in a plug form into the flowing gas stream (Fig. 7.48). The feeding technique is such that the plugs are tightly packed before being fed into the conveying pipe [27].

It has been found that the plugs are maintained as an entity along the whole length of the conveying line. A condition for successful operation of such a system is gas permeability through the plug as well as some cohesive forces within the plug.

(c) Double pulse system (Takt-Schub)

A method of effecting some solids flow control without any mechanical shut off valves is the use of a gas pulsing technique (Fig. 7.49). Essentially the blow vessel is fitted with two gas inlets each with their own shut off valve. One pipe is located above the material, whilst the second pipe is fitted to the exit from the blow vessel along the centre line of the conveying pipe [28].

By means of alternate pulsing of the valves it is possible to effect some control of the solids flow. A gas blast directed to the top of the material ensures that a quantity of material is forced into the conveying line. The second pulse will

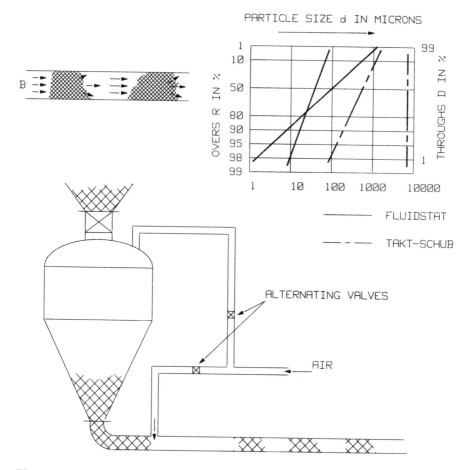

PARTICLE SIZE d IN MICRONS

————— FLUIDSTAT

— — — TAKT–SCHUB

Figure 7.49 Arrangement of Takt-Schub system (Buhler Brothers Ltd, Uzwil, Switzerland).

convey the 'plug' of material a distance along the conveying pipe. Eventually the conveying process is converted into a series of plugs moving down the line. The technique can only be applied to a limited range of products and is well suited to granular products.

(d) Plug pulse system

The plug pulse system is a refinement of the double pulse technique to meet the problems of free flowing materials. In this system a discharge valve is alternatively actuated with a gas pulse (Fig. 7.50).

The vessel is kept pressurized by an open gas supply. On opening of the discharge valve, a discrete amount of materials is deposited into the conveying

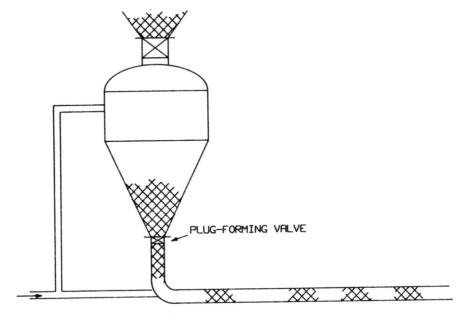

Figure 7.50 Plug pulse conveying system.

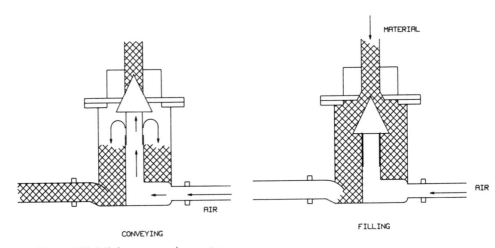

Figure 7.51 Minipot conveying system.

line. An air pulse is used to convey the plug down the line. Both the regulation of the gas pulse and the timing of the opening of the discharge valve are controlled by means of a variable timer. The timing settings are adjusted to suit a particular material. The most successful tests have been conducted using a pinch valve as the discharge valve.

A variation of the plug pulse system is the so called minipot. The minipot is one of the simplest forms of blow vessel configurations available (Fig. 7.51). Essentially the minipot consists of a weighted conical valve located on a central stem in the middle of the pot which also acts as the gas inlet pipe.

The mass of the cone is such that under normal conditions the cone is in the open condition thereby permitting the pot to be filled with solids. On a signal from a timer, a gas supply valve is opened permitting gas to flow along the central pipe. The gas flow and pressure are so arranged as to initially provide for the closing of the conical valve. Further gas flow percolates through the stem of the cone and provides sufficient gas to transport a plug of material. The volume of the pot is so arranged to permit a series of small plugs to move through the pipeline.

The minipot has been successfully applied to a large number of applications. Typically the transportation of cement, fly ash, lime and various granular products including fertilizers and plastic granules has been successfully achieved using such a minipot.

The minipot has been designed for ease of installation and normally uses a minimal amount of conveying gas.

7.6.6.4 Plug destroying systems

(a) Pressure sensing plug system

A further derivative of the basic plug phase principle is the pressure sensing plug system. The system consists of a series of gas injection stations along the conveying pipe, the distance between each station being governed by both the size of the line and the nature of the product being conveyed.

Located at each station is a pressure sensing booster valve, which automatically senses pressure changes and adjusts booster pressure to keep the material

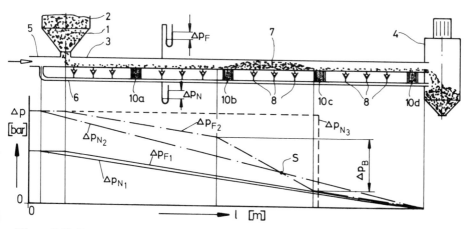

Figure 7.52 Pneumosplit system (Waeschle Maschinenfabrik GmbH, Ravensburg, West Germany).

flowing. By having individual stations, booster gas is injected only when and where it is required.

The pneumo split system (Fig. 7.52) thus facilitates a constant pressure gradient and a gentle handling of material. The boosters are so arranged that no one station can build a pressure higher than the one immediately upstream from it.

There are several techniques for pressure sensing including an electronic pressure sensing device and a mechanical sensing device. There is evidence of substantial improvements in overall conveying efficiency [24], when using a mechanical type system.

(b) The Fluid-Schub System

The similar Fluid-Schub system incorporates valves between the auxiliary line and the conveying pipe (Fig. 7.53). When a blockage causes the conveying pressure to rise, air is automatically routed through the auxiliary line until the plug is chipped away from its forward end.

7.6.6.5 *Some general comments on low velocity systems*

An attempt has been made to identify the various techniques used to promote low velocity pneumatic conveying. The final selection of the most suitable system is greatly dependent upon the characteristics of the material to be conveyed. More

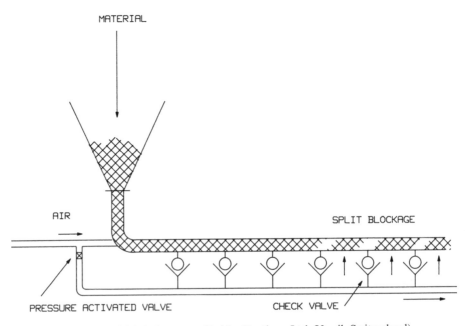

Figure 7.53 The Fluid-Schub system (Buhler Brothers Ltd, Uzwil, Switzerland).

details pertaining to the specific selection of a system are discussed in the chapter on dense phase conveying (Chapter 9).

The reader is cautioned to ascertain whether the system which is ultimately selected, will meet the requirements of a 'true' low velocity system. An important criterion in system selection is the ability to 're-start' the system in the event of a power failure.

7.6.6.6 Natural plug formation

In all the discussions relating to the selection of a low velocity conveying system, an awareness of the product characteristic is absolutely essential. There are some granular products which when fed from a bottom discharge blow vessel with a discrete quantity of gas, will form natural low velocity plugs. The system can be

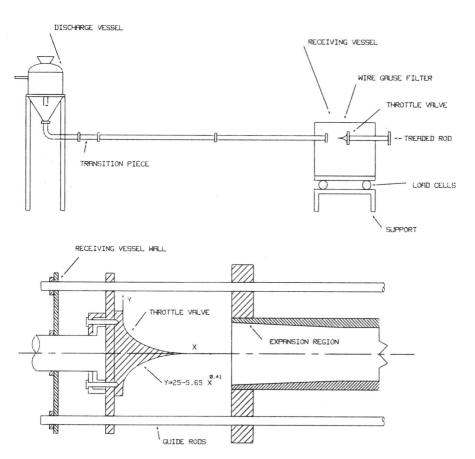

Figure 7.54 Arrangement of extruded flow systems.

'tuned' to produce the plugs without the need for any peripheral plug forming devices.

These natural plug forming products, include a wide range of plastic granules. It is found that when too much air is introduced into the system the product is transported as a normal dilute phase suspension. On reduction of the quantity of gas, it is possible to effect natural plug formation.

7.6.6.7 Extruded flow

As the name implies, extruded flow systems permit the conveying of certain granular materials as an ultradense plug. The plug extends for the length of the conveying pipe and the system is well suited to granular materials in which a certain amount of conveying gas can percolate through the material body.

A typical system consists of a blow vessel connected to a discharge line without any discharge valve. The flow of material is controlled by means of a specially designed conical valve situated at the discharge end of the system.

At the start of the conveying cycle the conical valve is adjusted far forward into the flared end of the discharge pipe, leaving sufficient clearance for gas to pass through the pipe whilst containing the flow of solids.

Once the conveying pipe is completely full of material the discharge valve is opened to allow material to flow. Both the shape of the conical discharge valve as well as the profile of the flared seal are critical. Work done by Shepherd [31] includes a number of observations of materials tested in the extruded flow.

Typically with a discharge valve at the end of the system Welschof [32], it is possible to control the flow of material whilst attaining mass flow ratios of the order of $\mu = 500$. No noticeable particle degradation has been observed even when conveying very brittle materials [31]. By virtue of the extruded flow concept, extremely low gas flow rates are required to affect transportation. The low gas flow rates facilitate the need for relatively modest gas–solids separation equipment. In Fig. 7.54 a typical arrangement of an extruded flow system is shown. In particular, it should be noted that the profiled discharge valve is located at the end of the conveying pipe.

7.7 CONCLUSIONS

In this chapter, an attempt has been made to highlight the various feeding devices used for pneumatic conveying systems. At all stages the reader has been cautioned to make sure that the selection of a suitable feeding device is based on a full knowledge of both the product and the process in which the transportation system is required.

An attempt has also been made to include most of the more popular commercial systems available on the market. Every effort has been made to ensure that at all stages the reader has been provided with enough information so as to make a suitable choice of a feeding system.

REFERENCES

1. Bennington, S.T. and King, A.L. (1972) *Jet Pumps and Ejectors—A state of the Art Review and Bibliography*, BHRA Fluid Engineering, Cranfield, November.
2. Bohnet, M. (1982) Aerodynamic calculation of gas/solid injectors, *Proc. Pneumatech I*, International Conference on Pneumatic Conveying Technology, Powder Advisory Centre, London, May.
3. Butters, G. (ed.) (1981) *Plastics Pneumatic Conveying and Bulk Storage*, Applied Sciences Publishers, Reading, p. 125.
4. Cramp, W. and Priestley, A. (1924) Pneumatic grain elevators, *The Engineer*, January 11, 18, 25, February 1.
5. Vogel, R. (1979) Dense phase vertical vacuum conveying in short length risers, *M.Sc. Dissertation*, Faculty of Engineering, University of Witwatersrand, Johannesburg, South Africa.
6. Cardoso, V.M.R. (1983) Vacuum conveying of crushed coal over short distances, *M.Sc. Dissertation*, Faculty of Engineering, University of Witwatersrand, Johannesburg, South Africa.
7. Reed, A.R. and Mason, J.S. (1983) The effect of suction nozzle geometry on the performance of pneumatic ship unloaders, *Proc. Int. Conf. on Bulk Materials Storage, Handling and Transportation*, Institution of Engineers, Australia, August.
8. Butters, G. (ed.) (1981) *Plastics Pneumatic Conveying and Bulk Storage*, Applied Sciences Publishers, Reading, p. 125.
9. Reed, A.R. and Mason, J.S. (1977) Estimating air leakage through rotary valves, *Bulk-Storage Movement Control*, January/February.
10. AMD Services, Johannesburg, South Africa.
11. Marcus, R.D. (1984) Minimum energy pneumatic conveying I—dilute phase *Journal Pipelines*, **4**, 113–21.
12. Cyclonaire Corporation, Nebraska, USA.
13. Stoes, H.A. (1983) *Pneumatic Conveying*, 2nd edn, Wiley, New York.
14. Marcus, R.D. and Benatar, G. The Mono powder pump, *Bulk Solids Handling*, Transtest Publications, August.
15. Weber, M. (1973) *Stromungs-Fordertechnik*, Krausskopf Verlag.
16. Waghorn, D.J. and Mason, J.S. (1976) The effect of aeration and position of inlet to conveying line on the discharge characteristics of a blow tank, *Proc. 1st Int. Conf. on Bulk Solids, Storage, Handling and Flow*, Stratford upon Avon, Powder Advisory Centre, UK, November.
17. Kraus, M.N. (1980) *Pneumatic Conveying of Bulk Materials*, 2nd edn, McGraw-Hill, New York.
18. Lohrmann, P.C. (1983) An investigation into aspects of the selection, design and operating characteristics of blow tank pneumatic conveying systems to suit a particular material requirement, *M.Sc. Dissertation*, Faculty of Engineering, University of Witwatersrand, Johannesburg, South Africa.
19. Lohrmann, P.C. and Marcus, R.D. (1984) Minimum energy pneumatic conveying II—dense phase, *Journal Pipelines*, **4**, 123–9.
20. Snow, C.L. (1984) Long distance pneumatic conveying of dried slime, *M.Sc. Dissertation*, Faculty of Engineering, University of Witwatersrand, Johannesburg, South Africa.

21. Sheer, T.J. (1986) Investigations into the use of ice for cooling deep mines. Personal communication, Chamber of Mines Research, South Africa.
22. Rizk, F. (1976) *Proceedings of Pneumotransport 3*, BHRA Fluid Engineering, Cranfield.
23. Wiggill, C. (1985) Long distance conveying of fly ash, *Internal Report*, Materials Handling Research Unit, University of the Witwatersrand, Johannesburg.
24. Govier, G.W. and Aziz, K. (1977) *The Flow of Complete Mixtures in Pipes*, Krieger Publishing Company, New York.
25. Butters, G. (ed.) (1981) *Plastics Pneumatic Conveying and Bulk Storage*, Applied Sciences Publishers, Reading, p. 123.
26. Flatt, W. (1980) Low velocity pneumatic conveying of granulated and pulverised products. Criteria for selecting the optimal pneumatic conveying system, paper J3, *Proceedings of Pneumotransport*, **5**, BHRA Fluid Engineering, Cranfield.
27. Hoppe, H. (1984) Gentle pneumatic transport of friable materials by means of modern conveying methods, *Proc. Pneumatech II*, Powder Advisory Centre, UK, September.
28. Tsuji, Y. and Morikawa, Y. (1982) *Int. J. Multiphase Flow*, **8**, 657–67.
29. Lippert, A. (1966) *Chem-Ing Tech*, **38**, 350–5.
30. Apsey, J.H. (1975) The pneumatic pulse phase powder conveyor, *Proc. Joint Symposium on Pneumatic Transport of Solids*, SAIMechE, SA Institute of Materials Handling, April.
31. Shepherd, N.G. (1979) Dense phase pneumatic conveying of coarse materials in the extrusion flow regime *Proc. Tech. Programme Int. Powder and Bulk Solids Handling and Processing Conf.*, pp. 499–508, May.
32. Welschof, G. (1962) Pneumatische Foerderung bei grossen Fordergutkonzentrat-ionen, *VDI Forschung*, **492**, 28,
33. Muschelknautz, E. und Krambrock, W. (1969) Vereinfachte Berechnung horizontaler pneumatischer Foerderleitungen bei hoher Gutbeladung mit feinkornigen Pro-dukten, *CIT*, **41**, 21, S. 1164.

8
Flow in standpipes and gravity conveyors

8.1 INTRODUCTION — STANDPIPES AND GRAVITY CONVEYORS

This chapter is concerned with the flow of solids under gravity. Two types of flow will be considered. In one solids flow downwards in a vertical or inclined tube generally known as a 'standpipe'. Standpipe flow is often encountered in the outlet of hoppers, in cyclone diplegs and particularly in transferring solids out of a fluidized bed. The other type of gravity flow considered here is analogous to open channel flow of a liquid. This is known as flow in a gravity conveyor or an air-slide. Solids flow down a channel tilted a few degrees to the horizontal (often between $1°$ and $8°$). The solids are fluidized by an upflow of gas close to the minimum fluidization velocity and flow down the channel like a liquid. In this chapter, the two types of gravity flow will be considered separately.

8.2 CLASSIFICATION OF STANDPIPE SYSTEMS

A standpipe is defined here as a vertical or inclined tube in which granular solids flow downwards. A standpipe has the capability of serving two important functions:

(a) To transfer solids from a point at a low pressure to a point at a higher pressure.
(b) To provide a seal against gas flow in one direction.

The importance of these two capabilities can be illustrated in a catalytic cracking plant for the production of gasoline. A typical catalytic cracker (Fig. 8.1) consists of two reactors through which an alumina catalyst (the solid) recirculates [1]. The catalyst from the combustion reactor flows down a tall standpipe (up to 20 m in height) through a slide valve and is then transported upwards through a riser tube to the other reactor. Note that the pressure at the top of the standpipe, p_1 (Fig. 8.1), is lower than that at the bottom of the standpipe, p_3. Pressure immediately above the slide valve near the lower end, p_2, is significantly above p_1 as a result of the 'head of solid' in the standpipe. In this case it is also important that p_2 is greater than p_3, giving $p_2 > p_3 > p_1$ during operation.

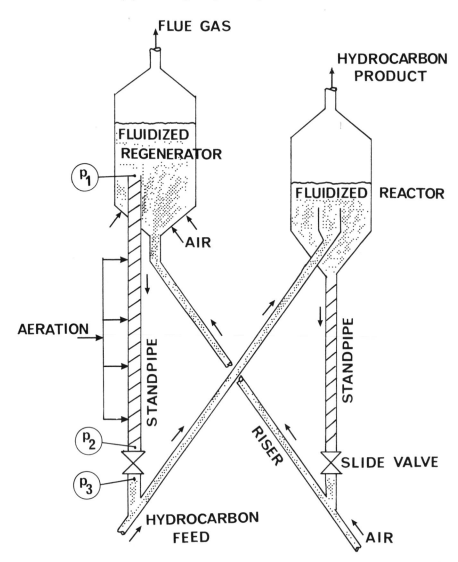

Figure 8.1 A hydrocarbon cracking plant for production of gasoline (after Matsen [1]).

That p_2 is greater than p_3 is important in this case as this will prevent upflow of hydrocarbon vapour through the slide valve and standpipe into the combustion reactor full of air. The tall standpipe thus serves the dual functions of transferring solid to a higher pressure and of preventing backflow of gas in the upward direction.

For a standpipe to exhibit these two capabilities, the system can only operate stably under a narrow range of parameters. An understanding of gas–solid

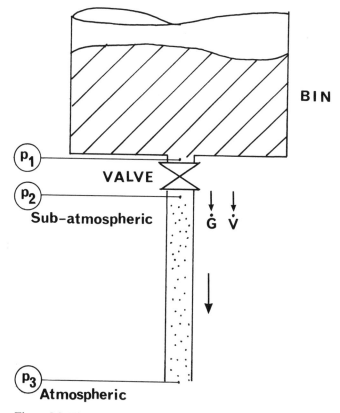

Figure 8.2 The simple standpipe.

downflow is important in the design and operation of standpipes. In this section, we shall consider the classification of standpipe systems.

8.2.1 The simple standpipe

Figure 8.2 describes the simple system generally with external pressure equal to atmospheric pressure. The only independent parameter is the degree of valve opening. The presence of the standpipe below the hopper as shown in Fig. 8.2 has the interesting effect of increasing the maximum solid discharge rate from the hopper [2]. This is made possible as the pressure below the valve is reduced to below atmospheric pressure. This will result in a positive pressure difference $(p_1 - p_2 > 0)$ to promote flow through the valve.

8.2.2 System with top and bottom terminal pressure as independent parameters

Figures 8.3(a) and 8.3(b) show a common type of standpipe with its top inside a bed of solids and a valve at its lower end. Aeration gas may or may not be

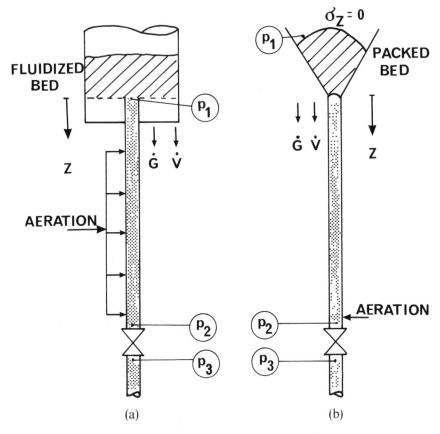

Figure 8.3 Standpipes with top and bottom pressure as independent parameters.

introduced along the pipe from an external source. Here the pressures p_1 and p_3 are fixed by factors external to the standpipe and are defined as independent parameters. Aeration rates and valve opening can also be independently manipulated and are the other independent parameters. At a given condition, the dependent parameters are solid flow rate, gas entrainment rate, flow pattern, pressure and voidage profiles in the standpipe. Figure 8.3(a) shows the top of the pipe immersed in a fluidized bed and Fig. 8.3(b) shows the top of the pipe connected to a packed bed of solids.

8.2.3 System with top terminal pressure as independent parameter

This system is identical to that described in Fig. 8.3(a) with the exception that p_3 is no longer an independent parameter. An example is the Sasol Synthoil reactor system [3] as shown in Fig. 8.4. Here p_3 is influenced by the solid recirculation rate and is not an independent parameter.

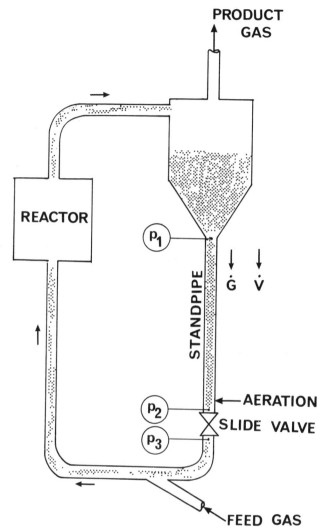

Figure 8.4 Standpipe with top pressure as independent parameter; the Sasol Synthoil reactor system (after Holtkamp *et al.* [3]).

8.2.4 System with top and bottom terminal pressure and solid rate as independent parameters

Figure 8.5 shows some of the industrial systems under this common category. Figure 8.5(a) shows a standpipe acting as an overflow of a fluidized bed. Figure 8.5(b) shows a cyclone dipleg and Fig. 8.5(c) shows the downcomer of a multistage fluidized bed. The solid feed rate to the standpipe is also an

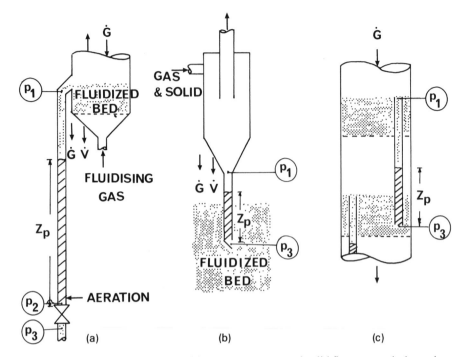

Figure 8.5 Standpipes with top and bottom pressures and solid flow rate as independent parameters: (a) fluid bed overflow standpipe; (b) cyclone dipleg; (c) standpipes in multistage fluidized beds.

independent parameter in addition to the two terminal pressures p_1 and p_3. In normal operation, the lower part of the standpipe is full of solids in dense phase flow while a thin suspension flows through the upper section. The dependent parameters are gas entrainment rate, flow pattern, pressure and voidage profiles and the height of the section full of solids (z_p in Fig. 8.5).

8.2.5 Summary of classification

In this section we have classified common industrial systems according to the independent parameters. Identification of the independent parameters of a standpipe system is necessary in design and operation. There are other criteria of classification such as flow pattern, type of hardware, pressure of operation, and so on [4]. The usefulness of these classifications is not as general as the present one [5].

8.3 CLASSIFICATION OF FLOW MODES IN A STANDPIPE

The flow mode in a standpipe can be either fluidized (i.e. particles are in suspension) or non-fluidized (i.e. particles are not in suspension as in moving- or packed-bed flow). Within each category, subdivision into two further flow patterns can be made [6]. These will be discussed below.

8.3.1 Non-fluidized flow

In non-fluidized flow, particles flow *en bloc* with little relative motion between them. The particles are not in suspension and the slip velocity between gas and solid is less than that required to support the apparent weight of the solid. The slip velocity (relative velocity), w, is defined by

$$w = -v/\varepsilon + c'/(1-\varepsilon) \qquad (8.1)$$

For non-fluidized flow w is less than that at incipient fluidization, i.e.

$$w < v_{min}/\varepsilon_{mf} \qquad (8.2)$$

where

$\quad v =$ superficial gas velocity (positive downwards)
$\quad c' =$ superficial solid velocity (positive downwards)
$\varepsilon, \varepsilon_{mf} =$ voidage, voidage at minimum fluidization
$\quad w =$ slip (relative) velocity, defined as positive upwards
$v_{min} =$ minimum fluidization velocity

Within the non-fluidized flow mode, Kojabashian [7] proposed the further subdivision into transition packed-bed flow, in which slip velocity is positive (i.e. upwards) and voidage increases with slip velocity; and packed-bed flow in which slip velocity is negative (downwards) and voidage is equal to that of a closely compact bed, ε_p independent of slip velocity. Knowlton *et al.* [8] suggested that in transitional packed-bed flow, the following linear relationship may be applicable:

$$\varepsilon = \varepsilon_p + \frac{(\varepsilon_{mf} - \varepsilon_p)w}{v_{min}/\varepsilon_{mf}} \qquad (8.3)$$

where ε_p is voidage of a vibrated bed of particles.

The acronyms TRANPACFLO and PACFLO have been suggested to describe transitional packed-bed flow and packed-bed flow respectively [6].

8.3.2 Fluidized flow

In fluidized flow, solids are in suspension. The relative (slip) velocity between solid and gas is greater than that at minimum fluidization and the voidage is greater than that at minimum fluidization, i.e.

$$w \geqslant v_{min}/\varepsilon_{mf} \qquad \varepsilon \geqslant \varepsilon_{mf} \qquad (8.4)$$

For a given gas–solid system, a unique relationship exists between slip velocity and voidage in fluidized flow, i.e.

$$w = f(\varepsilon) \tag{8.5}$$

Within the fluidized flow regime, further classification was proposed by Kojabashian [7]. His classification was later modified by Leung and Jones [9] to give two types of fluidized flow:

type I fluidized flow $(\partial v/\partial \varepsilon)_{c'} > 0$ (8.6)

type II fluidized flow $(\partial v/\partial \varepsilon)_{c'} < 0$ (8.7)

The use of equations (8.6) and (8.7) in predicting flow mode can be demonstrated by considering a gas–alumina standpipe. For this system, the following slip velocity–voidage relationship has been determined experimentally [6]:

$$w = 8.4\varepsilon^2 - 6.66\varepsilon + 1.36 \tag{8.8}$$

From equations (8.2), (8.6), (8.7) and (8.8), we can derive an equation to describe the demarcation between the two types of fluidized flow modes:

$$c' \gtrless (1 - \varepsilon)^2 (25.2\varepsilon^2 - 13.3\varepsilon + 1.36) \tag{8.9}$$

The greater and less than signs in equation (8.9) refer to type I and type II flow respectively.

A quantitative flow regime diagram for the gas–alumina system can be constructed from equation (8.9). This is given in Fig. 8.6 showing that voidage by itself does not define the flow regime. Type I and type II flow can occur over the entire range of voidage. A quantitative flow regime diagram similar to Fig. 8.6 can be constructed for any gas–solid system provided the voidage–slip velocity relationship for the system is available.

8.3.3 Summary of flow modes

In summary the four flow modes in standpipe flow are

(a) Packed-bed flow (PACFLO) in which

$$w < 0$$

$$\varepsilon = \varepsilon_p$$

and is independent of slip velocity.

(b) Transitional packed-bed flow (TRANPACFLO) in which

$$0 < w < v_{min}/\varepsilon_{mf}$$

and ε is a function of slip velocity.

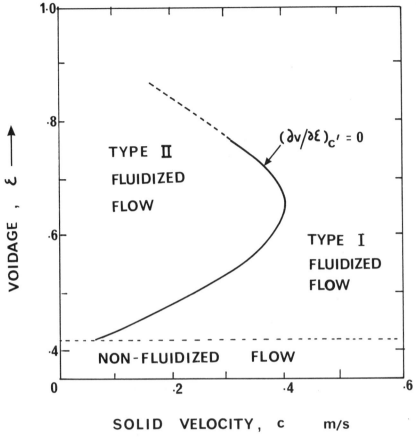

Figure 8.6 Demarcation between type I and type II fluidized flow (after Leung and Jones [6]).

(c) Type I fluidized flow, in which

$$w \geqslant v_{min}/\varepsilon_{mf}$$

$$\varepsilon \geqslant \varepsilon_{mf}$$

$$(\partial v/\partial \varepsilon)_{c'} > 0$$

(d) Type II fluidized flow, in which

$$w \geqslant v_{min}/\varepsilon_{mf}$$

$$\varepsilon \geqslant \varepsilon_{mf}$$

$$(\partial v/\partial \varepsilon)_{c'} < 0$$

8.4 EQUATIONS PERTAINING TO EACH FLOW MODE

8.4.1 Non-fluidized flow

For steady non-fluidized flow, two one-dimensional equations are available for describing pressure and normal stress. Following the nomenclature in Fig. 8.7, we can write two momentum equations [10]:

(a) Mixture momentum equation

$$\frac{d\bar{\sigma}_z}{dZ} + \frac{dp}{dZ} + \frac{4\tau_w}{D} - \rho_p(1-\varepsilon)g + c'\rho_p\left(\frac{dc}{dZ}\right) = 0 \tag{8.10}$$

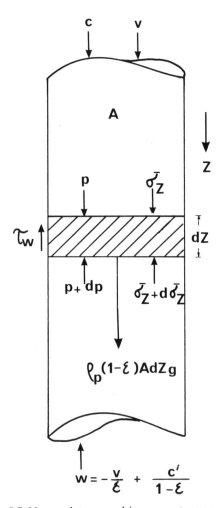

Figure 8.7 Nomenclature used in momentum equations.

where

$\bar{\sigma}_z$ = mean normal stress acting on solid
τ_w = wall shear stress
c = average actual solid velocity = $c'/(1 - \varepsilon)$

(b) Gas momentum equation [11]

$$dp/dZ = K_1 w \qquad (8.11)$$

where

$$K_1 = 150\eta(1 - \varepsilon)^2/(\psi d\varepsilon)^2 \qquad (8.12)$$

ψ = sphericity of particles

η = viscosity of gas

For packed-bed flow, voidage is a constant equal to the vibrated bed voidage, ε_p. For transitional packed-bed flow, equation (8.3) relating voidage and slip velocity may be used [8].

For fully developed flow and neglecting gas inertia, equation (8.10) can be simplified to

$$\frac{d\bar{\sigma}_z}{dZ} + \frac{dp}{dZ} + \frac{4\tau_w}{D} - \rho_p(1 - \varepsilon)g = 0 \qquad (8.13)$$

The normal stress profile can be obtained by integrating equation (8.13) once (dp/dZ) is calculated from equations (8.11) and (8.12). The wall shear stress can be estimated by

$$\tau_w = \mu_w \sigma_r \qquad (8.14)$$

$$\sigma_r = \bar{\sigma}_z(1 - \sin \delta)/(1 + \sin \delta) \qquad (8.15)$$

for a Coulombic solid, where

σ_r = radial compressive stress on solid
μ_w = coefficient of friction between particles and pipe wall
δ = internal angle of friction of particles

8.4.2 Fluidized flow

For fluidized flow, the normal stress acting on solids is zero and the mixture momentum equation becomes

$$\frac{dp}{dZ} + \frac{4\tau_w}{D} - \rho_p(1 - \varepsilon)g + c'\rho_p\left(\frac{dc}{dZ}\right) = 0 \qquad (8.16)$$

For fully developed flow, with a volumetric solid concentration greater than 0.2, wall friction effect and gas inertia may be neglected to give

$$dp/dZ = \rho_p(1 - \varepsilon)g \tag{8.17}$$

Voidage in fluidized bed flow can be estimated from a fluidization expansion equation. For bubbly fluidized flow, the equation proposed by Matsen [1] may be used:

$$w = [w_b(\varepsilon - \varepsilon_{mf}) + v_{min}(1 - \varepsilon)]/[\varepsilon(1 - \varepsilon)] \tag{8.18}$$

where w_b is the rate of rise of a single bubble in a fluidized bed.

For homogeneous fluidized flow, the equation of Richardson and Zaki [12] may be used instead of equation (8.18):

$$w = w_{f0}\varepsilon^{n-1} \tag{8.19}$$

where

w_{f0} = single particle settling velocity
n = exponent in the Richardson–Zaki equation

In a tall standpipe, or one operating at a very low pressure, the effect of gas compression as a result of pressure change along a standpipe may become very significant. In that case, variation of gas velocity along the pipe can be accounted for by applying the ideal gas equation or an appropriate equation of state for the gas [13].

8.5 FLOW THROUGH A VALVE

In many industrial standpipes, a slide valve, or some other restriction such as an L valve, a J valve, a flapper valve, etc. is present at the lower end for control of solid flow and pressure balance. Often such a restriction is necessary to promote dense phase flow and to provide adequate pressure build-up in the standpipe. In any analysis for standpipe flow, it is necessary to include the valve as part of the system under study. We shall deal with the characteristics of various types of valves in this section.

8.5.1 Flow through a slide valve

Flow of a gas–solid mixture through a slide valve can be modelled in terms of flow through an orifice. The characteristic equations for a valve are dependent on the state of the solids above the valve: fluidized or non-fluidized. The two cases will be considered separately.

8.5.1.1 Fluidized flow

A large volume of work has been published on the flow of fluidized solids through an orifice [14–19]. There is general agreement that the equation for describing solid flow rate is analogous to that for flow of a fluid through an orifice. The following equation by Judd and Dixon [17] may be used for flow of solids with a finite pressure difference across a valve:

$$\dot{G} = C_v A_o [A^2/(A^2 - A_o^2)]^{0.5} (2\rho_B \Delta p_o)^{0.5} \tag{8.20}$$

where

A = cross-sectional area of pipe above valve
A_o = cross-sectional area of opening in valve
C_v = valve coefficient
$\dot{G}$ = mass flow rate of solid
ρ_B = bulk density of solid–gas mixture above valve
Δp_o = pressure drop across valve

The magnitude of the coefficient C_v is dependent on the geometry of the valve and the properties of the solid. Values of C_v in the range of 0.68 to 0.98 have been obtained for flow of milled iron ore and silica–alumina catalyst [17, 20].

The correction factor $[A^2/(A^2 - A_o^2)]^{0.5}$ in the above equation is generally close to 1 for small valve openings and can often be neglected. For operators running a standpipe system, it is recommended that they obtain their own valve coefficient from plant measurements by plotting $\dot{G}/A_o$ versus $\Delta p_o^{0.5}$.

Equation (8.20) describes the flow of solids through a valve for a given valve opening and pressure difference. A separate equation is available to describe gas flow. As the gas inertia is negligible, pressure drop can be related to the frictional pressure drop for flow of gas relative to the solid in the valve [15, 16]. Using the Ergun equation to describe frictional pressure loss due to relative motion between gas and solid, the following equation relating gas and solid flow through a valve can be derived:

$$\Delta p_o = -K_1 w - K_2 w|w| \tag{8.21}$$

K_1 is given in equation (8.12) and K_2 is given by:

$$K_2 = 1.75\rho(1 - \varepsilon)D_o(A/A_o^2)/(24\psi d\varepsilon) \tag{8.22}$$

D_o = diameter of opening of valve.

8.5.1.2 Non-fluidized flow

In considering non-fluidized flow (or moving-bed flow) through a valve, two classes of flow may be distinguished, namely, solid flow with and solid flow without a significant fluid drag effect. With a significant fluid drag generated from the relative velocity between gas and solid, a pressure gradient in the gas is set up. For fine particles, even a very small relative velocity would generate a large pressure gradient which would have an important effect on solid flow. For coarse particles, a very high relative velocity would be required before fluid drag plays an important role.

Where fluid drag is not significant, pressure drop across the orifice is close to zero. With significant fluid drag, pressure drop can be positive or negative depending on the direction of the relative velocity. A common example is the use of an efflux tube at the outlet of a hopper at atmospheric pressure as shown in Fig. 8.2. The effect of the tube is to reduce the pressure at the outlet of the orifice to below atmospheric pressure. This creates a positive pressure drop across the orifice with a corresponding increase in solid discharge [2].

A large number of empirical and semi-empirical equations are available in the literature for estimating solid flow rates for the flow of granular solids through an opening with negligible fluid drag [21–24]. For flow through a circular orifice, the following equation by Beverloo *et al.* [23] may be used to estimate solid flow rate:

$$\dot{G}_o = 35\rho_p g^{1/2}(D_o - 1.4d_s)^{2.5} \tag{8.23}$$

where

d_s = specific surface area diameter of particle
$\dot{G}_o$ = solid flow rate through valve with no fluid drag effect

For a non-circular orifice opening, the equation can be written as

$$\dot{G}_o = 45\rho_p A'_o(gD'_{oh})^{0.5} \tag{8.24}$$

where

D'_{oh} = effective hydraulic diameter of the opening
$\quad = (D_{oh} - 1.4d_s)$, where D_{oh} is the hydraulic diameter of the opening
A'_o = the effective opening area calculated from D'_{oh}

The effect of fluid drag on moving-bed flow of solids through an orifice has been considered by a large number of workers [25–28]. Leung *et al.* [29] suggested that the equations for no slip can be combined with the equation for fluidized flow to give the following general equation:

$$\dot{G} = \dot{G}_o + C_v A_o(2\rho_B \Delta p_o)^{0.5} \tag{8.25}$$

The first term on the right-hand side of equation (8.25) refers to the residual flow for zero Δp_o. The second term describes the flow rate using a simplified version of equation (8.20) for fluidized flow. Equation (8.25) is useful for analysing standpipe operating conditions as it is applicable to moving bed flow and fluidized solids flow through an orifice or a slide valve.

8.5.2 Flow through non-mechanical valves

The L valve, J valve and V valve (Fig. 8.8) belong to a class of non-mechanical valves that employ a small amount of aeration gas to control the flow of particulate solids. These valves have no moving mechanical parts subject to wear and seizure. They are also relatively inexpensive and have been used to feed or

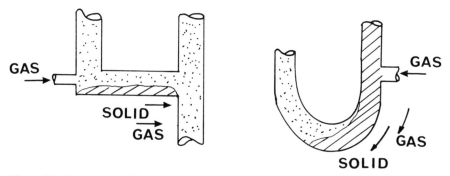

Figure 8.8 Non-mechanical valves: (a) the L-valve; (b) the J-valve.

control flow into either a fluidized bed or a pneumatic conveying line. Flow of solids can be stopped completely through such a valve by shutting off the supply of aeration gas.

The characteristics of L valves and J valves have been measured by Knowlton *et al.* [8] and Knowlton and Hirsan [30]. Their studies show that for a given system, pressure drop across a valve is a monotonic function of solid flow through the valve:

$$\Delta p_o = f(\dot{G}) \tag{8.26}$$

and a unique relationship exists between gas and solid flow rates through the valve:

$$f(\dot{G}, \dot{V}) = 0 \tag{8.27}$$

The general forms of the equations (8.26) and (8.27) are not known. For each valve, the equations have to be established experimentally. The two equations are analogous to equations (8.20) and (8.21) for flow through an orifice/slide valve.

The V valve (Fig. 8.9) is another non-mechanical valve recently developed at the Academica Sinica. It has an aperture in the vertical plane connecting to a V-shape channel. Compared with the L valve and the J valve, the V valve can operate over a larger range of flow rates and has a better seal against reverse flow of solids and gas. Detailed characteristics of the valve have been presented by Liu *et al.* [31] and Chong *et al.* [32]. While a design procedure for the V valve has been put forward by Chong *et al.* the procedure has yet to be tested experimentally.

8.6 STABILITY OF STANDPIPE FLOW

Perhaps the most intriguing problem facing standpipe operators is that of flow instability. Dramatic instability in standpipe operation often occurs in industrial

SOLID & GAS

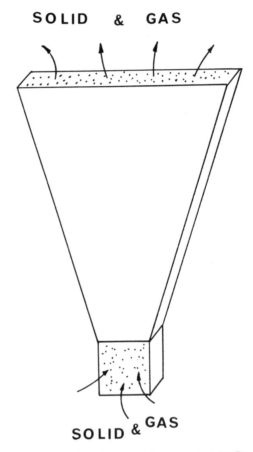

SOLID & GAS

Figure 8.9 The V-valve (after Liu *et al.* [31]).

operation and can lead to costly plant shutdowns. The four major types of instability are [33]:

(a) flooding instability.
(b) multiple steady states and bifurcation instability.
(c) Ledinegg type instability [34].
(d) Rangachari and Jackson type instability [35].

The various types of instability will be discussed below.

8.6.1 Flooding type instability

Flooding in a standpipe is defined by Leung [33] as

$$(\partial v/\partial \varepsilon)_{c'} = 0 \qquad (8.28)$$

Equation (8.28) indicates that any increase in v at a constant solid flux will result in a runaway increase in voidage causing the pipe to empty. Equation (8.28) corresponds to the demarcation of type I and type II fluidized flow described in Section 8.3.2. Thus operation close to the demarcation line is likely to be unstable and troublesome.

Matsen [1] suggested that instability would occur when the downward solid velocity is just sufficient to hold a bubble stationary in the standpipe, i.e.

$$\dot{G} = A\rho_p w_b(1 - \varepsilon) \tag{8.29}$$

It can be shown that equation (8.29) is a special case for flooding for bubbly flow with a characteristic bubble velocity of w_b. Thus Matsen's explanation of a 'stationary bubble instability' is a mechanistic description of the flooding instability.

8.6.2 Multiple steady states and bifurcation instability

Under certain operating conditions, multiple steady states have been predicted to occur by Leung and Jones and by Chen *et al.* [6, 36]. Figure 8.10 is a plot of solid flow rate versus $(p_3 - p_1)$. There are two operating lines in the figure: the upper line ABC and the lower line DEF. As $(p_3 - p_1)$ is gradually increased, the system may operate along AB until a critical point C is reached. Further increase in $(p_3 - p_1)$ will result in a stepwise drop to the lower operating solid rate at E. This sudden change is defined as bifurcation instability. Reducing $(p_3 - p_1)$ from point F will follow operation along FED in Fig. 8.10.

In the region corresponding to DE, two possible steady states are feasible, either along the upper line or the lower line. Chen *et al.* [36] verified the existence of such multiple steady states and the bifurcation instability both theoretically and experimentally in their simple laboratory standpipe. It remains to be seen how this understanding can be applied to the operation of more complex industrial standpipes.

8.6.3 Ledinegg [34] type instability

Ledinegg carried out a sensitivity analysis for gas–liquid flow in vertical boiler tubes. The system of algebraic equations is reduced to two—a supply equation and a demand equation. Solutions of the two equations are represented by points of intersection of the two curves representing the equations. The stability of a particular solution is analysed by a simple perturbation argument. The application of Ledinegg's analysis was extended to standpipe flow by Jones *et al.* [37]. They considered a standpipe system represented by Fig. 8.3(a). Their analysis shows two regions of stable fluidized operation: one at high voidage and the other at a voidage close to that at minimum fluidization. The intermediate voidage region for fluidized flow was shown to be unstable. The outcome of this analysis appears to be consistent with the fact that intermediate voidage fluidized flow is seldom observed in practice.

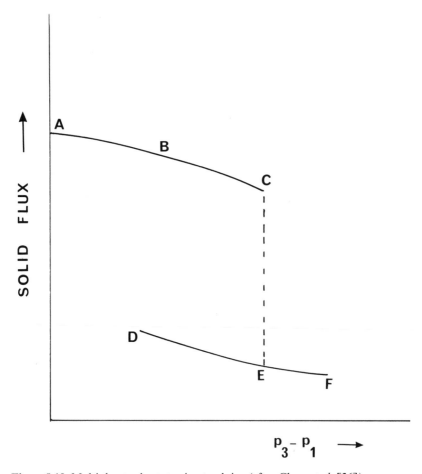

Figure 8.10 Multiple steady states in standpipe (after Chen *et al.* [36]).

8.6.4 Stability analysis of Rangachari and Jackson [35]

Rangachari and Jackson considered the stability of the simple system depicted in Fig. 8.2 with the valve fully open. They proposed a stability criterion based on the sign of $d(p_3 - p_1)/dc$. They suggested that stable operation can only be attained if the above differential is less than zero. Further work will be required to extend this work to more complex industrial systems.

8.6.5 A summary on instability

Several known mechanisms for instability in standpipe flow have been described in the literature. It should be stressed that a given flow system may be analysed to be stable from one viewpoint but unstable from another. Many of the proposed mechanisms for instability have yet to be verified in carefully executed experiments. Further work will be required here.

8.7 ANALYSIS OF INDUSTRIAL STANDPIPES— CASE STUDIES

Two case studies will be considered here for two types of standpipes. The first is an underflow standpipe as depicted in Fig. 8.3(a) where the top of the standpipe is inserted inside a fluidized bed. Here the independent parameters are the two terminal pressures p_1 and p_3, aeration rate and valve opening. The dependent parameters are solid rate, gas entrainment rate and voidage in the pipe. The second standpipe is an overflow standpipe (Fig. 8.5(a)) in which the solid flow rate is an additional independent parameter. The dependent parameters are the gas entrainment rate, voidage profile and the position of the interface between dilute phase and dense phase in the standpipe. Implications of the results of the analysis will also be discussed.

8.7.1 Underflow standpipe—Fig. 8.3(a)

The system under consideration is a 0.81 m diameter, 9.8 m tall standpipe in a hydrocarbon cracking plant. Alumina catalyst circulates through the standpipe at rates between 10 to 20 tonnes per minute. Design conditions for the operation of the standpipe and relevant data are summarized in Table 8.1.

For a given set of independent parameters for the system, there are four unknowns: $\dot{G}$, $\dot{V}$, ε and p_2 where p_2 is the pressure immediately above the slide valve. There are four equations describing behavior of the system: two equations pertaining to flow in the standpipe (equations (8.17) and (8.18)) and two equations describing flow through the side valve (equations (8.20) and (8.21)). These four algebraic equations can be solved numerically to give a set of predicted operating conditions for a given operation. Table 8.2 presents the results on the effect of

Table 8.1 Solid and system characteristics for an underflow standpipe in case study [38]

Pressure at top of standpipe, p_1	232 kPa
Pressure at bottom of standpipe below slide valve, p_3	239 kPa
Length of standpipe	9.8 m
Diameter of standpipe	0.81 m
Temperature in standpipe	930 K
Minimum fluidization velocity, v_{min}	0.02 m/s
Typical bubble velocity, w_b	0.32 m/s
Bulk density at minimum fluidization, ρ_B	760 kg/m³
Mean solid diameter	80 μm
Voidage at minimum fluidization, ε_{mf}	0.4
Valve coefficient, C_v, used in calculations	0.5

Table 8.2 Effect of slide valve opening on underflow standpipe operating conditions [38]. Actual operation observed in plant: valve—slightly open; solid rate—250 kg/s

Slide valve opening (% valve area)	Solid rate (kg/s)	Gas entrainment rate*	Voidage in standpipe
50	1190	0.65	0.41
25	620	0.34	0.42
10	240	0.14	0.48
6.7	No solution		

Gas entrainment rate is expressed as superficial velocity down a standpipe in m/s.

variation of valve opening and Table 8.3 presents the results on the effect of aeration rate. The aeration gas is introduced into the standpipe at a location immediately above the slide valve.

Table 8.2 gives the calculated results for the case of no aeration. The results show that there is a minimum valve opening and correspondingly, a minimum solid recirculation rate below which the system will not work. The minimum rate determines the turndown ratio for the above system. Although not shown in Table 8.2, it can be shown that the minimum solid rate can be varied by changing the terminal pressure difference, i.e. $(p_3 - p_1)$. Another consideration for smooth operation is to operate away from the flooding locus defined by equation (8.28). Taking a typical bubble velocity w_b to be about 0.32 m/s [1], the flooding solid rate for the gas–solid system corresponds to 120 kg/s.

To avoid flooding instability, it is recommended that the operating solid velocity should be kept 1.5 times above the critical rate or 0.5 times below the critical rate. This places further restriction on the operation of the standpipe.

Calculations were also carried out on the effect of aeration rate at a given valve opening. The results show that there is a critical aeration rate above which there is no solution. The critical point is analogous to point C in Fig. 8.10. Beyond this point there is a stepwise drop in solid rate resulting in the type of instability discussed in Section 8.6.2. The above conclusion is consistent with observed behaviour in the industrial standpipe.

8.7.2 Overflow standpipe—Fig. 8.5(a)

The system under study is depicted in Fig. 8.5(a) with a standpipe diameter of 66 mm and an overall height of 17.5 m [38]. The operating parameters and calculated operating conditions are summarized in Table 8.3 for a 50% valve opening. For a given set of independent parameters, i.e. $(p_3 - p_1)$, solid flux, valve opening and aeration rate, the system will have a region above the slide valve in dense phase (which may be in fluidized or non-fluidized flow) with an upper region in dilute phase flow analogous to solid raining down a tube. The position

Table 8.3 Data and calculated results on an overflow standpipe in case study

Data used:

$$p_3 - p_1 = 18.3 \, \text{kPa}$$
$$\text{Valve opening} = 50\%$$
$$\text{Total height of standpipe} = 17.5 \, \text{m}$$
$$\rho_p = 680 \, \text{kg/m}$$
$$\varepsilon_{mf} = 0.5$$
$$\dot{G}/A = 207 \, \text{kg/m}^2/\text{s}$$
$$D = 66 \, \text{mm}$$
$$\text{Particle diameter} = 315 \, \mu\text{m}$$
$$C_v = 0.6$$
$$\text{Internal angle of friction} = 60°$$

Calculated results:

Aeration rate (m/s)	Equilibrium height of dense phase section, z_p (m)	Voidage in dense phase section	Flow pattern in dense phase section
0.02	3.4	0.6	Fluidized
0.07	2.9	0.55	Fluidized
0.10*	2.5	0.5	Fluidized/ non-fluidized
0.11	3.8	0.49	TRANPACFLO
0.118	11.4	0.475	TRANPACFLO
0.122†	25.0	0.47	TRANPACFLO

*At this critical aeration rate, transition from fluidized flow to non-fluidized flow [TRANPACFLO] occurs in the dense region of the standpipe.
†The maximum z_p is that of the total height of the standpipe of 17.5 m.

of the interface, z_p, varies with change in independent parameters. When z_p reaches the total height of the standpipe, the system become inoperable. Table 8.3 summarizes the effect of aeration rate on z_p and the voidage in the lower dense phase section. The results show that the flow pattern in the lower region would change from fluidized flow to non-fluidized flow with increase in aeration gas rate. With further increase in aeration rate, z_p increases until the whole pipe is occupied by dense phase flow and the system becomes inoperable.

The results for two different valve openings are given in Fig. 8.11. At low aeration rates, lean phase in coexistence with dense phase fluidized flow occurs along BM in Fig. 8.11. At point M, voidage in the dense phase region reaches the transition value of voidage at minimum fluidization. Further increase in aeration rate will result in a change in flow pattern to non-fluidized flow in the lower section. The height of the non-fluidized dense phase region, z_p, increases with

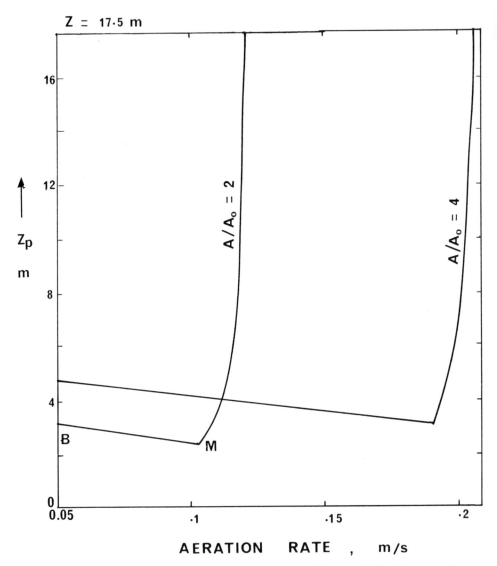

Figure 8.11 Calculated operating conditions of an overflow standpipe for two valve-openings, after Jones and Leung, [38].

increase in the aeration rate until the whole standpipe is occupied by non-fluidized flow. The corresponding aeration rate is the maximum aeration rate for operation for the particular set of independent parameters. In Fig. 8.11, we present the results for two valve openings. It is interesting to note that the range of operable aeration rates depends on valve opening. Thus, manipulating the valve at a fixed aeration rate may result in change from a stable operating point to an unstable operating point as shown in Fig. 8.11.

8.7.3 Summary of case studies

The two case studies above show that modelling of any standpipe system is possible with the equations described in this chapter. The reliability of the modelling predictions, however, is not certain. While trends predicted by models have been verified in practice, quantitative predictions from the models are often inconsistent with observed operating conditions. Nevertheless, the models are useful in understanding operation of existing standpipe systems. Comparison between predictions and operations may be used to develop empirical correction factors to the model equations.

8.8 GRAVITY CONVEYORS

8.8.1 Introduction

The gravity conveyor, also known as the air-slide, consists of an inclined channel in which fluidized solid particles flow under the influence of gravity (Fig. 8.12).

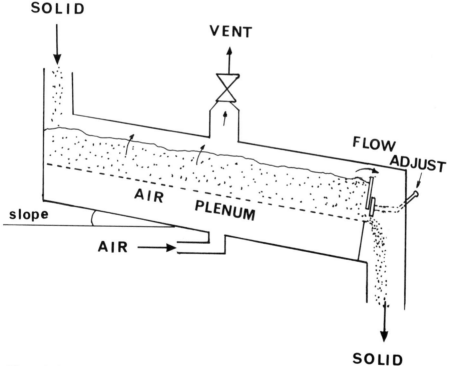

Figure 8.12 The gravity conveyor.

The particles are fluidized in the entire length of the channel by air through a suitable distributor. The flow of fluidized solids in a gravity conveyor is analogous to open channel flow of a liquid [39, 40]. It is particularly suitable to the transfer of fine grain bulk solids that fluidize readily, such as Geldart type A and B [41] particles. The inclination angle of the conveyor can vary over a range from 0.5° to 12°; most conveyors operate between 2° and 8° [42]. The gravity conveyor has the advantages of low solid velocity with little attrition losses, high mass flow rates and low specific power consumption. With special distributor design [43], operation at temperatures up to 850 °C is possible.

For design, the length to be conveyed, the mass flow rate and characteristics of solids to be conveyed are given. We are required to determine:

(a) The air supply rate and its pressure.
(b) The width and height of the fluidized zone.
(c) The angle of inclination of the conveyor.
(d) The design of auxiliary items such as height of conveyor, distributor, gas cleaning equipment, etc.

These matters will be taken up in this section.

8.8.2 Design procedure

Although much has been published on the gravity conveyor [39, 40, 42–48], there is still considerable uncertainty in its design. Most of the published analyses are based on an analogy between fluidized solid flow down the conveyor and open channel flow of a Newtonian or non-Newtonian liquid. For these analyses to be useful in designing a gravity conveyor, a knowledge of the viscosity of fluidized solids will be required. This information is generally not available. Thus the design of gravity conveyors is largely based on rules of thumb and actual operating experience. We shall discuss the design procedure below.

8.8.2.1 Operating gas velocity, v

The operating gas velocity refers to the velocity of air for fluidizing the particles in the entire length of the conveyor. For long conveyors it is important that distribution of air throughout should be uniform. This can be achieved by either having a large pressure drop across the distributor or by dividing the plenum air chamber into a number of sections with air flow rates to each section individually controlled.

The air velocity through the particles must be high enough to fluidize the particles for the solids to flow down the inclined channel. The horizontal solid velocity along the channel can be raised by increasing the fluidization gas velocity from v_{min} to a certain upper limit. Beyond this upper limit, solid velocity will not be influenced by the fluidization velocity [43]. The increase in solid velocity with fluidization velocity has been interpreted in terms of the reduction of apparent viscosity of the fluidized solids with fluidization velocity up to a certain value of gas velocity. The design fluidization velocity for a gravity conveyor should be that value at which further increase in velocity will not result in any significant increase in solid flow rate. The results of Singh *et al.* [43] and Woodcock and Mason [48] suggest that the optimal velocity should be 1.5 to 2 times the minimum fluidization velocity for the particles. For design, we recommend

$$v = 1.5v_{min} \tag{8.30}$$

For coarse materials with high v_{min}, the use of equation (8.30) will result in an unacceptably high operating velocity. In this case operation at much closer to the minimum fluidization velocity is recommended.

8.8.2.2 Width of conveyor, b

Both the width b, and the inclination angle have a direct effect on the maximum carrying capacity of a conveyor. In the absence of any operating data, it is difficult to estimate the required width of a conveyor for a given duty. With some operating data, it is possible to estimate the required width by extrapolation with the help of the following equation [49]:

$$b = K(\dot{G}/\rho_B)^{0.5} \tag{8.31}$$

where

$\dot{G}$ = maximum capacity of conveyor
K = a constant for a given system

In the absence of any operating data for a solid, the results of Singh *et al.* [43] may be used as a starting point for extrapolation. For a width of 150 mm, they reported a sand flow rate of up to 60 tonnes per hour with a density of sand of 2630 kg/m^3 and an angle of inclination of 2° for the gravity conveyor.

Another way of estimating the width of a conveyor is to follow the guidelines of Leitzel [42] given in Table 8.4. The capacities in the table are given in cubic

Table 8.4 Capacity of different width gravity conveyors [42]. To convert to kg/h, multiply capacity by bulk density of solid

Width of conveyor (mm)	Conveyor capacity m^3/h
100	15
200	55
300	125
400	280
500	560
600	730
750	1000
900	1500

metres per hour. This can be converted to kg/h by multiplying by the bulk density of the solids. The bulk density at minimum fluidization may be used in the calculations.

8.8.2.3 Height of fluidized layer, H

For a given system, the height of the fluidized solid zone in a gravity conveyor depends on the solid feed rate. The only equation available to estimate this height, H, was presented by Singh *et al.* [43], as follows:

$$H = \dot{G}/(0.5\rho_B bg)^{0.5} \tag{8.32}$$

Equation [8.32] however, is dimensionally inconsistent and should not be used directly. Experimental measurements combined with extrapolation using the equation is recommended. As a first approximate estimate, a value of 0.1 m may be assumed for the bed height in preliminary calculations.

8.8.2.4 Specification of air requirement

To specify the air requirement, we need to specify the volumetric flow rate and the delivered pressure. The volumetric flow rate can be calculated simply from a knowledge of the operating fluidization velocity and the total cross-sectional area of the fluidized bed. Using equation (8.30) for fluidizing velocity, the volumetric air flow rate is given by

$$\dot{V} = 1.5v_{min}bL \tag{8.33}$$

where

$b =$ width of conveyor
$L =$ length of conveyor

The pressure of the fluidizing air has to overcome line resistance and pressure drop across the distributor as well as the pressure drop across the bed. The latter can be calculated from a knowledge of the height of the bed, H, from

$$\Delta p_{bed} = g\rho_B H \tag{8.34}$$

The bulk density, ρ_B, may be taken as that at minimum fluidization. The pressure drop across the distributor should be adequate to distribute the fluidizing air uniformly throughout the entire length of the conveyor. A value of 0.5 times the pressure drop across the bed may be used as a rough estimate of the required pressure drop in the distributor. Line pressure loss can be estimated when the size, length and geometry of the line are specified.

In summary, the air blower should be sufficient to provide a flow rate of $\dot{V}$ given by equation (8.33) at a pressure of $(1.5\rho_B gH)$ plus line pressure drop. If the delivery pressure is considered excessive for economic reasons, we should consider the division of the air plenum into several sections with independent control of air flow rate into each section.

8.8.2.5 Angle of inclination

The angle of inclination of the gravity conveyor has an effect on conveyor capacity, air requirement and height of the fluidized solids, *H*. Increase in the inclination angle will increase the maximum capacity of the conveyor. For a given conveying rate, increase in inclination angle will result in a lower requirement of fluidizing gas and/or a lower operating height of the fluidized bed. In either case, the power required for supplying the air will be reduced.

No quantitative guidelines are available on the choice of angle of inclination. The choice is dependent on the flow properties of the solid to be conveyed, the type of distributors used, and to a lesser extent, on whether the conveyor is of the open type or the enclosed type. Table 8.5 from Leiztel [42] gives some guidance on the selection. The description of flow properties as poor to very good is necessarily vague. Geldart type A [41] particles may be considered to exhibit very good flow properties.

In many cases, the choice of inclination is dictated by the available elevation difference between solid feed and discharge points. If the elevation difference is insufficient to provide the necessary angle of inclination, a different kind of horizontal fluidized bed conveyor with zero degree of inclination may be used. In these conveyors, solids are propelled forward either by pressure difference or by a jet of air [50, 51].

8.8.2.6 Other considerations

A number of other considerations will have to be taken into account in the design of the complete gravity conveyor. These include the type of distributor to be used,

Table 8.5 Angle of inclination of enclosed and open types of gravity conveyor [42]

Flow characteristics of powder	Type of distributor	Angle of enclosed type conveyor	Inclination of open type conveyor
Poor	Ceramic	8	10
Poor	Fabric	10	12
Poor	Plastic	10	—
Poor	Metallic	10	12
Good	Ceramic	6	6–8
Good	Fabric	8	8–10
Good	Plastic	8	—
Good	Metallic	8	8
Very good	Ceramic	2–5	0–3
Very good	Fabric	4–7	2–4
Very good	Plastic	4–7	—
Very good	Metallic	4–7	2–4

whether the conveyor is enclosed or open, the removal of dust from the exhaust air, the need of inspection openings or whether there is a need to change the direction of flow of solids. All these matters and other accessories will have to be considered in the overall design.

8.8.3 A worked example

Design a gravity conveyor for conveying 30t/h of alumina particles with a density of $1300 \, kg/m^3$ and a mean particle diameter of $60 \, \mu m$, over a distance of 20 m.

Solution

(a) The minimum fluidization velocity has been calculated for the solid in Chapter 3 to be $v_{min} = 1.1 \times 10^{-3} \, m/s$.

(b) Set operating fluidization velocity as $1.5 v_{min}$ (equation (8.30)). Operating fluidization velocity $= 1.65 \times 10^{-3} \, m/s$.

(c) Estimate width of conveyor from equation (8.31) and the data of Singh et al. [43]. For the data of Singh et al., equation (8.31) becomes

$$150 = K(60/2630)^{0.5}$$

For the alumina conveyor

$$b = 150[(30/1300)/(60/2630)]^{0.5}$$
$$= 151 \, mm$$

An alternate method of estimating b is from Table 8.4 as follows:

voidage at minimum fluidization $= 0.4$

$$\text{bulk density of solid} = (1 - 0.4) \times 1300 = 780 \, kg/m^3$$
$$\text{capacity of conveyor} = (30 \times 1000)/780 = 38 \, m^3/h$$

From Table 8.4, conveyor width, $b = 158 \, mm$. Thus the results from the two different calculations are similar. For design, specify $b = 150 \, mm$.

(d) Estimate height of fluidized bed, H. As discussed in Section 8.8.2.3, no reliable equations are available for estimating H. An arbitrary value of 0.12 m is taken here as the design value for H.

(e) Estimate pressure drop across fluidized bed. From equation (8.34),

$$\Delta p_{bed} = 780 \times 9.81 \times 0.12 = 0.9 \, kPa$$

(f) Specify Δp across distributor of bed to be 0.5 times pressure drop across the bed:

$$\Delta p_{distributor} = 0.5 \times 0.9 = 0.45 \, kPa$$

(g) Estimate pressure of delivered air:

delivered pressure $= 0.9 \, \text{kPa} + 0.45 \, \text{kPa} + \text{line pressure loss}$

(h) Estimate air requirement

$$\dot{Q} = vbL$$
$$= 1.65 \times 10^{-3} \times 0.150 \times 20$$
$$= 5.0 \times 10^{-3} \, \text{m}^3/\text{s}$$

(i) Assume angle of inclination to be $2°$ as the solid belongs to Geldart type A with good flow properties.

REFERENCES

1. Matsen, J.M. (1973) *Powder Technology*, **7**, 93–6.
2. Richards, J.C. (1964) *British Coal Utilities Research Association Monthly Bulletin*, **28**, 465–80.
3. Holtkamp, W.C.A., Kelly, F.T. and Shingles, T. (1977) *Chemistry in South Africa*, March, 44–6.
4. Knowlton, T.M. (1979) *National Science Foundation Workshop on Fluidization and Fluid Particle Systems – Research Needs and Priorities* (ed. H. Littman), Rensselaer Polytechnic Institute.
5. Teo, C.S. and Leung, L.S. (1982) *Journal Pipelines*, **2**, 187–97.
6. Leung, L.S. and Jones, P.J. (1978) in *Fluidization* (eds J.F. Davidson and D.L. Keairns), Cambridge University Press, Cambridge, pp. 116–21.
7. Kojabashian, C. (1958) Properties of dense phase fluidized solids in vertical downflow, *Ph.D. Thesis*, Massachusetts Institute of Technology.
8. Knowlton, T.M. Hirsan, I. and Leung, L.S. (1978) in *Fluidization* (eds J.F. Davidson and D.L. Keairns), Cambridge University Press, Cambridge, pp. 128–33.
9. Leung, L.S. and Jones, P.J. (1978) *Powder Technology*, **20**, 145–60.
10. Hinze, J.O. (1962) *Appl. Sci. Res. Section A*, **11**, 33–46.
11. Yoon, S.M. and Kunii, D. (1970) *Ind. Eng. Chem. Process Design and Development*, **9**, 559–66.
12. Richardson, J.F. and Zaki, W.N. (1954) *Trans. Inst. Chem. Engrs*, **32**, 33–53.
13. Do, D.D., Jones, P.J., Leung, L.S. and Matsen, J.M. (1977) in *Proc. Particle Technology, Nuremberg*, (eds H. Brauer and O. Molerus), D23–46.
14. Massimilla, L., Betta, V. and Della Rocca, C.D. (1961) *AIChE J.*, **7**, 502–8.
15. Jones, D.R.M. and Davidson, J.F. (1965) *Rheol. Acta*, **4**, 180–92.
16. deJong, J.A.H. and Hoelen, Q.E.J.J.M. (1975), *Powder Technology*, **12**, 201–8.
17. Judd, M.R. and Dixon, P.D. (1976) The flow of fine dense solids down a vertical standpipe, Paper presented at AIChE Annual Meeting, Chicago, December.
18. Teo, C.S. (1985) A theoretical and experimental study of gas–solid flow in standpipes, *Ph.D. Thesis*, University of Queensland.
19. Jones, P.J. (1981) Downflow of gas–solid mixtures in bottom restrained vertical standpipes, *Ph.D. Thesis*, University of Queensland.

20. Judd, M.R. and Rowe, P.N. (1978) in Fluidization (eds J.F. Davidson and D.L. Keairns), Cambridge University Press, Cambridge, pp. 110–15.
21. Ketchum, M.S. (1919) *The Design of Walls, Bins and Grain Elevators*, McGraw-Hill, New York, p. 323.
22. Rausch, J.M. (1958) Gravity flow of solid beds in vertical towers, *PhD. Thesis*, Princeton University.
23. Beverloo, W.A., Leniger, H.A. and van de Velde, J. (1961) *Chem. Eng. Sci.*, **15**, 260–6.
24. Zenz, F.A. (1976) in *Fluidization Technology*, Vol. 2 (eds D.L. Keairns *et al.*) Hemisphere Publishiing, Washington, pp. 239–52.
25. McGougale, I.R. and Evans, A.C. (1966) *Trans. Inst. Chem. Engrs*, **44**, T15–T24.
26. Altiner, H.K. and Davidson, J.F. (1980) in *Fluidization* (eds J.R. Grace and J.M. Matsen), Plenum Press, New York, pp. 461–8.
27. Pullen, R.J.F. (1974) Studies of solids flowing downwards from a hopper through vertical pipes, *Ph.D. Thesis*, University of Leeds.
28. Shook, C.A., Carleton, A.J. and Flain, R.J. (1980) *Trans. Inst. Chem. Engrs*, **48**, T173–5.
29. Leung, L.S., Jones, P.J. and Knowlton, T.M. (1978) *Powder Technology*, **19**, 7–15.
30. Knowlton, T.M. Hirsan, I. (1978) *Hydrocarbon Process*, **57**, 149–56.
31. Liu, D.L., Li, X.G. and Kwauk, M.S. (1980) in *Fluidization* (eds J.R. Grace and J.M. Matsen), Plenum Press, New York, pp. 485–92.
32. Chong, Y.O., Teo, C.S. and Leung, L.S. (1986) *Powder Technology*, in press.
33. Leung, L.S. (1980) in *Fluidization* (eds J.R. Grace and J.M. Matsen), Plenum Press, New York, pp. 25–68.
34. Ledinegg, M. (1938) Unstabilitat der Stromung bei naturlichem und zwangumlauf, *Die Warme*, **61**, No. 48, 891–8.
35. Rangachari, S. and Jackson, R. (1982) *Powder Technology*, **31**, 185–96.
36. Chen, Y.M., Rangachari, S. and Jackson, R. (1984) *Ind. Eng. Chem. Fundamentals*, **23**, 354–70.
37. Jones, P.J., Teo, C.S. and Leung, L.S. (1980) in *Fluidization* (eds J.R. Grace and J.M. Matsen), Plenum Press, New York, pp. 469–76.
38. Jones, P.J. and Leung, L.S. (1985) in *Multiphase Science and Technology Series*, Vol. 2 (G.F. Hewitt, J.M. Delhaye and N. Zuber), Hemisphere Publishing, Washington, Chapter 5.
39. Keunecke, K. (1965) *VDI Forsch.*, **509**, 34–9.
40. Botterill, J.S.M. and Bessant, D.J. (1976) *Powder Technology*, **14**, 131–7.
41. Geldart, D. (1973) *Powder Technology*, **7**, 285–90.
42. Leitzel, R. E. (1978) *Proceedings of Pneumotransport 4*, BHRA Fluid Engineering, Cranfield D3.41–D3.51.
43. Singh, B., Calcott, T.G. and Rigby, G.R. (1978) *Powder Technology*, **20**, 99–113.
44. Woodcock, C.R. (1978) The flow of particulate bulk solids in air-assisted gravity conveyor, *Ph.D. Thesis*. Thames Polytechnic, London.
45. Isler, W. (1960) *Zement-Kalk-Gips*, **13**, No. 10, 482–6.
46. Botterill, J.S.M. and Abdul-Halim, B.H. (1979) *Powder Technology*, **23**, 67–8.
47. Woodcock, C.R. and Mason, J.S. (1976) *Proceedings of Pneumotransport 3*, BHRA Fluid Engineering, Cranfield E1.1–E1.16.
48. Woodcock, C.R. and Mason, J.S. (1978) *Proceedings of Pneumotransport 4*, BHRA Fluid Engineering, Cranfield D2.23–D2.40.
49. Mason, J.S. (1985), private communication.
50. Futer, E. (1969) *Mech. Eng.*, April, 21–3.
51. Stegmaier, W. (1978) *J. Powder Bulk Solids Technol.*, **2**, No. 1, 47–55.

9

An overview of high pressure systems including long distance and dense phase pneumatic conveying systems

9.1 INTRODUCTION

The recent surge in interest in dense phase and long distance pneumatic conveying has stimulated vendors to develop a number of new systems specially directed towards increasing their market share in bulk materials handling. The proliferation of such systems has met with varied success and in many situations a basic lack in understanding of the flow phenomena has resulted in inappropriate solutions being offered for a particular handling problem.

Of significance however, is the fact that researchers have yet to produce some theoretical base for the design of high pressure systems. The vendors have apparently got themselves into a situation where it is almost imperative for each company to have some unique 'plug' forming device in their stable. Those organizations who do not have access to such technologies are seen to be deficient in their expertise. Whilst there is no question of the fact that many of these systems provide the end user with significant advantages in terms of increased throughput, lower energy consumption, minimal particle degradation, ability to transport over distance in excess of 1000 metres etc., the question does arise as to whether the added cost of specialized hardware is always justified. In many situations, conventional pneumatic conveying systems suffice. (See Section 7.6.6.6.)

Whilst there is a dearth of adequate theoretical background to facilitate the design of high pressure systems, it is expedient to link some of the theoretical concepts presented in Chapter 4 with some experimental observations reported in the literature. This chapter has been written in an attempt to provide the reader with an additional insight into high pressure pneumatic conveying technology, from the viewpoint of practical experiences and relevant experimental observations.

9.2 HIGH PRESSURE SYSTEMS

The feeding of high pressure pneumatic conveying systems is fully described in Chapter 7. The prime reasons for moving towards the use of higher pressures lie firstly in the need to reduce the energy required to transport materials pneumatically, secondly to facilitate the transport of bulk materials over distances in excess of 1000 metres, and thirdly to handle delicate friable products.

The effectiveness of employing higher pressures to minimize energy consumption and minimize product degradation is well documented [1,2,3]. From studies conducted on a range of materials [1] it has been shown that much benefit can be obtained by imposing a higher initial pressure to a blow vessel system before opening the discharge valve (Fig. 7.28). The same studies [1] allude to the ability to upgrade an existing system (by increasing the discharge rate attainable or by increasing the conveying distance) by simply increasing the initial pressure in the blow vessel.

The transportation of materials at 'low' velocities implies the use of special features in terms of bypass pipes, special pressure sensing valves and the like (Section 7.6.6). By virtue of the fact that most of these systems rely on the product being conveyed as discrete plugs, the increased friction due to the plugs requires the use of higher pressures.

Long distance conveying, albeit in the dilute phase, also requires the necessary hardware to operate at high pressures. The automatic linking of high pressures to dense phase is thus a misnomer.

9.3 DENSE PHASE FLOW CLASSIFICATION

Whilst the definition of dense phase pneumatic conveying is based on an arbitrary solids load ratio $\mu > 30$ (Chapter 1), a more appropriate definition lies in the use of the state diagram (Section 6.2). It is expedient to define all flow conditions, in which the gas velocity v is below the saltation velocity, as being dense phase flow.

The dense phase flow regime can be further subdivided into three distinct regions [4]:

(a) Continuous dense phase where the material moves by saltation over a stable creeping bed.

(b) Discontinuous dense phase where particles move as groups or clusters; this region is sometimes referred to as:

pulse phase for granular products
plug phase for powdery products

(c) Solid phase where the solids are extruded through the pipe as a continuous slug.

Experimental results [2,3] suggest that the advantages of dense phase conveying can be maximized by reducing the conveying velocity as much as possible. However, solid phase conveying is generally limited to shorter pipes and granular materials [5]. As such, at present, maximum effort by vendors is being directed towards marketing systems which operate in the discontinuous phase regime.

9.4 A DESCRIPTION OF PLUG FLOW AND THE RELATIONSHIPS BETWEEN PLUG FLOW AND MATERIAL CHARACTERISTICS

A visual description of the flow in the discontinuous phase region has been presented by various researchers [6, 7, 8]. For all materials tested, as the gas flow rate was reduced, the following flow patterns were observed:

(a) The strands characteristic of continuous dense phase conveying changed into moving dunes or balls.

(b) The formation of discrete plugs eventually filling the entire cross section of the pipe.

During dune conveying, the efficiency is lowered by the re-acceleration of the individual particles through the solid mass. In contrast, wall friction causes the dominant energy loss during plug conveying. As such, since plug formation is the limiting case of discontinuous flow, the high operating pressures are generated by the increased wall friction.

The transient nature of discontinuous flow makes it virtually impossible to accurately predict the onset of plug formation. A plug could, for example, be formed in the dune conveying regime due to the collision of dunes of different size and velocity. This problem exists even in cases where plugs are well defined, since during conveying plug dimensions are found to vary considerably.

In a survey of existing theories and experimental investigations, it was found [9] that the material properties, and specifically the particle size distribution, has a significant bearing on plug flow behaviour. Most investigators [9] use as their datum the plugging of cohesionless material with similarly sized particles. Such materials provide experimental results which are qualitatively consistent with simple theory.

Konrad *et al.* [10] derived an equation to quantify the pressure drop required to move an isolated plug in a horizontal pipe. For a cohesionless material the equation [10] reduces to:

$$\frac{\Delta p}{L} = \frac{4\beta_\omega \lambda_\omega \rho_b}{D} + 2\rho_B g \beta_\omega \qquad (9.1)$$

where β_ω is the coefficient at wall friction, λ_ω is the ratio of axial to radial stress at the wall and ρ_B is the solid bulk density.

An implication of the analysis of Konrad *et al.* [10] is the fact that the pressure drop across a plug is proportional to the plug length; this observation was independently verified by Dickson *et al.* [11] and Lilly [12] for glass beads, polyethylene granules, aluminium spheres and a relatively fine powder—

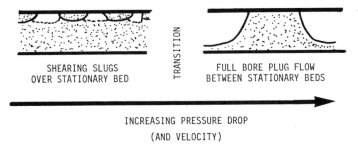

SHEARING SLUGS
OVER STATIONARY BED

TRANSITION

FULL BORE PLUG FLOW
BETWEEN STATIONARY BEDS

INCREASING PRESSURE DROP
(AND VELOCITY)

Figure 9.1 Flow transition at low velocity.

bentonite. The linear dependence of the pressure drop on the solid bulk density as described by Konrad *et al.* [10] was verified by Lilly [12].

Experimental observations [13,14,15] for uniform cohesionless materials indicate that the discrete moving plugs are separated by a stationary bed of particles which are deposited and then swept up by successive plugs. The acceleration of the stationary particles manifests itself as a forward stress, and thus increases the pressure drop. However, for a constant bed height, plug velocity and conveying rate, the theory predicts that the pressure drop is independent of plug length. Furthermore, uniform cohesionless material is reported to plug naturally (Section 7.6.6.6).

Natural plug formation implies that no special equipment is required to effectively convey this type of material in the discontinuous phase. In such situations, the pipe diameter must be chosen so as to limit the sum of plug lengths and hence the overall pressure drop in the pipe.

Visual observations [14] have indicated that if the gas velocity reduced to below a certain point, the material transport changes from 'full bore' plug flow, to the shearing of small product slugs over a large stationary bed (Fig. 9.1). It was further observed [14] that optimum efficiency was measured at the transition point between the two flow patterns. Implicit in this observation is that the lowest velocity at which material flows as a 'plug' throughout the pipeline is the 'optimum' velocity.

Not all materials are either uniform or cohesiveless, and Krambrock and Parekh [16] report, for a fine powder, an almost exponential dependence of the pressure drop on the plug length (Fig. 9.2).

The authors [16] found that above a critical length, the plug becomes immovable as the wall friction increases at a greater rate than the propulsive force. Similar observations for powders ($d \leqslant 66\,\mu$m) were reported by Lippert [7], which resulted in the development of various devices to limit the length of plugs.

The literature indicates an apparent discrepancy in the results observed by various researchers. A possible solution to the confusion has been provided by Wilson [17] who included the effects of stress on deformation within the plug. The deformation would effect the permeability of the plug, and hence the pressure

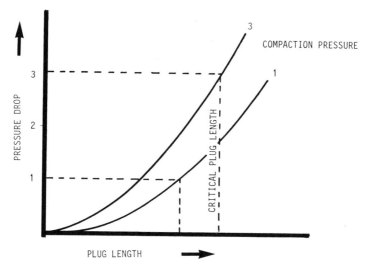

Figure 9.2 Pressure drop across a plug (fine powder).

gradient and stresses along its length. It was concluded [17] that the independent variables like plug length, pipe diameter and material properties could be reduced to the two basic independent parameters:

(a) Λ, 'a dimensionless measure of plug length'.
(b) W, 'an indicator of the fractional change in fluid pressure gradient with respect to the logarithms of the particulate normal stress'.

Thus, for a material like the glass beads used by Dickson *et al.* [11], which are nominally incompressible, $W = 0$; this would result in a linear pressure gradient whereas for a fine powder, a non-linear dependence of pressure drop on plug length is possible. The simpler conceptual model shown in Fig. 9.3 illustrates the importance of permeability in determining the pressure drop.

The model depicted in Fig. 9.3 can be illustrated by considering a sufficiently long plug of fine powder which has been rendered effectively impermeable through compaction. Because the aerodynamic drag on the individual particles would be negligible, the pressure drop would have to be sustained structurely by the individual particles. This is analogous to a plug moved entirely by mechanical means as described by Dickson *et al.* [11].

The model can be extended to take into account the performance of a material such as soda ash which is known to plug very easily when transported from a normal bottom discharge blow vessel system. The material is characterized by a wide particle size distribution. When a long plug forms, the small particles are driven between the large particles, reducing the permeability and decreasing the apparent wedge angle. The resulting fixed plug can often be moved only through reverse pressurization.

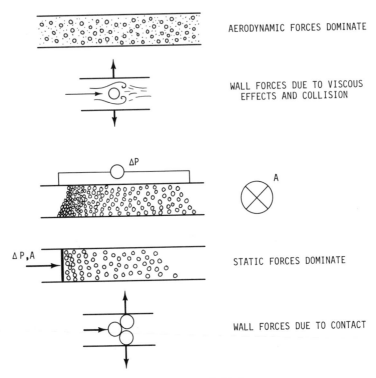

AERODYNAMIC FORCES DOMINATE

WALL FORCES DUE TO VISCOUS
EFFECTS AND COLLISION

STATIC FORCES DOMINATE

WALL FORCES DUE TO CONTACT

Figure 9.3 Effect of permeability on wall friction.

Wilson [17] reports that even for the materials exhibiting a non-linear pressure drop dependence on plug length, during successful conveying, the pressure drop is proportional to the plug length. This observation was confirmed by Tsuji and Morikawa [18] who observed that the pressure drop across a moving plug is less than that across a packed bed of the same particles. Evidently, turbulence and vibration prevents the terminal wedging of the conveyed particles.

Fine materials like cement, pulverized coal and fly ash, which are known to be successfully conveyed in the dense phase [19], can tolerate dune and plug formation without blockage. The property of these materials to fluidize easily suggests that the void fraction in the dunes is high, so that a certain amount of compression is possible before the particles wedge together to form an immovable plug.

The behaviour of a plug is often influenced by factors which resist mathematical analysis, requiring carefully controlled experimentation. For example the effect of particle shape on the pressure drop depends not only on the geometry of the individual particles, but also on their mutual orientation, etc.

9.5 SYSTEM SELECTION AND PRODUCT CHARACTERISTICS

In Section 7.6.6, a number of specialized systems specifically designed to promote discontinuous dense phase conveying were described. In particular, the hardware required to effect conveying in this flow regime was categorized according to three modes of operation:

(a) Gas injection or rejection systems.
(b) Plug forming systems.
(c) Defensive systems.

The effective selection of an appropriate system is normally dependent upon the characteristics of the product to be conveyed. Although characteristics like cohesiveness and friability may be considered in specialized applications (e.g. transporting carbon black), mean particle size and size distribution criteria are fundamentally important for effective selection.

In Fig. 9.4 a qualitative basis for the selecting of discontinuous dense phase systems is presented. Products in zone 3 conform to those which are relatively large and of a similar size. These products will form plugs having a pressure drop proportional to their length, whether stationary or moving. Existing conventional feeding techniques (Chapter 7) can be used, and the gas and solid feed rate and pipe diameter must be simply optimized to achieve energy efficient conveying. Since the material cannot form an immovable plug, the system can be

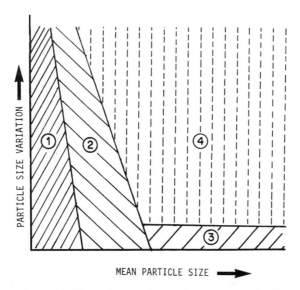

Figure 9.4 Discontinuous dense phase system selection.

stopped at any time and restarted without the need for a separate mechanism to break-up blockages.

Very fine powders like baking flour fall into zone 1 and can also be successfully conveyed using conventional equipment. The fluidization characteristics of the material facilitate the ability to transport such products at relatively high solids loading ratios. Even at high solids loadings, the stationary bed is small. However, if a plug is given any chance to form by either increasing the solids loading until the formation of a significant bed, or in the advent of a power failure or premature shutdowns, the resulting plug may be immovable. As such, a conventional system transporting such products may not achieve the desired reliability.

Ubiquitous materials like fly ash and pulverized coal lie near the border of zones 1 and 2. Whilst these products often exhibit favourable dense phase conveying characteristics, they often settle and create unstable slugging. Such materials are also relatively impermeable and could be expected to form immovable plugs. The key to promoting high solids loadings appears to be the promotion of fluidization. If the interstitial spacing is sufficient, the pressure drop across a fluidized plug would not be transmitted directly to the walls, leading to substantial energy savings. Furthermore, the pressure drop would be proportional to the plug length. Successful systems utilizing this approach include the bypass and turbo flow designs (Section 7.6.6.2).

Materials falling into zone 4 have a relatively large mean size as well as a wide particle size distribution. These materials are considered to be problematic for dense phase conveying. In a typical dense phase conveying situation, the fine particles will remain suspended in the gas stream, whilst the larger particles form an unstable bed. Further reduction of the gas velocity results in the formation of a plug consisting primarily of the large particles. This plug acts as a filter on the percolating air and the fine particles join the interstitial spaces, eventually blocking the pipe as a result of significantly altering the permeability. The fluidization/turbulence systems (Section 7.6.6.2) can also work successfully in this case, but the primary effect is not fluidization, but preventing particles packing together for any length of time, therefore avoiding exponential pressure drops and resulting blockage.

If the material to be conveyed is unusually cohesive, a plug forming system will yield good results. Although the pressure drop across a plug of fine material may be an exponential function of the plug length, the plug forming devices are so arranged as to limit the plug lengths to 0.3–0.4 metres long. By limiting the lengths of the plugs, pressure losses of acceptable magnitude are maintained. Normally the stationary bed between slugs is relatively small resulting in small forward stresses. As the plugs are relatively impermeable, they remain separated even over long conveying distances.

In constrast, these plug forming systems also appear to convey granular, permeable products efficiently. However, the resulting plugs can degrade rapidly, and so they appear to offer little advantage over conventional systems over longer distances.

Defensive systems such as the Pneumosplit and Fluidschub (Section 7.6.6.5) destroy plugs when they form. This usually constrains the system to operate in the strand or dune regime which appears to be less efficient than plug phase conveying. On the other hand, these defensive systems are applicable to materials having unusual properties and requirements. An example is unusually sticky materials, which tend to clump together in unpredictable manners. Such materials cannot be relied on to fluidize regularly, and can easily lead to clogging bypass pipes, so that a system which adds gas seems to be essential.

Whilst an attempt has been made to highlight the features of the various low velocity systems and to relate these features to specific characteristics of the product itself, it should be noted that at this stage the fundamentals of low velocity conveying still remain relatively unknown. Vendors of equipment are gaining more experience with a wider range of products and many preconceived ideas, as to which product is best suited to a particular mode of transport, are being shattered. Many claims are being made as to the effectiveness of certain systems, and the end user is cautioned to ensure that the selection of a system is based on a sound evaluation of the special features a particular system purports to have. In particular, perhaps the most common debate amongst vendors is not so much the lower velocity aspect, but more the low energy requirements for such systems. Ultimately an accurate assessment of the total energy consumption will facilitate the selection of an appropriate system.

Whilst many specialized systems operate at low velocities, there can be a correspondingly higher pressure requirement which, in some cases, offsets the benefits which can be derived from the lower velocity.

One undisputed feature of any of the systems described above is the ability to restart a system in the advent of a power failure. To many operators, this feature is singularly more important than any other feature.

9.6 DENSE PHASE SYSTEM DESIGN

Whilst there are continuous efforts being made to produce an adequate theoretical model for the design of dense phase conveying systems, very few researchers have been able to predict theoretical results which can compare with experimental evidence.

Weber [20] has produced an empirical correlation which has been shown to produce reasonable approximations to actual experimental results. The analysis of Weber is discussed in Section 4.24.

Using Weber's [20] analysis from equation (4.113),

$$p_1 = p_2 \exp\left(\frac{\beta \mu g L}{RT\ c/v}\right) \tag{9.2}$$

It has been found experimentally [20] that for most loose materials, β varies between 0.4 and 0.8, with a mean value $\beta = 0.6$.

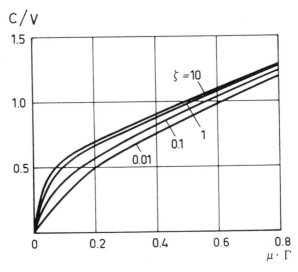

Figure 9.5 Relationship between c/v and $\mu\Gamma$.

Experimental data from actual dense phase systems indicate that the slip velocity ratio c/v depends upon the solids loading ratio μ, and two terms Γ and ζ as shown in Fig. 9.5 Now Γ is defined as

$$\Gamma = 0.5(\rho_1 + \rho_2)/\rho_B \tag{9.3}$$

where $0.5(\rho_1 + \rho_2)$ is the mean gas density, ρ_b is the bulk density of the solids and

$$\zeta = 4\lambda_Z^* B(Fr^5)\Gamma/(\pi\beta Fr_f) \tag{9.4}$$

From experimental results it has been found that

$$\lambda_Z^* \simeq 0.75 \qquad \beta \simeq 0.6 \qquad B \simeq 10^{-3}$$

From which

$$\zeta = 1.6 \times 10^{-3} Fr^5 \Gamma/Fr_f \tag{9.5}$$

Note that $Fr_f = w_f/(Dg)^{1/2}$.

Large values of ζ occur for the transport of fine powders with particle sizes in the range $10\,\mu m \leqslant d \leqslant 100\,\mu m$ at normal pressure and at air velocities in the range 10 m/s to 15m/s. Small values are encountered for the same products transported in the same pipe diameters but operating at pressures of several atmospheres, and velocities from 3 to 6 m/s. (A worked example using the above technique is presented in Chapter 14.)

Table 9.1 Experimental observations obtained from various dense phase systems [8]

No.	Material	L (m)	Z (m)	D (mm)	$\dot{G}$ (t/h)	$\dot{V}$ (m³/h)	Δp (kPa)	v (m/s)	$Fr(\Gamma)^{1/2}$	$\mu\Gamma$	μ	c/v	ρ_P (kg/m³)	ρ_B (kg/m³)
1	Cement raw meal	146	—	36	1.4	11.5	200	3.15	0.25	0.25	102	0.88	2690	1000
2	PAN powder	150	—	36	1.2	19	140	3.95	0.40	0.20	53	0.59	1190	500
3	Soda	200	30	100	35	1050	250	18	0.95	0.08	28	0.29	2030	1000
4	SiO$_2$ Filling material	30	—	65	4	100	30	7.3	0.89	0.30	33	0.25	2650	150
5	Moist sand	120	—	100	19.5	300	350	3.75	0.2	0.13	54	0.28	1800	1350
6	SiO$_2$ Filling material	58	—	70	1.4	30	14	2.1	0.175	0.2	39	1.12	2650	270
7	SiO$_2$ Filling material	10	—	70	1	29	2.3	2.25	0.175	0.13	29	0.83	2650	270
8	Organic product	37	1.5	66	4.1	63	70	3.6	0.2	0.12	54	0.25	1000	700
9	Soda	25	—	65	20	200	30	13	0.6	0.12	83	0.51	2030	1000
10	Light ash	1200	15	200	50	4000	350	13	0.5	0.12	10	0.52	2350	1200
11	PVC powder	115	20	70	7	240	65	13.5	0.9	0.03	24	0.36	1370	500
12	Rock salt (flexible pipe)	26	2	50	5.8	110	80	11	0.55	0.07	44	0.13	2200	1400
13	Organic product	6.5	—	20	0.4	8	17	6.5	0.70	0.05	41	0.11	1000	600
14	Organic product	25	10	70	17	300	120	13	0.95	0.10	47	0.10	1000	500
15	Alumina	130	15	100	8	300	250	5	0.35	0.17	22	0.15	2480	800
16	Powder for plastics	300	—	100	10	310	150	6.8	0.53	0.12	27	0.57	1050	350

In Table 9.1, experimental observations from several dense phase systems are presented. Note that

L = horizontal length of system
Z = vertical height
D = pipe diameter
$\dot{G}$ = solids mass flow rate
$\dot{V}$ = air volumetric flow rate
Δp = pressure drop across the total system
v = air velocity
Fr = Froude number
μ = solids loading ratio
ρ_p = actual particle density
ρ_B = bulk density of the solids

9.7 LONG DISTANCE PNEUMATIC CONVEYING AND PRESSURE LOSS MINIMIZATION

9.7.1 Introduction

To date, long distance pneumatic conveying systems have been widely accepted in the mining industry [21, 22] as a viable method of transporting building materials to underground workings. In many instances the technology has developed such that a complex of computer controlled batching stations with interconnecting pipe work is common place in many German coal mines. In some mines [23] piping systems in excess of 40 km have been installed connecting surface storage facilities to a multitude of tandem blow vessel systems located at storage stations underground. Single conveying loops in excess of 3500 metres long including a 1000 metre vertical drop are typical of such systems [23].

Whilst the main emphasis in the mining applications is the reliable transport of essential materials to the underground workings, little cognisance has been taken of the power consumption in these long distance systems.

Based on some information obtained from the mining systems, it would appear that the power consumed in these operations is excessive. As such, long distance pneumatic conveying systems have thus far received limited acceptance in industrial operations.

An essential element in the design of such long distance systems is the piping layout. Little work has been done on methods of sizing the piping system to ensure optimum performance of the system. What is known however, is that the piping systems can have a significant influence on the performance of a long distance pneumatic conveying system [24]. In addition, it has also been ascertained that most vendors use arbitrary methods of selecting the piping layout.

Table 9.2 Results on the conveying of dry gold slime

Parameter	Symbol	Unit	System 1	System 2	System 3	System 4
Volume of pressure vessels	V	m³	1 × 2	1 × 2	1 × 2	1 × 2
Conveying pipe length	ΔL	m	270	570	1037	1600 (900/700)
Number of diameter changes	S	—	0	0	0	1
Pipe diameter	D	mm	150	150	150	150/200
Air alone pressure loss	Δp_L	kPa	50	79	93	102
Maximum pressure loss with product	Δp	kPa	250	300	390	300
Maximum mass flow of solids	$\dot{G}$	t/h	30	28	22	24
Air mass flow	$\dot{Q}$	t/h	2.86	4.31	4.78	3.16
Solids loading ratio	μ	—	10.5	6.5	4.6	7.6
Initial air velocity	v_α	m/s	15.5	19.3	16.7	14.2
Final air velocity	v_ω	m/s	75.3	68.3	75.8	28.3
Froude number at inlet	Fr_α	—	12.3	15.9	13.8	11.7
Froude number at exit	Fr_ω	—	37.4	56.4	62.6	20.2

Whilst each supplier recognizes the need to use a stepped piping system, there appears to be little logic in deciding when to effect an increase in pipe diameter and further what such an increase should be. An important factor which is continuously stressed by the equipment suppliers is the relative initial costs of larger diameter piping when compared to smaller diameters and the need to bear in mind that ultimately the single most costly item in these systems is the piping.

The influence of the piping layout on the performance of a long distance system was highlighted in a series of tests carried out on the conveying of dry gold slime [24]. Results from these studies are shown in Table 9.2.

Referring to Table 9.2 and comparing systems 3 and 4, it can be seen that the introduction of a stepped pipe has a significant influence on the system performance. It can be seen that it is possible to obtain a slightly higher conveying rate (24 t/h, cf. 22 t/h) by increasing the pipe length from 1037 metres to 1600 metres by introducing a diameter change after 900 metres from $D = 150$ mm to $D = 200$ mm. Other important observations indicate that the inclusion of the stepped pipe (system 4) facilitates a lower system pressure loss ($\Delta p = 300$ kPa) when compared to the shorter single diameter pipeline (system 3) where the system pressure loss at a slightly reduced solids flow rate was ($\Delta p = 390$ kPa). Further, the discharge velocity in the stepped pipeline $v = 28.3$ m/s is considerably lower than that for the single diameter pipe $v = 75.8$ m/s—an important consideration when transporting highly abrasive products.

9.7.2 Design considerations—critical length

It is a well known fact that the throughput of a pneumatic conveying system, operating with a single diameter pipeline, is critically dependent upon the length of the pipeline. The system throughput decays almost exponentially with length as shown conceptually in Fig. 9.6. Extensive tests carried out on ordinary Portland Cement [25] clearly demonstrate this phenomenon (Fig. 9.7).

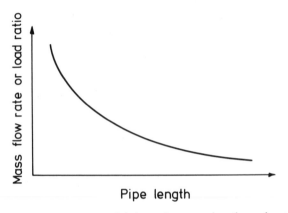

Figure 9.6 Exponential decay in conveying throughput.

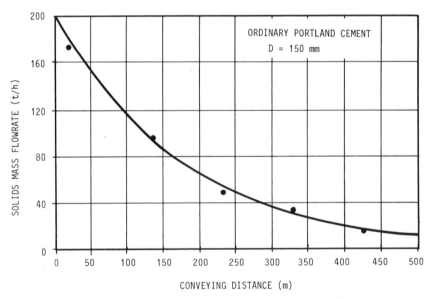

Figure 9.7 Throughput as a function of pipe length for ordinary Portland Cement.

Table 9.3

Material: anhydride, $d_{max} = 10\,mm$

Expression	Symbol	Dimension	Test number 1	2	3	4	5
Solids mass flow rate	$\dot{G}$	t/h	20	10	4.5	2	0.347
Air flow rate	$\dot{Q}$	t/h	3.5	3.5	3.5	3.5	3.5
Mass load ratio	μ	—	5.8	2.9	2.3	0.58	0.1
Pipe length	L	m	1000	1500	2000	2500	3000
Pipe internal diameter	D	mm	125	125	125	125	125
Pressure difference (max. available)	Δp_{max}	bar	3.3	3.3	3.3	3.3	3.3
Air coefficient	λ_L	—	0.0136	0.0136	0.0136	0.0136	0.0136
Solids coefficient	$\lambda_Z \times 10^3$	—	4.78	4.9	5.6	5.3	3
Max. air velocity	v_0	m/s	54.8	54.8	54.8	54.8	54.8
Initial air velocity	v_1	m/s	15.7	15.7	15.7	15.7	15.7
Mean air velocity	$\bar{v}$	m/s	35.2	35.2	35.2	35.2	35.2
Min. Froude number	Fr_{min}	—	14.2	14.2	14.2	14.2	14.2
Min. air density	ρ_0	kg/m³	1.43	1.43	1.43	1.43	1.43
Max. air density	ρ_1	kg/m³	5	5	5	5	5
Pressure drop ratio	$\Delta p_L/\Delta p_Z$	—	1:2	1:1	1:0.5	1:0.23	1:0.02
Dynamic pressure	p_{dyn1}	Pa	616.2	616.2	616.2	616.2	616.2

A more detailed analysis of this length dependency has been carried out using data published by Hunke [26], and using the various equations in Chapter 6, Table 9.3 has been drawn up. The tests [26] were conducted at a constant air flow rate ($\dot{Q} = 3500$ kg/h) whilst the solids mass flow rate was adjusted until the maximum available pressure drop ($\Delta p_{max} = 3.3$ bar) was attained. The decrease in system throughput with increasing pipe line length is clearly demonstrated and is shown graphically in Fig. 9.8. Clearly, the increase in pipe length results in more energy being required to convey the air through the system with correspondingly less blower power available to convey solids.

Increasing the length from 1000 metres to 3000 metres, leads to a reduction in the conveying rate from 20 t/h to 0.347 t/h—a reduction of 57 times. The results indicate that at 3000 metres, a critical length has been attained, for the particular conditions, at which the solids mass flow rate is virtually zero. Furthermore, the additional pressure drop factor λ_z rises slightly with the rapid decrease in the mass load ratio up to a certain point beyond which it falls off steeply. This critical point is highlighted in Fig. 9.9.

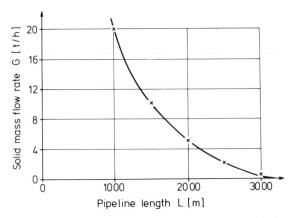

Figure 9.8 System throughput as a function of pipe length [26].

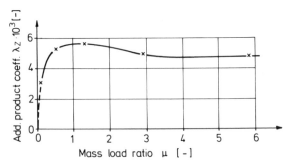

Figure 9.9 Variation of λ_z with mass load ratio.

An analysis of the pressure drop ratio indicates that for each additional 500 m length, the additional pressure drop is reduced to almost half of its initial value until the critical length is attained whereupon the reduction is about a factor of 10.

9.7.3 Design considerations—stepped pipe

Clearly, the use of a single diameter pipeline for long distance pneumatic conveying is unacceptable. The optimum use of a stepped pipeline facilitates the reduction in the total pressure loss for the gas alone, and hence renders more of the motive energy available for the transport of the solids.

Stepped pipes also facilitate some control on the conveying velocity resulting in some benefit in terms of particle degradation, wear and abrasion, etc.

The design process is based on dilute phase conditions. Fundamental to the design process is a knowledge of the minimum velocity at which the particles will be safely conveyed. The average particle velocity c can be estimated using equations from Section 4.11. However, it would be preferable to carry out some basic tests on the actual material making use of the techniques described in Chapter 6. It is also necessary to calculate the settling velocity using the state diagram or pressure minimum curve.

The basic design philosophy is based on the Froude number, Fr. The conveying gas will expand between two Froude numbers namely Fr_{min} and Fr_{max}. Once Fr_{max} is achieved, the pipe diameter should be increased. The appropriate selection of the diameter at the enlarged section is such that the conveying gas conditions on entering the enlargement should not fall below Fr_{min}.

The selection of the additional pressure loss coefficient is facilitated by the use of the appropriate λ_z–Fr–μ curves as described in Chapter 6.

A more refined technique using conditions of similarity is recommended in an attempt to attain the lowest possible pressure loss whilst minimizing the number of stages (Fig. 9.10). The technique is based on the λ_z vs Fr curve in which the mass load ratio μ is a parameter as shown in Fig. 9.10.

The curve demonstrates that for a single constant diameter straight conveying line, four or even more steps based on the Froude number can be selected. For each step, in the pipeline, the average λ_z coefficient can be chosen such that:

Step 1 lies between Fr_{min}–Fr_1–λ_{Z1}
Step 2 Fr_1–Fr_2–λ_{Z2}
Step 3 Fr_2–Fr_4–λ_{Z3}
Step 4 Fr_3–Fr_4–λ_{Z4}

The technique has been tested using limited reliable experimental data. Satisfactory results have been obtained albeit at this stage a lack of adequate data has limited the ability to finally verify all details of the theory. The technique has however been tested on full size commercial systems and has proved to be reliable.

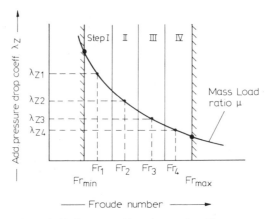

Figure 9.10 λ_Z versus Froude number Fr.

9.7.4 Design considerations—pipe length/pipe diameter ratio

Using the same marginal conditions as proposed in Fig. 6.22(a), (b), an investigation into the influence of the pipe length and pipe diameter has been carried out using data from full scale investigations [26]. The basic information from these tests is provided in Table 9.4. The evaluation of the results was carried out using the simplified equation (6.73), for an isothermal gas state. The tests were conducted using three different piping systems with diameters $D = 100$ mm, 125 mm and 150 mm, with pipe line lengths $\Delta L = 900$, 1320 and 1720 m respectively.

Assuming that the first test facility, $D = 100$ mm, $\Delta L = 900$ m is operating at optimum conditions, i.e. $Fr = 16.4$, the results (Table 9.4) indicate that in order to maintain a constant solids mass flow rate $\dot{G} = 15$ t/h at a constant pressure drop $\Delta p_{max} = 3.3$ bar, it is necessary to increase the air flow rate $\dot{Q}$ with increasing pipe diameter. The results stress the importance of being aware of the minimum Froude number Fr_{min}, which in this case is approximately $Fr_{min} = 16.5$.

For the second and third system, the increase in the ratio $\Delta L/D$ is in the proportions 1:1.17:1.27. Now, if the $\Delta L/D$ ratio was reduced to unity, the pressure loss for each system would be reduced by the same proportion.

Scaling up these system by maintaining a constant geometric ratio $\Delta L/D = 1$, and utilizing the additional energy for the conveying of solids, it is possible to obtain solids flow rates $\dot{G} = 21$ t/h and 27 t/h for the second and third systems. The corresponding mass load ratios are $\mu = 5.17$ and $\mu = 4.28$.

Implicit in this analysis is the fact that the second and third systems should have pipe lengths $\Delta L = 1128$ m and $\Delta L = 1354$ m respectively. These lengths would ensure maximum conveying rates at the marginal conditions.

Table 9.4

Expression	Symbol	Dimension	Test number		
			1	2	3
Solids mass flow rate	$\dot{G}$	t/h	15	15	15
Air flow rate	$\dot{Q}$	t/h	2.33	4.07	6.42
Mass load ratio	μ	—	6.5	3.7	2.3
Pipe length	ΔL	m	900	1320	1720
Pipe diameter	D	mm	100	125	150
Max. available pressure drop	Δp_{max}	bar	3.3	3.3	3.3
Min. air density	ρ_0	kg/m^3	1.43	1.43	1.43
Max. air density	ρ_1	kg/m^3	5	5	5
Max. air velocity	v_0	m/s	56.9	64.2	70.4
Initial air velocity	v_1	m/s	16.1	18.4	20.1
Mean air velocity	$\bar{v}$	m/s	36.5	41.3	45.3
Initial Froude number	Fr_α	—	16.4	16.6	16.6
Air coefficient	$\lambda_L \times 10^2$		1.42	1.3	1.2
Product coefficient	$\lambda_Z \times 10^3$		3.17	2.65	2.38
Pressure drop ratio	$\Delta p_L / \Delta p_Z$		1:1.45	1:0.75	1:0.46
Dynamic pressure	p_{dyn1}	Pa	656.1	846.4	1010
Geometrical ratio	$\Delta L / D$		9000	10560	11467
			1	1.17	1.27

9.7.5 Design considerations—influence of pipe diameter enlargements

In an attempt to highlight the various aspects discussed above, experimental tests carried out in a full size stepped pipe system will be analysed.

At the outset however, it should be noted that the minimum Froude number Fr_{min} on which all the analyses have been based is obtained experimentally and as such includes the influence of the acceleration of the solids. The proposed method is thus slightly optimistic and as such renders a 'safe' design.

It must be emphasized that the proposed design procedure recommends a change in pipe diameter once the maximum Froude number Fr_{max} is obtained. It should be noted that Fr_{max} is a function of the product and the conveying process. For example, for plastic materials Fr_{max} should correspond to that velocity before the formation of angel hairs (streamers).

In Table 9.5 experimental results obtained from a stepped pipe system over 2190 m are presented [26]. The analysis of the results has been based on the same simplifying assumptions used in the previous sections (Tables 9.3 and 9.4). Further, the influence of the acceleration at the feeder and the influence of the bends have not been considered.

Table 9.5

			Solids mass flow rate		
Solids mass flow rate			$\dot{G} = 15\,\text{t/h}$		
Air mass flow rate			$\dot{Q} = 2.33\,\text{t/h}$		
Mass load ratio			$\mu = 6.4$		
Available pressure drop			$\Delta p = 3.3\,\text{bar}$		

			Stage		
Expression	Symbol	Dimension	1	2	3
Pipe length	ΔL	m	107	1465	618
Pipe diameter	D	mm	100	125	150
Initial pressure	p_1	bar	3.99	3.68	1.78
Initial air density	ρ_1	kg/m³	4.6	4.3	2.1
Initial air velocity	v_α	m/s	17.6	12.1	17.26
Initial Froude number	Fr_α	—	17.8	11	14.26
Terminal pressure	p_0	bar	3.68	1.78	1.2
Terminal air density	ρ_0	kg/m³	4.3	2.1	1.43
Terminal air velocity	v_ω	m/s	19	24.8	25.6
Terminal Froude number	Fr_ω	—	19.2	22.5	21.1
Pressure difference/Stage	Δp	bar	0.31	1.9	0.58
Dynamic pressure	$p_{\text{dyn}1}$	Pa	712.4	314.8	312.8
Air coefficient	$\lambda_\text{L} \times 10^2$	—	1.7	1.6	1.5
Product coefficient	$\lambda_\text{Z} \times 10^3$	—	3.5	3.5	3.5
Integral coefficient	$\lambda \times 10^2$	—	3.94	3.84	3.74

Due to the lack of sufficient information, the results have been analysed using information from the previous examples from which a product factor $\lambda_\text{Z} = 3.4 \times 10^{-3}$ was obtained. It is clear that by lowering the Froude number Fr, an increase in the λ_Z factor is to be expected.

Using the available data and based on the above assumptions, the estimated pressure drop was found to be $\Delta p = 2.79$ bar. In terms of the basic assumptions this value is deemed to be acceptable when compared to the measured pressure drop $\Delta p_{\text{max}} = 3.3$ bar.

Assuming that the conditions presented in Table 9.4 for the 100 mm pipe are optimum, i.e. $Fr_{\text{min}} = 16.4$ and $\mu = 6.5$, then there is still enough margin for reducing the velocity or increasing the solids mass flow rate. The margin is approximately 8% when related to the velocity and about 15% when related to the pressure. As such, the correction leads to a mass load ratio $\mu = 7$.

A closer analysis of the results shown in Table 9.4 indicates that the whole question of acceleration of the solids needs to be addressed. In particular, it is evident that once the solids have been accelerated, the Froude number in the following enlarged pipe can be lower than that required for the feeding section.

In Table 9.5 it can be seen that the minimum Froude number in section 2 is

$Fr_{min} = 11$. This should be compared with section 1 in which $Fr_{min} = 17.8$ and section 3 in which the $Fr_{min} = 14.26$. The question arises as to whether the actual safe conveying velocity corresponds to $Fr_{min} = 11$. As such, it should be possible to convey the material in section 3 at a lower Froude number. With regard to section 1, the question of the acceleration of the solids still needs to be investigated. Ultimately the question arises as to whether in this particular system the minimum Froude number could be even less than 11.

9.8 CONCLUSIONS

An attempt has been made to consolidate some of the literature relevant to high pressure pneumatic conveying systems. Whilst there is no question of the fact that there are a large number of systems operating reliably throughout the world, the lack of any sound theoretical or empirical base is of concern.

A number of pointers have been suggested in an attempt to guide the reader towards some rational selection of an appropriate system and towards some design criteria for long distance piping systems.

REFERENCES

1. Lohrmann, P.C. and Marcus, R.D. (1984) Minimum energy pneumatic conveying II – dense phase, *J. Pipelines*, **4**, 123–9.
2. Jodlowski, C. (1984) Considerations on two phase gas/solid flow at low velocities, *Proc. Pneumatech II, Int. Conf. on Pneumatic Conveying* Technology, Powder Advisory Centre UK, September.
3. Hoppe, H. (1984) Gentle pneumatic transport of friable materials by means of modern conveying methods, *Proc. Pneumatech II, Int. Conf. on Pneumatic Conveying Technology*, Powder Advisory Centre UK, September.
4. Klintworth, J. and Marcus, R.D. (1985) A review of low velocity pneumatic conveying systems, *J. Bulk Solids Handling*, 747–54, August.
5. Shepherd, N. (1979) An investigation into the pneumatic transfer of fibrous and granular materials in the dense phase, *M.Sc. Dissertation*, Faculty of Engineering, University of Witwatersrand, Johannesburg, South Africa.
6. When, C.Y. and Simons, H. (1959) *AIChE J.*, **5**, 263–7.
7. Lippert, A. (1966) *Chem. Ing. Technol.*, **38**, 350–5.
8. Muschelknautz, E. and Krambrock, W. (1969) *Chem. Ing. Technol.*, **41**, 1164–72.
9. Flatt, W. (1980) Low velocity pneumatic conveying of granulated and pulverised products. Criteria for selecting the optimal pneumatic conveying system, Paper J3, *Proc. Pneumotransport 5*, BHRA Fluid Engineering, Cranfield, April.
10. Konrad, K., Harrison, D., Wedderman, R.M. and Davidson, J.F. (1980) *Proc. 5th Int. Conf. on The Pneumatic Transport of Solids in Pipes*, BHRA Fluid Engineering, Cranfield.
11. Dickson, A.J., Skews, B.W. and Marcus, R.D. (1978) Plug Phase Conveying, *Proc. 4th Int. Conf. on The Pneumatic Transport of Solids in Pipes*, BHRA Fluid Engineering, Cranfield.
12. Lilly, K. (1984) *M.Sc. Thesis*, Virginia Polytechnic Institute, Blacksbury, USA.

13. Konrad, K. and Davidson, J.F. (1984) *Powder Technology*, **39**, 191–8.
14. Hitt, R.J., Reed, A.R. and Mason, J.S. (1982) An investigation into two modes of slugging in dense phase horizontal pneumatic conveying, *Proc. Pneumatech I*, Powder Advisory Centre, UK.
15. Tomita, Y., Jotaki, T. and Hayashi, H. (1981) *Int. J. Multiphase Flow*, **7**, 151–66.
16. Krambrock, W. and Parekh, S. (1980) *Proc. 5th Int. Conf. on the Pneumatic Transport of Solids in Pipes*, BHRA Fluid Engineering, Cranfield.
17. Wilson, K.C. (1981) *Int. J. Bulk Solids Handling*, **1**, 295–9.
18. Tsuji, Y. and Morikawa, Y. (1982) *Int. J. Multiphase Flow*, **8**, 657–67.
19. Wypych, P.W. and Arnold, P.C. (1984) The use of powder and pipe properties in the prediction of dense phase pneumatic transport behaviour. *Proc. Pneumatech II*, Powder Advisory Centre, UK.
20. Weber, M. (1974) *Stromungs-Fordertechnik*, Krausskopf Verlag.
21. Cuerten, H.J. (1984) Industrial applications of long distance pneumatic conveying, *Proc. Pneumatech II*, Powder Advisory Centre, UK.
22. Clarke, I. (1982) Proposed methods of mechanized wide orebody stoping at depth in a South African gold mine, *Proc. 12th CMMI Congress*, (ed. H.W. Glen) pp. 403–16.
23. Heinrich Klockner Becorit Industrie, Heinrich Robert Coal Mine, Federal Republic of Germany.
24. Rizk, F. and Marcus, R.D. (1985) Einige Einflussgrossen Bei Der Langsftrecken – Pneuma – Forderung Von Fein – und Grobgut in Rohrleitungen, *Proc. Transmatic 85 Congress*, University of Karlsruhe, April.
25. Marcus, R.D. (1985) Cement discharge—Anglo Alpha cement, Internal Report, University of Witwatersrand, Johannesburg, Materials Handling Research Unit, January.
26. Hunke, H. (1982) Beitrug Zur Optimalen Auslegung Pneumatischer Fonderandlagen fur den Baustoff Naturanhydrit anhand von Betriebsuersuchen mit Grossen Forderlangen, *Dissertation*, Technical University Berlin.

10
Gas–solids separation

10.1 INTRODUCTION

One area which normally receives the least attention in the design of pneumatic conveying systems is that of the gas–solids separation system. Yet in many trouble shooting exercises, inadequate design in this area is often found to be the cause of unreliable plant operation or total failure. The gas–solids separation unit can have a profound influence on the performance of a system and is particularly critical in negative pressure and low pressure pneumatic conveying systems.

In particular the gas–solids separation unit has a bearing on:

(a) The overall pressure loss in the system.
(b) The possible loss of fines.
(c) Particle segregation.
(d) Particle breakdown.
(e) System cost.

Selection of a suitable system is governed primarily on the degree of separation required and the potential for the solids to create an environmental problem.

There are a number of techniques used for effecting gas–solids separation. Detailed theoretical consideration will not be discussed in this text; adequate references on the subject are available [1]. The most common techniques encountered in pneumatic conveying systems include cyclone separators, reverse jet filters, reverse flow filters, cartridge filters and mechanical shaking filters.

10.2 SELECTION CRITERIA

The selection of a suitable gas–solids separation unit is dependent on a number of factors and the following information is required to aid the selection process [2].

(a) Type of operation.
(b) Gas entrainment capacity (free gas delivered by the prime mover).
(c) Concentration of solids.
(d) Moisture and temperature of process and solids.
(e) Particle size distribution.
(f) Chemical properties of solids.

Table 10.1

Equipment	Percentage efficiency at		
	50 μm	5 μm	1 μm
Inertial collector	95	16	3
Medium efficiency cyclone	94	27	8
High efficiency cyclone	98	42	13
Shaker type fabric filter	>99	>99	99
Reverse jet fabric filter	100	>99	99

In addition to the above, other factors which must be considered include:

(g) The need for total recovery.
(h) Statutory requirements.
(i) Quality of the product.
(j) Intrinsic value of this product.
(k) Space availability for installation.

In terms of the appropriate selection of equipment, the efficiency of a dust collector system is defined as:

$$\eta_c = \frac{\rho_{c\alpha}^* - \rho_{c\omega}^*}{\rho_{c\alpha}^*} 100$$

where $\rho_{c\alpha}^*$ is the dust concentration in the dust laden gas and $\rho_{c\omega}^*$ is the dust concentration in the cleaned gas. Typically, the efficiency of gas cleaning equipment lies in the range $\eta_c > 99.98\%$. The efficiency of gas cleaning equipment at various particle sizes [3] is given in Table 10.1.

This definition of collector efficiency does not meet modern environmental pollution control legislation. Current thinking is to consider collection effectiveness in terms of the amount of material discharged into the atmosphere during a specified time period.

Example 10.1

A pneumatic conveying system is designed to transport 10 tonnes of solids per hour at a mass flow ratio $\mu = 10$. It is specified that a collector with a high efficiency must be installed.

Solution

Assume a collector efficiency $\eta_c = 99.98\%$. In terms of the conveying rate and the collector efficiency, the amount of dust discharging into the atmosphere will be $\dot{G} = 2$ kg/h yielding a dust concentration in the immediate vicinity of the

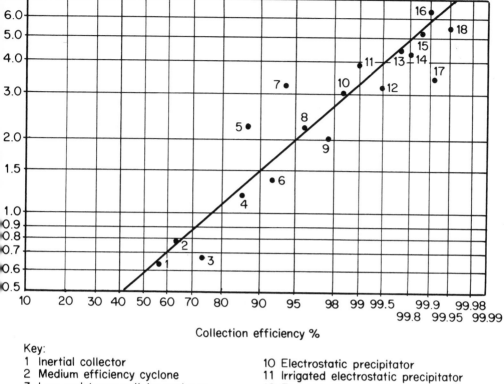

Key:
1 Inertial collector
2 Medium efficiency cyclone
3 Low resistance cellular cyclones
4 High efficiency cyclone
5 Impingement scrubber (Doyle type)
6 Self induced spray deduster
7 Void spray tower
8 Fluidised bed scrubber
9 Irrigated target scrubber (Peabody type)
10 Electrostatic precipitator
11 Irrigated electrostatic precipitator
12 Flooded-disc scrubber   low-energy
13 Flooded-disc scrubber   med.-energy
14 Venturi-scrubber   med.-energy
15 High-efficiency electrostatic precipitator
16 Venturi-scrubber   high-energy
17 Shaker-type fabric filter
18 Reverse-jet fabric filter

Figure 10.1 Relative costs of gas–solids separation systems.

collector $\rho_{c\omega}^{*} = 200\,\mathrm{mg/m^3}$ (taking the ambient air density $\rho = 1\,\mathrm{kg/m^3}$). Clearly, this emission rate is unacceptable and indicates the deficiency in the use of the above mentioned collector efficiency.

Modern environmental control laws of the type now in operation in West Germany (1985) classify the amount of emission permitted in terms of the characteristics of the dust itself. The legislation provides for categorizing the dust in terms of being harmful and harmless.

For harmless dusts, typical emission rates permitted for new installations allow a dust concentration of $150\,\mathrm{mg/m^3}$ for an emitted (cleaned gas) solid mass flow rate $\dot{G} \leqslant \mathrm{kg/h}$. Further, for a dust concentration of $75\,\mathrm{mg/m^3}$, the emitted solid mass flow rate is in the range $\dot{G} \geqslant \mathrm{kg/h}$.

The legislation for harmful dusts is far more stringent and requires even greater attention to the type of collector selected.

In terms of the relative costs for typical pneumatic conveying gas solids separation equipment, Fig. 10.1 is reproduced [3].

10.3 CYCLONE SEPARATORS—THEORY OF THE SEPARATION OF PARTICLES IN THE CENTRIFUGAL FIELD

In order to separate the particles in a flowing stream forces must be extended on them in a defined zone. These forces are gravitation, inertia and friction as well as electrostatic, adhesion and cohesion.

10.3.1 Separation in depositing chambers

This type of separation relies on the difference in densities of both media as well as the difference in velocities. In an expanded chamber (Fig. 10.2(a)) the gas velocity v is greatly reduced and taking the gravitational force into account, one can see that the larger particles will drop out earlier than the finer ones.

In an equilibrium state, the forces on a particle are the aerodynamic or drag force and the weight of the particle minus the air lifting force. Assuming that the particle has a spherical shape the balance of forces is as follows:

$$F_D = F_G - F_{lift} \tag{10.1}$$

$$F_D = C_D A \frac{\rho}{2} w_f^2 \tag{10.2}$$

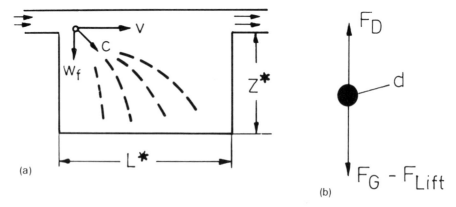

(a)

(b)

Figure 10.2(a) Depositing chamber with horizontal flow; (b) forces acting on a particle.

$$F_G = V_p \rho_p g \qquad (10.3)$$

$$F_{\text{lift}} = V_p \rho g \qquad (10.4)$$

where $A = \pi d^2/4$ and $V_p = \pi d^3/6$. Hence

$$C_D \frac{\pi d^2}{4} \frac{\rho}{2} w_f^2 = \frac{\pi d^3}{6} (\rho_p - \rho) g \qquad (10.5)$$

The drag coefficient can be estimated for:

(a) $Re_p < 1$, $C_D = 24/Re_p$ (Stokes' regime or laminar zone)

$$w_f = \frac{1}{18} \frac{\rho_p - \rho}{\rho} \frac{g}{v} d^2 \qquad (10.6)$$

(b) $10^3 < Re_p < 2 \times 10^5$, $C_D = 0.4{-}0.5$ (Newton's regime or turbulent zone)

$$w_f = \left(\frac{4}{3} \frac{\rho_p - \rho}{\rho} \frac{g}{C_D} d \right)^{1/2} \qquad (10.7)$$

The settling velocity w_f (turbulent zone) is depicted in Fig. 12.12(a), (b).
The limits for the separation of particles can be given by using the following expression:

$$\frac{w_f}{v} = \frac{Z^*}{L^*} \qquad (10.8)$$

$$w_f = v \frac{Z^*}{L^*} = w_f^*$$

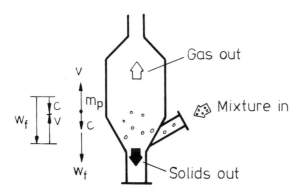

Figure 10.3 Depositing chamber with counter-current flow.

That means that, for a given geometric ratio Z^*/L^* and for the velocity v, the separation velocity w_f^* for a defined particle takes place, i.e. the boundary particle d^*.

In the case of a counter-current flow depositing chamber (Fig. 10.3) the separation efficiency η_s depends on the settling velocity w_f, i.e.

$$w_f \equiv v = \dot{V}/A \qquad (10.9)$$

Theoretically the separator efficiency

$$\eta_s = 100\% \qquad \text{for} \quad w_f^* > w_f$$

and

$$\eta_s = 0\% \qquad \text{for} \quad w_f^* < w_f$$

That means that there ought to be a very sharp cut in the efficiency curve. In reality the efficiency curve is smooth as shown in Fig. 10.4.

The boundary particle d^* is defined for a separation efficiency $\eta_s = 50\%$ for this particle band. Particles larger than d^* have a greater chance to deposit and those less than d^* have a lesser chance to segregate and will flow out with the carrier gas.

The following example illustrates the physical size of a typical separator.

An immense modification in the particle separation effects is obtained when using the centrifugal force, which also enables substantial cost reduction and even greater size reduction.

Introducing a mixture of gas–solids tangentially in a separator vessel with a given diameter D_C, one obtains an acceleration, a, in the centrifugal field, which leads to a multiple of the gravitational acceleration g.

Example 10.2

The dimensions of a depositing chamber should be roughly estimated.
Air volume rate, $\dot{V} = 15\,000\,\mathrm{m^3/h}$ carrying dust.

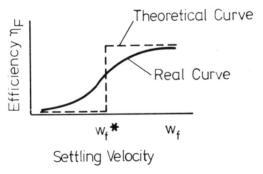

Figure 10.4 Schematic interpretation of a separation efficiency curve.

Air density, $\rho = 1\,\mathrm{kg/m^3}$
Particle density, $\rho_\mathrm{p} = 2500\,\mathrm{kg/m^3}$
Kinematic viscosity, $v = 18.1 \times 10^{-6}\,\mathrm{m^2/s}$

Case 1

Vessel diameter $D_\mathrm{s} = 4\,\mathrm{m}$ (assumption). Air mean velocity $v = w_\mathrm{f}^* = 0.33\,\mathrm{m/s}$.
Together with equation (10.6) one obtains:

$$d^* = 66 \times 10^{-6}\,\mathrm{m} = 66\,\mu\mathrm{m}$$

Case 2

If the boundary particle $d^* = 10\,\mu\mathrm{m}$ is required, then with equation (10.6) one
calculates w_f^* and then calculates the diameter of the separator.
For

$$d^* = 10\,\mu\mathrm{m} \rightarrow w_\mathrm{f}^* = 7.5 \times 10^{-3}\,\mathrm{m/s}$$
$$= 7.5\,\mathrm{mm/s}$$

with

$$\dot{V} = \frac{\pi D_\mathrm{s}^2}{4}\,w_\mathrm{f}^* = 7.5\,\mathrm{mm/s}$$

$$D_\mathrm{s} = \left(\frac{4\dot{V}}{\pi w_\mathrm{f}^*}\right)^{1/2} = 26.6\,\mathrm{m}$$

Case 3

If the dust particle had a particle density $\rho_\mathrm{p} = 1000\,\mathrm{kg/m^3}$ then $w_\mathrm{f}^* \approx 3 \times 10^{-3}\,\mathrm{m/s}$
and $D_\mathrm{s} \approx 40\,\mathrm{m}$.

In a cyclone with a diameter $D_\mathrm{s} = 0.3\,\mathrm{m}$ and with the initial velocity $v_\alpha = 15\,\mathrm{m/s}$
of the transport medium, the existing acceleration is of magnitude:

$$a = v_\alpha^2/R_\mathrm{C} = 225/0.15 = 1500\,\mathrm{m/s^2} \tag{10.10}$$

Dividing the acceleration a of the centrifugal field by that due to gravity g one
obtains the multiple factor of the acceleration ratio, i.e.

$$n = a/g = 1500/9.81 \approx 153$$

That means that in the centrifugal field one has in that special case 153 times
higher acceleration than in the gravitational field. Furthermore increasing the
separator diameter results yields a decrease of n. In Table 10.2 this effect is
demonstrated.

From Table 10.2 it can be seen that smaller separator diameters with the
higher multiple factor will yield higher separation efficiencies. This observation
is consistent with long term experiences in many operating plants.

Table 10.2 Acceleration factor for various cyclone sizes

Initial velocity, v_α (m/s)	Separator diameter, D_s (m)	Acceleration in the centrifugal field, a (equation (10.10)) (m/s²)	Multiple factor, $n\,(=a/g)$
15	3	$225/1.5 = 150$	≈ 15.3
	6	$225/3\ \ = 75$	≈ 7.6
	25	$225/12.5 = 18$	≈ 1.8

10.3.2 Separation in a centrifugal field

Consider a particle with the mass M_p in a centrifugal field rotating with a tangential velocity v_t (Fig. 10.5). The previous example has shown that the gravitational force is small in comparison with the force in the centrifugal field. The two decisive forces are the centrifugal and the drag forces. If the centrifugal force acting on a particle is higher than the corresponding drag force then the particle will flow towards the wall of the separator and due to gravity will whirl down to the outlet. In the other case, where the drag force exceeds the centrifugal force, the particle will follow the gas stream to the outlet, without separating the particle.

The balance between these two forces yields in the laminar zone:

$$F_D = F_C \tag{10.11}$$

$$3\pi\eta d v_R = \frac{\pi d^3}{6}\Delta\rho\,\frac{v_t^2}{R} \tag{10.11a}$$

$$d = 18\left(\frac{\eta}{\Delta\rho}\frac{v_R}{v_t^2}R\right)^{1/2} \tag{10.11b}$$

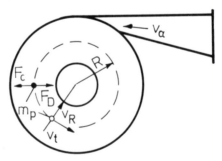

Figure 10.5 Top view of a particle in a centrifugal field.

In equation (10.11) v_R is the gas velocity in the radial direction, v_t the gas velocity in the tangential direction related to the radius R and $\Delta\rho = \rho_p - \rho$, the difference of densities.

In Fig. 10.6 a schematic interpretation of a cyclone is shown. The tangential inlet is narrowed so that the particles have the tendency not to hug the cyclone wall directly. This is taken into account with R. The actual inlet area is $b \times a$ and the initial velocity is v_α the outlet velocity is v_i in a pipe with inner diameter D_i. In this model the actual separation zone is defined by D_i and Z_i^*, a fictive cylindrical zone, where the radial velocity is equal to v_{Ri}.

Relating equation (10.11) to the outlet pipe, one obtains the following expression for the boundary particle size:

$$d^* = \left(18 \frac{\eta}{\Delta\rho} \frac{v_{Ri}}{v_{ti}^2} R_i \right)^{1/2} \tag{10.12}$$

Due to the inlet velocity v_α a rotating stream similar to a potential vortex is generated, which can be defined roughly as follows:

$$v_t R = \text{constant} \tag{10.13}$$

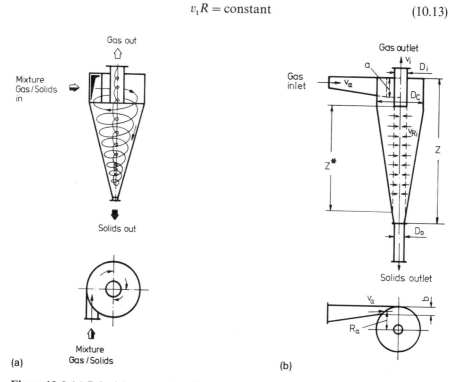

Figure 10.6 (a) Principle operation of a cyclone; (b) cyclone with a tangential gas-inlet rectangular form ($a \times b$).

Barth [4] found experimentally that the rotating velocity v_t increases towards the centre, where its maximum is attained at R_i, and then drops rapidly to zero.
   Therefore, the effectivity of a cyclone is mainly due to the magnitude of v_{ti}.
   The centrifugal force F_C is equal to

$$F_C = (F_G - F_{lift}) \frac{v_{ti}^2}{gR_i}$$ (10.14)

where

$$F_G - F_{lift} = \frac{\pi d^3}{6}(\rho_p - \rho)g$$ (10.14a)

Barth introduced an equilibrium between F_C and the drag force F_D corresponding to the fictive cylinder where the actual separation takes place. The radial velocity is:

$$v_{Ri} = \dot{V}/(\pi D_i Z^*)$$ (10.15)

10.3.3 Sink velocity in a centrifugal field

All the equations required for the derivation of the sink velocity in a centrifugal field can be written in a simplified form:

   (a) Drag force

$$F_D = C_D \frac{\rho}{2} w_f^2 A_p = C_D \frac{\rho}{2} w_f^2 \frac{\pi d^2}{4}$$ (10.16)

   (b) Balance of forces (Fig. 10.5)

$$F_D = F_C$$ (10.17)

$$= F_G - F_{lift}$$

$$\frac{24}{Re_p} \frac{\rho}{2} w_f^2 \frac{\pi d^2}{4} = F_G - F_{lift}$$ (10.18)

with $Re_p = w_f d/v$ and $v = \eta/\rho$, one obtains

$$F_G - F_{lift} = 3\pi \eta d w_{fR}$$ (10.18a)

with w_{fR} representing the radial sink velocity in a centrifugal field.
   The drag force for fine particles (laminar zone) is:

$$F_D = 3\pi \eta d v_R$$ (10.19)

From equations (8.18a) and (8.19) the following expression for the drag force is obtained:

$$F_D = (F_G - F_{lift}) \frac{v_R}{w_{fR}}$$ (10.20)

Together with the centrifugal

$$F_C = \frac{\pi d^3}{6} \Delta\rho \frac{v_{ti}^2}{R_i}$$ (10.21)

and from the drag force F_D equation (8.20) one obtains the boundary sink velocity in a centrifugal field:

$$w_f^* = \dot{V}g/(2\pi Z^* v_{ti}^2)$$ (10.22)

This settling velocity w_f^* represents the condition at which the particle size d^* will be separated at an efficiency of 50% (Fig. 10.4).

10.3.4 Associated pressure losses

Associated with the separation of particles in a centrifugal field is a corresponding pressure loss. High efficiency cyclones have relatively high pressure losses, which lead to high rotating velocities. Barth [4] has defined the pressure drop of a cyclone as follows:

$$\Delta p_C = \lambda_C \frac{\rho}{2} v_{ti}^2$$ (10.23)

λ_C represents the total loss factor occurring in a cyclone and $(\rho/2)v_{ti}^2$ stands for the kinetic energy of the vortex in the outlet pipe. The vortex velocity can be obtained by means of the impulse momentum. The difference in impulse momentum between the intake and exit across the sectional area of a cyclone is equal to the losses due to friction, i.e.

$$M_\alpha = M_i = M_f$$ (10.24)

where

$$M_\alpha = \dot{Q}_\alpha v_\alpha R_\alpha$$ (10.25a)

$$M_i = \dot{Q}_i v_i R_i$$ (10.25b)

$$M_f = \tau A_m R$$ (10.25c)

with

$$\tau = \lambda \frac{\rho}{2} v_t^2$$ (10.26)

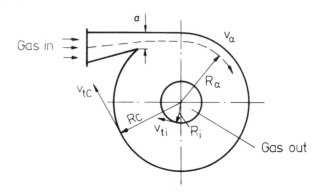

Figure 10.7 Cyclone with main velocities.

as the shear stress taking the friction loss into account, and $A_m = \pi DH$ as the mantel surface.

Substituting equations (10.25a), (10.25b), (10.25c) and (10.26) in (10.24), re-arranging and taking into consideration the potential vortex law $vR = \text{constant}$, one obtains:

$$\frac{v_{ti}}{v_i} = \frac{\pi R_i R_\alpha}{A_\alpha \alpha + \lambda \pi Z^* R_\alpha} \tag{10.27}$$

where (Fig. 10.7)

$$\alpha = \frac{v_\alpha R_\alpha}{v_{ti} R_C} \tag{10.28}$$

v_α is the initial velocity of the gas entering the cyclone along radius R_α, and v_{tC} is the tangential velocity related to the greatest radius, i.e. cyclone radius is R_C and v_{ti} is the inner tangential velocity along R_i.

Figure 10.8(a) represents the work carried out by Barth [4]. Figure 10.8(a) has been modified using different cyclone geometries and verified experimentally as shown in Fig. 10.8(b). It is necessary to modify the factor α to take into consideration various cyclone entrance configurations (Fig. 10.8(c)).

The pressure loss factor of a cyclone consists mainly of the friction losses in the cyclone body and in the outlet pipe. This model leads to

$$\lambda_C = \lambda_{C\alpha} + \lambda_{Ci} \tag{10.29}$$

$$\Delta p_{C\alpha} = \lambda_{C\alpha} \frac{\rho}{2} v_{ti}^2 \tag{10.30a}$$

$$\Delta p_{Ci} = \lambda_{Ci} \frac{\rho}{2} v_{ti}^2 \tag{10.30b}$$

where

$$\lambda_{C\alpha} = \frac{R_i}{R_C}\left[\left(1 - \frac{v_{ti}}{v_i}\frac{Z^*}{R_i}\lambda\right)^{-2} - 1\right]$$ (10.31)

and,

$$\lambda_{Ci} = \frac{K}{(v_{ti}/v_i)^{2/3}} + 1$$ (10.32)

Weidner [5] recommends $K = 4.4$ for sharp edged pipes and 3.4 for well rounded edged pipes. Taking the mass load ratio into consideration, one obtains a modified value for the λ factor:

$$\lambda = 0.005(1 + 3\,\mu^{1/2})$$ (10.33)

Example 10.3

A cyclone separator should be sized according to the following data:

$\dot{Q} = 1200\,\mathrm{kg/h}$
$t = 20\,^{\circ}\mathrm{C}$
$\rho_p = 1350\,\mathrm{kg/m^3}$
$G = 36\,\mathrm{t/h}$
$\mu = 3$

Step 1

$\rho_L \approx 1.2\,\mathrm{kg/m^3}$
$\dot{V} = 10\,000\,\mathrm{m^3/h}$
$= 2.78\,\mathrm{m^3/s}$

Note that the required pressure drop should be approximately 1000 Pa and the boundary particle size should be in the range $d^* \leqslant 10\,\mu\mathrm{m}$. Assumptions:

$v_\alpha = 12.5\,\mathrm{m/s}$
$A_\alpha = 0.2224\,\mathrm{m^2}$
$ba = 0.2723 \times 0.817\,\mathrm{m^2}$, where $b{:}a = 1/3$
$A_i = A_\alpha = 0.2224\,\mathrm{m^2}$
$D_i = 532\,\mathrm{mm}$
$D_C = 3D_i = 1596\,\mathrm{mm}$, where $D_C{:}D_i = 3$
$\quad = 4D_i = 2128\,\mathrm{mm}$, where $D_C{:}D_i = 4$
$Z^* = (10\text{--}20)R_i = 5\,\mathrm{m}$
$v_{Ri} = \dot{V}/\pi D_i Z^* = 0.333\,\mathrm{m/s}$

$$\frac{v_{ti}}{v_i} = \frac{\pi R_i R}{A_\alpha \alpha + \lambda\pi Z^* R_\alpha} = \frac{\pi \times 0.266 \times 0.928}{0.2224 \times 0.80 + 0.03\pi \times 5 \times 0.928} = 1.26$$

$$\alpha = (a/R_C = 0.2723/1.064) > 0.94$$
$$v_i = 12.5 \, \text{m/s}$$
$$v_{ti} = 15.76 \, \text{m/s}$$
$$w_f^* = 2.78 \times 9.81/(2\pi \times 5 \times 19.35^2) = 2.318 \times 10^{-3} \, \text{m/s}$$

$$d^* = \left(18 \frac{1.8 \times 1 \times 10^{-6}}{1350} \frac{0.333}{374.4} \times 0.266\right)^{1/2} = 7.5 \, \mu\text{m}$$

$$\lambda_{C\alpha} = \frac{1}{4}\left[\left(1 - 1.26\frac{5}{0.266}0.03\right)^{-2} - 1\right] = 2.73$$

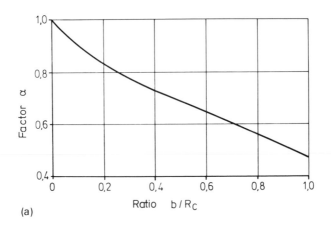

(a)

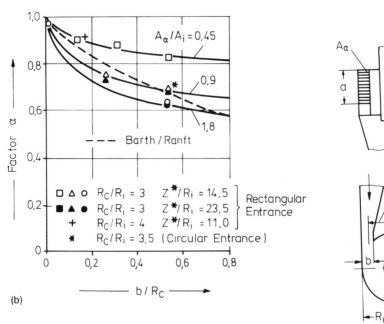

(b)

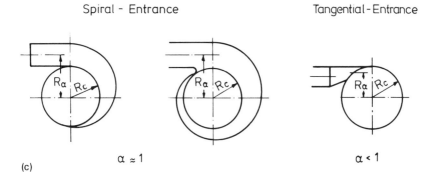

Spiral - Entrance   Tangential - Entrance

(c)

$\alpha \approx 1$ $\alpha < 1$

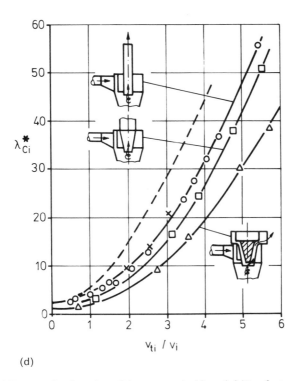

(d)

Figure 10.8 (a) Factor α is a function of the geometrical length b/R_C of a tangential cyclone; for cyclones with a spiral entrance $\alpha \sim 1$ (see (c) for cyclone entrance geometry). (a) has been modified using different cyclone geometries and verified experimentally as shown in (b). (b) Modified interpretation of factor; (c) cyclone entrance configurations; (d) λ_{Ci}^* as a function of the velocity ratio (Weidner [5]).

$$\lambda_{Ci} = \frac{4.4}{(1.26)^{2/3}} + 1 = 4.77$$

$$\lambda = 2.73 + 4.77 = 7.5$$

$$\Delta p = 4.738 \frac{1.2}{2} 19.35^2 = 1117.7 \qquad \text{(Pa)}$$

Cyclones installed in pneumatic conveying systems have normally larger dimensions than those for the same air flow rate. This facilitates separation at very low mass load ratios. Care should be taken to ensure an unobstructed free outflow for the solids. The cross-sectional area should take account of the aerated bulk solids density and the outflow velocity of the solids. Sealing apparatus such as rotary valves, screw feeders, double flap valves, etc. should be selected to account for the aerated bulk solids flow. The filling efficiency of the rotary feeder should not exceed $\phi \sim 0.3$–0.4.

Optimal cyclone sizes for high separation efficiencies are obtained with the following geometrical ratios:

$$R_C/R_i = 3\text{--}5$$

$$Z^*/R_i = 10\text{--}20$$

$$D_0 = 0.6 D_i$$

$$L_0 > 5 D_0$$

10.3.4.1 Modified method for calculating the pressure drop

A more refined method for calculating high efficiency cyclones has been developed by Muschelknautz and Brunner [6]. Barth's basic model has been used but slightly modified, e.g. equations (10.30a) and (10.30b) are now related to the axial gas velocity. This yields the modified equations:

$$\Delta p_{C\alpha}^* = \lambda_{C\alpha}^* \frac{\rho}{2} v_i^2 \qquad (10.34a)$$

$$\Delta p_{Ci}^* = \lambda_{Ci}^* \frac{\rho}{2} v_i^2 \qquad (10.34b)$$

$$\Delta p_C = (\lambda_{C\alpha}^* + \lambda_{Ci}^*) \frac{\rho}{2} v_i^2 \qquad (10.35)$$

The pressure drop factors equations (10.31) and (10.32) are modified and transformed to:

$$\lambda_{C\alpha}^* = \frac{R_i}{R_C} \left(\frac{v_{ti}}{v_i} \right)^2 \left[\left(1 - \frac{v_{ti}}{v_i} \frac{Z}{R_i} \lambda^* \right)^{-2} - 1 \right] \qquad (10.36)$$

and

$$\lambda_{Ci}^* = K\left(\frac{v_{ti}}{v_i}\right)^{4/3} + \left(\frac{v_{ti}}{v_i}\right)^2 \tag{10.37}$$

In equation (10.36) Z stands for the total height of the cyclone where the total friction occurs and the factor λ^* is in the vicinity of 5×10^{-3}. The value of K has been averaged to 4 as recommended from Weidner [5]. The results obtained by Weidner are shown in Fig. 10.8(d). This modified method delivers lower values of d^* than Barth's and the predicted pressure drop is in this case significantly higher.

10.3.5 Graphical estimation of cyclone geometry

The authors have calculated cyclones with spiral and tangential entrances, using the approved geometry. The results of this investigation are shown in a set of curves (Fig. 10.9). The third set of curves, Figs 10.13 and 10.14 yield the entrance velocity according to the previously determined pressure drop.

By means of these sets of curves optimal operating cyclones and high efficiencies are obtainable. It should be noted that these curves were calculated by using all available data in the literature.

Boundary conditions for the calculation of curves Figs 10.9–10.14 are as follows:

(a) Gas

Ambient temperature, $t_0 = 20\,°\text{C}$
Dynamic viscosity, $\eta_0 = 18.188 \times 10^{-6}\,\text{Ns/m}^2$
Ambient pressure, $p_0 = 1053.2\,\text{mbar}$
Gas density, $\rho_0 = 1.2\,\text{kg/m}^3$

(b) Particle

Particle density, $\rho_p = 1000\,\text{kg/m}^3$
Boundary particle size, $d_0^*\,\mu\text{m}$

(c) Cyclone geometry and factors

Entrance velocity, exit velocity, $v_\alpha = v_i = 10, 12.5, 15, 17.5$ and 20 m/s
Diameter ratio ($\equiv$ cyclone type) $D_C/D_i = 5, 4, 3$ and 2
Height/diameter ratio ($\equiv$ size) $Z^*/D_i = 10, 8, 6$ and 4
Diameter ratio, $D_0/D_i = 0.7$
Factor (Fig. 10.8) $\alpha = 1$ (spiral)
$$\alpha = \phi_c(b/R_c)$$
Friction factor, $\lambda = 2 \times 10^{-2}$
$$\lambda^* = 5 \times 10^{-3}$$
Constant, $K = 4$

Example 10.4

It is required to design a high efficiency cyclone with a boundary particle

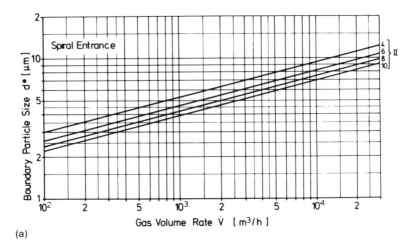

(a)

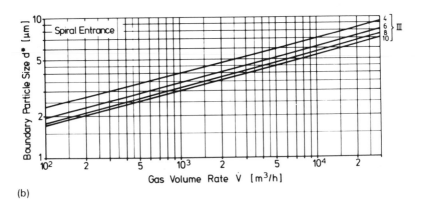

(b)

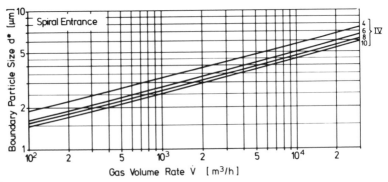

(c)

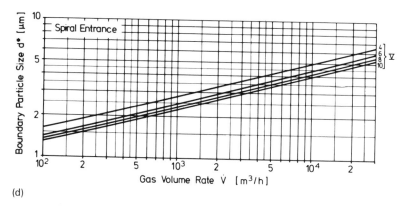

(d)

Figure 10.9 Boundary particle size as a function of the gas volume rate: (a) type II spiral cyclone; (b) type III spiral cyclone; (c) type IV spiral cyclone; (d) type V spiral cyclone.

size $d^* \approx 5\,\mu$m. The volumetric air flow rate is $10\,000$ m^3/h (Example 10.3). This example is worked out by means of Figs 10.9–10.14.

Step 1

For a boundary particle size of $d^* = 5\,\mu$m and for a volumetric air flow rate of 10^4 m^3/h one obtains from Fig. 10.10(d), the type of size for a cyclone with a tangential entrance. Intersection point delivers: type V/size 6.

Step 2

From Fig. 10.12 the appropriate pressure drop $\Delta p_C = 32.6$ mbar is obtained.

Step 3

The initial entrance velocity can be obtained by means of Fig. 10.14 and the corresponding type V/size 6. The intersection point lies at $v_\alpha \approx 12$ m/s.

Step 4

For an air flow rate of $10\,000$ m^3/h and a boundary particle size $d^* = 5\,\mu$m, the established data are:

1. Type V and size 6
2. Pressure drop $\Delta p_C = 32.6$ mbar
3. Entrance velocity $v_\alpha = 12.5$ m/s

The main geometrical data are:

1. Type V $\rightarrow R_C/R_i = 5$
2. Size 6 $\rightarrow Z^*/R_i = 6$
3. Inlet area = outlet area = 0.22 m^2

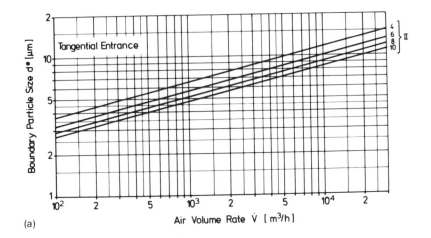

(a)

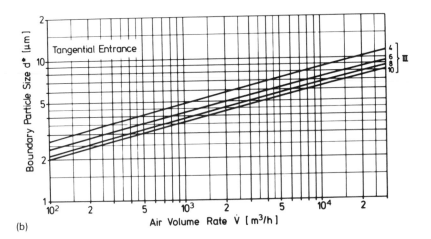

(b)

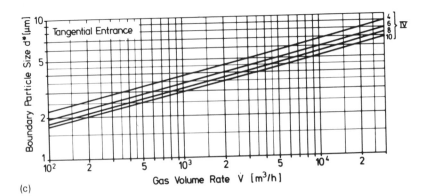

(c)

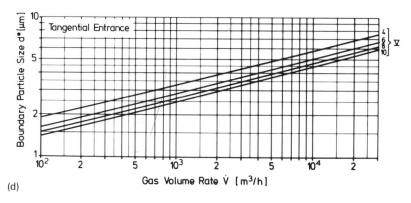

(d)

Figure 10.10 Boundary particle size as a function of the gas volume rate: (a) Type II tangential cyclone; (b) Type III tangential cyclone; (c) Type IV tangential cyclone; (d) type V tangential cyclone.

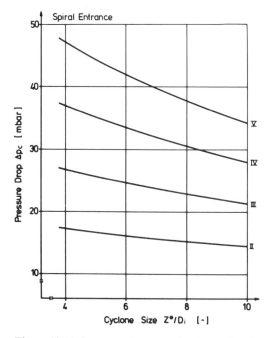

Figure 10.11 Pressure drop as a function of cyclone size (spiral).

4. Inlet size: $ab = 272 \times 816 \, mm^2$
5. Outlet diameter $D_0 \approx 0.6 \, D_i \, mm$

For the other gas states, the data from these curves must be corrected. The density, ρ, of the conveying media is determined by the local pressure p_x, the gas

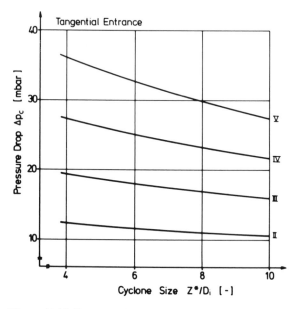

Figure 10.12 Pressure drop as a function of cyclone size (tangential).

constant R_x and the local temperature t_x.

$$\rho_x = \frac{p_x}{R_x(273 + t_x)} \qquad (10.38)$$

The correct pressure drop of the cyclone is:

$$\Delta p_{Cx} = \Delta p_C \frac{\rho_x}{\rho_0} \qquad (10.39)$$

where Δp_C is calculated for a gas with $\rho_0 = 1.2\,\text{kg/m}^3$.

   The boundary particle size equation (10.12) is to be corrected using the following expression:

$$d_x^* = \sqrt{d_0^* \frac{\eta_x \Delta \rho_x}{\eta_0 \Delta \rho_0}} \qquad (10.40)$$

All data with index 0 are defined in boundary conditions for the calculation of curves, Figs 10.9–10.14.

10.3.5.1 Barth's simplified assumptions for calculating v_{ti}/v_i

The ratio of impulse momentum

$$\alpha = \frac{M_\alpha}{M_C} = \frac{v_\alpha R_\alpha}{v_{tC} R_C}$$

$$M_i = M_C - M_L \qquad (10.41)$$

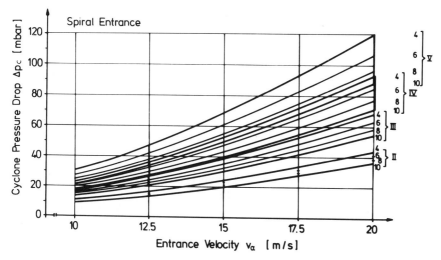

Figure 10.13 Pressure drop as a function of entrance velocity (spiral).

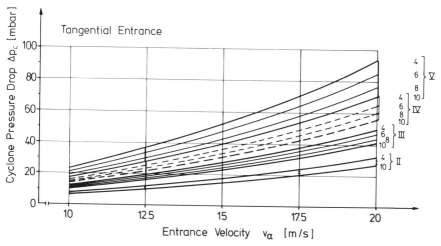

Figure 10.14 Pressure drop as a function of entrance velocity (tangential).

with

$$M_C = 2\pi\lambda R_i R_C Z^* \frac{\rho}{2} v_i v_{iC} \tag{10.42}$$

and $R_f = (R_i R_C)^{1/2}$ as a friction radius and Z^* the height of this fictive cylinder.

The remaining part of the cyclone, where the potential vortex causes pressure losses, is neglected, thus;

$$\frac{v_{ti}}{v_i} = \left(\frac{A_\alpha}{A_i} \frac{R_i}{R_\alpha} \alpha - \frac{Z^*}{R_i} \lambda \right)^{-1} \tag{10.43}$$

10.3.5.2 Muschelknautz's modifications taking the mass load ratio into consideration

$$M_i = M_C - (M_L + M_p) \tag{10.44}$$

where M_p stands for the impulse momentum. λ of Barth's equations has been modified to

$$\lambda = \lambda_L + \lambda_z'(\eta \, \mu)^{1/2} Fr_i \left(\frac{\rho}{\varepsilon \rho_p}\right)^{1/2} \left(\frac{R_i}{R_C}\right)^{5/8} \tag{10.45}$$

This interpretation is very similar to the pressure drop due to the particles in a gas stream, where $\lambda = \lambda_L + \lambda_z \mu$ in Chapter 6.

It has been found that $\lambda_z' = 0.25$. Due to the mass load ratio, a selective separation of particles in a cyclone is not possible. This occurs already for values of $\mu_B \geqslant 0.1$ (boundary mass load ratio).

This ratio of particle size is a result of a balance of forces namely the centrifugal force in relation to the drag force, i.e.

$$\frac{F_C}{F_D} = \frac{\dot{Q} v_i^2 / R_i}{\dot{Q} v_R / w_{fo}} = \frac{v_i^2 w_{fo}}{v_R R_i} \tag{10.46}$$

For characterization purposes of the dust particles, the velocity w_{fo} and the particle size d in equation (10.6) are defined as average values, i.e. $d = d_{50\%}$ in the particle size distribution curve and w_{fo} represents the corresponding fall velocity.

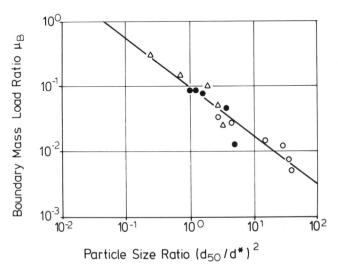

Figure 10.15 Boundary mass load ratio as a function of particle size ratio.

Substituting w_{fo} from equation (10.6) in equation (10.46) one obtains:

$$\frac{F_C}{F_D} = \left(\frac{d_{50\%}}{d^*}\right)^2 \qquad (10.47)$$

Fig. 10.15 (Muschelknautz and Brunner [6]) shows the boundary mass load ratio μ_B as a function of the particle size ratio $(d_{50\%}/d^*)^2$. This representation yields:

$$\mu_B = \frac{0.1}{(d_{50\%}/d^*)^{1.5}} \qquad (10.48)$$

Example 10.5

A dust laden gas should be cleaned. An existing cyclone is to be checked whether it could operate for the imposed conditions. An estimation of the separation efficiency and of the expected pressure drop is required.

Step 1

All available geometrical data:

1. Cyclone
   Type III, $D_C/D_i = 3$
   Size, $Z/D_i = 7.25$
   Ratio, $b/R_C = 0.27$
   Factor, $\alpha = 0.75$
   Diameter, $D_i = 250$ mm
2. Gas
   Air volume rate, $\dot{V} = 2000$ m³/h
   Air density, $\rho = 1.2$ kg/m³
   Dynamic viscosity, $\eta = 18.15 \times 10^{-6}$ N s/m²
3. Solids
   Solid mass flow rate, $\dot{G} = 600$ kg/h
   Particle density, $\rho_p = 1700$ kg/m³
   Voidage, $\varepsilon \approx 0.35$
   Particle size, $d_{50\%} = 20$ μm
   Fall velocity, $w_f = 2$ cm/s

Particle size distribution related to the mass of solids retained in the sieve (residue) is given in Table 10.3.

Step 2

1. Mass load ratio, $\mu = \dot{G}/\dot{Q} = 0.25$
2. Air axial velocity, $v_i = 11.318$ m/s
3. Froude number, $Fr_i = 7.226$
4. Assumed efficiency, $\eta = 99\%$

Table 10.3

Residue (Weight %)	Bandwidth (μm)	Average particle size (μm)
1	0–2	1
2	2–4	3
7	4–8	6
27	8–16	12
53	16–32	24
10	> 32	48

5. λ factor (equation (10.45)), $\lambda = 0.0125$

$$\lambda^* = \left[0.005 + 0.25 \, (0.99 \times 0.25)^{1/2} \left(\frac{7.226 \times 1.2}{0.35 \times 1700} \right)^{1/2} \left(\frac{1}{3} \right)^{5/8} \right]$$

$$= 0.00125$$

6. Area ratio, $A_\alpha / A_i \approx 0.9$

7. Radii ratio, $\dfrac{R_\alpha}{R_i} = \dfrac{R_C}{R_i} \left(1 - \dfrac{1}{2} \dfrac{b}{R_C} \right) = 2.6$

8. Velocity ratio (equation (10.43)),

$$\frac{v_{ti}}{v_i} = \frac{1}{0.9 \, (1/2.6) \, 0.75 + 0.0125 \times 14.5} = 2.27$$

9. Tangential velocity, $v_{ti} = 25.69 \, \text{m/s}$
10. Radial velocity, $v_{Ri} = 0.57 \, \text{m/s}$
11. Boundary particle size, (equation (10.12))

$$d^* = \left(\frac{18 \times 18.15 \times 10^{-6} \times 0.57}{1699 \times 660} 0.125 \right)^{1/2} = (20.75 \times 10^{-12})^{1/2}$$

$$= 4.6 \times 10^{-6} \, \text{m}$$

$$= 4.6 \, \mu\text{m}$$

12. Boundary mass load ratio (equation (10.48)),

$$\mu_B = \frac{0.1}{(20/4.6)^{1.5}} = 0.011$$

Table 10.4

Average particle size $d_{50\%}$	Ratio $d_{50\%}/d^*$	Fractional efficiency × residue η_F
1	0.217	$0 \times 0.01 = 0.00$
3	0.65	$0.07 \times 0.02 = 0.0014$
6	1.3	$0.47 \times 0.07 = 0.0329$
12	2.6	$0.95 \times 0.27 = 0.2565$
24	5.2	$0.99 \times 0.53 = 0.5247$
48	10.4	$1.0 \ \times 0.10 = 0.1$
		0.9155

13. Immediate separation efficiency,

$$\eta_i = \frac{\mu - \mu_B}{\mu} = \left(\frac{0.25 - 0.011}{0.25}\right)100 = 95.6\%$$

14. Selected separation in fractional form for 4.4% (Table 10.4). Fractional efficiencies have been obtained from Fig. 10.16, curve d [6].
15. Absolute value, $\eta_F = 4.4 \times 0.9155 = 4.028$

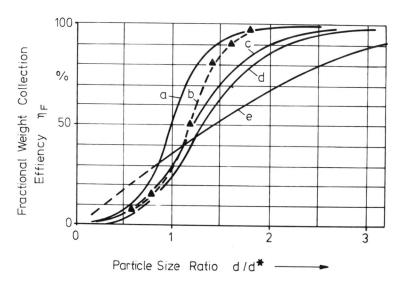

Figure 10.16 Weight collection efficiency as a function of particle size ratio.

16. Cyclone efficiency,

$$\eta_C = \eta_i + \eta_F$$
$$= 95.6 + 4.028$$
$$= 99.628\%$$

17. Pressure drop factor (equation (10.36)),

$$\lambda^*_{C\alpha} = 0.38 \times 5.153 \left(\frac{1}{(1 - 2.27 \times 14.5 \times 0.0125)^2} - 1 \right)$$
$$= 0.38 \times 5.153 \times 1.887 = 3.695$$

18. Pressure drop factor λ^*_{Ci} is obtained from graphs in Fig. 10.8(a). These graphs take into consideration the geometrical shape of the outlet pipe as shown in the diagrams. The calculated $v_{ti}/v_i = 2.27$ and the circular outlet ($A = $ constant) corresponds to a factor $\lambda^*_{Ci} = 12$.

19. The total pressure drop of the cyclone is (equation (10.35)):

$$\Delta p_C = (\lambda^*_{C\alpha} + \lambda^*_{Ci}) \frac{\rho}{2} v_i^2 = (3.695 + 12) \times \frac{1.2}{2} \times 11.318^2$$
$$= 1206.3 \, \text{N/m}^2$$

20. If one would neglect the influence of the solids the ratio of velocity v_{ti}/v_i (equation (10.43)) rises to 3.36 and the tangential velocity $v_{ti} = 38 \, \text{m/s}$. The λ^*_{Ci} factor is then equal to 23 which leads to a high pressure loss. Due to the solids in the air stream the potential vortex in the cyclone is reduced which is coupled with a pressure reduction.

21. Estimation of the boundary particle size and pressure drop using Figs 10.9–10.14 will be demonstrated in step 3. Required data:
    Air volume, $\dot{V} = 2000 \, \text{m}^3/\text{h}$
    Cyclone type III, $F_C/C_i = 3$
    Cyclone size, $Z^*/D_i = 7.25$

Step 3

From Fig. 10.10(b) one obtains the boundary particle size $d^* \simeq 4$.

Step 4

From Fig. 10.12 one estimates the pressure drop $\Delta p_C = 17.0 \, \text{mbar}$

Figure 10.17(a) Various entrance configurations; (b) cyclone entrance configurations showing cyclone body; (c) special cyclone configurations.

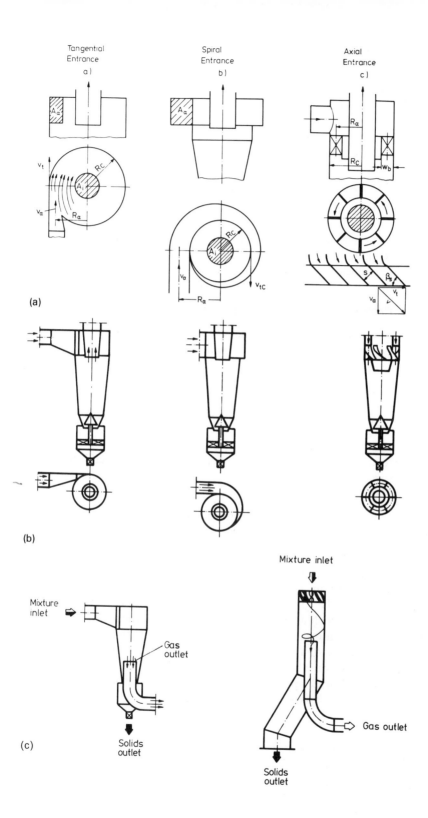

Tangential
Entrance
a)

Spiral
Entrance
b)

Axial
Entrance
c)

(a)

(b)

(c)

Mixture
inlet

Gas
outlet

Solids
outlet

Mixture inlet

Gas outlet

Solids
outlet

Step 5

From Fig. 10.14 one obtains the entrance velocity $v_\alpha \approx 11$ m/s.

Step 6

Correction of d^* (equation (10.40)):

$$d_x^* = 4\left(\frac{18.15 \times 10^{-6} \times 1700}{18.188 \times 10^{-6} \times 1000}\right)^{1/2} = 4 \times 1.3 = 5.21$$

The estimation of the particle size and the entrance velocity are very close to the calculated values. The estimated pressure drop is higher than the calculated one, due to the influence of the mass load ratio. Nevertheless these graphs permit a good estimation for the efficiency of the cyclone.

10.3.6 Proven cyclone geometries and configurations

There are a number of possible cyclone configurations. The following figures depict some configurations which are known to produce reliable performance.

10.3.6.1 Entrance geometry

Various techniques are used to introduce the laden gas stream into the cyclone housing (Fig. 10.17).

It should be noted that in Fig. 10.17(b) the cyclone housing is fitted with a settling chamber. The settling chamber is designed to fulfil three distinct functions:

(a) To centre the vortex generated by the cyclone.
(b) To prevent re-entrainment of the solids.
(c) To act as a storage hopper.

The conical reflector fitted to the product outlet of the cyclone effectively centralizes the vortex so as to ensure good separation. The device stabilizes the flow inside the cyclone.

Located below the conical reflector is a vortex breaking device consisting of three flat plates which also support the cone. The purpose of these plates is to break the vortex in order to avoid re-entrainment of the separated solids.

The conical reflector and vortex breaking device are located in a hopper which also serves as a storage bin for the separated solids. The design of such storage bins is discussed in Chapter 11. A critical factor in the design of the bin is to ensure that the solids flow unaided out of the bin.

10.3.6.2 Special cyclone configurations

In Fig. 10.17(c) two cyclone designs are shown with the clean gas outlet located at the base of the cyclone.

10.4 FABRIC FILTERS

10.4.1 Introduction

The increasing utilization of pneumatic conveying systems for fine particle transportation is leading to the wider use of fabric filters to ensure almost complete gas–solids separation.

Essentially fabric (or fibrous) filters depend for their operation on the impingement and settlement under gravity, as the particles move at a low velocity through the interstices of the filter fabrics in use. Each fabric has its own 'special' features, the most successful being one which has a nap or felt type construction.

The selection of the most appropriate fabric must, in addition to cost, take into consideration both the chemical and physical characteristics of the particles and the process. Typical characteristics of various filter fabrics are shown in Tables 10.5 and 10.6.

10.4.2 Modes of operation

Fabric filters are categorized according to whether they operate on an intermittent or continuous basis.

In Fig. 10.18, the pressure drop characteristics of both types of fabric filters are shown.

Ideally, a fabric filter should impose a constant resistance to gas flow so that at no time does the performance of the filter have a profound influence on the performance of the pneumatic conveying system. As such, the period of operation of an intermittent filter must not exceed a point when the pressure loss is such that it could precipitate deposition or blockage of the conveying system. In such a

Table 10.5 Properties of filter fabrics [7]

Fabric	Temperature limitation (°C)	Chemical resistance	
		Acids	Alkalis
Cotton	80	Poor	Good
Wool	95	Good	Poor
Nylon	95	Poor	Good
Polypropylene	95	Excellent	Excellent
Orlon	125	Good	Fair
Dacron	135	Good	Fair
Dynel	70	Good	Good
Glass	287	Excellent	Poor
Nomex	200	Fair	Good
Polyethylene	74	Good	Good
Teflon	200	Excellent	Excellent

Table 10.6 Properties of filter fabrics [7]

Fibre type	Natural fibre		Polyamide			Polyacrylonitrile (PVC)		Polypropylene	Polyester (PE)		Polyacrylonitrile (PAN)			PTFE	Glass
Trade name	Wool	Cotton	Nylon 6	Nylon 66	Nomex	Fibravyl	Cevyl T	PP	Diolen	Trevira	Dralon T	Redon R	Dolan	Teflon	Gevetex
Operating temperature (°C)	95	85	100	120	210	60	90	100	150	150	140	140	130	260	300
Peak temperature (°C) (short duration)	120	110	110	130	320	70	100	130	200	200	160	160	160	275	600
Humidity absorption (%) (20°C and 65% RH)	14–16.5	7–8.5	4	4–4.5	2.5–3	0	0	0.04	0.4	0.4	1	1.3	1–2	0	0.3
Acid resistance	Good	Poor	Fair	Fair	Good	Very good	Very good	Very good	Good	Good	Good	Good	Good	Excellent	Good
Alkaline resistance	Poor	Very good	Very good	Very good	Very good	Very good	Very good	Good	Fair	Fair	Fair	Fair	Fair	Excellent	Fair

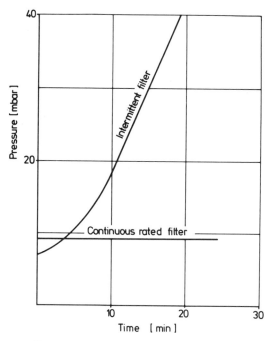

Resistance to air flow characteristic for an intermittent
and continuously rated filter

Figure 10.18 Operational characteristics of fabric filters.

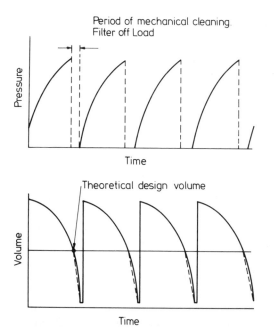

Figure 10.19 Cleaning cycle for mechanically shaken intermittent filters.

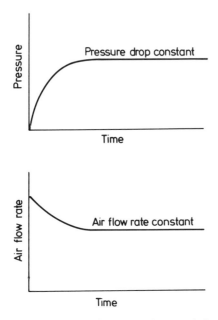

Figure 10.20 Performance characteristics of a continuous fabric filter system.

system, the period of operation of the filter must be limited to an upper pressure threshold; thereafter, the filter must be isolated from the process to facilitate a bag cleaning operation.

The cleaning process for intermittent filters is usually effected mechanically. Typical pressure–time and volume–time characteristics for such filters are shown in Fig. 10.19(a), (b), respectively.

In contrast, the performance characteristics of a continuous filter system where the dust is continuously removed are shown in Fig. 10.20(a), (b).

10.4.3 Fabric filter sizing

A crucial element in efficient pneumatic conveying system design is the correct sizing of the fabric filter system. Undersizing will normally create excessive pressure losses and result in a consequential reduction in system performance. Overdesign can result in unnecessary additional capital outlay or overloading of the filter system due to a lower pressure loss resulting in a greater mass of material being conveyed.

The sizing of a fabric filter is based on a factor known as the gas/cloth ratio. Essentially, the gas/cloth ratio is based on the gas flow per unit area of cloth which will produce a pressure drop which falls within limits. Pressure drop across such a filter is normally of the order of 200 mm water gauge (20 mbar).

The gas/cloth ratio is defined as

$$\gamma = \frac{\dot{V}}{A_{\mathrm{F}}} \tag{10.49}$$

where $\dot{V}$ is the volumetric flow rate of the gas at ambient conditions (m³/min) and A_{F} is the fabric filter area (m²).

The gas/cloth ratio has dimensions of velocity and is sometimes referred to as the *face velocity* or *approach velocity*. The value of γ is dependent upon the particle size and in many situations the physical characteristics of the particle. The range of values for γ is $0.5 \leqslant \gamma \leqslant 4$ where γ is measured in m/min.

Low values of the gas/cloth ratio γ (implying large filtration area) are for fine products or those products which are cohesive in nature. In Fig. 10.21, the gas/cloth ratio is plotted as a function of the mean particle size for various dust concentrations.

In this gas the dust concentration ρ_{α}^{*} is in units of g/m³, whilst the particle size is in microns (μm) and the gas/cloth ratio γ is in m/h. Typically for this situation $30 \leqslant \gamma \leqslant 240$.

As a rule of thumb, a fabric filter system (for most industrial applications) can be sized using a gas/cloth ratio range $0.8 \leqslant \gamma \leqslant 2$. Typically, for ordinary Portland Cement, it is accepted to use a gas/cloth ratio $\gamma = 1.5$. Referring to Fig. 10.21, for the case of ordinary Portland Cement a dust concentration $\rho_{\alpha}^{*} = 1000$. (In this case, using the above definition, the approach velocity is of the order of $v_{\mathrm{FV}} = 1.5$ m/min.)

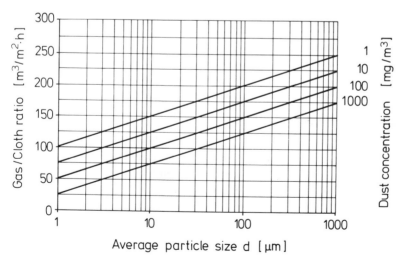

Figure 10.21 Gas/cloth ratio as a function of particle size and dust loading.

Example 10.6

A conveying system designed to transport ordinary Portland Cement through a $D = 100\,\text{mm}$ diameter pipe, was supplied with an air flow rate $\dot{V} = 11\,\text{m}^3/\text{min}$ FAD. The cement is conveyed on a batch basis using a bottom discharge blow vessel. What size filter is recommended if the conveying rate is $\dot{G} = 60\,\text{t/h}$, and ambient air density $\rho = 1.2\,\text{kg/m}^3$? (The mean particle size $d = 15\,\mu\text{m}$.)

Solution

The mass flow ratio, $\mu = \dot{G}/\dot{Q}$, where

$$\dot{Q} = \dot{V} \times \rho \times 60 = 792\,\text{kg/h}$$

$$\mu = \frac{60 \times 10^3}{792} = 75.8$$

Assume a system separation efficiency $\eta = 98\%$.

On the basis of this, 2% of the solids will be continuously in contact with the fabric filter. As such 1200 kg/h of cement impinges on the filter.

Dust concentration: Referring to Fig. 10.21 and extrapolating for $\rho_\alpha^* = 1818$ and a mean particle size $d = 15\,\mu\text{m}$, we obtain a gas/cloth ratio $\gamma = 70\,\text{m/h}$, which yields a face velocity $v_{\text{FV}} = 1.2\,\text{m/min}$.

On the basis of $v_{\text{FV}} = 1.2\,\text{m/min}$, the filter can now be sized using equation (10.49):

$$A_F = \frac{\dot{V}}{\gamma} = \frac{11}{1.2} = 9.2\,\text{m}^2 \tag{10.49}$$

However, since a single blow vessel is being used, there will be a slight overloading of the filter system when the last batch of cement is transported with the air remaining in the vessel at high pressure (Section 7.6.3). As such, in order to cope with the surge of high velocity air and to obtain a stock size filter, it would be expedient to select a filter with an area $A_F = 12\,\text{m}^2$.

10.4.4 Construction of fabric filter units

In most cases fabric filters consist of either a cylindrical or rectangular envelope bag supported by a wire cage. The wire cage keeps the bag open and provides the necessary sealing lip to locate the bag assembly in a plenum chamber. The filtration process normally occurs from the outside in, with the cleaned gas moving through the wire cage into the plenum chamber and then to atmosphere (Fig. 10.22).

Most filter systems are constructed such that all maintenance can be done from the outside thereby obviating the need for going inside the filter housing.

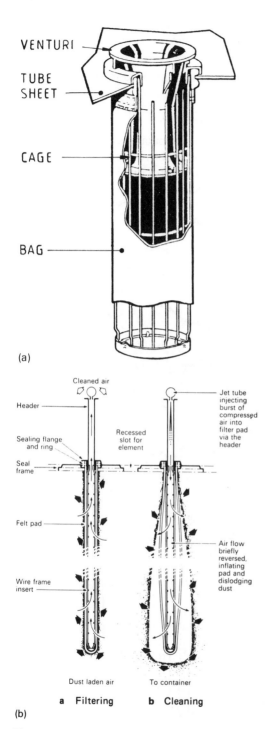

VENTURI

TUBE
SHEET

CAGE

BAG

(a)

Cleaned air

Header

Sealing flange
and ring

Seal
frame

Felt pad

Wire frame
insert

Recessed
slot for
element

Jet tube
injecting
burst of
compressed
air into
filter pad
via the
header

Air flow
briefly
reversed,
inflating
pad and
dislodging
dust

Dust laden air

To container

a Filtering   **b Cleaning**

(b)

Figure 10.22 Arrangement of (a) cylindrical and (b) envelope bag filter system.

10.4.5 Bag cleaning techniques

There are basically three cleaning techniques employed in fabric filter systems: reverse jet, reverse flow, and mechanical shaking.

(a) The reverse jet cleaning system (Fig. 10.23)

The reverse jet cleaning system is the most popular technique for pneumatic conveying systems. A series of nozzles is located above the mouth of each bag and supported in the plenum chamber. The nozzles are connected to a high pressure air supply via a series of solenoid actuated valves.

On activation of the solenoid valve, a jet of high pressure compressed air is expelled through the nozzle downwards into the bag. The expanding jet of air

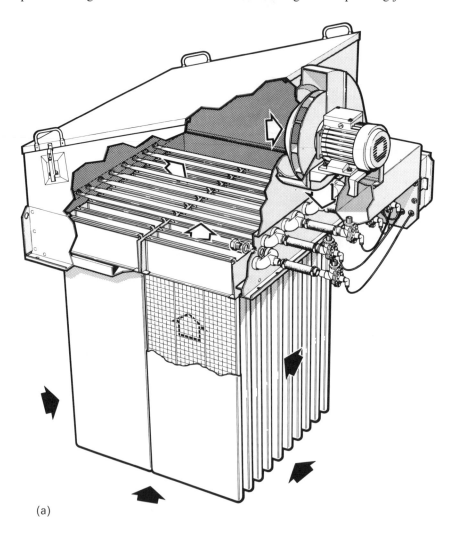

(a)

entrains additional air flow from the plenum chamber. The air jet provides a 'shock' blast of sufficient magnitude and volume to shake the dust off the bag. The loosened dust drops to the bottom of the filter housing. When sequencing the solenoid valves, it is possible to effect continuous cleaning of each bag whilst providing for continuous gas/solids separation. Thus, whilst a bank of bags is being cleaned by the reverse jet, the remaining bags in the system are actively filtering the dust laden gas.

The activation of the solenoid valves is controlled by means of an electronic timing device, which can vary both the duration of the pulse and the interval between pulses. Normally the duration time can be adjusted between 0.05 and 0.2 seconds.

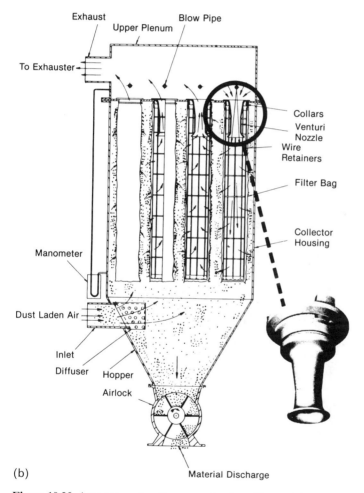

(b)

Figure 10.23 Arrangements of reverse jet bag filters: (a) Dust Control Equipment, Leicester, UK; (b) Mikro-Pulsive, Brandt Engineering, South Africa.

The cleaning action is a function of the impulse available from the pressure of the cleaning gas and the duration of the pulse. The cleaning gas pressure lies in the range 300–10 000 kPa. The selection of the appropriate solenoid valve to ensure effective cleaning is dependent upon this pressure.

The maximum length of a bag is a matter of much dispute, with some suppliers claiming high cleaning efficiency with reverse jets operating on bags in excess of 3 m in length. In general, it is accepted that reverse jet cleaning is most efficient in bags less than 2 m long.

(b) Reverse flow filters (Fig. 10.24)

Reverse flow filters use a similar bag construction as the reverse jet units, but employ low pressure air for cleaning. In these filters a bank of bags is sequentially segregated from the rest of the cleaning system and a low pressure high air flow is diverted into the sealed-off banks of bags. The air effectively 'reverses' the flow and thereby removes the dust clinging to the filter bags. A fairly complex mechanical system is normally employed to effect the sealing off and to connect

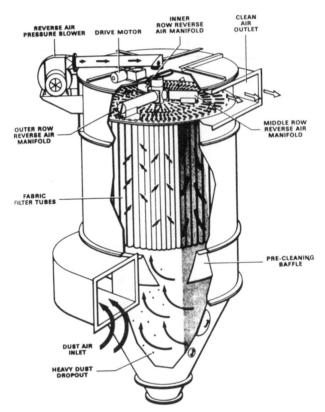

Figure 10.24 Arrangement of reverse flow bag filter (CEA-Carter-Day Co., USA).

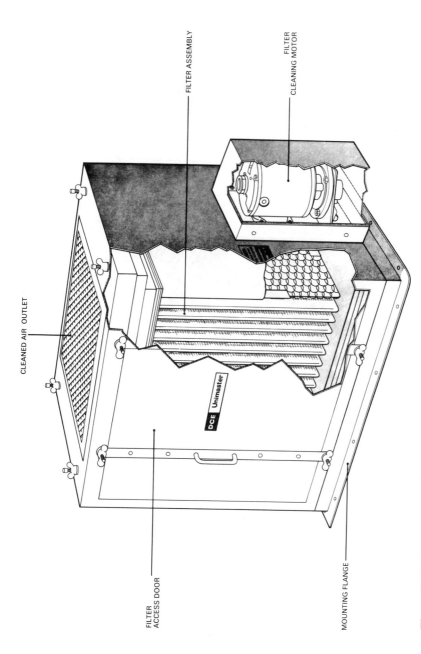

CLEANED AIR OUTLET

FILTER ASSEMBLY

FILTER CLEANING MOTOR

FILTER ACCESS DOOR

MOUNTING FLANGE

DCE Unimaster

Figure 10.25 Arrangement of mechanical shaking filter (Dust Control Equipment, Leicester, UK).

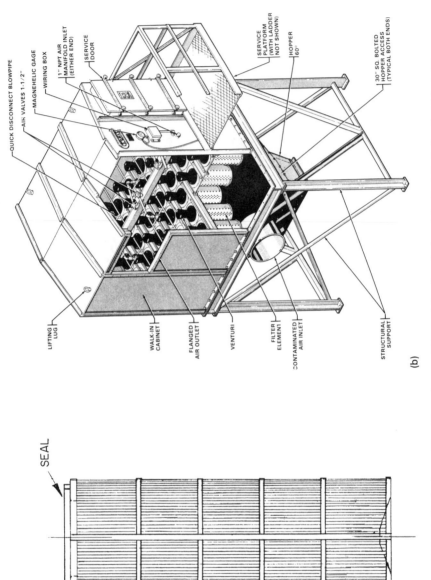

SEAL

(a)

(b)

QUICK DISCONNECT BLOWPIPE

AIR VALVES 1-1/2"

MAGNEHELIC GAGE

WIRING BOX

1" NPT AIR MANIFOLD INLET (EITHER END)

SERVICE DOOR

SERVICE PLATFORM (WITH LADDER NOT SHOWN)

HOPPER 60°

30" SQ BOLTED HOPPER ACCESS (TYPICAL BOTH ENDS)

LIFTING LUG

WALK-IN CABINET

FLANGED AIR OUTLET

VENTURI

FILTER ELEMENT

CONTAMINATED AIR INLET

STRUCTURAL SUPPORT

Figure 10.26(a) Typical cartridge filter element (General Services Industrials (Pty) Ltd, South Africa); (b) arrangement of cartridge filter systems (Donaldson Co. Inc, Minneapolis, USA).

the sealed off compartments to the low pressure blower. Such filtration systems normally include as part of the package a suitably sized blower to effect the reverse flow.

(c) Mechanical shaking filters (Fig. 10.25)

Mechanical shaking filters are becoming less popular in pneumatic conveying applications. Essentially the bags are supported in frames which in turn are connected to either a cam arrangement or a vibrating device to effect bag cleaning.

In most cases the cleaning operation requires the filter unit to be isolated from the main dust source whilst the cleaning operation is underway (Fig. 10.25). Mechanical cleaning filter systems, normally employ an electronic control device which ensures that a system is inoperable during the cleaning phase.

10.4.6 Cartridge filters (Fig. 10.26)

A relatively new innovation to dust cleaning is the use of paper cartridge filter elements instead of bags in reverse jet filters. The construction of the filter housing and cleaning mechanism is similar to that employed in reverse jet filters. However, the use of a paper element provides a significant space advantage.

By virtue of the pleated construction, large filtration areas are available in a relatively compact arrangement. As such, in applications such as large mobile vacuum systems, the ability to reduce the volume and the mass of the filter housing is extremely beneficial.

As with all filter elements, it is essential that a cartridge filtration unit be selected with the full knowledge of both the quality of the dust and the conveying process. There is a wide variety of cartridge elements available on the market. The majority conform to the normal paper element similar to those used on the intake manifold of large diesel engines. However, more recently with the advance of materials such as teflon, cartridges are being constructed with these more modern materials thereby enhancing the range of products which can be effectively separated using these systems.

10.4.7 Arrangement of filter housing (Fig. 10.27)

A most important aspect of fabric filter systems is the design of the housing into which the fabric filter unit is located. In most cases the filter unit housing is also required to provide some form of storage capacity for the separated solids.

It is now accepted practice to use a properly designed housing instead of the earlier practice in which a cyclone was used as a pre-separation unit to a bag filter system. As such, the design of the housing normally provides for a certain amount of cyclonic action to provide the necessary pre-separation of coarse particles.

In a circular housing construction, the conveying pipe is tangentially mounted onto the filter housing whilst, in a square or rectangular housing, the stream of gas laden solids is directed towards an impact plate to effect the pre-separation.

The essential features of the design of the housing must take into consideration

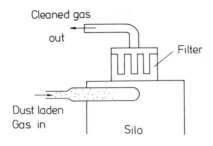

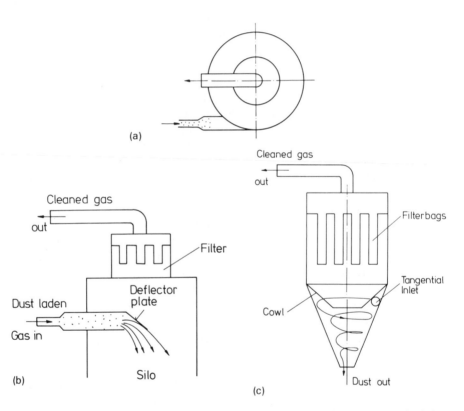

Figure 10.27(a) Tangential inlet arrangement for a circular filter housing; (b) inlet arrangement for a rectangular filter housing; (c) cowl inlet arrangement.

some of the elements of cyclone design. It is also normal practice to design the housing with the inlet pipe of a diameter larger than that of the conveying pipe. As such, on approaching the filter housing, the increased pipe diameter provides for a reduction in velocity thereby facilitating a certain degree of drop-out of solids before entering into the filter housing.

A number of arrangements are available from manufacturers in which various techniques are employed to locate the tangential inlet into the filter housing. One manufacturer, for example, will ensure that the tangential inlet pipe is located in the filter house immediately below a cowl arrangement. In Fig. 10.27(c), the arrangement is shown. Essentially this arrangement provides for some additional pre-separation and thereby minimizes the dust loading on the filter bags.

A further important element in the design of the filter housing is to ensure that the diameter of the filter housing is such that it regulates the approach velocity to the bags. As such in terms of the discussions in Section 10.5.3, a filter housing must be designed to take into consideration the total gas flow rate into the filter system. On the basis of this, it is possible to ensure that the diameter of the housing is such that the face velocity is controlled in terms of the desired gas/cloth ratio.

A number of problems can arise due to inadequate design of the filter housing. In particular an inadequately designed filter housing can result in a reverse vortex forming inside the filter, which can result in a re-entrainment of the dust particles thereby increasing the loading on the filter bags. In such situations, it is common practice to arrange for a vortex breaking device to be fitted into the filter housing (Fig. 10.28). A typical solution is to include a honeycomb type structure in the filter housing which effectively assists with the straightening out of the flow before the dust laden solids impinge on the bags.

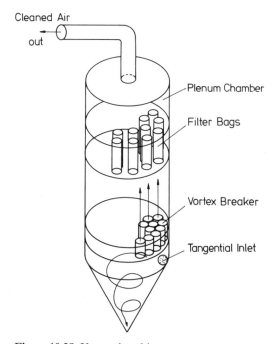

Figure 10.28 Vortex breaking arrangement.

There are a number of additional ways of introducing the dust laden gas into a filter system. In particular, the counter current system (Fig. 10.29) is recommended for systems which have a predominance of coarse material.

For fine particle suspensions the co-current system (Fig. 10.30), in which the gas–solids suspension is introduced either axially or radially through a channel in the bag house, is recommended. Clearly such a system cannot be used for abrasive materials.

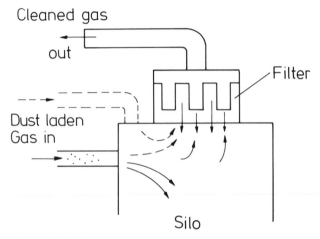

Figure 10.29 Counter current filter system.

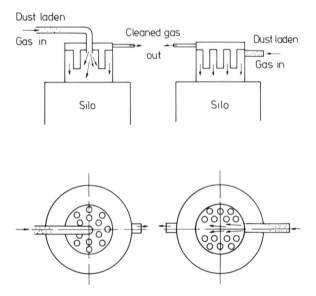

Figure 10.30 Co-current filter systems.

10.4.8 Dust explosions and earthing of filters

The question of providing adequate protection in the event of a dust explosion is a complex topic in its own right. System designers must be aware of the fact that almost any dust is explosive at a critical concentration.

By virtue of the large volume of the filter housing such critical dust concentration levels can occur at the end of a conveying period. Further, it is not uncommon to find high static electrical discharges occurring during a pneumatic conveying process. The advent of such a discharge occurring in a filter housing can initiate a dust explosion.

There are numerous techniques [8] available to safely vent a filter housing in the event of such an explosion taking place. The use of bursting discs and vent panels correctly sized is often recommended. In highly explosive environments safety regulations demand the use of an inert gas to suppress a dust explosion. In certain situations nitrogen is used as the conveying gas.

It is accepted practice to ensure that in high risk systems, the bags and the bag cages are earthed to the body of the filter. Such earthing procedures ensure the effective discharge of any static build-up.

10.5 CLEANING BY SOUND

The use of high frequency sound waves for the 'sonic activation' of powders [9] is gaining widespread acceptance as an effective and economic method of enhancing the performance of gas–solids separation equipment. Sound waves are generated using a special Tyfon type sound emitter. The waves are generated at frequencies of the order of 200 Hz to 400 Hz.

The sound emitter is located in the filter or cyclone housing (Fig. 10.31) and is

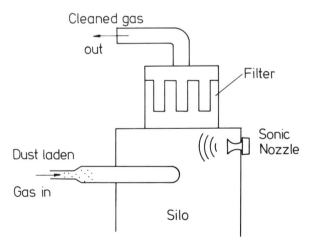

Figure 10.31 Arrangement of sonic horn in a filter housing.

operated intermittently to achieve maximum benefits. In addition to enhancing the cleaning of fabric filter systems, the high frequency sound waves also assist with the flow of the separated material out of the filter housing.

10.6 CONCLUSIONS

In this chapter an attempt has been made to provide the reader with an overview of the field of gas–solids separation. Essentially the selection of a suitable gas–solids separation device should be made in consultation with the suppliers of the equipment.

It would be impossible in such a text to adequately cover all the facets of gas–solids separation. System designers are cautioned to ensure that when designing systems for specialist applications, the expert advice of suitably competent gas cleaning engineers is sought.

An attempt has been made, however, to provide the reader with a comprehensive dissertation on cyclone design. It is believed by the authors that this section could be of assistance.

REFERENCES

1. Suurovsky, L. (1981) *Solid-Gas Separation, Handbook of Powder Technology*, Vol. 3 (eds. J.C. Williams and T. Allen), Elsevier, Amsterdam.
2. Stairmand, C.J. (1969) *Selection of Gas-Cleaning Equipment—A Study of Basic Concepts*, Filtration Society, London, September.
3. Duckworth, A. (1973) *Lecture Course Pneumatic Transport of Solids in Pipes*, University of Witwatersrand, Johannesburg, South Africa.
4. Barth, W. (1956) *Brennstoff-Warme-Kraft*, **8**.
5. Weidner, G. (1954) Die Bestimmung derDruckverluste von Zyklonabschedern, *VDI-Tagungsheft*, No. 3, 20.
6. Muschelknautz, E. and Brunner, K. (1967) Untersuchungen an Zyklonen, *Chem. Ing. Technol.*, **39**, 531–8.
7. Kayser, A. Spinnerei und Weberei, Einbeck, West Germany.
8. Bodurtha, F. T. (1980) *Industrial Explosion Prevention and Protection*, McGraw-Hill, New York.
9. *Cleaning by Sound*, Kockumation AB, Malmö, Sweden.

11

Some comments on: the flow behaviour of solids from silos; wear in pneumatic conveying systems; ancillary equipment

11.1 INTRODUCTION

There are a number of additional facets in the design of pneumatic conveying systems which in their own right could form the basis of a separate handbook. An awareness of the intricacies of silo and hopper design, wear in pneumatic conveying systems and the type and characteristics of a number of essential hardware components are deemed to be important information for the system designer.

In many instances, a lack of appreciation of efficient silo design or the dos and don'ts for designing systems for abrasive products have resulted in the condemnation of total systems. This chapter has been written with the specific objective of providing the reader with some insight into the additional factors relevant to the design of pneumatic conveying systems. The reader is cautioned to obtain specialist assistance for those systems which are being designed for products which are highly abrasive or have very poor flow characteristics.

The chapter is concluded with some discussion related to those essential components which, together with feeding devices discussed in Chapter 7 and gas–solids separation devices discussed in Chapter 10, make up a total conveying system.

11.2 THE FLOW OF SOLIDS FROM BINS

11.2.1 Introduction

An essential element in the successful operation of any pneumatic conveying system is the flow of solids from storage bins into the feeding device. The ability to ensure reliable and continuous flow from any storage device is fundamental to ensuring that a system will meet design criteria.

The 'correct' design of a storage bin requires the full appreciation of techniques such as those developed by Jenike [1] and others [2]. In this text the authors intend to alert the reader only to those essential elements which, when combined with an accepted design technique, will provide a successful bin design. It is not the intention of this text to provide the reader with all the information relating to the design of such storage systems.

11.2.2 Common flow problems from a silo bin

Essentially, there are two common flow problems associated with the incorrect design of a silo: (a) bridging; (b) ratholing.

(a) Bridging

The bridging phenomenon results in an arch or a bridge forming across the opening of a hopper. The strength of the bridge is such that it supports the total load of solids above it. Bridging occurs when the outlet of the silo $D < D_{min}$; where D_{min} is the calculated minimum diameter required to effect uninterrupted solids flow. (Bridging can occur even though the cone angle θ might be of the same magnitude as that obtained from accepted silo design theory.)

(b) Ratholing

The ratholing phenomenon is characterized by the formation of a channel throughout the solid mass. In this case the phenomenon is dependent upon the correct selection of the cone angle θ. Ratholing will occur even though the hopper opening conforms to he $D \geqslant D_{min}$.

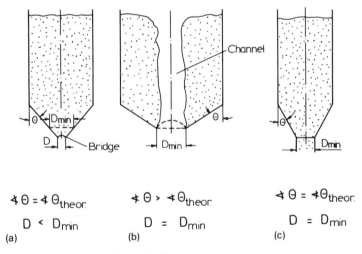

Figure 11.1 Flow problems in silos.

The bridging and ratholing phenomena are shown in Fig. 11.1(a), (b) alongside a 'correctly' designed silo which will promote mass flow (Fig. 11.1(c)).

11.2.3 Characteristic flow of granular and powdered products from a storage bin

Essentially the flow of granular and powdered products from a storage bin conforms to two flow situations: (a) mass flow; (b) funnel flow. In Fig. 11.2 the characteristics of mass flow and funnel flow are depicted.

(a) Characteristics of a mass flow bin

Mass flow from a bin implies that the total volume of the stored solids is in motion. As such, uniform and steady state flow can be attained. A mass flow bin is devoid of any channelling, surging, flooding, hang-ups or bridging. The flow is also independent of the head of the stored solids and as such these bins guarantee a minimum of consolidation of the products, no dead space, minimal degradation, consolidation and spoilage. In summary, the flow from a mass flow bin is aptly described as providing the user with a 'first in and first out' situation.

(b) Characteristics of a funnel flow bin

Funnel flow is best understood by considering the flow from a bin with a flat bottom or gentle slope. In such a situation the flow occurs in a channel in the centre of the bin. The flow is always from the top of the stored solids to the centre.

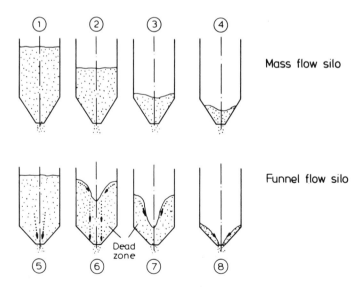

Figure 11.2 Mass flow and funnel flow.

During the flow of solids through the channel, a dead zone occurs in all other parts of the bin. Funnel flow leads to 'first in and last out' and has disadvantages such as flooding, material degradation, consolidation, etc.

In some situations a poorly designed bin, or conditions of continuous filling and drawing out of product, can lead to 'first in and never out'. Solids with a wide particle size distribution tend to segregate out, leaving the coarse particles in the dead zone whilst the fine particles flow through the channel.

The ultimate selection between mass flow and funnel flow must, in addition to taking into consideration the product characteristics and the process, take cognizance of the fact that a mass flow bin is generally more costly and will by virtue of its construction occupy considerably more headroom.

11.2.4 Factors influencing the flow of solids from a bin

There are three essential factors which must be considered when designing a storage hopper or bin.

(a) Geometric form of hopper

The essential elements which must be considered include:

(1) Cone angle (2θ).
(2) Size of outlet (D_{min}).
(3) Shape (circular or rectangular).
(4) Hopper construction material (ϕ_x).

(b) Product characteristics

(1) Particle size and shape.
(2) Particle size distribution.
(3) Particle density and bulk density.
(4) Cohesivity of the product.
(5) Fluidizability.
(6) Floodability.
(7) De-aeration characteristics.

(c) Additional factors

(1) Influence of humidity.
(2) Temperature of product and process.
(3) Storage time.
(4) Ambient conditions.

11.2.5 Stress distribution in a silo

In order to appreciate the various forces imposed by the stored solids on the walls of a silo, the stress distribution for a typical conical bottom silo will be discussed

(Fig. 11.3). As a starting point, the stress distribution for the case of the silo carrying a liquid is shown as the hydrostatic pressure. Clearly, the stress distribution is uniform and is a function of the level of the liquid in the silo, i.e. the highest pressure occurs at the bottom of the conical hopper.

Substituting the liquid with a granular product results in a stress distribution as indicated by σ_1 (the principal stress or major consolidation stress) curve. It can be seen that at the highest level in the silo, the stress distribution for the solids is similar to that of the liquid. Due to the friction between the particle and the wall of the silo, the σ_1 curve deviates with growing depth.

After a certain head of solids it will be noted that the σ_1 stress distribution remains constant until the transition zone in which the silo changes shape from a cylinder to a cone. In this zone, there is a sharp increase in the value of the stress σ_1. It will be further noted that beyond the transition, the stresses in the cone decrease linearly towards the outlet. Theoretically, the stress attains a value of zero at the peak of the cone.

An important feature of the storage of products in a silo is the advent of consolidation.

The unconfined yield stress, f_c, is best understood by referring to the simple model depicted in Fig. 11.4. A cohesive bulk solid is loaded into a cylindrical former, and subjected to a normal stress σ_1 which is representative of the mass of the solids in a silo. On careful removal of the former, a cylinder of the bulk solids will remain. If the unconfined cylinder is now subjected to a stress, the bulk solid will initially resist the load until a point is reached where the bulk solid cylinder yields. The stress at which yielding takes place is the unconfined yield stress f_c. It will be noted that the unconfined yield stress, f_c, follows the same pattern as the

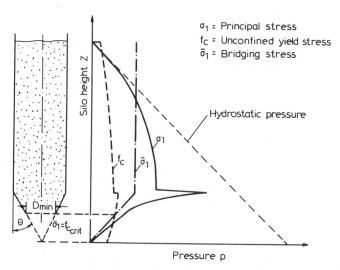

Figure 11.3 Stress distribution in a silo.

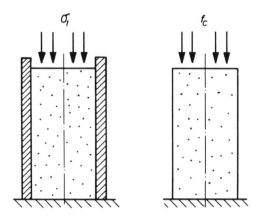

Figure 11.4 Simplified model to illustrate the unconfined yield stress.

principal stress σ_1. This stress is dependent upon the principal stress and as such follows similar trends.

The bridging stress, $\bar{\sigma}_1$, is a function of the silo diameter having a constant value in the cylindrical part of the silo and decreasing from the transition to the bottom of the cone. The intersection of $\bar{\sigma}_1$ and f_c yields a critical point where bridging of the solids is possible. In the case where the bridging stress, $\bar{\sigma}_1$, is greater than the unconfined yield stress, no bridging is possible. However, if the unconfined yield stress, f_c, is greater than $\bar{\sigma}_1$, then bridging is possible.

A critical component in the silo design is the selection of the minimum opening, D_{min}, to ensure free flow of the solid material. The selection of D_{min} is dependent upon $f_{c(crit)}$, the critical unconfined yield stress. It should be noted that $f_{c(crit)}$ occurs at the intersection of $\bar{\sigma}_1$ and f_c.

11.2.6 Experimental methods for measuring the flow characteristics of bulk solid materials

11.2.6.1 Introduction

The final design procedure for silos is dependent upon the acquisition of certain fundamental flow properties of the material. Whilst there are several techniques available to provide design information, perhaps the most common and most successful technique lies in the use of the Jenike shear cell. Other techniques include the ring shear cell developed by Walker; the powder tester of Hosakawa; the torsional shear cell of Peschl, etc. Discussions in this text will be confined to the Jenike shear cell.

11.2.6.2 The Jenike shear cell

The Jenike shear cell (Fig. 11.5) is composed of a base located on a frame of the apparatus, a ring resting on top of the base and a cover. The bottom of

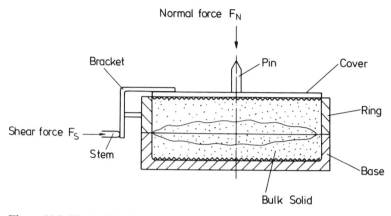

Figure 11.5 The Jenike shear cell.

the cover and the inside of the base are roughed to increase the adhesion of
the tested solid. The base and the ring are filled with material to be tested.

A pre-consolidation load is applied to the material in order to ensure a
homogeneous sample. The skill of the operator lies in the preparation of the
samples and, in particular, the ability of reproducing the same porosity for
each test specimen.

A vertical force F_N (normal force) is applied to the cover. A horizontal shear
force F_S is applied by means of a stem which acts on a bracket attached to the
cover. The stem acts in the plane of contact between the ring and the base. A
part of the shearing force is transferred from the bracket to the ring through
a loading pin. This ensures a sufficiently uniform distribution of the shearing
force F_S across the cell.

The shear force is measured by means of a load cell and a typical shear rate
is of the order of 2.7 mm/min. The shear cell tester enables the evaluation of
the following information:

(a) The effective angle of internal friction ϕ_e.
(b) The kinematic angle of friction ϕ_i.
(c) The major principal or consolidating stress σ_1.
(d) The unconfined yield stress f_c.
(e) The bulk density in the cell $\rho_{B(cell)}$.

A second test involving the use of a plate located on the base is performed to
obtain design data relevant to the interaction between the material and the
hopper wall. The plate is thus representative of a sample of the proposed material
to be used in the construction of the silo. From these tests the following
information is obtained:

(f) Angle ϕ_w, the wall friction angle where $\phi_w = \tan^{-1}(\tau/\sigma)$.

11.2.7 The Jenike flow categorization technique

Jenike proposed a method of categorizing the flow of bulk solids in terms of a factor ff_c known as the flow function which is obtained by plotting the unconfined yield stress, f_c, against the major consolidation stress, σ_1.

11.2.8 The Jenike design theory

Whilst it is not the intention of this text to provide a detailed description of the Jenike design theory, a brief summary of the salient features of the technique will be highlighted.

11.2.8.1 Results from shear cell analysis

Once an accepted testing procedure has been performed, using a shear cell, on the bulk solids, a number of observations are obtained which facilitate the plotting of the $\tau - \sigma$ diagram (Fig. 11.6). The shear cell analysis is performed to yield at least three yield loci, obtained by using a Mohr semicircle technique as shown in Fig. 11.6.

From this diagram the following information can be obtained:

(a) The major consolidation stress σ_1.

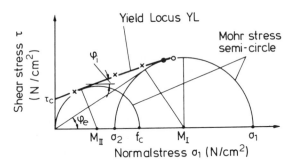

Figure 11.6 The τ–σ diagram.

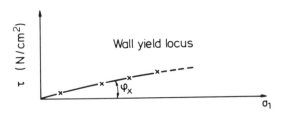

Figure 11.7 τ–σ diagram for a plate.

(b) The unconfined yield stress f_c.
(c) The kinematic angle of friction ϕ_i for the product.
(d) The effective angle of internal friction ϕ_e of the product.

In addition, from tests carried out using a plate of the material to be used for the construction of the silo, the shear cell analysis permitted the construction of the $\tau - \sigma$ diagram as shown in Fig. 11.7. From this diagram the friction factor between the bulk solid and the silo construction material, ϕ_x, is obtained.

11.2.8.2 Flow factor, ff

Extensive observations lead to the conclusion that a bulk solid will flow if a bridge (Fig. 11.1) does not develop across the channel. In mass flow bins, such a situation cannot occur. In funnel flow bins, however, it is necessary to ensure that the bulk solids are not capable of sustaining an empty, vertical pipe of excessive height (Fig. 11.2).

For an obstruction to occur in a channel, the bulk solid has to be consolidated to such a degree that it develops sufficient strength to support the weight of the solids above it. As such, the higher the consolidating pressure, σ_1, in a channel, and the lower the pressure, $\bar{\sigma}_1$, which acts in an obstruction, the lower the flowability of the channel. This is expressed by the flow factor

$$ff = \sigma_1/\bar{\sigma}_1 \tag{11.2}$$

Jenike has consolidated his theory in a set of curves which provide information dependent upon whether the channel is conical or axisymmetric, plane flow or symmetric and for various values of effective angle friction ϕ_e.

In funnel flow a stable pipe or rathole may form above the outlet and for effective discharge the size of the outlet, and hence the diameter of the rathole, should be sufficiently large to ensure that the rathole will collapse and flow can be initiated. Critical rathole diameters are normally calculated for the consolidation pressures experienced when the bin or silo is filled. The dimensions of this critical diameter have been dependent upon ϕ_e, f_c and the bulk specific weight of the product. Critical rathole dimensions determined in this way give the maximum upper bound values likely to occur in practice.

In the initial work of Jenike it was proposed that the critical rathole diameter be calculated on the basis of the major consolidating pressure experienced on discharge. Funnel flow under these conditions involves the application of a flow factor which depends upon ϕ_e and the slope of the channel. A different set of curves is available for this case.

For design purposes, Jenike recommended a flow factor $ff = 1.7$ for funnel flow hoppers. Critical rathole diameters determined by this method, being based on the flow consolidation pressures, are normally underestimated. However ratholes determined in this fashion indicate a lower bound value which may be approached if the bin is being emptied whilst it is also being filled.

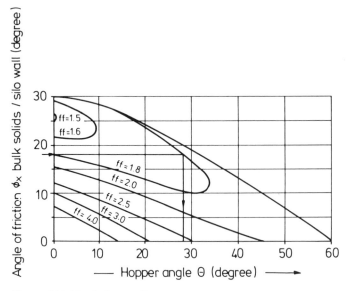

Figure 11.8 Typical mass flow curve.

Figure 11.8 is typical of one curve from a series of similar curves produced by Jenike for mass flow hoppers with different cone geometries. Similar curves for funnel flow are also available. The curve is a plot of the angle of friction, ϕ_x, against the cone angle, θ, with the flow function, ff, as a parameter for a constant effective angle of internal friction ϕ_e.

Having obtained the flow factor from a curve typical of that shown in Fig. 11.8, it is now possible to construct a curve in which f_c, $\bar{\sigma}_1$ is plotted against the principal stress σ_1. Fig. 11.9 is typical of such a plot.

In Fig. 11.9 the flow function, ff_c, is plotted from at least three yield loci curves as shown in Fig. 11.6. Further, the flow function ff as obtained from Fig. 11.8 is also represented on this curve. At the intersection of the ff_c and ff

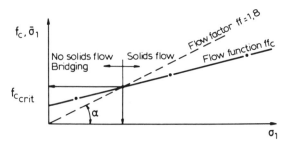

Figure 11.9

curves, the critical unconfined yield stress $f_{c(crit)}$ is obtained as well as the corresponding major consolidation stress, σ_1.

The diagram illustrates that all conditions to the left of the intersection point represent the no solids flow condition (bridging). All conditions to the right of the intersection point represent the solids flow condition.

Example 11.1

Design a mass flow hopper for a product for which a shear cell analysis provided the following data:

    (a) $\phi_e = 30°$
    (b) $\phi_i = 55°$
    (c) $\phi_x = 18°$
    (d) $\rho_{B(cell)} = 600\ \text{kg/m}^3$.

Solution

With the values of ϕ_e and ϕ_x it is possible to obtain the flow factor using Fig. 11.8. With $\phi_x = 18°$ a horizontal line will intersect the boundary curve at $\theta = 32°$. However, for adequate design safety it is customary to accept a low value of the angle θ. As such, moving horizontally along the $\phi_x = 18°$ line to a low value of θ results in the intersection of the $ff = 1.8$ boundary. Thus for this situation one obtains the following:

$$ff = 1.8 \qquad \theta = 28.5°$$

The intersection of the $ff = 1.8$ curve and yield loci curve yields a value of the

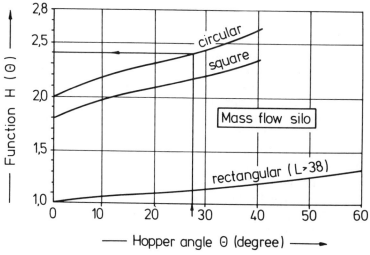

Figure 11.10

critical unconfined yield stress $f_{c(crit)}$.

$$f_{c(crit)} = 620 \, \text{N/cm}^2$$

Using the value of the cone angle, $\theta = 28.5°$, a second set of curves yields a factor: $H(\theta) = 2.4$ (for a circular outlet for this example (Fig. 11.10)). Using the above information it is now possible to calculate the minimum outlet diameter for mass flow:

$$D_{min} = H(\theta) \frac{f_{c(crit)}}{g \rho_{B(cell)}}$$

$$= \frac{(2.4)(620)}{(9.806)(600)}$$

$$= 0.253 \, \text{m}$$

In terms of the above, the silo will conform to the following:

(a) Cylindrical shape.
(b) Cone angle $\theta = 28.5°$.
(c) Opening 300 mm.

The design of funnel flow hoppers employs a similar procedure, but with different curves.

11.3 FLOW AID DEVICES FOR SILOS AND HOPPERS

11.3.1 Introduction

Whilst every effort should be made to design silos and hoppers according to accepted practice, there are a number of situations where flow aid devices fulfil an important role in the promotion of flow. In addition to providing 'first aid' for those situations where incorrect design procedures were adopted, flow aid devices are also used in situations where it is desired to use an existing installation for another product with different flow properties. Further, some flow aid devices are specifically incorporated into silo and hopper design to provide a controlled feed of product out of the silo.

Whilst in many instances, flow aid devices provide a relatively inexpensive solution to hopper flow problems, and their installation more often than not is based on a 'suck it and see principle', there is now an increasing awareness of putting more science into the art. As such, many vendors of flow aid devices are attempting to characterize their equipment to provide effective selection criteria for each application.

There is a wide range of these devices on the market. While some devices require minimal reconstruction of the existing silo, others require fairly substantial structural modifications before such a device can be installed.

In addition to providing a number of advantages in terms of flow assistance and flow control, many flow aid devices are used to reduce the height of the conical section of a silo. The ability to have an almost flat bottomed silo has a number of significant cost benefits.

In many situations, flow aid devices provide for a shallower conical hopper and hence a reduction in the overall height of the silo installation. It has been shown [3] that for each 300 mm of increased height of a wall of a 21.5 m diameter silo, an additional cost of $3000 is incurred.

The concept of additional costs in terms of height in the silo installation is further illustrated [3] by considering a hopper with a 3 m opening and a steel cone with a 60° angle of slope. To increase the angle of slope from 60° to 61° would require a vertical wall height increase of about 1.1 m. If the designer steepens the angle by 5° to 65° to protect against very stubborn materials, and he still wishes to retain the same storage capacity, he will end up with a structure with an extra 4.1 m of wall height with an additional cost of $40 500.

11.3.2 Types of flow aid devices

In general, flow aid devices conform to five basic types:

(a) Fluidization.
(b) Air assisted.
(c) Vibration.
(d) Hopper liners.
(e) Mechanical assistance.

The devices vary in complexity and in many cases a particular device might be better suited for a particular product.

11.3.2.1 Fluidization

There are a large number of flow aid devices using the concept of fluidization or aeration. The basic principle involves the mixing of the product with air thereby facilitating the flow of the product in a liquid like manner. Such devices are normally used for fine powdered products in which the particle size is such that the addition of air will promote flow. (See air activated gravity conveyors discussion—Chapter 8.)

Fluidization devices are produced in a variety of forms, from small nozzles in which the air is passed through a porous medium which distributes the air uniformally over the area of the nozzles, to large air pads normally used to line flat bottomed silos, thereby obviating the need to have a large conical section at the base of the silo. Other configurations include the use of specially constructed mushroom head devices with nozzles located behind the head of the mushroom. The mushroom head protrudes into the hopper wall, and the air which is passed into the head exits from the nozzles and effectively scours an area of the hopper wall providing an air envelope which facilitates the flow of the product.

In some instances, whole sections of the conical hopper are lined with an aeration sump whilst one device includes the use of a flexible diaphragm which distributes the air in the hopper as well as providing an additional benefit in terms of vibrating the product in the vicinity of the hopper outlet. The vibrations are set up as a result of the head of product resting on top of the diaphragm. The air escaping behind the diaphragm tends to lift the diaphragm which in turn is subjected to a force due to the mass of material on it. The successive movement of the product and the diaphragm creates the vibrations.

It is of vital importance to ensure that the air supply to the fluidization devices is clean and above all dry. In most cases, low pressure air is recommended with a maximum supply pressure of the order of 20 kPa. Typically, turbo blowers are commonly used for such applications. Moist air can create severe problems which lead to caking and eventual blockage of the fluidization device. In many cases, the use of too high an air pressure results in the formation of channels in the vicinity of the device.

A range of fluidization devices used to promote solids flow from bins is shown in Fig. 11.11.

11.3.2.2 Air assisted flow aid devices

The use of air assisted flow aid devices is gaining widespread acceptance as a viable method of promoting solids flow from storage devices. Much effort is being put into identifying a design procedure to facilitate both the sizing and the location of these devices [3].

Essentially, these devices make use of high pressure, high energy air blasts strategically located such that the air blast effectively breaks down 'dead' areas or bridges in a silo or hopper.

The device consists of a high pressure air receiver fitted with a specially designed large orifice quick release valve. The quick release valve is pilot operated and is normally electrically actuated to facilitate the use of a timing device. The air receivers are pressurized to about 700 kPa and the volume of air for each blast is controlled by the size of the air receiver. Depending upon the application, various size air receivers are available all working on the same principle.

The devices are located by simply fitting a 50 mm pipe to the wall of the silo or hopper and therefore connecting the flow aid device to the connecting pipe. There are a number of well documeted case histories of successful implementation of these devices [3].

A typical air assisted flow aid device is shown in Fig. 11.12 below.

11.3.2.3 Vibration

The use of vibratory devices to promote flow of solids from a silo is extensive and a large number of variations in design are available. In many situations,

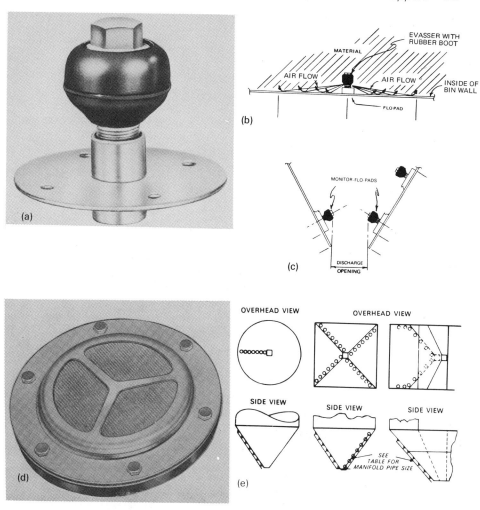

Figure 11.11 Typical fluidization devices to promote flow from storage bins; (a) evasser flo-pad (Monitor Manufacturing, USA–Flow Controls, South Africa); (b) Operation of evasser flo-pad; (c) Typical installation of evassers at discharge of bin; (d) Air pad aeration device (Monitor Manufacturing, USA–Flow Controls, South Africa); (e) Installation of air-pad devices in bins and hoppers.

vibratory devices, by virtue of their controllability are also used to provide a regulated discharge rate.

Invariably, the vibratory devices available conform to two types:

(a) External clamp-on vibrators.
(b) Internal fitted devices.

The devices are either pneumatically or electrically actuated such that both the

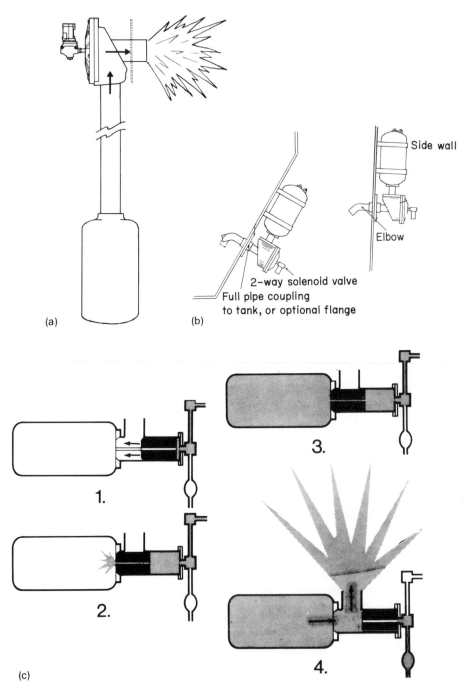

(a)

Side wall

Elbow

2-way solenoid valve
Full pipe coupling
to tank, or optional flange

(b)

1.

2.

3.

4.

(c)

Figure 11.12 Typical air assisted flow aid devices: (a) Air blaster flow aid device (Monitor Manufacturing, USA–Flow Controls, South Africa); (b) Installation of air blasters; (c) Filling and discharging cycle of a flow aid device (Big Blaster Air Cannon, Martin Engineering Co., Illinois, USA).

frequency and the amplitude of the vibrations imparted to the stored solids can be varied.

The external devices are located at various positions in the silo, but in general it is more common to find such devices fitted to the conical hopper.

By virtue of the fact that the external devices are fitted to the silo, extra care must be exercised in the selection of an appropriate vibrator. Vibrators that are too large for the structure can cause failure due to fatigue or can result in some of the structural members going into resonant sympathetic vibration which will produce unwanted vibrations elsewhere in the system. The judicious selection and location of such devices can result in an efficient and often relatively cost effective first-aid solution to a hopper flow problem.

The internal devices have proved to be most effective in promoting flow as well as providing an effective solids flow control. The vibratory bin discharger is a popular device providing a number of useful features. The device consists of a self-contained conical hopper with outlet chute fitted with a series of vibrators. The unit is located on the base of the silo by means of anti-vibration mounting brackets and a flexible rubber skirt provides the transition piece between the device and the silo hopper.

The vibratory bin discharger is totally isolated from the main structure and as such does not impart any vibrations to the rest of the system. One distinct drawback of such a device is the fact that in a first-aid situation, fairly substantial structural modifications must be effected to install a vibratory bin discharger.

A second internal device is the so called 'bridge breaker' [4], so designed that it can be fitted into an existing installation with minimal structural modifications. The 'bridge breaker' consists of a series of vibrating screens located inside the hopper. Vibrations are transmitted to the screens by means of external vibrators connected to the screens by means of large bolts which pass through the walls of the hopper. An isolation mount isolates the vibrations from the hopper and also provides a seal to prevent product from flowing through the holes in the hopper wall.

The 'bridge breaker' device thus induces vibrations into the product, close to the walls where flow problems normally occur. The amplitude of the vibration is between 2 mm and 4 mm and the frequency is approximately 20 Hz.

The type and construction of the screens is an important aspect of a 'bridge breaker' selection. Two types of screens are available: mesh screen and rib cage screen. Further, the shape of the screens is selected to suit both the shape of the hopper and the type of product. Screens conforming to triangular, rectangular and diamond shapes are available to meet a specific application.

Mesh screens are used for all applications involving powders and granular material up to about 20 mm in size. The rib cage screen construction is used for large particle sizes and fibrous materials.

In Fig. 11.13 the two types of internal type vibratory flow devices are depicted.

Whilst the effective use of vibrations to promote flow of granular or powdered solids is undisputed [5], there are situations where 'over' vibration can promote

Internal Vibrating Screens

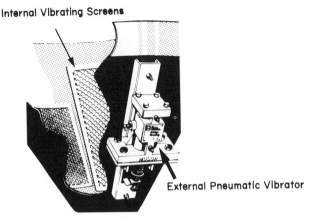

External Pneumatic Vibrator

Mucon Bridge Breaker
(Mucon, Basingstoke, England)

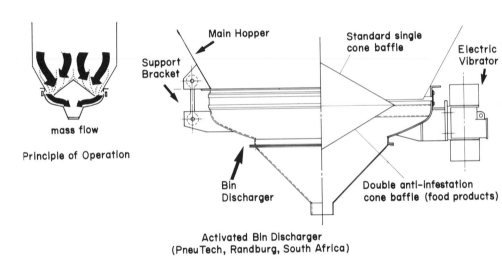

mass flow

Principle of Operation

Main Hopper

Support
Bracket

Standard single
cone baffle

Electric
Vibrator

Bin
Discharger

Double anti-infestation
cone baffle (food products)

Activated Bin Discharger
(PneuTech, Randburg, South Africa)

Figure 11.13 Internal type vibratory flow aid devices.

consolidation with attendant problems of total hold-up in the hopper. Certain fine powders compact when vibrated to such an extent that they become virtually solid and almost impossible to extract.

In many situations, the control of vibratory equipment is thus very important. As such, many installations are fitted with timing devices which control 'on'/'off' times of vibratory equipment to prevent consolidation.

The influence of vibrations in improving the flow characteristics of products from bins and hoppers has been extensively investigated by Roberts [5]. The author [5] has determined the influence of frequency and amplitude on the

Table 11.1 Influence of vibrations on hopper geometry [5]

Hopper geometry	Unvibrated conditions	Vibrated conditions $f = 200$ Hz; $X_p = 0.1$ mm
Half angle, α (deg)	19	33
Opening size, B (mm)	0.9	0.6

reduction of both the bulk strength and the wall or boundary friction for various storage conditions.

In a typical test, the influence of vibrations on the flow characteristics was determined as shown in Table 11.1. The data presented in Table 11.1 show the significant increase in hopper half angle α and reduction in the opening dimension that is possible when vibrations are applied.

11.3.2.4 Hopper liners

The use of special low coefficient of friction hopper liners to promote hopper discharge is becoming more acceptable as an economically viable technique. The improvement in fixing techniques and the further refinement in plastic technology has resulted in widespread use of special grades of plastic for hopper lining.

Thomas [6] in a paper on hopper linings outlines a number of features, which must be taken into account, when selecting a suitable liner for a particular application. He [6] lists a number of selection factors:

(a) Corrosion and water absorption.
(b) Operating temperatures.
(c) Ease of installation and maintenance.
(d) Safety factors including toxicity, flammability.
(e) Impact and wear resistance.
(f) Static build-up.
(g) Particle size and hardness.
(h) Influence on bin structure.

Perhaps one of the more significant aspects which must not be overlooked is the fact that a low friction lining could result in a change from funnel flow to mass flow in a bin. The flow transition will result in larger stresses being exerted in the transition region where the vertical walls join the start of the hopper section. These forces could be critical in old bins or bins which have not been adequately constructed to withstand the additional loads.

Bin wall and liner wear patterns can also change markedly as there is more sliding abrasion at the wall surfaces in a mass flow hopper than there is in the case of funnel flow. Recognition of these wear patterns will caution the user to employ thicker liners in such critical areas.

One of the more successful lining materials is ultra high molecular weight polymer (UHMW), which is an extremely long chain polyethylene based material with a molecular weight of 4–16 million. The exceptionally long chains result in a product with outstanding mechanical properties such as toughness, good sliding properties, abrasion resistance, etc. When compared to other products, UHMW has significant advantages and meets a large number of hopper lining requirements. From a cost point of view, UHMW is cheaper than PTFE, stainless steel, polyurethane and ceramic tiles. The material also provides a unique combination of abrasion and corrosion resistance.

11.3.2.5 Mechanical assistance

There are a number of mechanical devices which can be fitted to silos and hoppers which will promote flow. Invariably, these devices are used in very large silo installations and are unlikely to be encountered in systems employing pneumatic conveyors.

The installation of mechanical devices normally requires major structural changes and as such, these systems cannot really be considered as 'first-aid' devices.

Mechanical devices include, rotary ploughs, screw activators, paddle feeders and circular bin discharges.

11.4 WEAR IN PNEUMATIC CONVEYING SYSTEMS

11.4.1 Introduction

Of all the factors which limit the widespread application of pneumatic conveying systems, it can be said that wear plays the predominant role. Whilst wear in pneumatic conveying systems is a reality, experience has shown that with careful design and the selection of appropriate materials, wear problems can be substantially minimized. As technology improves and operators gain more experience, a number of simple and inexpensive techniques are available to increase the life of systems in which wear is a major problem.

A large number of wear studies have been undertaken by many research workers. It is clear that these studies have produced a diversity of opinions. This is not surprising, by virtue of the fact that one is dealing with a complex flow phenomenon.

Many studies have been purely subjective and in many cases inadequate experimental data have resulted in incorrect conclusions being drawn from such experimental investigations. Many of the studies have produced specific rather than general results and caution must be exercised when using the evidence from such studies for a similar yet different application.

The reader is cautioned to ensure that wear studies are evaluated in terms of a 'horses for courses' criteria in which in certain applications a particular wear resistant material might perform admirably whilst the same material might produce disastrous results in a different application.

There are some basic observations which hold true for all suspensions and these observations will be summarized in the following subsections.

11.4.2 The erosion mechanism

In the study of erosion of metals, there usually exists an incubation period during which little erosion occurs. This incubation period is followed by an accelerated rate period and then a steady state period [7]. Ductile and brittle materials have different responses to multiple solids impacts. These responses are associated with the angle of attack. Ductile materials perform best at large angles of attack whilst brittle materials erode less at low angles of attack. Review papers on the erosion of materials have been prepared by the National Materials Advisory Board [8], Adler [9] and Ruff and Widerhorn [10].

Many erosion theories on ductile materials use the constant flow stress concept to represent the material behaviour. Erosion of ductile materials has been considered as a gouging action like the tool cutting mechanism by Finnie [11, 12]. Bitter [13, 14] considered erosion as a cutting wear and a deformation wear mechanism. Bitter's model seems to follow the experimental findings closely. Optical microscopy and high speed photography were used by Winter and Hutchings [15, 16] to characterize the impact event. They concluded that material removal can occur by ploughing deformation or by two types of cutting deformation.

Assuming surface degradation occurs through a mechanism like fatigue for multiple particle impact Mamoun [17] developed an expression for erosion of ductile metals. Jahamir [18] used a delamination theory to account for erosion. Bellman and Levy [19] observed platelets which became detached from the surface by subsequent impacts. The platelets have also been found by Follansbee [20].

Erosion of metals can consist of discrete isolated impact craters or more uniformly eroded surfaces. The latter are more common for multiple impacts and consist of materials removal processes involving accumulative deformation. The mechanisms of the accumulative deformation are not well defined but heat generated at the surface and particle are probably involved in the process.

For ceramics, erosion takes place by a brittle process where material removal occurs mainly by chipping. This chipping process consists of two cracking regimes: an elastic and plastic regime [21]. Several types of fractures have been observed in the elastic regime, from single cone cracks [21]. Hardness and fracture toughness are the two parameters that control the erosion.

11.4.3 Experimental investigations on the influence of impact angle and surface material

The work reported by Tilley [22] shows the influence of impact angle and surface material on erosion. In Fig. 11.14 results of this work indicate that the three materials tested display different erosion rates and respond differently to varying angles of impact. Tilley's work was carried out using sand particles in the range 60–125 μm impinging on a flat plate at velocities of 100 m/s.

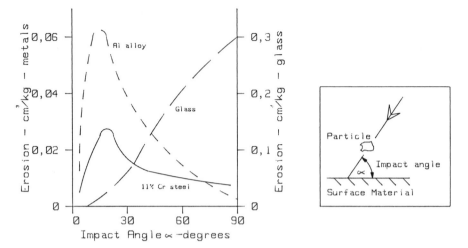

Figure 11.14 Variation of erosion with impact angle for various surface materials.

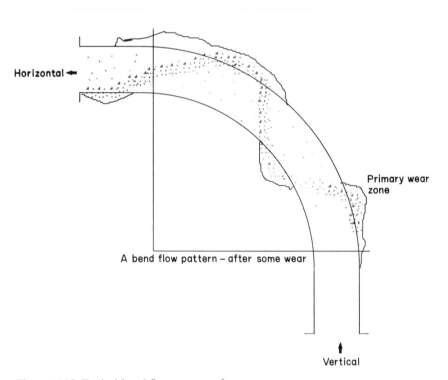

Figure 11.15 Typical bend flow pattern after some wear.

Alumunium alloy suffers maximum erosion at an angle of 20° and offers good erosion resistance at normal impact angles of 90°. This pattern is typical of ductile materials. 11% chromium steel exhibits characteristics of both a ductile and a brittle material. Of interest, is the impact angle at which maximum erosion takes place for both the aluminium and the chrome steel. This impact angle of the order of 20° must be viewed in the light of actual observations on flow through bends in pneumatic conveying systems.

Typically, the primary wear point occurs at an angle of incidence of the order of 20° within a bend. In Fig. 11.15, results from experiments carried out by Mason and Smith [23] are shown. These observations have been confirmed in many industrial situations.

11.4.4 Surface ripples

Ductile materials tend to form so called surface ripples at low values of impact angle. This phenomenon has been observed by both Sheldon and Finnie [24] and more recently by Snow [25] on studies carried out on the pneumatic transport of dried slimes in gold mining applications. Typical observations by Snow [25] are shown in Fig. 11.16. The surface ripples shown in this figure were observed in a horizontal pipe. The ripples are fairly regular in formation. Average conveying velocities of the order of 40 m/s were used in these studies.

11.4.5 Influence of particle size

As would be expected, most experimental observations show a clear increase in erosion with increase in particle size. In Fig. 11.17, results obtained by Sheldon and Finnie [24] are indicative of erosion obtained when an aluminium surface was eroded by angular silicon carbide particles moving at velocities of the order of 150 m/s.

11.4.6 Influence of particle velocity

Perhaps the single most important parameter in wear and erosion in pipelines is the particle velocity. Much work has been done to find a correlation between erosion and velocity. In simplistic terms the relationship between erosion and velocity can be stated as

$$\text{Erosion} = \text{constant} \times \text{velocity}^N$$

The exponent N varies from $N = 2$ for ductile materials to $N = 6$ for brittle materials. As a guideline, it is generally accepted $N = 3$ for most industrial situations. The influence of velocity and particle size in terms of erosion is shown in Fig. 11.18.

Figure 11.18 is a logarithmic plot showing the variation of the specific erosion with velocity for 230 μm sand conveyed at a solids loading $\mu = 2$ [26]. Results for four sets of tests conducted over a wide range of conveying velocities are shown in the figure. It is interesting to note that the slope of all four lines is of the order of 2.65, thus in this case the exponent $N = 2.65$.

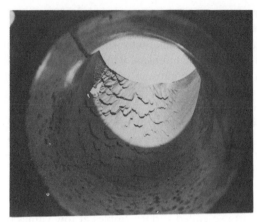

Inside of pipe

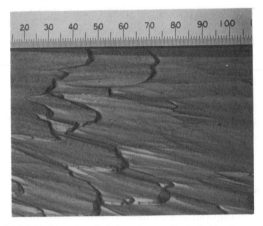

Close-up view of
surface ripples

Figure 11.16 Inside of a pipe showing surface ripples from the pneumatic transportation of gold mine slimes.

11.4.7 Effect of particle hardness

The influence of particle hardness has received little attention from researchers. Goodwin et al. [27] carried out studies on the impact of sand moving at 130 m/s at right angles to 11% chromium steel. It was found that the erosion is related to hardness by the expression

$$\text{specific erosion} = \text{constant} \times h_{\text{p}}^{2.3}$$

where h_{p} is particle hardness in kg/mm^2.

It is clear that much more work is required in this area. Implicit in any evaluation of hardness is the influence of particle sharpness and shape.

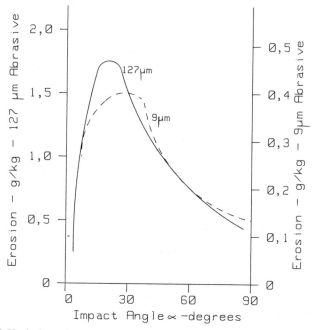

Figure 11.17 Variation of erosion with impact angle and particle size for aluminium.

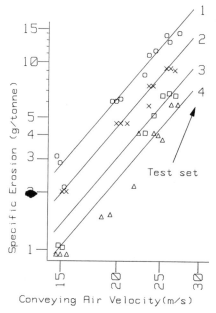

Figure 11.18 Variation of specific erosion with conveying velocity.

11.4.8 Effect of solids loading

Solids loading has been found to have a pronounced influence on the erosion rate in pneumatic conveying systems. In a study in which 17 μm sand was transported through 90° mild steel bends, Mills and Mason [28] established the following correlation:

$$\text{specific erosion} = 5.5\,(\text{solids loading})^{-0.26}$$

Graphically, the results are shown in Fig. 11.19.

From Fig. 11.19, it can be seen that the specific erosion expressed in grams of material removed per tonne of material conveyed through the system has a pronounced dependency upon phase density. An increase in phase density results in a decrease in the specific erosion.

11.4.9 Depth of penetration

More recently [29] additional studies on the influence of solids loading on specific erosion have confirmed the trend depicted in Fig. 11.19. The authors [29] however allude to the more realistic situation of 'depth of penetration' which ultimately has more significance in terms of the life of a pipeline or bend. Mills and Mason [30] found that in terms of the depth of penetration, there is a marked

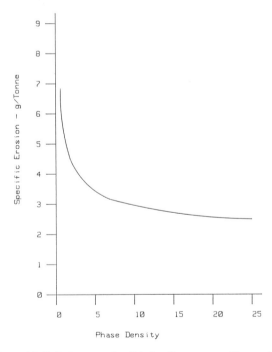

Figure 11.19 Influence of solids loading on specific erosion.

increase with solids loading and that the depth of penetration has an over-riding effect on the mass loss. As such, they found [30] that the mass of product that can be conveyed through a bend before failure occur actually decreases with increasing solids loading.

Agarwal *et al.* [29] illustrate the significance of depth of penetration using results obtained from experimental observations of profiles taken around the outer bend wall surface of two bends. The bends were located at different sections in a recirculating test rig: results indicate that for one bend a mass loss of 16 g was recorded and had a maximum depth of wear of about 0.7 mm. The second bend had a greater depth of wear for a mass loss of only 9 g. The first bend failed after losing 62 g of material whilst the second bend failed after a loss of only 39 g of material.

11.4.10 Evaluation of wear resistant materials

Many experimental techniques employed to evaluate the wear resistance of various materials are open to criticism in terms of the unrealistic testing procedures. Further, wear evaluation in which large samples of specialist materials are required can be prohibitively expensive. A technique developed by Wright [31] in which a number of samples of various wear resistant materials can be simultaneously evaluated has received widespread approval in terms of providing reliable data.

The technique provides for the construction of a target consisting of a sandwich of the various wear resistant materials to be tested. In the study [31] such targets were fitted to the primary and secondary wear zones in a long radius bend. The technique provides for the simultaneous evaluation of the materials, all of which are subjected to the same solids loadings, solids velocity and impact angle. Within each sandwich target, a mild steel sample was also included. The mild steel was used as the datum from both the wear point of view and the cost. A relative abrasion resistance index (RAR) was used for comparative purposes. RAR is defined as the volume loss per unit surface area with respect to mild steel.

A typical target test arrangement is shown in Fig. 11.20.

11.4.11 Minimizing wear

There are a number of techniques and golden rules which when practised can minimize the effects of wear in pneumatic conveying installations.

The most significant wear problems occur at bends or any discontinuity in a pipeline system. When transporting an abrasive product, extra precautions need to be taken to ensure careful alignment of the piping. In extreme cases, it is worthwhile employing special pipe joining techniques with machined spiggots at the flanges to minimize discontinuity at the joints.

There are a number of useful techniques to reinforce bends to prolong the life of the system. Bend reinforcement is usually effected by providing a thick protective layer of wear resistant lining on the back of a bend. Various methods of applying such linings are depicted in Fig. 11.21.

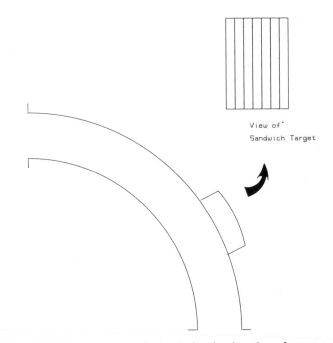

View of
Sandwich Target

Figure 11.20 Arrangement of a bend showing location of target tests.

In severe cases it is common practice to include a so called 'dirt box' in bend construction. Such a system provides for a situation in which the product which is being conveyed fills the box and creates a buffer zone in which the product being conveyed comes into contact with the same product.

In some cases, success has been achieved by re-designing the bend profile itself. In extensive trials [32] the replacement of a radiused bend with a T-bend has proved to be most successful. The T-bend has outlasted the radiused bend which was failing after some 200 tonnes of 50 mm quartzite rock was transported through it. The T-band concept was introduced after virtually every type of commercially available wear resistant liner was evaluated in the radiused bend configuration. Further tests [33] carried out over several years have proved the same configuration for T-bends can be used for Y-bends.

The basic premise behind the success of T- and Y-bend configurations appears to lie in the fact that there is only one point of impact during a change in flow direction. With a radiused bend, several changes in direction occur resulting in a sliding type wear. Typical profiles for T- and Y-bends are shown in Fig. 11.22.

In many highly abrasive conveying situations regular maintenance of the pipelines includes the rotation of pipes through 120°. This technique facilitates a more uniform wear pattern resulting in considerable increase in the life of horizontal piping. Pipe suppliers can provide pipes with special indicators which mark the 120° intervals.

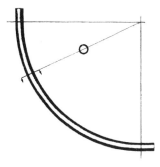

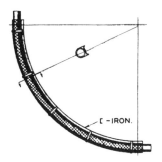

STANDARD PIPE BEND: Commonly used for non-abrasive materials. Minimum recommended radius varies from four feet in smaller pipe sizes to eight feet in larger sizes.

HOSE BEND: When handling materials, such as alum, that tend to adhere to a pipe bend, bends utilizing hose are provided. These are attached to a formed channel.

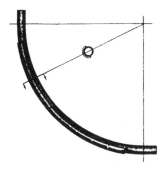

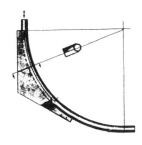

REINFORCED PIPE BENDS: For handling mildly abrasive materials, pipe bends with attached reinforcement are recommended. Welded-on (above) or bolted-on (below) reinforcement prolongs the life of the system at points where wear is greatest.

PIPE BENDS WITH BEARING BOXES: For handling highly abrasive materials, wearing boxes should be attached to pipe bends. Two common types are illustrated: single compartment wearing box (above), and concrete-filled wearing box (below) for greatest protection against system erosion.

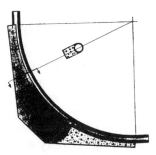

Figure 11.21 Bend reinforcing techniques (GATX-Fuller, Bethlehem, PA, USA).

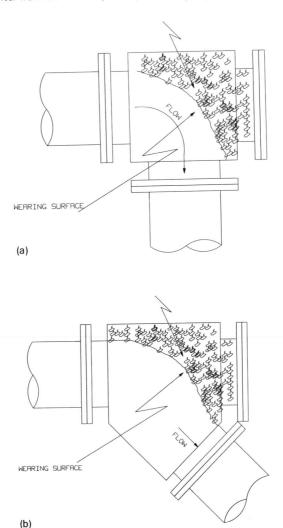

Figure 11.22 Bend profiles for (a) T- and (b) Y-bends.

The wear rate distribution across the pipe wall for a dilute phase system conveying quartzite rock has been investigated by Mohlmann [33]. A typical wear profile is shown in Fig. 11.23. In addition to showing a significant increase in wear rate for the bottom of the pipe, the influence of velocity is also indicated.

It is interesting to note that no difference in wear rate at the bottom of the pipe for the low and high velocity situations was measured. However, for the top and the side of the pipe a lower wear rate is recorded for the low velocity situation. The difference in velocity between the low velocity and high velocity situations was approximately 30%.

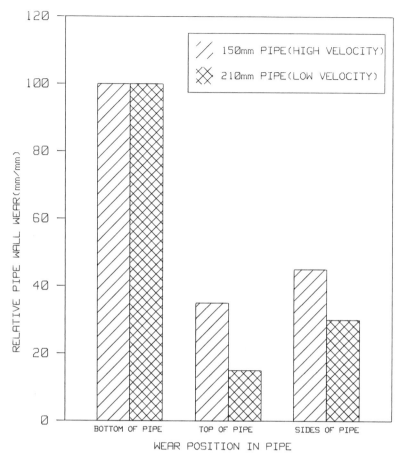

Figure 11.23 Relative wear along the bottom, sides and top of a horizontal pipe.

11.4.12 Interpretation of results from wear studies

The problems of incorrect interpretation of results obtained from wear studies can best be illustrated by considering two experimental investigations [31, 33].

In the first study [31], gold slimes were transported through a dilute phase system whilst in the second study [33], 50 mm lumps of quartzite rock were transported. Target tests described in Section 11.4.10 were used to evaluate a number of wear resistant materials. The relative abrasion resistance tests for both situations are shown in Fig. 11.24.

For the gold slimes, the polyurethane material (Ureline) proved to be the most effective with a wear resistance of over seven times that of mild steel. On the other hand, the same material (Ureline) had a wear resistance of one third of that of mild steel when subjected to the transportation of 50 mm lumps of quartzite.

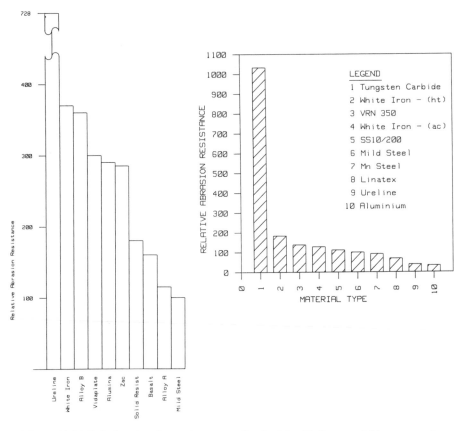

Figure 11.24 Relative abrasion resistance studies for (a) gold slimes and (b) quartz rock.

The above illustrates the point that wear resistant materials behave significantly different when subjected to different conveying situations. As such caution must be exercised when placing any reliance on the observations from experimental studies for wear situations very different from the envisaged application.

11.5 ANCILLARY EQUIPMENT

11.5.1 Introduction

One aspect of pneumatic conveying system design which is not documented in the literature is the ancillary equipment required to engineer a complete system.

The unsuspecting engineer who has eventually established all the criteria for a system design is then confronted with the problem as to what types of piping, bends, valves, etc. he should use in his system. In this section aspects of ancillary equipment for a system will be discussed. Discussions will be limited to a few of the more important ancillary components. Full details pertaining to specifications, pressure ranges, abrasion resistance, etc. must be obtained from reliable suppliers of such equipment.

11.5.2 Valves

Apart from the rotary airlocks discussed in Chapter 7, there are several types of control valves available to ensure flow control into and out of pneumatic conveying systems.

Valve selection must take into consideration such aspects as wear, upper temperature limits and maximum pressure or vacuum which the valve must seal against. There are several valves available, some specially developed for pneumatic conveying systems; other more common engineering valves can also be used. Valve technology is a science on its own and little justice can be done to it in a text of this nature. However, some of the valves used in pneumatic conveying systems will be discussed.

11.5.2.1 Non-return valves (Fig. 11.25)

It is good practice to protect all air supply lines by means of suitable non-return valves. These valves come in various forms and include flap type, poppet and wafer check types. Care must be taken to select a valve with a low pressure loss— this applies especially to dilute phase systems.

11.5.2.2 Butterfly valves (Fig. 11.26)

Butterfly valves are used extensively in blow vessel systems and are used as material feed valves, vent valves and in certain cases discharge valves.

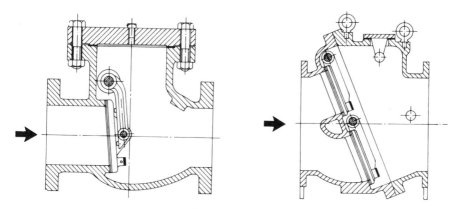

Figure 11.25 Typical non-return valves used for protection of air supply systems (Premier Valves, Transvaal, South Africa).

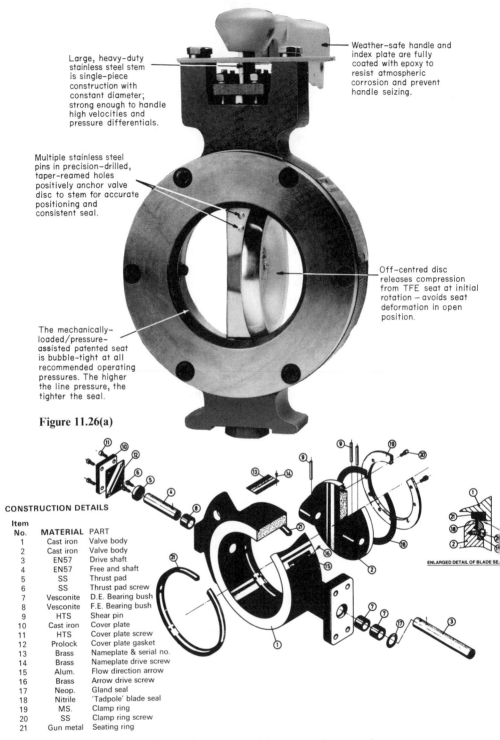

Large, heavy-duty stainless steel stem is single-piece construction with constant diameter; strong enough to handle high velocities and pressure differentials.

Weather-safe handle and index plate are fully coated with epoxy to resist atmospheric corrosion and prevent handle seizing.

Multiple stainless steel pins in precision-drilled, taper-reamed holes positively anchor valve disc to stem for accurate positioning and consistent seal.

Off-centred disc releases compression from TFE seat at initial rotation – avoids seat deformation in open position.

The mechanically-loaded/pressure-assisted patented seat is bubble-tight at all recommended operating pressures. The higher the line pressure, the tighter the seal.

Figure 11.26(a)

CONSTRUCTION DETAILS

Item No.	MATERIAL	PART
1	Cast iron	Valve body
2	Cast iron	Valve body
3	EN57	Drive shaft
4	EN57	Free and shaft
5	SS	Thrust pad
6	SS	Thrust pad screw
7	Vesconite	D.E. Bearing bush
8	Vesconite	F.E. Bearing bush
9	HTS	Shear pin
10	Cast iron	Cover plate
11	HTS	Cover plate screw
12	Prolock	Cover plate gasket
13	Brass	Nameplate & serial no.
14	Brass	Nameplate drive screw
15	Alum.	Flow direction arrow
16	Brass	Arrow drive screw
17	Neop.	Gland seal
18	Nitrile	'Tadpole' blade seal
19	MS.	Clamp ring
20	SS	Clamp ring screw
21	Gun metal	Seating ring

ENLARGED DETAIL OF BLADE SE

Figure 11.26(b) Typical butterfly valves used in pneumatic conveying processes.

Commonly referred to as a quarter-turn valve, the butterfly valve is also suited to automatic control by mounting an actuator on the valve stem. It is often said that the secret to butterfly valves is in the rubber technology, but irrespective of the quality of the rubber an incorrectly installed valve will provide endless problems.

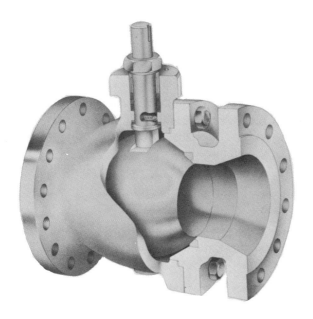

Figure 11.27 Typical arrangement of a full bore ball valve (Industrial Petroleum Valves Int Ltd, Germiston, South Africa).

Care must be exercised in ensuring that the valve shuts correctly. Any gap between the blade and the outer seal will provide a pathway for small particles under pressure to escape, resulting in rapid erosion of the valve blade and rubber seal.

Experience has shown that within reason the pressure losses across a butterfly valve in pneumatic transport systems are minimal. The use of butterfly valves in pipelines is also common in many systems, and as long as the correct selection of the valve has been effected, such valves can withstand the relatively high erosion which takes place during the conveying process.

11.5.2.3 Ball valves (Fig. 11.27)

Another member of the quarter-turn family, ball valves provide an uninterrupted flow path when fully opened. There are many ball valves operating successfully in pneumatic conveying systems, especially in high temperature applications (up to 200 °C). Ball valves are commonly used as discharge valves for brittle materials where it is undesirable to cause any particle degradation. Hence, the capacity of having a full bore valve is an advantage.

11.5.2.4 Pinch valves (Fig. 11.28)

Another form of valve which provides an uninterrupted flow path is the so called 'pinch valve' (or more sophisticated sleeve valve).

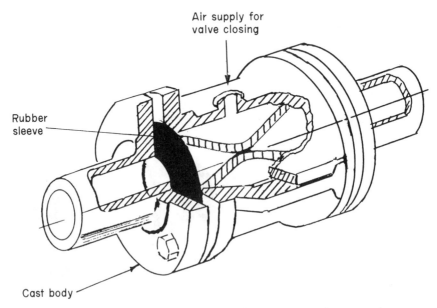

Figure 11.28 A typical pinch valve used in a pneumatic conveying system (Bush & Wilton–Sowerby Engineering Co, Johannesburg, South Africa).

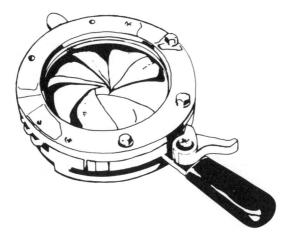

Figure 11.29 Typical arrangement of an iris type valve (Mucon, Basingstoke, England).

These valves are closed by supplying high pressure compressed air to the casing which surrounds the flexible sleeve. The flexible sleeve is then pushed in to form an airtight seal.

One distinct advantage of these valves is their ability to shut in the flow of material and still form an airtight seal.

11.5.2.5 Iris valves (Fig. 11.29)

A valve well suited to controlling the discharge of material from a hopper is the so called 'iris valve'. The iris valve can be adjusted to provide a variable opening and is capable of containing material in large hoppers of silos. By virtue of the variation of the orifice, such valves are often used for control of solids flow out of hoppers and into pneumatic conveying systems.

A wide range of liners is available to make up the diaphragm of the iris. Selection of the valve material is dependent upon the type of solids which is contained in the hopper.

11.5.2.6 Diverter valves (Fig. 11.30)

Diverter valves are used to change the direction of flow in pneumatic conveying systems and these valves are available in various forms. Multiway diverter valves can direct the flow from a single line into any one of a number of branch lines.

One problem with diverter valves lies in their inability to seal under high pressures, and it is often found that line diversions for high pressure systems are made up of a series of pinch valves.

The change in flow direction through a diverter valve is effected either by a rotating thimble inside the valve housing or by use of a flap type valve which shuts off one branch line and opens another.

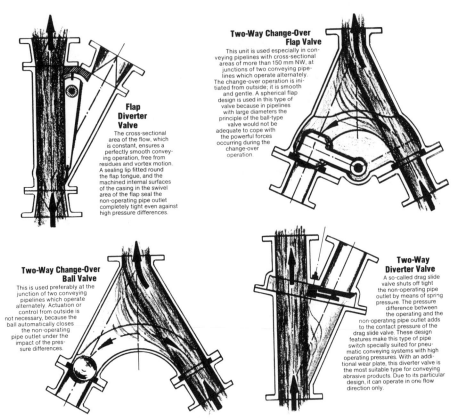

Flap Diverter Valve

The cross-sectional area of the flow, which is constant, ensures a perfectly smooth conveying operation, free from residues and vortex motion. A sealing lip fitted round the flap tongue, and the machined internal surfaces of the casing in the swivel area of the flap seal the non-operating pipe outlet completely tight even against high pressure differences.

Two-Way Change-Over Flap Valve

This unit is used especially in conveying pipelines with cross-sectional areas of more than 150 mm NW, at junctions of two conveying pipelines which operate alternately. The change-over operation is initiated from outside; it is smooth and gentle. A spherical flap design is used in this type of valve because in pipelines with large diameters the principle of the ball-type valve would not be adequate to cope with the powerful forces occurring during the change-over operation.

Two-Way Change-Over Ball Valve

This is used preferably at the junction of two conveying pipelines which operate alternately. Actuation or control from outside is not necessary, because the ball automatically closes the non-operating pipe outlet under the impact of the pressure differences.

Two-Way Diverter Valve

A so-called drag slide valve shuts off tight the non-operating pipe outlet by means of spring pressure. The pressure difference between the operating and the non-operating pipe outlet adds to the contact pressure of the drag slide valve. These design features make this type of pipe switch specially suited for pneumatic conveying systems with high operating pressures. With an additional wear plate, this diverter valve is the most suitable type for conveying abrasive products. Due to its particular design, it can operate in one flow direction only.

Figure 11.30 Diverter valve arrangements (Johannes Moller, Hamburg, West Germany).

11.5.2.7 Dome valve (Fig. 11.31)

The dome valve has been especially developed to provide many of the features required for pneumatic conveying systems. Essentially, the dome valve takes the form of half a ball valve which in the closed position activates an inflatable seal. Once the valve attains its final rest position, the seal inflates and provides for an airtight arrangement.

The valve can withstand high pressures and temperatures and is manufactured from abrasion resistant materials. A unique feature of the valve incorporating the half ball concept is the fact that it is possible to shut off the flow of materials. Once the material has been cut off by the closing valve, the inflatable seal carries out the sealing function.

Dome valves are extensively used in high pressure blow vessel arrangements particularly in those applications where large particles are being transported through the blow vessel system. Fitted as a material inlet valve, the dome valve provides for an effective seal in a most hostile environment. A large number of such valves are found in coal conveying systems and in particular outstanding

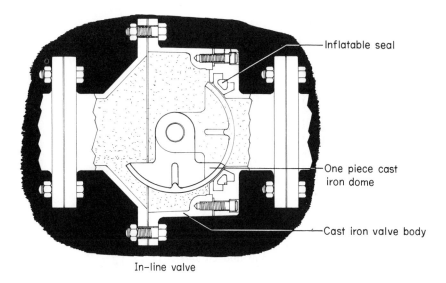

In-line valve

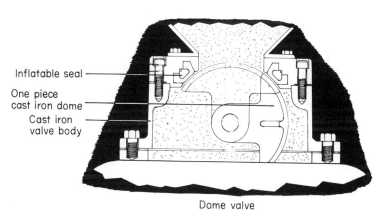

Dome valve

Figure 11.31 Typical arrangements of dome type valves (Simon Macawber South Africa (Pty) Ltd).

success has been reported in the design of feeding systems for the transportation of large quartzite rocks [33].

11.5.2.8 Slide valves (Fig. 11.32)

The slide valve also conforms to 'full bore' valves and is rapidly gaining acceptance as a flow control valve. Recent developments have produced a valve which is not only highly wear resistant, but can also provide a positive seal against high pressures.

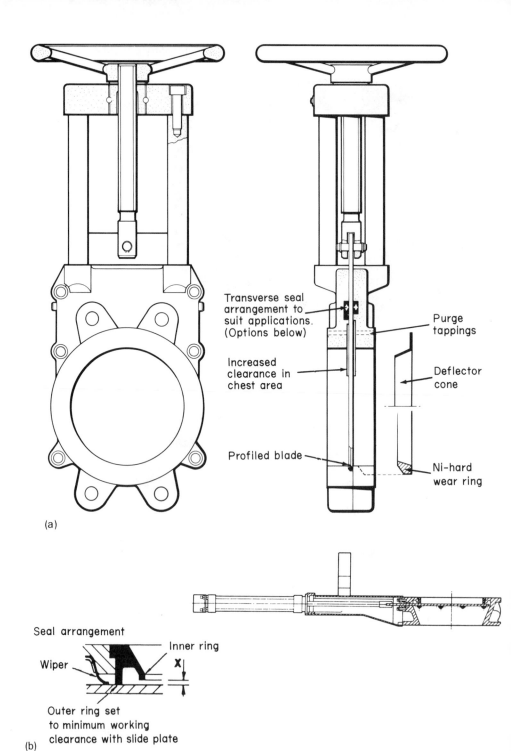

(a)

Transverse seal arrangement to suit applications. (Options below)

Increased clearance in chest area

Profiled blade

Purge tappings

Deflector cone

Ni-hard wear ring

Seal arrangement

Wiper

Inner ring

X

Outer ring set to minimum working clearance with slide plate

(b)

Figure 11.32 Arrangements of slide valves.

One advantage of such a slide valve is its low height. Since the valve consists of a casing and a relatively thin wafer even large diameter valves have a face-width of the order of 70 mm.

Slide valves are also extensively used for the control of solids flow from silos and hoppers as well as being used as material feed valves in blow vessel applications.

11.5.2.9 Disk valves (Fig. 11.33)

Disk valves are a recent innovation and they too provide a full bore opening. The valve consists of a moving disk which in the closed position mates against a seal.

The valve is well suited to low pressure blow vessel applications and can withstand limited pressures. Such valves are also used for vacuum applications where it is desired to shut off various hoppers in sequence in a batching operation.

11.5.3 Rigid piping and pipe couplings (Fig. 11.34)

Piping is one of the components in a pneumatic transport system which is often taken for granted. It is only when wear problems occur that the engineer fully realizes the importance of piping.

The correct installation of a piping system is most important and, as pointed out above, care must be exercised to ensure that where possible misalignment is avoided; that the pipe is free of blemishes and undented. Any irregularity in the piping will promote wear in that particular area.

In general the majority of low pressure fan systems employ thin gauge tubing which is either rectangular or circular in cross section. Because the pressures are low wall thicknesses are usually small.

The higher pressure systems including dense phase systems normally use a standard medium gauge steel piping. Methods of connecting these pipes include welding, slip-on couplings and flanges. Welding the piping is normally undesirable, especially if maintenance work is required on a particular piece of pipe.

The use of plastic based pipes is receiving considerable interest, but in dilute phase high velocity systems static electrical effects can cause problems. More recent developments with the inclusion of carbon fillers in the pipes, are resulting in the development of antistatic plastic piping systems. It is predicted that the use of plastic pipes will be well suited to the conveying of foodstuffs and/or chemically corrosive materials. Interesting observations in terms of the wear resistance capabilities in slurry applications using plastic piping indicate that such piping might have further important applications in the pneumatic transport industry.

Aluminium piping and stainless steel piping is also used in many pneumatic conveying applications. A special technique of treating the internal surfaces of aluminium pipes to provide a 'rough' surface has been found to be particularly successful in minimizing the formation of angel hairs in the plastics conveying industry. There are also situations in which fibre cement pipes are used, especially in the cement industry where it is possible to have the ideal wear resistance situation in which like materials are in contact with each other.

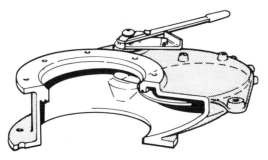

The Disc valve in an open position
The Disc is completely inside the recess and does not obstruct the flow of material.

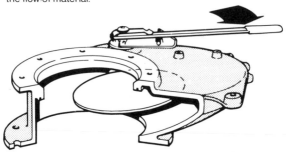

The half closed position
The Disc in this position does not contact the seals and remains free to "float" a small amount on the radial support arm.

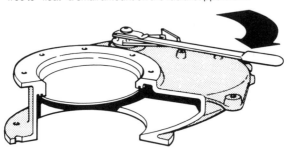

Fully closed
The Disc contacts the seals over the last few degrees of hand lever movement and, with a mild wedging action, provides a complete seal both through the valve and to the environment.

Figure 11.33 Arrangement of a disk valve (Mucon, Basingstoke, England).

A wide range of special wear resistant piping is now available for pneumatic conveying applications. Care should be exercised in terms of selecting piping for a particular application. Wear resistant liners together with specially constructed high carbon steel pipes are used in a large number of mining applications. The selection of the liner or the pipe must also take into consideration such aspects of impact and corrosion.

FLANGE CONNECTION

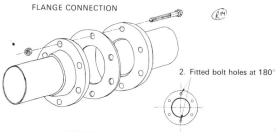

2. Fitted bolt holes at 180°

ASSEMBLY

1) Full face or ring gasket can be used. (Latter often preferable) gasket should be as thin as possible. Attention to be given to selection of gasket material
2) Important to ensure bores are matched to give an uninterrupted bore. This can be achieved using two fitted bolts in close toleranced machined bolt holes. Alternatively a more expensive spigot flange can be used.

1) BEW (BACK WELD AND EXPANDED)
This offers an uninterrupted bore, with only a back fillet and the bore expanded onto the flange. This is an economical alternative.

2) TYPE 5
This attachment also offers an uninterrupted bore. The weld bead in the bore requires grinding smooth after welding.

3) TYPE 6
The inside bore weld is a fillet weld which will result in an unacceptable discontinuity in the bore. However, it would be acceptable if lined with polyurethane or equivalent with the flange face lining machined to give square corner to bore.

4) TYPE 4
This ensures an uninterrupted bore, however, the flange face requires machining after attachment, which is expensive.

VIKING JOHNSON COUPLING

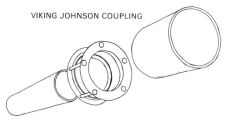
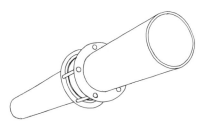

Note
1) Rubber ring sealing on outside diameter of pipe.
2) When assembled, there is a gap giving rise to turbulent flow.
3) Can accommodate slight misalignment.
4) Requires attention to anchoring.

Figure 11.34 Pipe coupling techniques.

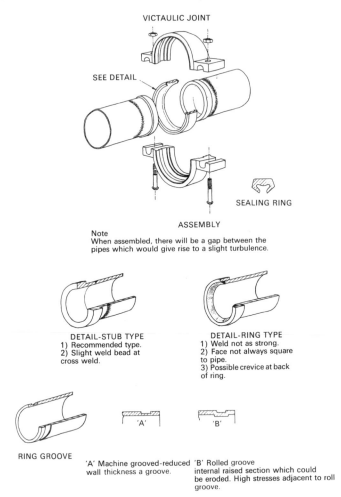

Figure 11.34 Continued

Although there is limited experimental evidence available, the limited inform-ation would indicate that pneumatic conveying systems should either follow a horizontal or vertical route and should definitely not allow for piping to be inclined at all. Limited evidence indicates that incline piping systems result in tremendous problems in terms of blockages, increased wear and significantly higher pressure losses per unit length. It is clear that currently the norm is to avoid the use of incline piping at all costs.

11.5.4 Flexible piping

The use of flexible piping in pneumatic conveying systems includes: discharge houses from bulk tankers, vacuum hoses, bellows to connect piping to silos mounted on load cells, etc. In addition, flexible piping is used for bends which are either unconstrained or are clamped to a rigid former to provide a rigid type bend.

The form of flexible piping used can vary from rubber, wire reinforced rubber, plastic and metallic flexible tubing. Discharge and vacuum hoses sometimes tend to build up static charge, but it has been found that wire reinforced materials provide an effective way of dissipating any static build-up.

There are several good reasons why flexible piping should be used for bends. Primarily, it is the convenience of being able to rapidly replace a worn out bend and secondly there are instances in which increased life has been achieved by using flexible piping for such bends.

One interesting application in the use of flexible piping is in the discharge of cement from rail tankers. Flexible hose is fixed at regular intervals to supports— a certain amount of sag is allowed between these supports. As the material moves through the flexible pipe it will 'snake' its way along thereby moving as a plug system. It is claimed that this technique facilitates greater discharge rates from bulk road and rail tankers.

11.6 CONCLUSIONS

In this chapter an attempt has been made to provide the reader with some insight into the flow behaviour of solids from silos, wear in pneumatic conveying systems and a limited discussion on some ancillary equipment often found in pneumatic conveying installations. The chapter must be seen to be providing the reader with just an insight rather than going into too much detail. The careful selection of appropriate devices for hopper discharge, the selection of wear resistance materials and the use of ancillary equipment must be carried out with due cognizance of the conveying process. Assistance from reputable suppliers or those people expert in silo and hopper design is often necessary for the effective operation of pneumatic conveying systems. An unfortunate consequence of the various items of hardware discussed in this chapter is the fact that engineers often do not attach enough importance to the components discussed above. Such lack of attention often results in the unreliable operation of a pneumatic conveying system.

REFERENCES

1. Jenike, A.W. (1964) *Bulletin 123*, University of Utah, USA.
2. Arnold, P.C., McLean, A.G. and Roberts, A.W. (1980) *Bulk Solids Storage, Flow and Handling*, Tunra, University of Newcastle, Newcastle, NSW, Australia.
3. Stahura, R.P. (1985) Introduction to flow aids, *Proc. Int. Materials Handling Conference*, SAI Materials Handling, SAI Mech. E., University of Witwatersrand, Johannesburg, Sept.
4. Simpson, K. (1935) Bridgebreakers, *Proc. Int. Materials Handling Conference*, SAI

Materials Handling, SAI Mech. E., University of Witwatersrand, Johannesburg, Sept.

5. Roberts, A. (1985) Effect of vibration on bulk solids flow, *Proc. Int. Materials Handling Conference*, SAI Materials Handling, SAI Mech. E., University of Witwatersrand, Johannesburg, Sep.

6. Thomas, R. (1985) Hopper linnings, fact or fiction? *Proc. Int. Materials Handling Conference*, SAI Materials Handling, SAI Mech. E., University of Witwatersrand, Johannesburg, Sept.

7. Kang, C.T., Chang, S.L., Berks, N., and Pettit, F.S. (1983) *Proc. JMIS-3*.

8. (1977) National Materials Advisory Board, National Academy of Sciences, USA, Report No. NMAB-334.

9. Adler, W.F. (1979) NTIS, Report No. ETI-CR79-680.

10. Ruff, A.W. and Weiderhorn, S.M. (1979) *Erosion by Solid Particles Impact; Treatise on Materials Science and Technology*, Vol. 16, (ed. C.M. Preece), Academic Press, New York.

11. Finnie, I. (1960) *Wear*, **3**, 87.

12. Finnie, I., Levy, A. and McFadden, D.H. (1977) *Fundamental Mechanisms of Erosive Wear of Ductile Materials by Solid Particles; Erosive: Prevention and Useful Applications*, (ed. W.F. Adler), ASTM STP 664.

13. Bitter, J.G.A. (1963) *Wear*, **6**, 5.

14. Bitter, J.G.A. (1963) *Wear*, **6**, 169.

15. Winter, R.E. and Hutchings, I.M. (1975) *Wear*, **34**, 141.

16. Winter, R.E. and Hutchings, I.M. (1974) *Wear*, **29**, 181.

17. Mamoun, M.M. (1975) Technical Report ANL-75-XX3, Argonne National Laboratory.

18. Jahamir, S. (1980) *Wear*, **61**, 309.

19. Bellman, R. Jr and Levy, A. (1980) Technical Report, Lawrence, Berkeley Laboratory, LBL-10289.

20. Follansbee, P.S. (1980) *Ph.D. Thesis*, Carnegie-Mellon University, Pittsburgh.

21. Evans, A.G. and Willshaw, T. R. (1977) *Mater. J. Sci.*, **12**, 97.

22. Tilly, G.P. (1969) Erosion caused by air borne particles, *Wear*, **14**, 63–79.

23. Mason, J.S. and Smith, B.V. (1972) The erosion of bends by pneumatically conveyed suspensions of abrasive particles, *Powder Technol.*, **6**, 323–35.

24. Sheldon, G.L. and Finnie, I. (1966) On the ductile behaviour of nominally brittle materials during erosive cutting, *Trans. ASME*, **88b**, 307–92.

25. Snow, C. (1984) The pneumatic transfer of dried slimes over long distances, *M.Sc. Dissertation*, University of Witwatersrand, Johannesburg, Feb.

26. Smoldyrew, A.Y.E. (1980) *Pipeline Transport—Principles of Design*, Terraspace Inc., p. 265.

27. Goodwin, J.E., Sage, W. and Tilly, G.P. (1970) Study of erosion by solid particles, *Proc. Inst. Mech. Engrs*, **184**, Part I, 279–92.

28. Mills, D., and Mason, J.S. (1981) Conveying velocity effects in bend erosion, *J. Pipelines*, **1**, 69–81.

29. Agarwal, V.K., Mills, D. and Mason, J.S. (1985) Some of aspects of bend erosion in pneumatic conveying system pipelines, *Bulk Solids Handling*, **5**, No. 5, 1085–90.

30. Mills, D. and Mason, J.S. (1981) The significance of penetrative wear in pipe bend erosion, *Proc. Int. Conf. on Optimum Resources Utilization Through Tribo-Technology and Maintenance Management*, Indian Institute of Technology, Delhi, Dec.

31. Marcus, R.D., Wiggil, C. and Rizk, F. (1985) Parameters influencing long distance pneumatic conveying systems, *Bulk Solids Handling*, **5**, No. 4, 739–46.
32. Marcus, R.D., Burgess, H., Fenderico, D.M., Fritella, A. and Vogel, R. (1980) The application of pneumatic conveying techniques to the mining industry, *Proc. 5th Int. Conf. on the Pneumatic Transport of Solids in Pipes*, BHRA Fluid Engineering, Granfield.
33. Mohlmann, J.D. (1985) Parameters influencing the pneumatic conveying of large rock particles, *Ph.D. Thesis*, Faculty of Engineering, University of Witwatersrand, Johannesburg.

12

Control of pneumatic transport

12.1 BASIC MATERIAL FLOW AND CONTROL THEORY

For pneumatic transport the basic principle of analysis is the material balance of the solids transported. A number of different situations could arise for the control of the solids flow. The macro approach to the control analysis will be considered first then more detailed distributed models of the actual solids flow will be explored.

The simplest analogue of flow of solids is to compare the system to an equivalent liquid situation. Figure 12.1 shows an input–output situation from a solids storage tank. In pneumatic transport one is probably concerned in delivering a constant outflow of mass. If M is the amount of solids in the storage or feeder unit then one can write

$$\frac{dG}{dt} = \dot{G}_\alpha - \dot{G}_\omega \qquad (12.1)$$

where α and ω refer to initial and terminal states respectively.

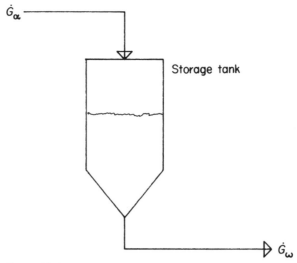

Figure 12.1.

A method of maintaining the output constant is to set up a reference level in the feeder and maintain the tank pressure constant. The level or amount of solids in the tank can be continuously measured:

$$\varepsilon' = G_{ref} - G \tag{12.2}$$

where G_{ref} is the reference amount of solids in the tank. The error can be set proportional to the inlet flow of solids so that

$$G_\alpha = K\varepsilon' \tag{12.3}$$

This is only one type of control that can be employed. Various control schemes can be incorporated at this point in the analysis. The basic differential equation (12.1) is expanded to yield

$$\frac{dG}{dt} + KG = KG_{ref} - \bar{G}_0 \tag{12.4}$$

With Laplace transforms one has

$$G(s) = \frac{1}{s + K}[KG_{ref}(s) - \bar{G}_0(s) + G(0)] \tag{12.5}$$

The signal-flow diagram for this case is shown in Fig. 12.2.

Another set-up that is common in pneumatic transport has a rarer analogue in the liquid systems—a blow tank arrangement. A blow tank or delivery tank with solids can be pressurized to deliver the solids into and through a pipeline. An input beyond the initial charge to the tank is lacking. Figure 12.3 shows this

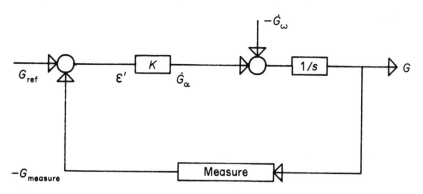

Figure 12.2.

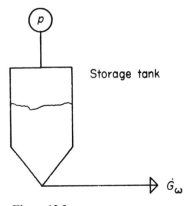

Figure 12.3.

arrangement. The balance of solids can be written as

$$\frac{dG}{dt} = -\dot{G}_\omega \qquad (12.6)$$

If one measures the output flow rate continuously as can be done with modern flow devices, an error signal can be set up as

$$\varepsilon = \dot{G}_{\omega ref} - \dot{G}_\omega \qquad (12.7)$$

The outflow of mass from the tank is dependent on the amount of mass in the unit and the applied pressure. Using a linear combination for this phenomenon one has

$$\dot{G}_\omega = \alpha G + \beta p_{tank} \qquad (12.8)$$

The pressure in the tank can be related to the error signal by a proportional control such that

$$p_{tank} = K(\dot{G}_{ref} - \dot{G}_\omega) \qquad (12.9)$$

Combining the above expressions one has

$$\frac{dG}{dt} = -[\alpha G + \beta K (\dot{G}_{\omega ref} - \dot{G}_\omega)] \qquad (12.10)$$

Applying Laplace transforms one finds

$$G(s) = \frac{1}{s + \alpha} [G(0) - \beta K (\bar{\dot{G}}_{\omega ref}(S) - \bar{\dot{G}}_\omega(s))] \qquad (12.11)$$

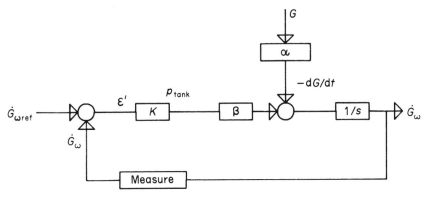

Figure 12.4.

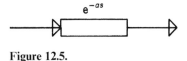

Figure 12.5.

The signal-flow diagram for this control is shown in Fig. 12.4.

12.2 TRANSPORT LAGS

The movement of the solids through a line can produce a lag time in the process. This transport of course is the very essence of pneumatic conveying. The lag time Δt can be represented as distance of the transport line divided by the solids velocity, L/c. In describing the process in the form of a signal-flow diagram (Fig. 12.5) the term e^{-as} in the Laplace transform form must be added for the lag time term. The constant a depends on the details of the solids movement in a given line. In the signal-flow format one has inserted the lag time term before the $1/s$ terms. One should note that screw conveyors can also be represented in the same lag format.

12.3 ANALYSIS OF GAS – SOLID FLOW BY TRANSFER FUNCTIONS

Pneumatic transport systems can be analysed by transfer functions if the process described is of first order. The analysis can begin by considering a driving force pressure drop as

$$p_\alpha - p_\omega = p_{in} - p_{out} \tag{12.12}$$

At steady state this driving force is balanced by the frictional (f), gravitational (g) and electrostatic (el) forces present in the system; thus

$$p_{in} - p_{out} = \Delta p_f + \Delta p_g + \Delta p_{el} \qquad (12.13)$$

For the unsteady state the balance must be modified with Newton's second law as [1]

$$Q\frac{dv}{dt} + G_p\frac{dc}{dt} = A(p_{in} - p_{out}) - A(\Delta p_f + \Delta p_g + \Delta p_{el}) \qquad (12.14)$$

where Q is the mass of fluid in the line and G_p is the mass of solids in the line. If a valve or bend is in the line, these pressure losses can be added to the above equation.

One now inserts a perturbation into the above variables. The variable will be composed of a steady state value and a fluctuating component:

$$p_{in} = \bar{p}_{in} + p_{in}^1 \qquad (12.15)$$

$$p_{out} = \bar{p}_{out} + p_{out}^1$$

$$\Delta p_f = \Delta \bar{p}_f + \Delta p_f^1$$

$$\Delta p_g = \Delta \bar{p}_g + \Delta p_g^1$$

$$v_f = \bar{v}_f + v_f^1$$

$$c_p = \bar{c}_p + c_p^1$$

Inserting these definitions into equation (12.14) one obtains

$$Q\frac{dv^1}{dt} + G_p\frac{dc^1}{dt} = (p_{in}^1 - p_{out}^1) - A(\Delta p_f^1 + \Delta p_g^1) \qquad (12.16)$$

since

$$\bar{p}_{in} - \bar{p}_{out} = \Delta \bar{p}_f + \Delta \bar{p}_g$$

The Laplace transform can now be taken from equation (12.16):

$$Q[sv(s) - v^1(0)] + G[sc(s) - c^1(0)] = A[p_{in}^1(s) - p_{out}^1(s)] - A(\Delta p_f^1(s) + \Delta p_g^1(s)]$$

$$(12.17)$$

A number of different assumptions can be employed at this point to develop the specific transfer functions.

Setting $v^1(0)$ and $c^1(0)$ equal to zero and the gravity fluctuations term as negligible one has

$$Qsv(s) + G_psc(s) = A[p_{in}^1(s) - p_{out}^1(s)] - A[\Delta p_f^1(s)] \qquad (12.18)$$

If the gas velocity fluctuation is smaller than the particle velocity and the frictional fluctuation is dominated by the particle fluctuation, one can write

$$G_p s c(s) = A[p^1_{in}(s) - p^1_{out}(s)] - A\left(\frac{\partial(\Delta p_f)}{\partial c}\right) c(s) \qquad (12.19)$$

Solving for $c(s)$

$$c(s) = \frac{A[p^1_{in}(s) - p^1_{out}(s)]}{G_p s + A\partial(\Delta p_f)/\partial c} \qquad (12.20)$$

Letting $\Delta p^1_T = p^1_{in}(s) - p^1_{out}(s)$

$$\frac{c(s)}{\Delta p^1_T} = \frac{A^{-1}\partial c/\partial(\Delta p_f)}{1 + M_p s/A(\partial(\Delta p_f)/\partial c)} = \frac{K}{1 + \tau s} \qquad (12.21)$$

Thus from transfer analysis the time constant is

$$\tau = \frac{M_p/A}{\partial(\Delta p_f)\partial c} \qquad (12.22)$$

and the gain is

$$K = \frac{1}{A}\left(\frac{\partial c}{\partial(\Delta p_f)}\right) \qquad (12.23)$$

The term $\partial(\Delta p_f)/\partial c$ can be written in terms of the friction factor with

$$\Delta p_f = \lambda^*_Z \rho_p (1 - \varepsilon)\frac{c^2}{2}\frac{L}{D} \qquad (12.24)$$

Now taking the derivative gives

$$\frac{\partial(\Delta p_c)}{\partial c} = \frac{\rho_p}{D} c L(1 - \varepsilon) \qquad (12.25)$$

Resubstituting these terms into the time constant and gain factor with some simplifications, such as $G_p = LA(1 - \varepsilon)\rho_p$,

$$\tau = \frac{D}{\lambda^*_Z c} \qquad (12.26)$$

$$K = \frac{4}{\pi \lambda^*_Z c \rho_p (1 - \varepsilon) L D} \qquad (12.27)$$

Thus the response time of a gas–solid system can be estimated in the above fashion.

12.4 STABILITY OF PNEUMATIC TRANSFER SYSTEMS

The question of how stable a pneumatic transport system, is often posed when design of a new arrangement or modification in existing units is made. The word stable may mean simply that a small perturbation in the line pressure and velocity will not upset the steady flow condition enough to cause the system to change to a

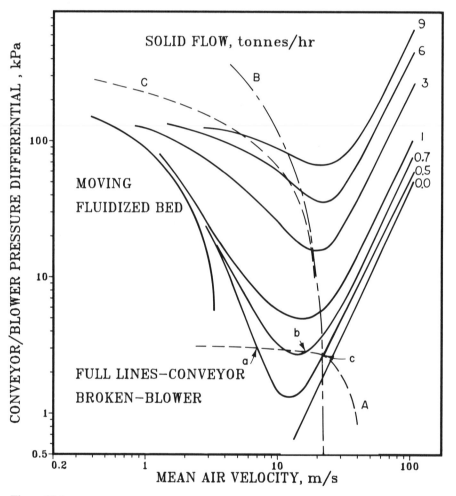

Figure 12.6.

choking flow condition. Leung, Wiles and Nicklin [2] and Doig [3] were the first to consider such an excursion of gas–solid flows. They were interested in the coupling of a blower and a transport line and how one unit interacted with the other. Figure 12.6 shows a plot of the blower curve on the gas–solid pressure drop–velocity phase diagrams. A perturbation in the pressure drop caused by a sudden blockage of the line can drive the flow from point (c) to (b) and then to point (a) which is located near the dangerous choking regime. The coupling of such blower and transport lines is not to be taken lightly for stable pneumatic transport operations. Chapter 6 has more detail on this subject.

Another way of viewing stability is to investigate the basic gas and solid equations describing pneumatic transport and then to apply standard mathematical analysis to probe the conditions of stability. The essential part of such an analysis is to be able to relate this mathematical stability back to physical phenomena occurring in actual pneumatic systems. In an effort to explore this important aspect of pneumatic transfer two linear approaches will be considered along with one non-linear analysis.

12.5 STABILITY ANALYSIS WITH TAYLOR SERIES LINEARIZATION

The basic dynamic equations for this stability analysis are the same as equations (4.25) and (4.26). The non-linear terms in these equations deal with the slip velocity and velocity of the fluid or particle in a squared format. The Taylor series linearization will be applied to these terms in an expansion around the steady state velocities. For example,

$$(v - c)^2 \approx (v^* - c^*)^2 + 2(v^* - c^*)(v - c - v^* + c^*) \tag{12.28}$$

where the velocity can be broken into a steady and a fluctuatory component $c = c^* + \tilde{c}$ and $v = v^* + \tilde{v}$

Employing these expansions in the dynamic equation one obtains finally the transformed linear system

$$\frac{d\tilde{c}}{dt} = \alpha_0 + \alpha_1 \tilde{c} + \alpha_2 \tilde{v} \tag{12.29a}$$

$$\frac{d\tilde{v}}{dt} = \beta_0 + \beta_1 \tilde{c} + \beta_2 \tilde{v} \tag{12.29b}$$

which upon combination will yield a second-order differential equation

$$\frac{d^2\tilde{c}}{dt} = \gamma_1 \frac{d\tilde{c}}{dt} + \gamma_2 c_p + \gamma_3 \tag{12.30}$$

Analysis for the stability of equation (12.30) involves simply finding the region in which the eigenvalues of the solutions go positive showing a growth factor and thus instability. The eigenvalues of equation (12.30) are easily expressed as

$$m = \frac{-\gamma_1 \pm (\gamma_1^2 - 4\gamma_2)^{1/2}}{2} \qquad (12.31)$$

The constants in the above equations can be shown as

$$\gamma_1 = -(\alpha_1 + \beta_2)$$
$$\gamma_2 = (-\alpha_2\beta_1 + \alpha_1\beta_2)$$
$$\gamma_3 = \alpha_2\beta_0 - \alpha_0\beta_2$$

and

$$a_0 = -\frac{1}{\rho_p}\frac{dp}{dx} - g + \frac{3C_{DS}\varepsilon^{-4.7}}{4d}\frac{\rho_f}{\rho_p}[-(v^* - c^*)]^2$$

$$-\frac{\lambda_z^*}{2D}\begin{cases} -c^{*2} & \text{squared format} \\ -(v^* - c^*)^2 & \text{slip format} \end{cases}$$

$$a_1 = \left\{ \frac{3C_{DS}\varepsilon^{-4.7}}{4d}\frac{\rho_f}{\rho_p}[2(v_s^* - c^*)] \right\}$$

$$-\frac{\lambda_z^*}{2D}\begin{cases} c^{*2} & \text{squared format} \\ 2(v^* - c^*)^2 & \text{slip format} \end{cases}$$

$$d_0 = a_0; \quad d_1 = -(a_1 + a_2); \quad d_2 = a_1 + a_2$$

and

$$b_0 = -\frac{1}{\rho}\frac{dp}{dx} - g - \frac{3C_{DS}\varepsilon^{-4.7}}{4d}\frac{1 - \varepsilon}{\varepsilon}[-(v^* - c^*)^2] - \frac{2F_L}{D}(v^{*2})$$

$$b_1 = +\frac{3C_{DS}\varepsilon^{-4.7}}{4d}\frac{1 - \varepsilon}{\varepsilon}[2(v^* - c^*)]$$

$$b_2 = \frac{-2F_L}{D}(2v^*)$$

$$\beta_0 = b_0; \quad \beta_1 = -b_1; \quad \beta_2 = (b_1 + b_2)$$

One will note that for the α parameters two choices are given as to the frictional representations for the solid friction factors. The first is a particle velocity format such as that of Konno and Saito [4] while the second is a slip velocity representation.

Exploring the eigenvalues of equation (12.30) shows that positive eigenvalues are generated to the left of the minimum point on the pressure drop with velocity curve at constant solids flow. This is the region experimentally that shows a sharp increase in pressure drop moving toward a choking condition. This linearization process has served to describe the basic characteristics of the gas–solid flow system.

12.6 LINEAR STABILITY ANALYSIS — JACKSON APPROACH

The second linear stability analysis to be discussed is one that has been pioneered by Jackson [5] for fluidization and adopted by Grace and Tuot [6] for pneumatic transport. The approach of Jackson considers the continuity equations for the solids and the gas along with the dynamic equation of the solids alone. The dynamic equation of the solids does not include the pressure drop term. Defining the velocity and number density perturbation as

$$v = v^* + \tilde{v}$$

$$c = c^* + \tilde{c}$$

$$n = n_0 + \tilde{n}$$

and inserting these into the continuity and dynamics equation and ignoring all but the first order terms, one obtains

$$\nabla.\tilde{v} = \frac{c}{1 - n_0 c}\left(\frac{\partial \tilde{n}}{\partial t} + v^* \nabla \tilde{n}\right) \tag{12.32}$$

$$\nabla.\tilde{c} = -\frac{1}{n_0}\left(\frac{\partial \tilde{n}}{\partial t} + c^* \nabla \tilde{n}\right) \tag{12.33}$$

$$\times n_0 G\left(\frac{\partial \tilde{c}}{\partial t} + c^* \frac{\partial \tilde{c}}{\partial x}\right) - n_0 \rho c^*\left(\frac{\partial \tilde{v}}{\partial t} + v^* \frac{\partial \tilde{v}}{\partial x}\right)$$

$$+ g\tilde{n}(m_p - \rho c^*) - \beta_0(\tilde{v} - \tilde{c}) - \tilde{n}\beta_0^1(v^* - c^*)$$

$$= 0 \tag{12.34}$$

In equation (12.34)

$$\beta_0 = (1 - \varepsilon)\frac{(\rho_p - \rho)g}{(v^* - c^*)} \tag{12.35}$$

The procedure involves using the function

$$\tilde{n} = f(t)\exp\left[i(k_x)\right] \tag{12.36}$$

to be inserted in equations (12.31), (12.32) and (12.33) to produce a second order differential equation in $f(t)$ whose solution produces again two eigenvalues defined as

$$s_1, s_2 = \frac{b}{2a}\{\pm[1 + 4(\alpha - 1)(C^2/b^2) - 4i(C/b)(ae - 1)]^{1/2}$$

$$- [1 + 2i(C/b)(1 + q)]\} \qquad (12.37)$$

where,

$$a = 1 + \rho_p \varepsilon/\rho(1 - \varepsilon)$$

$$b = \rho_p - \rho(1 - \varepsilon)(v^* - c^*)$$

$$C = k(v^* - c^*)$$

$$e = 1 - 2\varepsilon + \varepsilon n_0 \beta_0^1/\beta_0$$

$$q = c^* a(v^* - c^*)$$

For stability the growth term in distance is given as

$$\Delta x = \mathrm{Im}(s_1)/k\,\mathrm{Re}(s_1) \qquad (12.38)$$

Interpretation is understood by the concept that the smaller the positive values of Δx are the easier the system becomes in its ability to form clusters of particles indicating instability. In this analysis one notes that

$$k = \pi/50d \qquad \frac{n_0\beta_0'}{\beta_0} = \frac{(\eta - 1) - \varepsilon_s(\eta - 2)}{\varepsilon_s}$$

where $\eta = 4.7$ by Richardson and Zaki and $\varepsilon_s = 0.43$ for a packed bed. Table 12.1 shows some values for the growth distance Δx for typical systems; the larger Δx the more stable the system.

Joseph, Larourre and Klinzing [7] have employed this analysis to explore the effect of electrostatic forces on the stability of pneumatic transport. They found the electrostatic forces decreased the growth distances thus indicating a less stable system.

Table 12.1 Growth distances ($\Delta x(m)$) for 100 μm particles with air at 6m/s

T (K)	ρ (KPa)	ρ_p (kg/m^3)	ε 0.7	0.8	0.9	0.98
300	101	7800	0.144	0.152	0.190	0.43
300	101	2600	0.21	0.20	0.26	0.73
1300	101	2600	0.53	0.35	0.39	1.55
300	101	480	3.4	1.62	1.62	12.4

12.7 STABILITY VIA THE LIAPUNOV ANALYSIS

The former analyses considered stability of gas–solids flows from the linearization aspect. The results which have been obtained in this fashion appear to agree adequately with the experimental findings especially in the phase plane analysis. To include the non-linear terms in the analysis would generally require a numerical solution with graphical interpretation of the findings. In the area of stability analysis in other fields of endeavour the second method of Liapunov stands out as a technique of great utility. Not only are the non-linear terms able to be handled in this technique but also regions of stability can be established without great computational difficulties. The second method of Liapunov is based on a generalization of the idea that if a system has an asymptotically stable equilibrium state then the stored energy of the system displaced with a region of attraction decays with increasing time until it finally assumes its minimum value at the equilibrium state.

The idea of a Liapunov function is more general than that of energy and is far more widely applicable. The Liapunov functions are functions of independent variables $V_1, \ldots, V_n$ and t and can be denoted as $V(y, t)$ or $V(y)$ if t is not explicit. The sign of the function $V(y)$ and its time deriviative $\dot{V}(y)$ give information about the stability, asymptotic stability or instability of the equilibrium state under study without directly solving for the detailed solution.

Global asymptotic stability can be guaranteed for a system if it is possible to formulate a scalar function (the Liapunov function) with continuous first partial derivatives such that:

(a) $V(y) = 0, y = 0$
(b) $V(y) > 0, y = 0$
(c) $V(y) \to \infty, \|y\| \to \infty$
(d) $\dot{V}(y) = dV/dt < 0, y \neq 0$ (12.39)

LaSalle and Lepchetz [8] have shown that if conditions (a), (b) and (d) are satisfied within a bounded region defined by $V(y) < C$, where C is some positive constant, then the system is asymptotically stable in that bounded region.

A possible Liapunov function is the quadratic form

$$V = y^T p_y$$ (12.40)

where p in a two dimensional system is a matrix

$$\begin{bmatrix} p_{11} & p_{12} \\ p_{21} & p_{22} \end{bmatrix}$$

If p is chosen as the identity matrix, then the Liapunov function is merely the norm of the state vector y. The basic gas–solids equations given by equation (4.25) and (4.26) can serve as the basic starting point for this analysis. One transformation is necessary to form a system of equations in which the steady state has a vector coordinate of zero. This is achieved by the following transforms:

$$\tilde{c} = c - c^* \tag{12.41}$$

$$\tilde{v} = v - v^* \tag{12.42}$$

where c^* and v^* are the steady state solutions of equations (4.25) and (4.26). It should be noted that the pressure drop is assumed constant in this analysis. In the new system the equations can be written as

$$\frac{d\tilde{c}}{dt} = \frac{3}{4}\frac{C_{DS}}{d}\frac{\rho}{\rho_p - \rho}[(\tilde{v} + v^*) - (\tilde{c} + c^*)]^2 - g - \frac{1}{\rho_p}\frac{\partial p}{\partial x} - \frac{\lambda_Z^*}{2D}(\tilde{c} + c^*)^2 \tag{12.43}$$

$$\frac{d\tilde{v}}{dt} = -\frac{3}{4}\frac{C_{DS}\rho}{d(\rho_p - \rho)}[(\tilde{v} + v^*) - (\tilde{c} + c^*)]^2 - \frac{\lambda_Z^*}{2D}(\tilde{v} + v^*)^2 - \frac{1}{\rho}\frac{\partial p}{\partial x} \tag{12.44}$$

The Liapunov function which is taken to be the norm of the state vector is

$$V(U) = \tilde{v}^2 + \tilde{c}^2 \tag{12.45}$$

and

$$\frac{dV}{dt} = 2\tilde{v}\frac{d\tilde{v}}{dt} + 2\tilde{c}\frac{d\tilde{c}}{dt} < 0 \tag{12.46}$$

The above equations can be substituted in this equation in order to define the boundary between the regions of stable and unstable conditions. One sets $dV/dt = 0$ and solves for the resultant cubic equation for c at varying values of v. By doing this while varying one system parameter such as particle size, density etc. it is possible to assess the effect of that parameter on the shape and size of the region of stability. Figure 12.7 shows a typical result of the application of the Liapunov method to gas–solids flow. The figure shows increasing circles of stability as the flow increases in the phase plane $\Delta p/L$ versus v at a constant $\dot{G}$. One finds the centre of the circle as the steady state solution. If a perturbation exists in the system and the perturbation does not violate the circle's boundary, the system will return to the steady state when the perturbation is removed. If the perturbation crosses the circle's boundary, the system can go to another steady state or go unstable if it crosses the stability boundary line. There are certain limitations to the Liapunov second method that must be mentioned:

(a) The stability conditions obtained from a particular v function are sufficient but may not be necessary to ensure stability.

(b) Failure to find a V function can give no information on stability conditions.

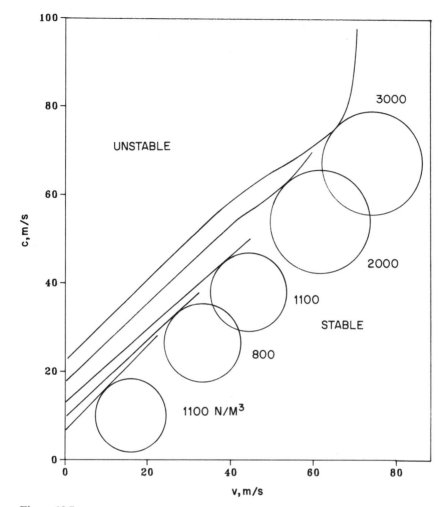

Figure 12.7.

(c) Although a particular V function may prove that the equilibrium state under consideration is stable in a region which includes this equilibrium state, it does not necessarily mean that the motions outside this region are unstable.

REFERENCES

1. Weber, T.W. (1973) *An Introduction to Process Dynamics and Control*, Wiley, New York.
2. Leung, L.S. Wiles, R.I. and Nicklin, D.J. (1971) *Ind. Eng. Chem. Process Design Development*, **10**, 183.

3. Doig, I.D. (1975) *S. African, Mech. Eng.*, **25**, 394.
4. Konno, H. and Saito, S.J. (1969) *Chem. E. Japan*, **2**, 211.
5. Jackson, R. (1963) *Trans. I. Chem. E.*, **41**, 13.
6. Grace, J.R. and Tuot, J. (1979) *Trans. I. Chem. E.*, **57**, 49.
7. Joseph, S., Larourre, P.J. and Klinzing, G.E. (1984) *Powder Technol.*, **38**, 1.
8. LaSalle, J. and Lepchetz, S. (1981) *Stability by Liapunov's Direct Method with Applications*, Academic Press, New York.

13
Instrumentation

In order to ensure a reliable pneumatic transport system it is necessary to measure and monitor the flow conditions from delivery to transport and recovery. When beginning to search for instrumentation to perform such functions, one goes directly to the single phase experience. Flowmeters and pressure sensing devices come first to mind. Quickly one finds the flowmeters to be inadequate and special care must be shown in the use of the sensing devices so they are not damaged or clogged. With the advent of computer control measured signals need to be changed into electrical impulses of voltages or currents to be transmitted to the computer where detailed logic is only limited by one's creativity. Pneumatic transport is and will be controlled in this manner.

In this chapter an attempt will be made to describe two classes of instrumentation, namely: instrumentation used primarily in research type environments; and instrumentation which has been devised to operate in an industrial environment.

13.1 STANDARD INSTRUMENTATION

Early on in the design of instrumentation for pneumatic transport BCR devised a coupled orifice/venturi system. The principle was to place the two units in series. The orifice would respond only to the gas changes while the venturi responded to the two-phase system accounting for the solids flow. Figure 13.1 shows an example of these coupled instruments. Davies [1] and Crowe [2] have explored the use of the Venturi meter as applied to pneumatic transport in further detail. The data show that the pressure drop between the carrier pipe and the Venturi throat vary linearly with solids flow at a given mass flow rate. The systems studied considered a relative low loading rate (up to 1.5). The standard Venturi having an angle of 21° was found to perform adequately. The Venturi arrangement was in a vertical pipe. Figure 13.2 shows the configuration of the Venturi studied by Crowe.

13.2 TRANSDUCERS

The pressure waves and fluctuations behaviour in a two-phase gas–solid system can give much information about the flow condition within the flow line. The use of transducers to measure these pressure waves is essential since almost

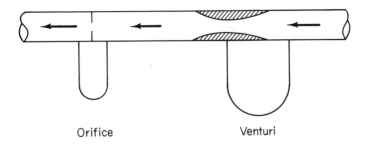

Figure 13.1 Coupled Venturi/orifice meter for gas–solids flow measurements.

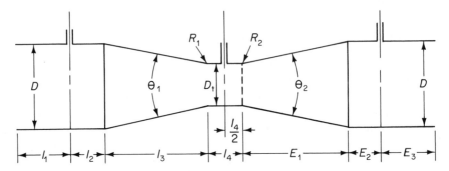

Figure 13.2 Vertical Venturi device used by Crowe [2].

instantaneous readings can be obtained. The reason this is very important is because often any upset in the pneumatic system propagates so quickly that before you know it, the system is plugged which will necessitate the dismantling of the unit for removing the plug. Careful monitoring of the pressure transducer readings is therefore imperative. One experience along these lines involved the transport of a solid synthetic fuel which had been pulverized. Initially the material conveyed steadily without any problem. As time increased, 1/2 to 3/4 of an hour, the pressure drop as shown by the transducers increased and eventually the flow ceased. Upon opening the line it was found that particles had fused together because of the frictional heating until the entire line was plugged.

The use of transducers is essential. However, care must be taken in their use. The simple insertion of a transducer in the line is not enough to ensure adequate functional operation. Most pneumatic transport systems convey a wide distribution of particles even though the mean value of the particle size may be large. Attrition of particles in the line can add to the percentage of fines one obtains in the conveying line. One way of preventing fines from finding their way into the operational part of the transducer is to use transmitters with diaphragm seals. These devices are usually made of a volume of liquid enclosed, without any air space, with sensitive diaphragms of thin metal located at either end of the cylindrical element. The pressure from the line pushes on the diaphragm and transmits the pressure through the enclosed liquid to other diaphragms which act upon the air column in contact with the transducer's active surface.

Other devices also exist in order to prevent fine particle migration into the transducer's inners. A variety of filters can be employed from glass wool to pressed metal. The latter can be formed in a variety of shapes the most notable being a cylindrical shape to match the pipe diameter and thus transmit an average circumferential pressure to the transducer. This setup can permit back purging of the metal filter if problems of plugging occur in the filter [3].

Some people have chosen not to use a filter, but to constantly purge the connecting line between the tranducer and the tube wall. Even with such a precaution, to eliminate fines at the transducer face, fine particle migration has occurred which almost seems to defy the laws of gravity.

13.3 CROSS-CORRELATION PROCEDURES

Of late, the use of cross-correlation applied to two-phase flow has seen some exciting applications. Cross-correlation of signals has been available for a number of years and probably has its practical application mostly in the field of turbulence. Hot wire, hot film anemometers and Laser Doppler Velocimetry (LDV) systems have the possibility of cross-correlating signals. Some manufacturers produce a cross-correlator unit for any kind of electronic signals. One of the most practical aspects of the cross-correlation procedure is the ability to use a variety of signal devices. The essential element is that the device can detect flow fluctuations which generally arise from any pneumatic conveying system. If one considers the signals from two measuring devices placed a fixed distance apart as $A(t)$ and $B(t)$, the cross-correlation can be written as

$$R_{AB} = \int_{-\infty}^{\infty} [A(t)B(t + \tau)] \, dt \qquad (13.1)$$

where τ is the delay time between the signals. This delay time can be changed

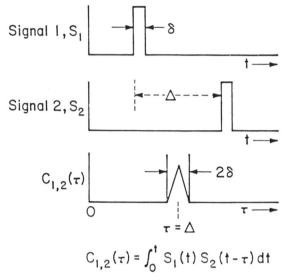

$$C_{1,2}(\tau) = \int_0^t S_1(t)\, S_2(t-\tau)\, dt$$

Figure 13.3 Cross-correlation technique.

according to the analysis. The procedure involves changing the delay time over a range in order to calculate various values of R_{AB}. When a maximum value in the cross-correlation coefficients is obtained at a particular delay time τ, this is designated as the true signal delay time between the two signals at points A and B. Figure 13.3 shows the application of this principle to a simple signal. Since one has fixed the distance between the measuring signals, the particle velocity of the solids flowing pneumatically can be found as

$$C = \frac{\text{distance between signal } A(t) \text{ and } B(t)}{\text{time at max. } R_{AB}} \tag{13.2}$$

Another important factor concerning this type of signal measuring is that it can be performed electronically and as such, can serve to be incorporated into a control system for pneumatic transport. Figure 13.4 shows a typical cross-correlation signal and its behaviour with delay time.

The probes that can be utilized for the cross-correlation procedure are wide and varied. The Auburn International dielectric meter can be employed very effectively as a probe as shown by Mathur and Klinzing [4]. Smith and Klinzing [5] have used a cylindrical element as an electrostatic measuring probe with success while Mathur and Klinzing [6] have also used a commercial electrostatic probe manufactured by Auburn International to obtain the cross-correlation between two signals. It has been suggested that any light probe can also serve the purpose of detecting signals that can be cross-correlated. The simple light probe to be described is one possibility.

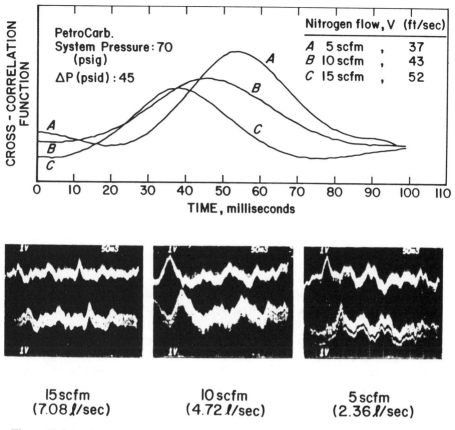

Figure 13.4 Typical cross-correlation signal.

13.4 A CORIOLIS FORCE METER

A unique flow meter that can be applied to two-phase flow systems such as gas–solid pneumatic flow, is the Micro-Motion Coriolis force flow meter. The basic principle relies on the Coriolis force that is placed on flow around a U-bend arrangement. The Coriolis force produces a twist on the U-arrangement which is dependent on the amount of mass flowing through the tube. The meter is generally made of the same diameter as the flow line in which it is inserted. The twisting motion is detected by electro-optical switches. Figure 13.5 shows a general diagram of this unit. Mathur [7] has performed extensive tests on this apparatus as to its suitability in measuring nitrogen–coal flow over a wide range of solids–gas loadings. The Micro-Motion was tested in the horizontal and vertical flow direction, the latter serving as a bend in the flow line. Since the flow path is in a U-shape, the energy loss through such a system is larger than a regular bend. Figure 13.6 shows the findings for the pressure loss through

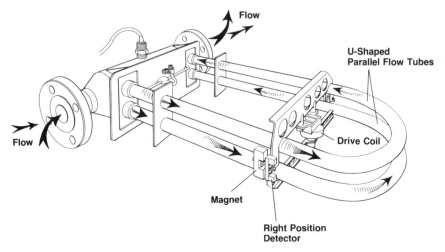

Figure 13.5 Coriolis force meter.

a Micro-Motion meter. For low loading conditions in the horizontal flow set-up, large pressure fluctuations were introduced in the flow lines due to the U-bend pattern. As the solids loading increased, this pulse disappeared.

One aspect of using this meter that has not been answered is the degree of erosion seen by the meter since it represents such abrupt changes in the flow pattern for the gas–solid flow. Figure 13.7 shows the meter's response to varying flow rates of gas and solids combined. The linear behaviour of the meter is marked.

13.5 DIELECTRIC METER

Auburn International manufacture a dielectric meter which measures the dielectric constant of the flowing gas–solid mixture on a volume basis. The dielectric constant is a measure of the capacitance of a substance related to the capacitance of air. The Auburn probe is seen in Fig. 13.8 with its various parallel electrodes around the circumference of the cylindrical probe. These electrodes are the signal measuring devices and their operation is pulsed over a frequency of 208 Hz in order to give an average value for the dielectric. The value of the dielectric is directly proportional to concentration of solid material within the probe or, as in this case, within the pipe since the Auburn meter has the same diameter as the transporting pipe. This latter situation reduces erosion to an absolute minimum. The dielectric constant of air is 1.0 and that for water is 78.9; thus, any moisture in the system will strongly influence the Auburn meter reading. Figure 13.9 shows the application of the Auburn dielectric meter to the pneumatic transport of coal. The reference measurement for the flow rate of coal is a weigh cell. One sees the linearity of the plot to be highly justified. The Auburn meter can thus be used as a two-phase gas–solid flowmeter and is

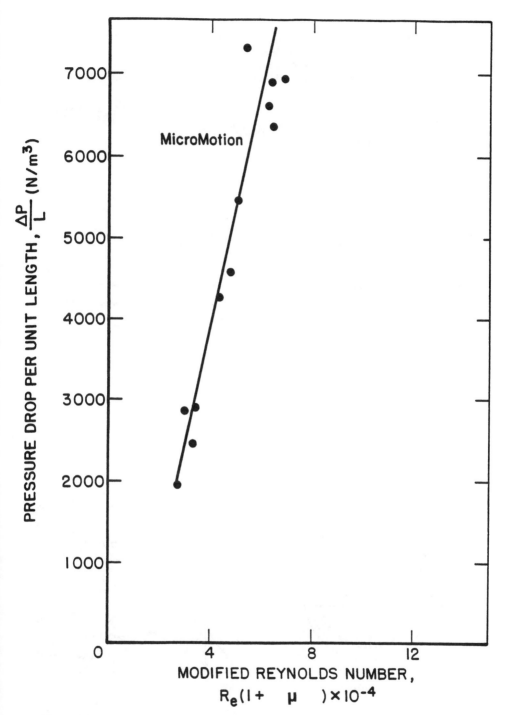

Figure 13.6 Pressure loss through a Micro-Motion meter.

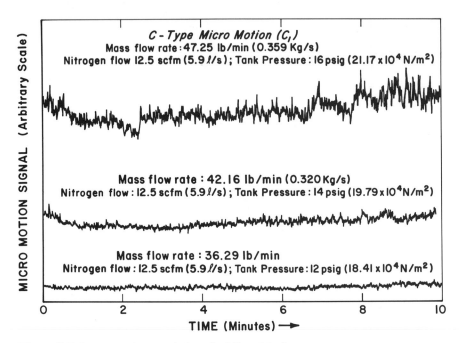

Figure 13.7 Response characteristics of a Micro-Motion meter.

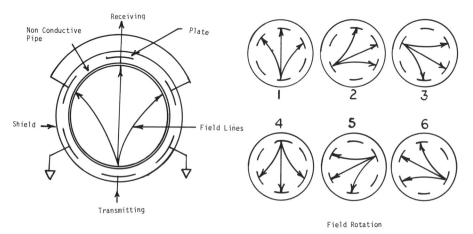

Figure 13.8 The Auburn probe.

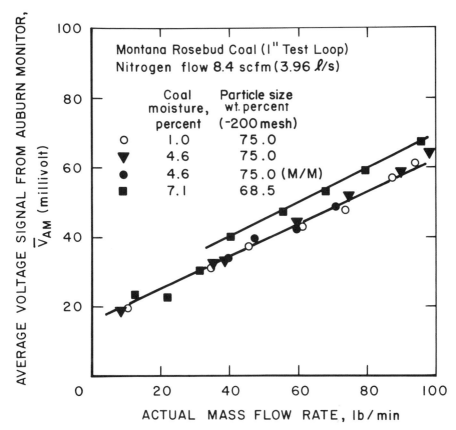

Figure 13.9 The Auburn probe used to monitor the transport of coal.

found to respond to changes in flow almost instantaneously. This latter fact presents the Auburn meter as an excellent candidate for a flow control device in pneumatic transport. Should the moisture content of the transport gas or conveyed solids vary several percent over the desired test run, then the calibration curve will switch to a higher monitor reading. Figure 13.10 shows how well the Auburn dielectric meter responds to flow fluctuations in pneumatic transport systems.

The Auburn meter can also be calibrated to yield the voidage of the flow. What is essential for the calibration is its use as a volume that contains solids under a known voidage condition. A packed bed of coal or sand can be used as a reference. As one knows from experience, the manner in which the packing takes place can influence the voidage. The voidage for such systems can vary from about 0.34 to 0.50. The voidage can be checked by a variety of fluid displacement methods, water or mercury for example. With the Auburn meter reading at this packed bed condition as a reference the reading obtained in the

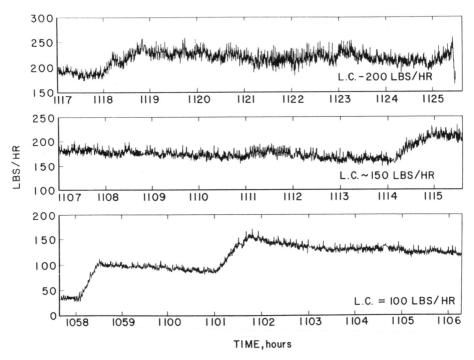

Figure 13.10 Response of Auburn probe to fluctuating flows.

flow condition can be directly transported to the flow voidage. This procedure has been successfully applied to pneumatic transport of coal by Mathur.

The Auburn dielectric meter thus has a great deal of versatility to its use. Flow indicator, flow meter, particle velocity measurement by cross-correlation and voidage meter are all within its repertoire. The checking of the basic definition of voidage can be seen by the plot shown in Fig. 13.11. One notes the linearity is well established.

13.6 LOAD CELLS

Inventories of solids in a system can be monitored by the use of load cells. Usually a solid state sensor will transform the compression force on a unit into an electrical signal. A wide range of capacities are available. The cells can be located on the three support elements of a storage or delivery tank. The empty tank deflection of the cells can be zeroed. If the load cells are located on the delivery and receiving receptacles, the difference can be used as a crude solids flow meter. Generally the response on the load cell differences are not sufficient to serve as an instantaneous measure of the flow rate. They are, however, excellent units for calibration of most instantaneous flow measuring units and

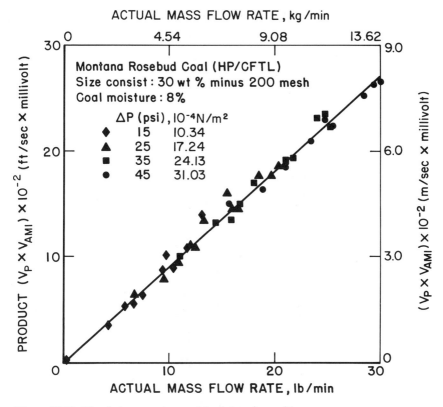

Figure 13.11 The Auburn meter used to determine voidage.

balancing inventories. It is desirable to have a load cell system on most pneumatic transport systems. Figure 13.12 shows a typical load cell installation.

13.7 PARTICLE TAGGING

The tagging of particles with a substance that can be detected as the particles move in the flow is another technique in order to obtain the particle velocity as a transfer line. The most common tagging elements have been radioactive. Certain short lived radioisotopes have been stated as being safe for usage; however, care must be taken in their use. Disposal and contamination are problems once the experiments have been conducted. Brewster and Saeder [8] have employed a non-radioactive tagging material which is a powdered point pigment which is phosphorescent, ZnS:Cu. The pigment can be attached to particles by use of a sodium silicate solution. Transparent viewing sections in the transport line are needed for the set-up. A light source energized the pigment which is on the tagged particles. Two detector cells are placed at a

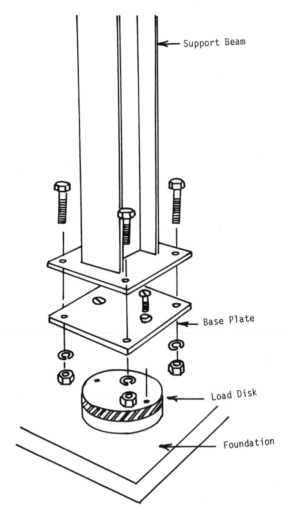

Figure 13.12 Typical load cell installation.

fixed distance apart along the length of the transport line. The detectors consist of photomultiplier tubes which measured the light signal emitted by the tagged particles and as such provided a means to determine the transport time between the fixed detectors.

13.8 ELECTROSTATIC BASED METERS

Using the basic principle that conveyed solids in a gas stream generate static charges on the solids, provided the material conveyed and the conveying line are different and the relative humidity of the gas is less than about 75%, a

Figure 13.13 Electrostatic based meter.

number of flow meters have been proposed. To date the only commercial meter is manufactured by Auburn International. This meter is a flow/no flow indicator rather than a quantitative device (Fig. 13.13). As indicated previously Mathur and Klinzing [6] have employed two of these meters successfully as sensors to obtain the particle velocity.

A number of prospective meters based on electrostatic generation have appeared in the literature. Soo and his coworkers [9, 10, 11] have been most active in the development of flow measuring devices based on electrostatics. Some of the designs have consisted of probes placed in the flowing media while others have had the same diameter of the pipe, thus creating no flow disturbance; with the ball probe inserted in the flow stream mass flow profiles were obtained as the probe traversed the tube diameter. These investigators have tested a number of different substances with their devices, most noticeably work with coal [11].

King [12] employed pin electrodes in order to measure the electrostatic charge generated in pneumatic transport of plastic particles in an effort to devise a flow meter. He looked at a signal probe for the noise level generated as related to the number of particle–wall interactions which is directly proportional to the mass flow rate of material flowing. Cross-correlation techniques were also employed in his study with the pin electrodes. Figures 13.14 and 13.15 show the physical arrangement and responses.

Along the lines of cross-correlation and wall probes, Smith and Klinzing [5] used two metal ring probes placed at a fixed distance apart in a plastic conveying pipe in order to measure the particle velocity. The metal (A1) rings were 1/2″ in width and the same diameter as the pipe. The rings were coupled directly to a Keithly 610 C electrometer. Each signal was recorded simultaneously on a tape recorder. An analogue to digital converter was employed to take the analogue signal to a minicomputer for performing the cross-correlation. This operation was found to be reliable for flow measurements. When attempting

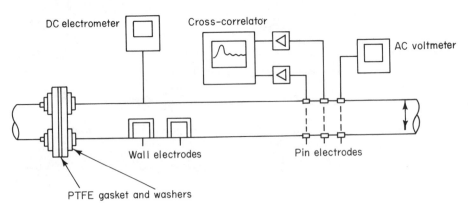

Figure 13.14 Physical arrangement of electrostatic probe.

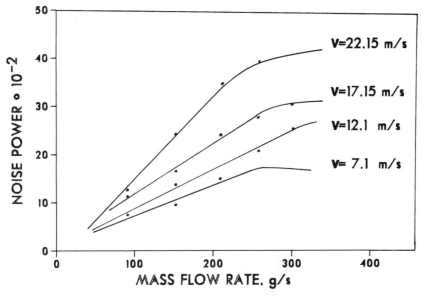

Figure 13.15 Typical response from electrostatic probe.

to measure the electrostatic charges, any number of probes can be employed. The signals can be measured easily by a good quality electrometer which has an output device for recording and analysis. The probe inserted in or through the wall should be metal (nickel, copper, or aluminium) surrounded by a non-conductor. In that way even grounded pipe systems can have the electrostatic signals measured.

13.9 ACOUSTIC MEASUREMENTS

Acoustic devices can also be employed in the measurement of two-phase flow systems. The basic principle is the attenuation of the sound wave seen by the gas and solid as being substantially different. In fact, the sonic application can be paralleled to the light application and a Doppler velocimeter can be developed based on the sonic principle. Most noteworthy in the field of sonic application to gas–solid flow systems is the work at Argonne National Laboratory (ANL).

Sheen and Raptis [13] at ANL have tested a microphone system as a flow/no flow device on an experimetal coal gasification facility. The char flow was monitored since line blockages were a recurrent problem. A high temperature microphone was placed near the char return line. The presence of char in the attenuation path causes absorption and scattering of acoustic energy generated by the associated stream of eductor. The amount of attenuation

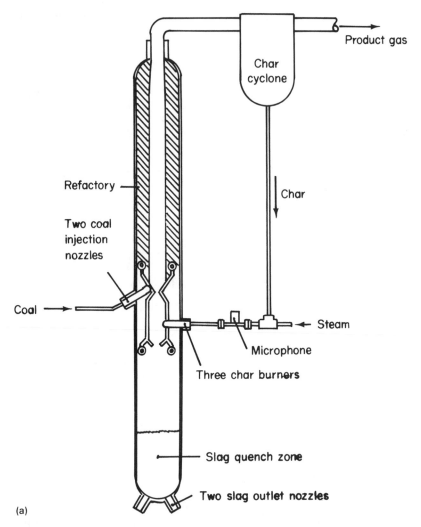

Figure 13.16(a) Physical arrangements of acoustic meter. Reproduced by permission of A.C. Raptis, Argonne National Laboratory.

indicates the amount of char present. Figure 13.16(a) shows the physical arrangement of the system.

A commerical sound velocimeter is now on the market [14]. This unit has been applied successfully to liquid–solid systems; however, testing on gas–solid systems has not been made. The unit's arrangement is seen in Fig. 13.16(b). The flow tube is a pipe section made of the same material and diameter as the conveying line. The sonic pulse is sent from the transmitting transducer diagonally across the flow to a receiving transducer. A pulse repetition rate is

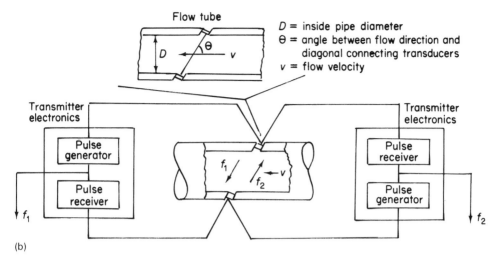

Figure 13.16(b) Sound velocimeter.

determined that is dependent upon the transit time of the pulse through the fluid. A similar pulse is generated by sending pulses in the opposite direction since the motion of the fluid system will slow down the pulses travelling upstream. The transit times of the upstream and downstream pulses will be different and this difference is a direct measure of the flow rate.

In the use of the acoustic devices it should be noted that since particulate flow will abrade or erode the pipe wall, the acoustic signal could change with time because the device's metal covering could erode and change the path of the sound waves.

13.10 SCREW CONVEYORS

The screw conveyor can be used as a solids metering device since a prescribed amount of material is delivered to feed stream per unit time. There are problems generally with lumpy and sticky materials and general packing of powder. The screw feeder has in general three sections: the feed inlet, a choke and a conveying section [15]. Figure 13.17 shows this arrangement. The feed section solids flow into the cavity and are carried over the shaft. At high speeds or short feed sections, there may not be adequate time to fill the cavity and the conveying capacity is reduced. Varying or tapered pitch flights are preferred in the design to provide an even draw-off. The choke section is at least two pitches long and provides a flow control by limiting the flow area. This will minimize the possibility of solid flooding. The conveying section core has an increase in pitch to prevent packing. Thomson [15] reports on the character of the powder in relation to the screw feeder performance. For heavy mineral sand, fertilizer prills

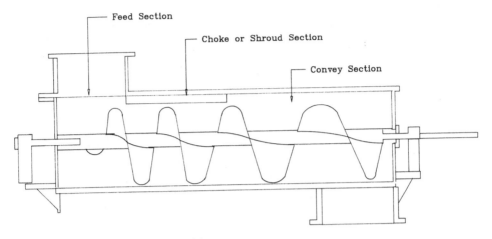

Figure 13.17 Screw feeder assembly.

Table 13.1 Screw conveyor test data

Solids	Screen analysis (Tyler) as poured	Bulk density (kg/m³)
Mineral sand (free flowing)	41% on 80 mesh 95% on 150 mesh 100% on 200 mesh	2051
Fertilizer prill	50% on 20 mesh 99% on 48 mesh	960
Plastic cubes	3 mm cube	449
Polymer powder (fluidizes and floods readily)	11% on 100 mesh 77% on 150 mesh 3% under 250 mesh	176

and powdered polymer he found increasing efficiency of transfer. The particle sizes are listed in Table 13.1. The heavy mineral sand tended to backflow, with the pellets and prills not aerating and the polymer powder being readily fluidized.

13.11 LIGHT MEASURING DEVICES

The light measuring devices to monitor and measure gas–solid flow can work on an attenuation basis or on the Doppler shift basis. The attenuation principle can be applied more directly to a flow system at a much lower cost than the laser Doppler velocimeter. The latter system can yield individual particle velocities, thus it is limited to dilute phase flow systems.

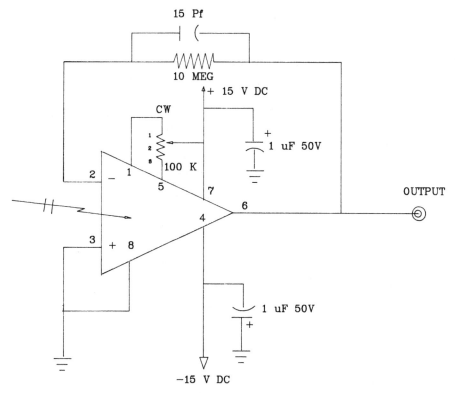

Figure 13.18(a) Op/amp diagram, United Technology with 450 photodiode.

The simplest light measuring device is shown in the electronic schematic in Fig. 13.18(a). This consists of a light source (a halogen lamp) and a photodiode op/amp to receive the light signal and change it into an electrical impulse. The device must be placed on a viewing window across the transport line or set into the wall of the conveying line with a transparent protection cover for the lamp and photodiode. The halogen lamp employed in this set-up seems more than adequate to be employed in some fairly dense pneumatic transport systems.

Calibration of the output device with a load cell would provide another possibility for a flow measuring device. The use of two of these light probes at a fixed distance apart would provide a basis for cross correlation and particle velocity determination; Kerker [16] employed this latter technique to find the particle velocities as a function of distance in his study.

Chao *et al.* [20] have developed twin diode optical probe where the source and detector are made of minature Ge–As–P diodes. One diode is the source while the other is the detector. A large intensity of light from the powered diode renders the probe insensitive to background deposition on the surface.

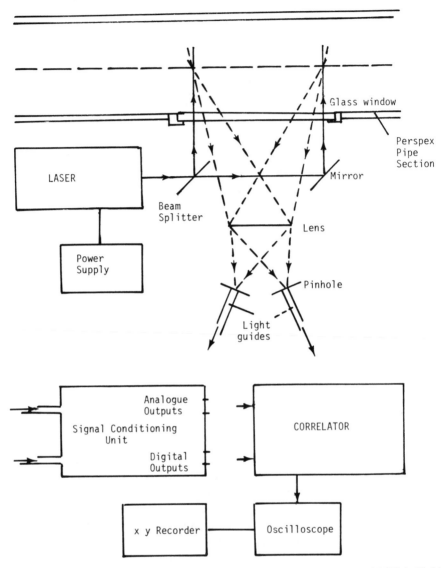

Figure 13.18(b) Laser Doppler velocimeter. Reproduced by permission of **BHRA** Fluid Engineering, UK.

The Laser Doppler Velocimeter systems have been applied as research tools to obtain basic information on the behaviour of gas–solid flow. Pfeffer and his associates [17] have uncovered some unique behaviour of the particles which seems to fall in line with turbulence measurements of other researchers [18]. Scott [19] has employed the LDV system to measure the particle velocity in a dilute pneumatic transport system. Over the range studied by Scott, he found for 4 mm diameter particles a linear behaviour between the particle velocity and the superficial gas velocity. The arrangement used by Scott is shown in Fig. 13.18(b).

13.12 OTHER TECHNIQUES FOR PARTICLE VELOCITIES

One of the oldest methods to obtain the particle velocities is to use a system of two simultaneously acting solenoid valves; in this arrangement the amount of solids trapped in the flow element is measured. By the weight of the solids and their volume the voidage can be found as $c = (G/G)L$. Rizk [23], Hariu and Molstad [21], Capes and Nakamura [22] and Saroff *et al.* [24] made extensive use of this procedure.

Ikemori and Munakata [25] used an impulse meter to measure the particle velocities. They employed a capture device for the particles which was coupled with a tension gauge to measure the force imparted to the system.

13.13 INSTRUMENTATION FOR INDUSTRIAL APPLICATIONS

13.13.1 Introduction

In this section a number of commercially available instruments will be described. Whilst most of these instruments are used for the monitoring and control of pneumatic conveying systems, more recent developments are facilitating the online monitoring of the flow parameters during the conveying process.

The control requirements in pneumatic conveying systems are normally limited to sensing a flow/no flow situation, whilst the most popular range of instruments are those used for monitoring levels in bins, hoppers and blow vessels. In the latter application, level probes are an essential component in the fully automatic operation of blow vessels.

13.13.2 Bulk material flow detector (Fig. 13.19)

This instrument emits a microwave beam and detects a doppler shift in frequency of reflected waves. It detects movements of bulk materials in or on the following feeder systems:

(a) Pipelines, ducts (pneumatic or gravitational feed).
(b) Air activated gravity conveyors.
(c) Material transfer points on: vibrating chutes; conveyor belts; worm feeders; and bucket chains.

Contactless detection of bulk material flow in transport systems made of

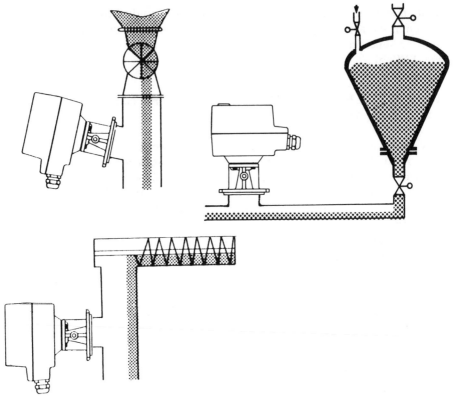

Figure 13.19 Typical application of bulk material flow detectors (Endress and Hauser, South Africa).

non-conducting material is possible, as the detector can be mounted externally without any holes in the transport duct itself.

This type of instrument is insensitive to build-up and is insensitive to air currents and dust in the air stream (particularly important for pneumatic conveying).

The sensitivity response is adjustable and a continuous adjustment of switching delay up to 10 seconds is useful in some applications with intermittent short breaks in material flow.

13.13.3 Bulk solids impact flowmeter

This type of instrument can be used for measuring the mass flow of bulk solids at transfer points between and/or after:

(a) Conveyors.
(b) Vibratory feeds.
(c) Rotary valves.

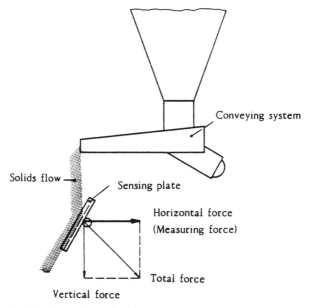

Figure 13.20 Measuring principle (Endress and Hausser, South Africa).

(d) Bucket elevators.
(e) Screw conveyors.
(f) Drag link conveyors.

The measuring principle is illustrated in Fig. 13.20. Instruments of this type are available in measuring ranges of 0–40 kg/h to 0–1000 t/h. The accuracy of such installations is often dependent on the degree of expertise employed in engineering and executing the installation, but typically accuracies of 1% are attainable.

(a) Physical Principles

The solids flow for flow rate measurement is directed over the sensing plate of the solids flowmeter.

The pulse generated on impact is processed by the flowmeter (Fig. 13.20). The physics of the measurement is based on Newton's law of dynamics, whereby force F is equal to the time change of the pulse mv, or

$$F = \frac{\Delta(mv)}{\Delta t} = \frac{m\Delta v}{\Delta t} = ma \tag{13.3}$$

The definition is as follows: 'force = mass × change in velocity', whereby it is assumed that mass remains constant. Newton's law can also be expressed as follows:

$$F = \frac{\Delta(mv)}{\Delta t} = \frac{m\Delta v}{\Delta t} = \frac{m}{t}\Delta v \tag{13.4}$$

$$F = q_m \Delta v \tag{13.5}$$

$$q_m = F\frac{1}{\Delta v} = Fk \tag{13.6}$$

where

q_m = flow rate, gravimetric
a = acceleration
Δv = difference between impact velocity and fall-off velocity
F = force
t = time
m = mass
k = constant

This law shows that the flow rate q_m is proportional to impact force. The solids flowmeter only evaluates the horizontal force. It is important that the other parameters are maintained constant; this can be achieved by selecting the optimum installation conditions.

(b) The basic equation for the solids flowmeter

To calculate the horizontal measuring force, the following simplified formula has been developed (Fig. 13.21):

$$F_M = 100 q_m h^{1/2} \sin \alpha \sin \gamma \tag{13.7}$$

F_M = the horizontal force in cN $(1\,\text{cN} \approx 1\,\text{g})$ generated by the impact on the sensing plate
q_m = flow rate in t/h
h = fall height in m

h is the vertical height between the point of impact on the sensing plate and the point at which the material begins to fall by gravity. The formula is correct, provided that the initial velocity is almost zero.

α = sensing plate angle to the horizonal
γ = angle of impact = angle between flow and sensing plate

Equation (13.7) contains Newton's law of dynamics, whereby the factor Δv was divided by $h^{1/2}$, $\sin \alpha$, $\sin \gamma$ into simple measurable divisions, since $v = (h \times 2 \times g)^{1/2} = h^{1/2}(2g)^{1/2}$. The constant factor $2g^{1/2}$ is contained in the factor 100 in equation (13.7). The horizontal vector of velocity, i.e. impact force,

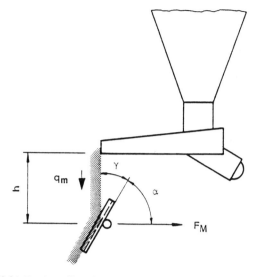

Figure 13.21 Basic calibration (Endress and Hausser, South Africa).

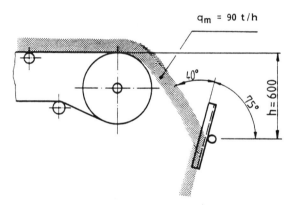

Figure 13.22 Impact flow meter (Endress and Hausser, South Africa).

is calculated with the sine of the angle α of the sensing plate and the angle of impact γ.

Figure 13.22 shows the impact flowmeter geometry.

13.13.4 Mass flow measurement of pneumatically conveyed solids

A key measured variable in all conveying operations is the rate of solids flow. In the case of pneumatic conveying this can be done directly by measuring the solids entering the conveying pipe gravimetrically with a bulk flowmeter such as an impact sensing plate or a weighing container, or volumetrically with suitable metering systems.

Direct measurement in the pipe is possible using a cross-correlation and concentration measuring technique. A system employing this technique is made up of four components: two sensors in the line, a correlator, and a concentration transmitter.

The need for two sensors becomes clear when one considers the basic equation for flow measurement in pneumatic conveying:

$$\dot{G} = \dot{V}_p \rho_p C_t = c A \rho_p C_t \tag{13.8}$$

where

$\dot{G}$ = mass flow rate
$\dot{V}_p$ = volume flow rate
ρ_p = solids density
C_t = volume concentration
A = pipe cross-sectional area
c = solids velocity

In contrast to measurement of single-phase flow, two-phase flow necessitates determination of a second independent variable in addition to the solids velocity, namely volume concentration.

If it is assumed that the solids density ρ_p remains constant, for a given pipe diameter with cross-sectional area A one can combine the two factors A and ρ_p into a constant or a calibration factor K, thus arriving at the simplified equation

$$\dot{G} = K c C_t \tag{13.9}$$

Figure 13.23 shows the general design of the measuring line. The concentration sensor is coupled to the concentration transmitter to form an independent measuring line for concentration. The correlator calculates the mean solids velocity from the two signals received from the velocity sensor and combines it with the concentration signal and the calibration factor to arrive at the mass flow rate.

(a) Velocity sensor

The correlation measuring principle is used to measure the velocity. The two statistical noise signals required for this are generated in two precision capacitors as shown in Fig. 13.24.

The solid particles carried along in the gas produce a change in the non-conductor in the precision capacitor, thus altering the capacitance. Since the particles follow a random path as a result of collisions with each other and the pipe wall rather than travelling along a straight line through the pipe, the

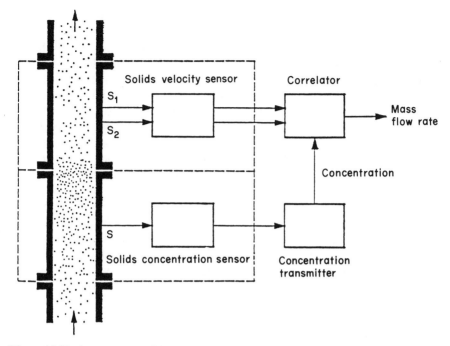

Figure 13.23 Arrangement of flow meter in the conveying pipe (Endress and Hausser, South Africa).

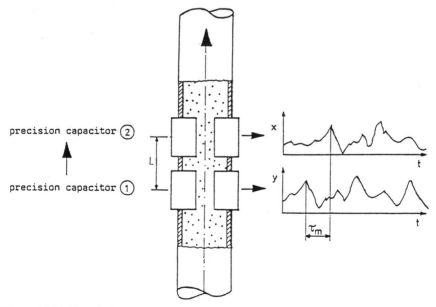

Figure 13.24 Correlation measurement of velocity (Endress and Hausser, South Africa).

noise signals obtained through time tend to change randomly as shown diagramatically in Fig. 13.24. If the distance L between the two capacitors is kept reasonably short, the noise signal obtained at capacitor 2 will show a similar pattern as the arrangement of the particles in the pipe does not change rapidly. If the particle arrangement could be frozen on its journey from the first to the second capacitor, the two signal patterns would be identical and the correlation would be 100%. If the two capacitors are set too far apart for the flow in question, the particles would mix so much along the distance L that there would be no similarity between the noise signals. In this case the correlation would be zero. With optimal capacitor spacing, which depends on the velocity range and the scanning frequency of the correlator, correlations of the order of 60% to 80% are obtained in actual practice. The comparison of the two noise signals with respect to similarity is a mathematical/statistical process. The signal from capacitor 1 is delayed in the correlator until the similarity between the signals reaches a maximum, or, in the ideal case, until they are identical.

The correlator calculates the necessary delay time τ_m, which corresponds exactly to the time required for the particles to travel from capacitor 1 to capacitor 2, from the cross-correlation function (CCF) as shown in Fig. 13.25. The CCF reaches a peak precisely at this interval τ_m. Along the ordinate of Fig. 13.25, the correlation coefficient is derived from 0 to 100% as the measurement of similarity of the two signals.

From the transit time τ_m the velocity is derived:

$$v = L/\tau_m$$

This is an absolute measurement and the correlative velocity measurement need not be calibrated. This system requires the selection of a location in the conveying system that will provide a symmetrical flow profile and therefore a reliable measurement of mean flow velocity. Depending on particular obstacles to

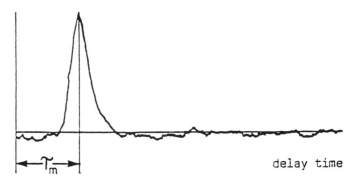

Figure 13.25 Cross-correlation function (Endress and Hausser, South Africa).

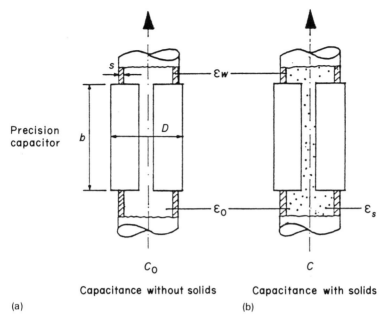

Precision
capacitor

Capacitance without solids

(a)

Capacitance with solids

(b)

Figure 13.26 Principle of capacitive concentration (Endress and Hausser, South Africa).

regular flow, e.g. bends, constrictions or enlargements, inlet runs of about 10–20 times pipe diameter and outlet runs of about 5–10 times pipe diameter should be maintained.

(b) Concentration sensor

The concentration sensor evaluates the absolute change in capacitance caused in a precision capacitor by the solid particles as shown in Fig. 13.26. If gas alone, without any solids, were flowing through the pipe, the capacitor would have a certain basic capacitance, its so-called empty pipe capacitance C_0, as expressed by the equation:

$$C_0 = \frac{0 \cdot b - D}{(D\pi/4) + (2s/\varepsilon w)}$$

C_0 depends on the geometry of the capacitor, the width of the capacitor plates, w, the diameter, D, and on the non-conductor in the capacitor—as determined by the wall thickness, s, of the inside tube and the dielectric constants (DC) of the tube material and the gas. If the solids are conveyed with the gas, the non-conductor and the capacitance C of the capacitor both change. The ratio of the capacitance C with solids in the pipe to the empty pipe capacitance C_0

$$\frac{C}{C_0} = 1 + \frac{1 - (1/\varepsilon s)}{1 + (2s/\frac{1}{4}D\varepsilon w)}$$

is proportional to the concentration C_t, which is required to calculate the mass flow rate.

Because this measurement is dependent on the dielectric constants of the gas and solids as well as on the specific geometry of the measuring pipe, it requires (unlike the velocity measurement) calibration with the particular material being conveyed.

The capacitance change ΔC occurring with the solids in comparison with the empty pipe capacitance ($\Delta C = C - C_0$) is very small. Unless a certain minimum solids loading μ is present, the reliability of the capacitive measurement cannot be guaranteed.

Empirically, it is found that:

$$\mu > 5 (\text{kg solids/kg gas})$$

is required for reliable measurement. Figure 13.27 illustrates what this loading level represents in terms of different phases of pneumatic conveying.

As shown in Fig. 13.27 the minimum solids loading of $\mu = 5$ restricts the use of capacitive concentration measurment to the low-load range of dilute phase conveying. Otherwise this method covers the entire range of pneumatic conveying right up to the clogging limit.

(c) Transmitters

Correlator

The heart of the entire measuring line is the correlator, which calculates the mean solids velocity from the two noise signals received from the velocity sensor and combines this figure with the concentration signal and a calibration factor according to the concentration equation to arrive at the desired mass flow rate.

Transmitter for concentration measurement

This transmitter receives the signal from the concentration sensor and supplies a standardized current input to the correlator.

13.13.5 Level detection

In many pneumatic conveying systems it is necessary to detect the levels or presence of materials in charging hoppers, blow vessels, chutes (blocked chute detection) etc. A variety of instrument types are available depending on the circumstances in each application.

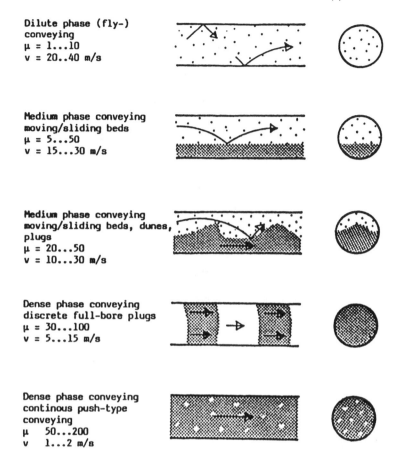

Dilute phase (fly-)
conveying
μ = 1...10
v = 20..40 m/s

Medium phase conveying
moving/sliding beds
μ = 5...50
v = 15...30 m/s

Medium phase conveying
moving/sliding beds, dunes,
plugs
μ = 20...50
v = 10...30 m/s

Dense phase conveying
discrete full-bore plugs
μ = 30...100
v = 5...15 m/s

Dense phase conveying
continous push-type
conveying
μ   50...200
v   1...2 m/s

Figure 13.27 Conveying conditions showing the changes in solids loading.

(a) Capacitance switches (Fig. 13.28)

The principle of operation is that a capacitance probe and the wall of the container or vessel form the plates of a capacitor.

When the probe is covered with material, this material acts as a dielectric between the capacitor plates changing the capacitance. Thus change is detected electrically and a signal is obtained to indicate the presence of material at the probe and/or actuate the mechanism filling or emptying the vessel.

Robust capacitance probes are available which can withstand high temperatures (up to 25 °C) and abrasive dusts and powders such as fly ash.

If a capacitance probe is being used for low level detection in a blow vessel, the electronic switching unit should be fitted with an adjustable switching delay to prevent the system switching when momentary 'bridging' of the material occurs above the probe during discharge.

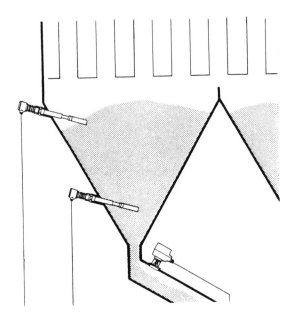

Figure 13.28 Arrangement of capacitance probes in a hopper (Endress and Hausser, South Africa).

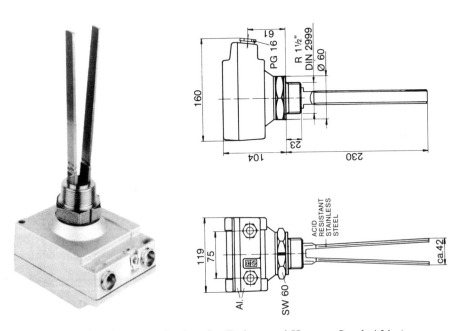

Figure 13.29 Vibrating prong level probe (Endress and Hausser, South Africa).

(b) Vibrating level limit switches (Fig. 13.29)

These consist of a probe which is constructed so that it can easily be vibrated at its natural resonant frequency. They can either be of the 'tuning fork' type or consist of a single tine.

The frequency of vibration of the probe is changed by the filling material in a vessel, and this is detected by a piezo crystal and electrical circuitry.

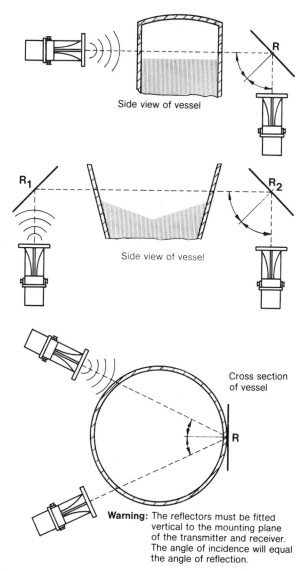

Side view of vessel

Side view of vessel

Cross section of vessel

Warning: The reflectors must be fitted vertical to the mounting plane of the transmitter and receiver. The angle of incidence will equal the angle of reflection.

Figure 13.30 Arrangement of microwave level detectors in typical industrial applications.

These level switches can be adjusted to switch for either full or empty conditions. They are suitable for use in fine grained solids and powders but should not be positioned in the path of material flow streams which will result in the wear of the probe over time. These probes need no adjustment and have no moving parts. They are available for 'zone 10' hazardous areas which allows their use for detecting levels of flammable dusts.

(c) Microwave barriers (Fig. 13.30)

A microwave system comprising a transmitter, receiver and electronic switching unit can be used for detecting the presence of material at a point in a container. The transmitter and receiver are mounted opposite each other on either side of the container or vessel. When the filling material fills the space in between, the microwave beam emitted is absorbed and this is detected by the receiver.

This is a non-contact non-intrusive method. It requires electrically non-conductive walls for the vessel in order to operate. If the vessel is made of conductive material windows of suitable material such as glass, plexiglass or basalt can be used.

Advantages of this type of system include:

(a) It is unaffected by light, sound, condensation, heat, wind, dust.

(b) With non-conductive vessels it is easy to retrofit, there are no sealing problems and it is simple to change the switch point.

13.13.6 Nuclear level measurement and detection (Fig. 13.31)

If it is not possible to insert a level detecting device into a vessel, and the walls are constructed of electrically conductive material (precluding the use of microwave barriers) nuclear level sensing devices may provide a solution.

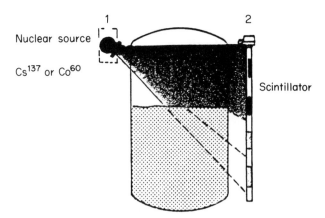

Figure 13.31 Continuous level measurement using nuclear source (Endress and Hausser, South Africa).

(a) Level limit switches

An isotope (usually ^{60}Co or ^{137}Cs) emitting gamma radiation is mounted in a shielded source container on one side of the vessel. The source container has a window (which can be opened and shut) which beams a stream of radiation across the vessel where it is detected, e.g. by a Geiger-Muller tube. When the vessel is filled with material, the radiation is attenuated by the material and this is detected.

An electronic switching unit coupled to the detector provides switching signals to actuate alarms and/or filling and emptying mechanisms.

The use of nuclear level switches usually requires registration and certification by relevant State Authorities concerned with safe use and handling of atomic energy.

(b) Nuclear continuous level management

In such a system the source container has a window which beams a plane of radiation across the vessel and down the length over which the level is to be measured. A strip detector is placed on the other side of the vessel which, in conjunction with an electronic transmitter, is able to determine the level of the material in the vessel. These detectors are of the scintillation counter type.

The more advanced systems available offer simple calibrating procedures and automatic compensation for decaying source strengths. As with nuclear level limit switches State certification is usually required.

REFERENCES

1. Davies, G.S. (1981) *Proc. Powtech 81*, Birmingham, England.
2. Crowe, C.T. (1982) Final Report on Contract DOE DE-FG22-80PC30212.
3. Klinzing, G.E. (1981) *Gas-Solid Transport*, McGraw-Hill, New York.
4. Mathur, M.P. and Klinzing, G.E. (1983) *CE Symp. Series*, 222.
5. Smith, R. and Klinzing, G.E. (1989) *AIChE J.*, in press.
6. Mathur, M.P. and Klinzing, G.E. (1983) *Fine Particle Soc. Meeting*, Honolulu, August.
7. Mathur, M.P. (1982) *Proc. 1982 Symp. on Instrumentation and Control for Fossil Energy Processes*, Houston, Texas, June.
8. Brewster, B.S. and Seader, J.D. (1980) *AIChE J.*, **36**, 325.
9. Cheng, L., Tung, S.K. and Soo, S.L. (1980) *Trans. ASME J. Eng. Powder*, **91**, 135.
10. Soo, S.L., Ihrig, H.G. Jr, and El Kouch, A.F. (1969). *Trans. ASME J. Basic Eng.*, **82D**, 609.
11. Cheng, L. and Soo, S.L. (1970) *J. Appl. Phys.*, **41**, 585.
12. King, P. (1973) *Proceedings of Pneumotransport 2*, Paper D2, BHRA Fluid Engineering Cranfield.
13. Sheen, S.H. and Raptis, A.C. (1979) *Tech. Memorandium*, No. TMO7, Argonne National Laboratory, Sept.
14. Zacharias, E.M. Jr and Franz, D.W. (1973) *Chemical Engineer*, January 22.
15. Thomson, F.M. (1971) *Bulk Material Handling*, Vol. 2 (ed. M.C. Hawk), University of Pittsbugh.

16. Kerker, L. (1977) *Verfahrentechnik*, **11**, No. 9, 549.
17. Kolansky, M.S., Weinbaum, S. and Pfeffer, R. (1969) *Proceedings of Pneumotransport 3*, BHRA Fluid Engineering, Cranfield.
18. Corino, E.R. and Brodkey, R.S. (1969) *J. Fluid Mech.*, **37**, 1.
19. Scott, A.M. (1978) *Proceedings of Pneumotransport 4*, Paper A3, BHRA Fluid Engineering, Cranfield.
20. Chao, B.T., Perez-Blanco, H., Saunders, J.H. and Soo, S.L. (1979) *Proc. Symp. on Powder and Bulk Handling of Solids Conf.*, Philadelphia, May.
21. Hariu, O.H. and Molstad, M.E. (1949) *Ind. Eng. Chem.*, **41**, 1148.
22. Capes, C.E. and Nakamura, K. (1973) *Can. J. Chem. Eng.*, **51**, 31.
23. Rizk, F. (1973) *Dissertation*, Universität Karlsruhe.
24. Saroff, L., Gromicko, F.H., Johnson, H.E., Strakey, J.P. and Haynes, W.P. (1976) *Proc. 69th Annual Meeting AIChE*, Chicago.
25. Ikemori, K. and Munakata, H. (1971) *Proceedings of Pneumotransport 1*, BHRA Fluid Engineering, Cranfield.

14

System design and worked examples

14.1 INTRODUCTION

In an attempt to illustrate the various concepts discussed in the preceding chapters, a number of worked examples relating to pneumatic conveying systems will be presented in this chapter. Where possible each example has been structured so as to illustrate a number of facets of the theory, whilst an attempt has also been made to design each problem so that it relates to practical pneumatic conveying problems.

The authors have also included some system design procedures proposed by various researchers. Whilst each procedure has been evaluated for specific applications, the reader is cautioned to note the limitations and boundary conditions of the various techniques.

In some examples, a number of new concepts are presented as well as the introduction of some useful charts to facilitate the quick acquisition of data.

14.2 MOISTURE CONTENT IN AIR

It is required to convey a hygroscopic powder which when exposed to air above a moisture content of 60% becomes cohesive. An existing blow vessel system is available, complete with a screw compressor fitted with an aftercooler capable of delivering air at 20 °C above ambient conditions. The compressor is coupled to the blow vessel through a pressure reducing valve. The compressor is regulated to operate between 10 bar and 9.5 bar. The blow vessel system is rated at 3 bar and the maximum ambient temperature is 35 °C. The existing compressor/aftercooler system should be investigated to determine whether an additional external drying system is required.

Solution

The problem can be solved using two sets of curves and assuming isothermal air expansion. The curves to be used are:

(a) The temperature/mass concentration of water in air curve for 100% relative humidity (Fig. 14.1).
(b) The temperature/mass concentration of water in air for 1 bar (Fig. 14.2).

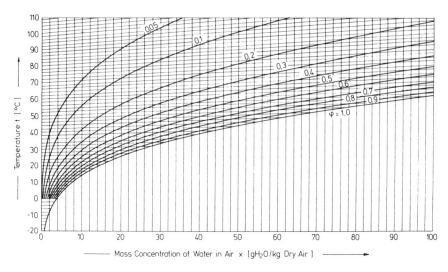

Figure 14.1 Mass concentration of water in air (100% relative humidity).

Taking an ambient temperature $t = 26\,°C$ (Fig. 14.1) and a relative humidity $\phi = 100\%$, it will be seen that the mass concentration of water in air $X = 22\,g\,H_2O/kg$ dry air.

The ambient air will be compressed to a pressure of 10 bar gauge (11 bar absolute) with a corresponding rise in temperature which can be calculated using equation (2.23)

$$T_2 = T_1 \left(\frac{p_2}{p_1} \right)^{(k-1)/k}$$

where $\kappa < 1.6$ for compression with friction.

$$T_1 = 26 + 273.15 = 299.15\,K$$

$$p_2 = 11\,bar$$

$$p_1 = 1\,bar$$

$$T_2 = 299.5 \left(\frac{11}{1} \right)^{(1.6-1)/1.6} = 735.21\,K$$

$$t_2 = 462\,°C$$

The air is cooled by the aftercooler, and referring to Fig. 14.2 at 75 °C the air at a pressure of 11 bar will be saturated (dew point). The aftercooler will drop the air temperature to $t = 46\,°C$. This implies that water will drop out of the air stream

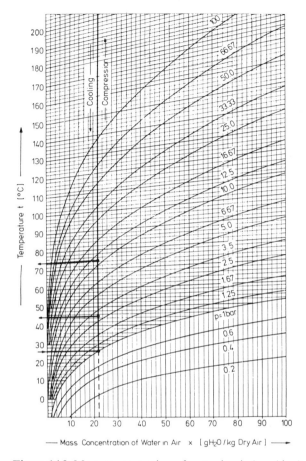

Figure 14.2 Mass concentration of water in air ($p = 1$ bar).

at $t = 46\,°C$. It should be noted that the mass concentration of water in the air $X = 6\,g\,H_2O/kg$ dry air (Fig. 14.2).

The air is expanded from $p = 11$ bar absolute to the conveying condition $p = 4$ bar absolute. Moving along the $X = 6\,g\,H_2O/kg$ dry air curve to the $p = 4$ bar absolute curve, the new dew point will be $t = 27\,°C$.

The conveying process will involve the expansion of the air at $p = 4$ bar absolute and $X = 6\,g\,H_2O/kg$ dry air to $p = 1$ bar absolute. Referring to Fig. 14.1, air with $X = 6\,g\,H_2O/kg$ dry air would have a dew point temperature $t = 6\,°C$ at $\phi = 100\%$ at 1 bar.

However, the air entering the conveying system is $t = 46\,°C$ and based on isothermal conditions, it will leave the system at the same temperature.

Transposing the conditions of the conveying air, $t = 46\,°C$, $X = 6\,g\,H_2O/kg$ dry air, to Fig. 14.1 we obtain an intersection point with the $\phi = 0.1 = 10\%$ relative humidity curve.

As such, the existing equipment will yield totally safe conveying conditions. No additional drying equipment is required.

14.3 THE DESIGN OF INDUSTRIAL VACUUM SYSTEMS

14.3.1 Introduction

An increasing awareness of the importance of minimizing industrial health hazards has resulted in an increasing interest in the use of industrial vacuum systems. These systems are generally designed to handle intermittent loads such as spillages or the cleaning of boilers and the like during scheduled maintenance periods.

There are a number of techniques for designing these systems; however, since they operate under extremely dilute phase conditions, invariably, little cognizance is taken of the presence of the solids. As such most industrial vacuum systems are designed taking into consideration an air alone situation.

Since many of these systems involve a relatively complex network of pipes, inlet ports, valves, cleaning tools, flexible hoses, etc. a set design procedure is recommended [1] in order to take into account the various loss factors associated with such systems. The design procedure, proposed in this text, has been tested and proved to be extremely reliable. The procedure has been substantially simplified using some basic assumptions some of which might not be totally acceptable to the purist.

14.3.2 Design philosophy

Invariably, the greatest pressure loss in the system occurs within the tool and the flexible hose used to connect the tool to the inlet port, which in turn is connected to a branch pipe or to the main piping system. The first basic assumption in the design procedure is to assume that the same volume of air enters each tool and flexible hose assembly regardless of the location in the industrial vacuum system.

Under normal applications, the variations caused by the location of an inlet port are minor and as such this assumption has been proved to be acceptable.

The selection of a system is based on the assessment of the volume of air required at two conditions:

(a) An assessment of the lowest possible volume of air entering each inlet port in use. This value is dependent upon the envisaged applications, and is selected according to Table 14.1. The quantity of air entering the exhauster at a lower pressure loss is thus obtained.

(b) The second condition is obtained from the maximum volume of air at each inlet port in use.

The two conditions thus obtained can be plotted as a load line on the performance curves of a commercially available exhauster. The interaction between the load line and the exhauster curve facilitates the selection of a suitable exhauster and motor.

14.3.3 Design procedure

The evaluation of the air and vacuum required for a particular system can be simplified by following a set procedure:

(a) Determine the number of inlet ports and location of tubing, separator system and exhauster.

(b) Prepare a sketch in sufficient detail to show inlet port locations, length of run for each branch and main with fitting type and location, and location of separator and exhauster unit.

(c) Starting at the most remote inlet port, proceed systematically toward the exhauster, tabulating for the most remote branch and each section of the main:

(i) The number of inlet valves in use served by the branch and main.

(ii) The number of 90° bends and 45° turns.

(iii) The measured length of pipe and corresponding pipe diameter.

(d) Starting at the most remote inlet port, size the branch and section of the mains in accordance with the minimum volume found in Table 14.1 for the desired system, and the minimum velocity in Table 14.2.

Table 14.1 Maximum and minimum volume per hose/tool combination and corresponding pressure drop for an industrial vacuum system

Application	Nominal size of tools/hose	Minimum volume and pressure drop		Maximum volume and pressure drop	
		Volume, $\dot{V}$ (m³/min)	Pressure drop (kPa)	Volume, $\dot{V}$ (m³/min)	Pressure drop (kPa)
Bench use	$D = 25\,mm$ $L = 2.4\,m$	1.13	8.43	2.27	27.5
White rooms or areas with very low dust content	$D = 40\,mm$ $L = 15.2\,m$	1.70	10.76	2.83	28.27
Usual industrial	$D = 40\,mm$ $L = 15.2\,m$	2.27	18.4	2.83	28.27
High vacuum industrial	$D = 40\,mm$ $L = 7.6\,m$	2.55	12.73	4.25	32.87
Heavy spills— cleaning rail roadcars and ships	$D = 50\,mm$ $L = 15.2\,m$	3.96	13.93	6.23	32.53
High vacuum and heavy cleaning	$D = 50\,mm$ $L = 7.6\,m$	5.1	12.77	8.50	32.00

Table 14.2 Recommended conveying velocities for industrial vacuum systems

Nominal pipe diameter, D (mm)	Horizontal runs of branches and mains and vertical down flow risers		Vertical upflow risers	
	Minimum velocity (m/s)	Recommended maximum velocity (m/s)	Minimum velocity (m/s)	Recommended maximum velocity (m/s)
40	9	15	13	19
50	10	18	15	21
65	11	20	16	24
80	12	21	19	26
100	14	25	21	30
125	15	27	24	33
150	17	30	25	37

Notes:
(a) For materials with bulk density in the range $400\,\text{kg/m}^3 \leqslant \rho_b \leqslant 1500\,\text{kg/m}^3$ use lower velocities.
(b) For materials with bulk density in the range $2000\,\text{kg/m}^3 \leqslant \rho_b \leqslant 3000\,\text{kg/m}^3$ use higher velocities.

(e) Using Figure 14.3, determine the pipe size for the branch and each section of main and tabulate the pipe loss (Pa/m) of run.

(f) Using Table 2.8, determine the equivalent length of pipe and tabulate for each 90° and 45° bend in the air stream.

(g) Add actual measured length of run for the branch and each section of the main to the equivalent length of pipe determined under (f) above and tabulate as total length.

(h) Multiply the pipe loss from (e) above by the total length determined in (g) above and tabulate.

(i) Using the maximum volume as shown in Table 14.1, repeat steps (d)–(h) and tabulate. Ignore velocity.

(j) For the separator and interconnecting piping allow $\Delta p = 1.6\,\text{kPa}$ pressure loss for the lower volume and $\Delta p = 3.3\,\text{kPa}$ pressure loss for the higher volume and tabulate.

(k) Determine the total pressure loss for the lower and higher volumes taking all components into consideration. This pressure loss is representative of conditions at the exhauster inlet for both air flow conditions.

(l) The volume of air entering the exhauster inlet is under a negative pressure. As such, the air will expand and a greater volume of free air will enter the various nose nozzles. This is computed as follows:

$$\dot{V}_c = \left| \frac{101.325}{p_0 - \Delta p_T} \right| \dot{V}_a \qquad (14.1)$$

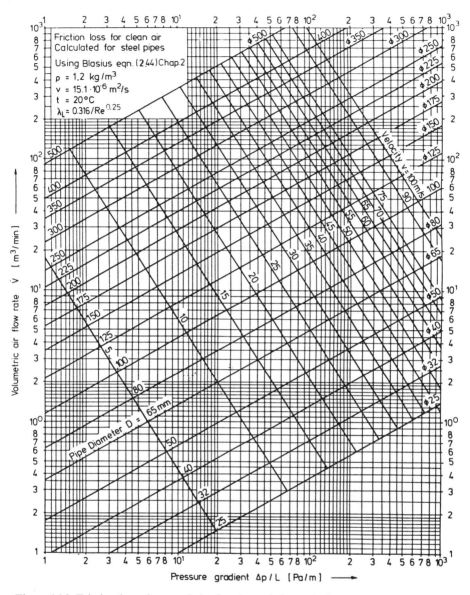

Figure 14.3 Friction loss characteristics for clean air in steel pipes.

where

$\dot{V}_c$ = the volumetric air flow at exhauster inlet conditions to facilitate exhauster selection using standard performance curves.

$\dot{V}_a$ = the actual total free air entering the inlet ports in use under atmospheric conditions.

p_0 = prevailing atmospheric pressure (kPa).
Δp_T = suction inlet pressure to exhauster determined from above technique.

(m) If it is required to direct the discharge from the exhauster through a piping system which could create an additional pressure loss, then this loss must be calculated and added to the exhauster inlet pressure drop.

(n) Once the total pressure against which the exhauster must operate is known, then a correction for altitude must be applied. For sea level conditions, the total pressure drop is used with the standard performance curves. If the installation is at an altitude, then the following correction must be made:

$$p_f = \left(\frac{101.325}{p_0} \right) \Delta p_T \qquad (14.2)$$

where

p_f = equivalent vacuum (kPa) which must be used with standard performance curves for an exhauster
p_0 = atmospheric pressure (site conditions)
Δp_T = total pressure drop against which the exhauster must operate on site.

Once the volumes entering the inlet to the exhauster and the pressures against

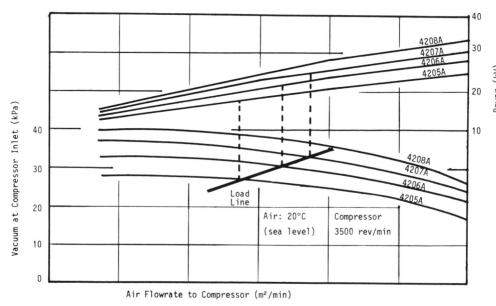

Figure 14.4 Exhauster performance curves.

which the exhauster must operate are known, two points—one representing the lower volume and lower pressure drop and another representing the higher volume and greater pressure drop—are plotted on a set of exhauster performance curves (Fig. 14.4). These points are then connected with a straight line called the load line which must interact with one or more standard exhauster performance curves. The appropriate exhauster is selected at the intersection between the load line and the performance curve. Select exhausters whose performance curve intersects the load line near the greater volume for heavy materials, and near the point of the lower volume for light dust and dirt.

Example

An industrial vacuum system is required for a medium industrial application in which four operators must be able to operate at any one time. Each operator must be equipped with a flexible hose and tools. The site condition is 2000 metres above sea level. The piping layout is as shown in Fig. 14.5. The system is to be designed taking into account the sizing of an appropriate exhauster and specifying the diameter of the branch and main pipes.

Solution

Referring to Table 14.1, for a normal industrial application the following is recommended:

(a) Flexible hose, $D = 40\,\text{mm}$, $L = 15.2\,\text{m}$
(b) Minimum volume, $\dot{V} = 2.27\,\text{m}^3/\text{min}$
(c) Minimum pressure loss, $\Delta p = 18.4\,\text{kPa}$
(d) Maximum volume, $\dot{V} = 2.83\,\text{m}^3/\text{min}$
(e) Maximum pressure loss, $\Delta p = 28.27\,\text{kPa}$

The most remote point in the system is point A and this point will be used as the datum for all calculations:

(1) Starting with the 40 mm hose at point A, it is known that the minimum volume which must pass through this hose is $\dot{V} = 2.27\,\text{m}^3/\text{min}$ (Table 14.1)
(2) From Fig. 14.3 and consulting Table 14.2 at a volume $\dot{V} = 2.27\,\text{m}^3/\text{min}$ it can be seen that a pipe diameter $D = 50\,\text{mm}$ will provide a safe velocity for a vertical upflow riser.
(3) Since the branch B–C is relatively long and since it is a horizontal pipe, consulting Table 14.2 and Fig. 14.3, it can be seen that it is acceptable to select the pipe diameter for this section $D = 65\,\text{mm}$. A larger diameter is preferable in terms of minimizing the pressure loss, as long as the recommended safe velocities as per Table 14.2 are adhered to.
(4) At point C, a second active inlet is introduced thus doubling the amount of air entering the branch. As such, the volume of air is $\dot{V} = 4.5\,\text{m}^3/\text{min}$.
(5) Consulting Fig. 14.3 and Table 14.2 it can be seen that the selection of a pipe diameter $D = 80\,\text{mm}$ will meet all constraints.

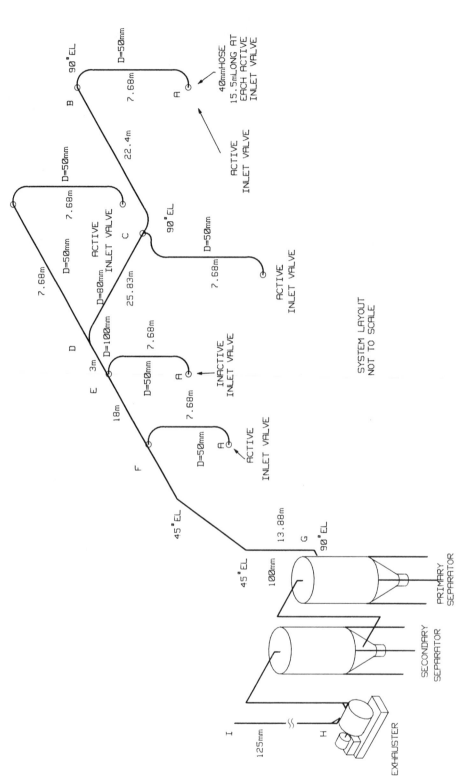

Figure 14.5 Layout of central vacuum system.

(6) The branch line C–D with two active inlet ports intersects a second branch line with one active inlet at point D. It should be noted that by virtue of the argument put forward in (3) above, since the second branch line is short, it is acceptable to retain its diameter $D = 50\,\text{mm}$.

(7) At point D, by virtue of three active inlet ports, the minimum air flow rate increases to $\dot{V} = 6.8\,\text{m}^3/\text{min}$. Once again, using the methods above, it will be seen that a pipe diameter from point D onwards of $D = 100\,\text{mm}$ will suffice.

(8) At point F a fourth active inlet is introduced increasing the minimum air flow rate $\dot{V} = 9.1\,\text{m}^3/\text{min}$ and once again a pipe diameter $D = 100\,\text{mm}$ meets all the requirements.

(9) On the basis of the above analysis, Table 14.3 is drawn up using the schematic layout of the system and Table 2.8 for equivalent lengths for the 90° and 45° bends:

(10) Once the system has been sized in terms of the most suitable pipe diameters, it is necessary to consider the pressure losses generated by virtue of the air flowing through the system. A table is drawn up itemizing each component of the total pressure loss.

(11) The pressure losses in Table 14.4 must be adjusted to include the losses in the separator and the additional loss created by the 38 metres of piping with $D = 125\,\text{mm}$ attached to the discharge of the exhauster. Allowing 1.6 kPa for the separator, and referring to Table 14.4, for the minimum volume condition

$$\Delta p_T = 21.5 + 1.6 + 0.49$$

$$= 23.6\,\text{kPa}$$

Table 14.3

Section	No. of active inlet ports	Pipe diameter (mm)	Bends 90°	Bends 45°	Equivalent loss* elbows (m)	Length of pipe (m)	Total equivalent length of pipe (m)
40 mm hose	1						
A–B	1	50	2	1	2.68	5	7.68
B–C	1	65	1		1.37	21	22.4
C–D	2	80	1		1.83	24	25.83
D–E	3	100				3	3
E–F	3	100				18	18
F–G	4	100	1	2	4.88	9	13.88

*From Table 2.8 and taking the loss in a 45° elbow to be half that in a 90° elbow, e.g. for section A–B for a 50 mm pipe: $\Delta L = 2(1.07) + 0.5(1.07) = 2.68\,\text{m}$.

Table 14.4

Section	Total equivalent length of pipe (m)	Minimum volume conditions for each active port				Maximum volume conditions for each active port			
		Air flow rate, $\dot{V}_a$ (m³/min)	Velocity, v (m/s)	Pressure drop (Pa/m)	Total pressure drop (Pa)	Bin flow rate, $\dot{V}_a$ (m³/min)	Velocity, v (m/s)	Pressure drop (Pa/m)	Total pressure (Pa)
40 mm hose					18.4×10^3				28.27×10^3
A–B	7.68	2.27	19.3	88.5	679.7	2.83	24.0	130.1	999.2
B–C	22.4	2.27	11.4	25.4	569.0	2.83	14.2	37.4	837.8
C–D	25.83	4.5	14.9	31.5	813.6	5.7	18.9	47.6	1229.5
D–E	3	6.8	14.4	22.4	67.2	8.5	18.0	33.1	99.3
E–F	18	6.8	14.4	22.4	403.2	8.5	18.0	33.1	595.8
F–G	13.88	9.1	19.3	37.3	517.7	11.3	24.0	54.7	759.2
				Subtotal	21 468.4			Subtotal	32 790.8

(where $\Delta p = 13\,\text{Pa/m}$ for the discharge pipe). For the maximum volume condition

$$\Delta p_T = 32.8 + 1.6 + 0.71$$
$$= 35.1\,\text{kPa}.$$

(where $\Delta p = 18.8\,\text{Pa/m}$ for the discharge pipe).

(12) To obtain the equivalent volumetric air flow rate entering the exhauster at standard conditions, it is necessary to obtain the local atmospheric pressure p_0. From Table 2.5, at an altitude of 2000 m, $p_0 = 789\,\text{mbar}$ $= 79.95\,\text{kPa}$.

For minimum volume conditions:

$$\dot{V}_a = 9.1\,\text{m}^3/\text{min}$$
$$\Delta p_T = 23.6\,\text{kPa}$$
$$\dot{V}_c = \frac{101.325}{79.95 - 23.6} \times 9.1 = 16.36\,\text{m}^3/\text{min}$$

For maximum volume conditions:

$$\dot{V}_a = 11.3\,\text{m}^3/\text{min}$$
$$\Delta p_T = 35.1\,\text{kPa}$$
$$\dot{V}_c = \frac{101.325}{79.95 - 35.1} \times 11.3$$
$$= 25.53\,\text{m}^3/\text{min}$$

(13) In order to correct the inlet vacuum for altitude: for minimum volume

$$p_f = \frac{101.325}{79.95} \times 23.6 = 29.9\,\text{kPa}$$

For maximum volume

$$p_f = \frac{101.325}{79.95} \times 35.1 = 44.5\,\text{kPa}$$

(14) The air flow rate and vacuum obtained for the minimum and maximum conditions provide the load line for the selection of an appropriate exhauster.

14.4 DILUTE PHASE PNEUMATIC CONVEYING SYSTEM DESIGN (METHOD 1)

14.4.1 Introduction

The following example will illustrate a design procedure to be adopted when calculating the parameters to specify a total dilute phase system. The procedure is based on the technique described in Chapter 6.

It must be emphasized that the techniques proposed in this text rely on the accurate determination of the conditions prevailing at the pressure minimum. As such, this example is based on the assumption that some basic tests have been conducted to obtain the necessary information.

14.4.2 The problem

You are required to design a dilute phase system to transport 3.9 t/h of polystyrol over a distance of 120 m which includes a 20 m vertical lift and two bends (Fig. 14.6).

Polystyrol has the following characteristics:

$$d = 2.5 \, \text{mm (oval–cylindrical shape)}$$

$$\rho_p = 1050 \, \text{kg/m}^3$$

$$\rho_B = 520 \, \text{kg/m}^3$$

You are required to convey the material in a carbon steel pipe using a rotary valve. The system must operate as a positive pressure system and the design must also include the sizing of a cyclone separator. The system is to be installed at sea level conditions with an ambient temperature $t = 20 \, ^\circ\text{C}$.

14.4.3 Experimental observations

From a series of tests conducted on the product the following information was obtained from the pressure minimum curve:

Figure 14.6 Layout of conveying system.

Maximum load ratio, $\mu = 5.5$

Froude number, $Fr_{min} = 20$

Additional pressure drop coefficient, $\lambda_Z = 5 \times 10^{-3}$

14.4.4 Estimation of pipe diameter

The pipe diameter can be estimated using conditions prevailing at the pressure minimum. Using μ and Fr we obtain the following equation:

$$D = \left(\frac{4\dot{G}}{\pi g^{1/2} \mu Fr \rho_0} \right)^{0.4} \tag{14.3}$$

$$= \left(113 \times 10^{-6} \frac{\dot{G}}{\mu Fr \rho_0} \right)^{0.4}$$

where

$Fr = Fr_{min}$
$\dot{G} = $ solids mass flow rate (t/h)
$\rho_0 = $ is the density of the air at ambient conditions, i. e. at the intake to a vacuum system and the discharge from a pressure system (Fig. 6.22)

Using equation (14.3) to determine the pipe diameter:

$$D = \left(113 \times 10^{-6} \frac{3900}{(5.5)(20)(1.2)} \right)^{0.4}$$

$$= 102.2\,\text{mm}$$

There is a standard range of pipes available and in this case a 100 mm pipe is selected as being the closest sized pipe, i.e $D = 100$ mm. The pipe diameter selected is based on the first estimation and does not take into account the pressure loss. An iterative approach will assist with the final selection of the pipe diameter.

14.4.5 Estimation of the pressure drop

$$\Delta p = \Delta p_L + \Delta p_A + \Delta p_Z + \Delta p_G + \Delta p_B + \Delta p_C$$

where

$\Delta p_L = $ pressure loss due to air (equation (2.44))
$\Delta p_A = $ acceleration pressure loss (equation (6.71))
$\Delta p_Z = $ additional pressure loss due to solids (equation (6.38)) for both horizontal

and vertical sections. This assumes that λ_z is identical for both horizontal and vertical lines

Δp_G = lift pressure loss due to gravity (equation (6.72)) and is considered for the vertical line only

Δp_B = bend pressure loss (equation (4.91))

Δp_C = pressure loss in the cyclone (Chapter 10)

As a first approximation, the pressure loss in the system is estimated assuming a cyclone pressure loss $\Delta p_C = 10\,\text{mbar}$:

(a) Air alone pressure loss, Δp_L

$$\Delta p_L = \lambda_L \frac{\rho_0}{2} v^2 \frac{\Delta L}{D}$$

where

$$\lambda_L = 0.316/Re^{0.25} \qquad \text{(equation (2.44))}$$

$$Re = vD/v \qquad \text{(equation (2.40))}$$

where

$$v = 15.1 \times 10^{-6}\,\text{m}^2/\text{s} \qquad \text{(Table 2.6)}$$

The air mass flow rate

$$\dot{Q} = \dot{G}/\mu = 3900/5.5$$
$$= 709.1\,\text{kg/h}$$

The air velocity

$$v = \frac{\dot{Q}}{A\rho(3600)}$$

$$= \frac{(709.1)(4)}{\pi D^2 (1.2)(3600)}$$

For $D = 100\,\text{mm}$, $v = 20.9\,\text{m/s}$

$$Re = 0.133 \times 10^6$$

$$\lambda_L = 0.0164$$

$$\Delta L = 100 + 20 = 120\,\text{m (total length)}$$

$$\Delta p_L = (0.0164)\left(\frac{1.2}{2}\right)(20.9^2)\frac{(120)}{(0.1)}$$

$$\Delta p_L = 5157.9\,\text{Pa}$$

(b) Acceleration pressure loss, Δp_A

$$\Delta p_A = \mu v_1 \rho_1 c \qquad \text{(equation (6.71))}$$

Note in this case, since v_1 and ρ_1 are not available, the system will be designed using conditions prevailing at the end of the pipe line, i.e. assuming incompressible flow in which $v_1 = v_0$ and $\rho_1 = \rho$.

Using Fig. 6.26(a) for a particle size $d = 2.5$ mm:

$$c/v = 0.5$$

using $v = 20.9$ m/s, $c = 10.45$ m/s.

$$\Delta p_a = (5.5)(1.2)(20.9)(10.45)$$

$$= 1441.5 \text{ Pa}$$

(c) Additional pressure loss due to presence of solids

It should be noted that this example has been calculated assuming that $\lambda_{Zv} = \lambda_{Zh}$, i.e. the additional pressure drop coefficient due to the solids is assumed to be the same in both the vertical (v) and horizontal (h) pipe. To be on the safe side λ_{Zh} is taken since in practice $\lambda_{Zh} > \lambda_{Zv}$.

From equation (6.38):

$$\Delta p_Z = \mu \lambda_Z \frac{\rho_0}{2} v^2 \frac{\Delta L}{D}$$

$$= (5.5)(5 \times 10^{-3}) \frac{1.2}{2} (20.9^2) \frac{120}{0.1}$$

$$= 8648.8 \text{ Pa}$$

where $\lambda_Z = 5 \times 10^{-3}$ is obtained from experimental observation.

(d) The lift pressure loss, Δp_G

From equation (6.72)

$$\Delta p_G = \rho^* g \Delta Z$$

Now,

$$\rho^* = \frac{\mu \rho_0}{c/v}$$

$$= (5.5)(1.2)/(0.5)$$

$$= 13.2 \qquad \text{(the conveying bulk density)}$$

$$\Delta p_G = (13.2)(9.806)(20)$$

$$= 2588.9 \text{ Pa}$$

(e) Bend pressure loss

From equation (4.91)

$$\frac{\Delta p_B}{\Delta p_Z} = 210\left(\frac{2R_B}{D}\right)^{-1.15}$$

Assume a bend radius $R_B = 7D = 700$ mm. Now $\Delta p_Z = 8648.8$ Pa for 120 metres (from (c) above)

$$\Delta p_Z = 72.1 \text{ Pa/m}$$

The equivalent length of bend

$$\Delta L_{eq} = 2\pi R_B/4 \qquad \text{(for } 90° \text{ bend)}$$
$$= 2\pi(0.7)/4$$
$$= 1.1 \text{ m}$$
$$\Delta p_{Z\,bend} = (72.1)(1.1)$$
$$= 79.3 \text{ Pa}$$
$$\Delta p_B = (79.3)(210)\left(\frac{2 \times (0.7)}{0.1}\right)^{-1.15}$$
$$= 800.7 \text{ Pa}$$

Since there are two bends in the system:

$$\Delta p_B = 1601.4 \text{ Pa}$$

(f) Total pressure loss (first iteration)

$$\Delta p = 5157.9 + 1441.5 + 8648.8 + 2588.9 + 1601.4 + 1000$$

where $10 \text{ mbar} \simeq 1000$ Pa. Therefore $\Delta p = 20\,438.5$ Pa $= 20.44$ k Pa

(g) Estimation of Froude number

In order to verify whether the initial estimation at the pipe diameter conforms with the minimum Froude number criterion:

$$Fr_1 > Fr_{min}$$

At the feed point:

$$p_1 = p_0 + \Delta p = 100 + 20.44$$
$$= 120.44 \text{ kPa}$$

(Note: p_0 has been assumed to be $p_0 = 100\,\text{kPa}$ and not $p_0 = 101.325\,\text{kPa}$).

$$\rho_1 = p_1/RT$$

Assuming isothermal conditions $t_1 = 20\,°\text{C}$

$$\rho_1 = \frac{120.44}{(0.207)(293.15)}$$

$$= 1.43\,\text{kg/m}^3$$

Initial velocity v_1:

$$v_1 = \frac{\dot{Q}}{\rho_1 A(3600)}$$

$$= \frac{(709.1)(4)}{\pi(0.1)^2(1.43)(3600)}$$

$$= 17.54\,\text{m/s}^1$$

Froude number Fr_1:

$$Fr_1 = v/(Dg)^{1/2}$$

$$= 17.54/((0.1)9.806)^{1/2}$$

$$= 17.71$$

Since $Fr_1 < Fr_{\min}$, the system cannot operate using this pipe diameter.

(h) Second iteration

The designer has two alternatives available to satisfy the Froude number relationship whilst retaining a solids mass flow rate $\dot{G} = 3.9\,\text{t/h}$:

(a) selection of a smaller pipe diameter, or
(b) reducing the mass load ratio μ.

Both options will ensure an initial Froude number (Fr_1) such that $Fr_1 > Fr_{\min}$. The first iteration produced a Froude number about 12% below the minimum Froude number. Allowing an additional 18% for uncertainty, the air mass flow rate will be increased by 30%. The increase of 30% produces

$$\dot{Q} = 922\,\text{kg/h}$$

This leads to the following data:

$$v_0 = 27.17\,\text{m/s}$$

$$Fr_0 = 27.44\,\text{m/s}$$

$$\mu = 4.23$$

From experimental data:

$$\lambda_Z = 4 \times 10^{-3}$$

Using the above data the following was calculated:

$$\lambda_L = 0.0153$$

$$\Delta p_L = 8132.1 \text{ Pa}$$

$$\Delta p_A = 1872.9 \text{ Pa}$$

$$\Delta p_Z = 8993.2 \text{ Pa}$$

$$\Delta p_{Gv} = 1991.0 \text{ Pa}$$

$$\Delta p_B = 1664.8 (2 \text{bends})$$

$$\Delta p = 23\,654.0 \text{ Pa}$$

Using this information and the same procedures as above:

$$\rho_1 = 1.58 \text{ kg/m}^3$$

$$v_1 = 20.64 \text{ m/s}$$

$$Fr_1 = 20.84$$

Thus $Fr_1 > Fr_{min}$ and hence the systems will operate.

It should be noted that the simplifying assumptions used in this example are acceptable for those situations in which there is a predominance of horizontal pipes. In the case where the proportion of vertical piping is greater, it is essential to calculate λ_Z^* as per equation (6.54). The reader is advised to consider Figs 6.7 and 6.26 in which the state diagram and the velocity ratio for horizontal and vertical flow (for Styropor) respectively are shown.

14.4.6 Rotary valve leakage

The total air requirements for a system must take into consideration the leakage through the rotary valve. In terms of Section 7.4.3 the following information is relevant:

Assume conveying pressure 1.25×10^5 Pa

Solids volume flow rate, $\dot{V}_p = \dot{G}/\rho_b$

$$= \frac{3900}{0.52} = 7500 \text{ dm}^3/\text{h}$$

$$= 7.5 \text{ m}^3/\text{h}$$

From selection charts:

$$\text{Valve diameter, } D_v = 250\,\text{mm}$$

$$\text{Valve length, } L_v = 300\,\text{mm}$$

$$\text{Valve speed, } V_s = 15\,\text{rev/min.}$$

Side and tip clearance, 0.13 mm
  Now

$$p_\alpha/p_\omega = 1.25$$

$$k = 0.88 \text{ (by interpolation. See Example 7.2)}$$

Hence

$$k = 0.88 - 0.2$$

$$= 0.68$$

Rotor leakage area

$$A = 2(0.3)(0.13 \times 10^{-3}) + 2(0.25)(0.13 \times 10^{-3})$$

$$= 0.000078 + 0.000655$$

$$= 0.143 \times 10^{-3}\,\text{m}^2$$

Clearance leakage (equation (7.7))

$$\dot{V}_c^* = (0.6)(0.68)(0.143 \times 10^{-3})[2(0.25 \times 10^5)/1.45]^{1/2}$$

$$= 0.66\,\text{m}^3/\text{min}$$

where

$$\rho_\alpha = 1.45\,\text{kg/m}^3$$

Carry over leakage

$$\dot{V}_p^* = \frac{\pi}{4}(0.25)^2(0.3)(15)$$

$$= 0.22\,\text{m}^3/\text{min}$$

The total air leakage

$$\dot{V}_T^* = \dot{V}_c^* + \dot{V}_p^*$$

$$= 0.66 + 0.22$$

$$= 0.88\,\text{m}^3/\text{min at 1.25 bar}$$

$$= 1.1\,\text{m}^3/\text{min free air}$$

$$\dot{V}_c^* = 66\,\text{m}^3/\text{h free air}$$

$$\dot{Q}_{\text{leakage}} = (0.88)(1.45)(60)$$
$$= 76.56 \, \text{kg/h}$$
$$\simeq 77 \, \text{kg/h}$$

Total air requirements

$$\dot{Q}_{\text{T}} = \dot{Q} + \dot{Q}_{\text{leakage}}$$
$$= 922 + 77$$
$$= 999 \, \text{kg/h}$$

14.4.7 Selection of cyclone

Since the product consists essentially of large particles with no dust, gas–solid separation can be effected by means of a cyclone:

(a) Using Fig. 10.12 and selecting a geometrical size $Z^*/D_i = 10$, selecting cyclone type II a pressure loss $\Delta p_c \simeq 10 \, \text{mbar}$.

(b) Using an air volumetric flow rate

$$\dot{V} = \frac{\dot{Q}}{\rho_c} = \frac{922}{1.2} = 768.3 \, \text{m}^3/\text{min}.$$

(c) Using Fig. 10.10(a) for $\dot{V} = 768.3 \, \text{m}^3/\text{min}$ and selecting size 4, the boundary particle size $d^* = 6 \, \mu\text{m}$.

(d) From Fig. 10.14 for a pressure loss $\Delta p_c = 10 \, \text{mbar}$, an entrance velocity $v_\alpha = 12.5 \, \text{m/s}$ (Type II, size 4).

It should be noted that the cyclone selected using the procedures described in Chapter 10 will provide a high efficiency. For the product with $d = 2.5 \, \text{mm}$ it can be seen that the cyclone is overestimated.

14.5 DILUTE PHASE PNEUMATIC CONVEYING SYSTEM DESIGN (METHOD 2)

14.5.1 Introduction

The design procedures described in Section 14.4 rely on the determination of experimental data prior to calculating the system pressure loss. Weber [2] describes a method for dilute phase system design which makes use of a number of selection charts to obtain certain fundamental conveying properties.

The Weber [2] technique has been evaluated by the authors using experimental data obtained from dilute phase conveying of polyethylene pellets. Whilst the method appears to provide good correlation for granular products, some discrepancies have been observed for fine powders.

The technique, which relies on empirical data, must be used with circumspection. The technique is useful inasmuch as it provides the designer with ballpark figures which as a first approximation can be very useful.

14.5.2 The problem

It is required to calculate the pressure drop for a dilute phase conveying system transporting wheat in a positive pressure mode. The following information is available:

Material	Wheat
Desired solids mass flow rate	$\dot{G} = 324\,\text{kg/h}$
	$= 0.09\,\text{kg/s}$
Particle density	$\rho_p = 1400\,\text{kg/m}^3$
Particle size	$d = 2\,\text{mm}$
Pipe diameter	$D = 40\,\text{mm}$
Horizontal length	$L = 16\,\text{m}$
Vertical lift	$Z = 6\,\text{m}$
Solids loading	$\mu = 4.85$
Pipe friction for air	$\lambda_L = 0.02$
Pipe coefficients for solids	$\lambda_Z^* = 0.002$
Air density	$\rho = 1.23\,\text{kg/m}^3$
Bend constant	$B = 0.5$
Number of bends	2

14.5.3 The solution

(a) Transport velocity

From equation (6.13)

$$\mu = \dot{G}/(\rho v A)$$

Thus,

$$v = \dot{G}/(\rho \mu A)$$
$$= (0.09)(4)/[\pi(0.04)^2(4.85)(1.23)]$$
$$= 12\,\text{m/s}$$

(b) Settling velocity

In this technique, the settling velocity is obtained from charts in which the settling velocity w_{f0} is plotted as a function of the particle diameter d, with the particle density ρ_p as parameter.

Figure 14.7(a), (b) represents the settling velocity in calm air for round particles varying in size $1\,\mu\text{m} \leqslant d \leqslant 100\,\mu\text{m}$ and $100\,\mu\text{m} \leqslant d \leqslant 10\,000\,\mu\text{m}$ respectively. Clearly the settling velocity is also dependent upon particle shape and of course

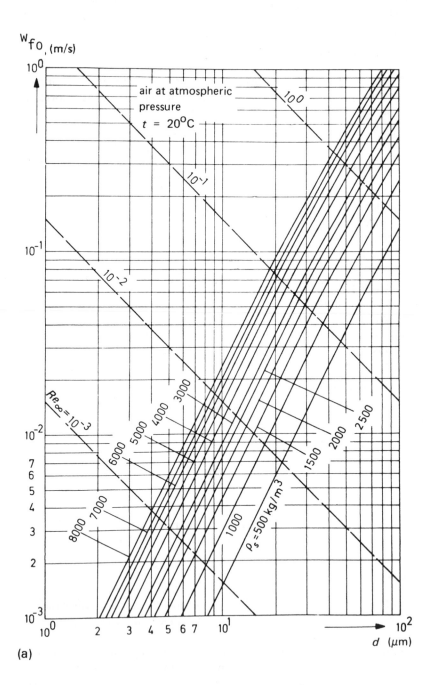

$^{W}f_{0}$ (m/s)

air at atmospheric
pressure
$t = 20°C$

d (µm)

(a)

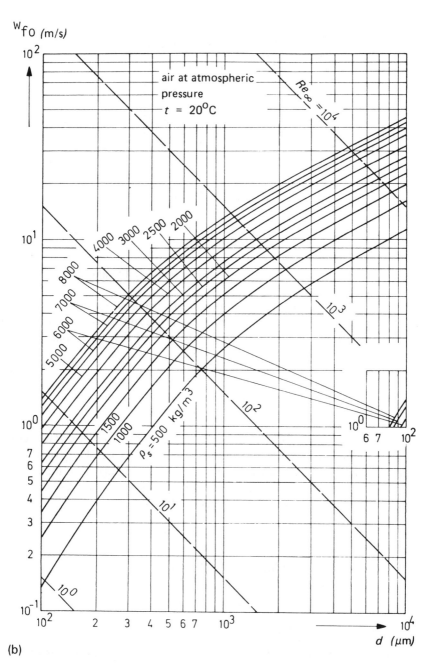

Figure 14.7 Settling velocity in calm air for round particles.

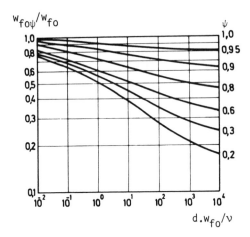

Figure 14.8 Effect of particle shape on settling velocity.

for pneumatic conveying systems it is also necessary to take particle–particle interaction into account.

The effect of particle shape is accounted for by using the sphericity factor ψ as per equation (3.13). Graphically, the influence of the sphericity factor on settling velocity is illustrated in Fig. 14.8. It should be noted that for a sphere $\psi = 1$.

From Fig. 14.7(b), at a grain size $d = 2\,\text{mm}$ and a particle density $\rho_p = 1400\,\text{kg/m}^3$:

$$w_{f0} = 8\,\text{m/s}$$

To account for the influence of the pipe diameter, the free fall settling velocity obtained in Fig. 14.7 must be corrected. In the case of a particle falling through a pipe, the displacement of the gas due to the particle volume creates an additional retarding effect. The free fall velocity of the particle is reduced taking both the particle and pipe diameter into account:

$$w_f/w_{f0} = 1 - (d/D)^2 \tag{14.4}$$

where w_f is the actual settling velocity of the particle.

$$w_f = 8[1 - (3/40)^2] \simeq 8\,\text{m/s}$$

(c) Friction coefficient, λ_z

The additional pressure drop factor due to impact and friction λ_z^* is obtained from the relationship:

$$v/c = 1 + w_{f0}[\lambda_z^*/2gD]^{1/2} \tag{14.5}$$

Table 14.5

Material	Steel (heat treated)	Steel (not treated)	Aluminium	Copper
	λ_Z^* for pipes made of			
Glass balls ($d = 4\,mm$)	0.0025	0.0032	0.0051	0.0053
Wheat	0.0032	0.0024	0.0032	0.0030
Coal (3–5 mm)	0.0023	0.0019	0.0007	0.0012
Coke (cylinders 5 mm long, $d = 4.5\,mm$)	0.0014	0.0034	0.0040	0.0019
Quartz (3–5 mm)	0.0060	0.0072	0.0185	0.031
Silica carbide (3 mm)	—	—	0.0360	—
Crushed glass balls ($d = 2.5\,mm$)	—	0.0123	—	—

where λ_Z^* is obtained from experimental observations. Typical values for λ_Z^* are shown in Table 14.5. (The technique described above should be compared with the method of obtaining λ_Z^* in Section 6.7.6.)

From Table 14.5, $\lambda_Z^* = 0.0024$. Using equation (14.5)

$$\frac{c}{v} = \{1 + 8[0.0024/(2)(9.81)(0.04)]^{1/2}\}^{-1}$$

$$= 0.7$$

Now since

$$V = 12\,m/s$$

$$c = 8.4\,m/s$$

To obtain the additional pressure drop factor in a pipe, due to the solids flowing in an air stream, λ_z, use is made of Fig. 14.9.

Figure 14.9 represents the variation of the effective friction coefficient λ_z due to the presence of the solids, with the Froude number Fr with λ_Z^* as a parameter. Both the horizontal and vertical conditions are catered for in Fig. 14.9.

Now the Froude number

$$Fr = v/(gD)^{1/2}$$

$$Fr^2 = v^2/(gD)$$

$$= 144/(9.81)(0.04)$$

$$= 367$$

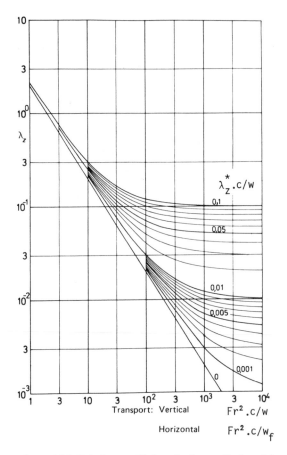

Figure 14.9 Friction coefficient λ_z for vertical and horizontal pneumatic conveyance.

$$(c/w_f)Fr^2 = (8.4/8)(367)$$

$$= 385$$

From Fig. 14.9

$$\lambda_z = 0.007$$

(d) Pressure loss

(1) Acceleration pressure loss (see equation (6.70))

$$\Delta p_A = \Delta p_{Agas} + \Delta p_{Asolids} \tag{14.6}$$

$$= \rho v^2/2 + \mu v \rho c$$

$$= (1.23)(12^2)/2 + (4.85)(12)(1.23)(8.4)$$

$$= 88 + 601$$

$$= 689\,Pa$$

(2) Lift pressure loss

In this case, the pressure loss due to elevation of solids

$$\Delta p_G = (1 + \mu)\rho g Z \qquad (14.7)$$
$$= (1 + 4.85)(1.23)(9.81)(6)$$

where $Z = 6$ metres. Hence

$$\Delta p_G = 423 \, \text{Pa}$$

(3) Frictional pressure loss

The Weber [2] technique separates the contributions due to gas and solid components

$$\Delta p = \Delta p_L + \Delta p_Z$$
$$= \rho v^2 L (\lambda_L + \mu \lambda_Z)/2D$$
$$= (1.23)(144)(16 + 6)[0.02 + 4.85(0.007)]/(2 \times 0.04)$$
$$= 2627 \, \text{Pa}$$

(4) Pressure loss due to bends

$$\Delta p_B = B(1 + \mu)\rho v^2 / 2$$
$$= (0.5)(1 + 4.85)(1.23)(12^2)/2$$
$$= 518 \, \text{Pa}$$

(5) Total pressure loss

$$\Delta p_T = 689 + 601 + 423 + 2627 + 518$$
$$= 4257 \, \text{Pa}$$

14.6 DILUTE PHASE PNEUMATIC CONVEYING SYSTEM DESIGN (METHOD 3)

14.6.1 Introduction

An alternative method of calculating the pressure drop in a dilute phase system has been derived from several sources [3]. The technique initially developed by Hinkle [4] is useful inasmuch as the various equations can be resolved to being pipe diameter dependent. As such, it is possible to resolve all equations to a form in which the pipe diameter can be used as a final factor in the system design. This approach is particularly useful for sizing a system according to the prime mover which will be selected.

14.6.2 The problem

It is required to convey polythene granules at a rate of 10 t/h over a route shown in Fig. 14.10. A roots type blower will be used preferably without an air cooler. To prevent streamers (angel hair formation), the maximum air velocity at discharge is 28 m/s and the maximum air temperature is 75 °C. Assume that the particles are cylinders with diameter 2 mm and length 2 mm. The particle specific gravity is 0.92. The maximum air temperature is 30 °C and the air density is 0.96 kg/m³ at

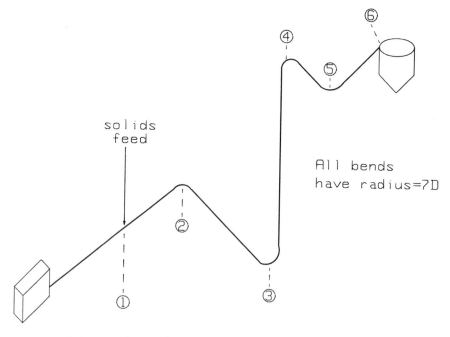

```
Length  1-2=35m
        2-3=25m
        3-4=40m
        4-5=10m
        5-6=15m
  Total  125m
```

All bends
have radius=7D

solids
feed

Figure 14.10 Layout of conveying system.

75 °C and atmospheric pressure. Assume a rough pipe (able to prevent streamers) with a roughness $\varepsilon = 0.25$ mm.

Find the smallest pipe diameter which will give an acceptable pressure drop.

14.6.3 The solution

(a) Maximum blower delivery pressure for 75°C

From equation (2.23), for adiabatic compression

$$T_2 = T_1 \left(\frac{p_2}{p_1} \right)^{(k-1)/k}$$

where

$$\kappa = 1.4$$

$$T_1 = 273 + 30 = 303 \text{ K}$$

$$T_2 = 273 + 75 = 348 \text{ K}$$

$$348/303 = (p_2/p_1)^{0.285}$$

$$p_2/p_1 = (1.15)^{3.5} = 1.62$$

Since atmospheric pressure $p_0 = 101.3$ kPa

Blower delivery pressure $= 0.62(101.3)$

$$= 62.8 \text{ kPa}$$

(b) Data derived from particle properties

(1) Equivalent diameter

The equivalent diameter for a cylindrical particle is found by determining the diameter of a sphere having the same volume as the cylindrical particle:

$$\pi d_s^3/6 = (\pi d_c^2/4)h \tag{14.9}$$

where

d_s = diameter of sphere
d_c = diameter of cylinder
h = height of cylinder

Hence

$$\pi d_s^3/6 = \pi (2^2/4)(2)$$

$$d_s = 2.29 \text{ mm}$$

(2) Shape factor

From Section 3.3.2:

$$\psi = \frac{\text{surface area of sphere of diameter } d_s}{\text{surface area of cylinder of diameter } d_c \text{ and height } h}$$

$$= \frac{\pi(2.29)^2}{2\pi(2^2/4) + \pi(2)(2)}$$

$$= 0.87$$

(3) Drag coefficient

For a cylindrical particle the drag coefficient

$$C_D = 0.7(5.31 - 4.88\psi)$$
$$= 0.7[5.31 - 4.88(0.87)]$$
$$= 0.73$$

(c) Particle velocity

The Hinkle technique uses the following expression for particle velocity:

$$c = v(1 - 0.008d^{0.3}\rho_p^{0.5}) \tag{14.10}$$
$$c/v = 1 - 0.008(2.29)^{0.3}(920)^{0.5}$$
$$= 0.69$$

(d) Solids friction factor

The solids friction factor λ_z is defined as:

$$\lambda_z = \frac{3\rho C_D D}{2\rho_p d}\left(\frac{v - c}{c}\right)^2$$

$$= \frac{3(0.96)(0.73)D\bar{p}(0.45)^2}{2(920)(2.29)(10^{-3})}$$

$$= 0.10\,\bar{p}D$$

where $\bar{p}$ is the pressure in the atmosphere at the midpoint of the section under consideration. Note that ρ is proportional to the average pressure in each section of the pipe network; as such $\rho = \bar{p}(0.96)$ in this example.

(e) Pressure drop relationship

To account for compressibility and to allow for the fact that the air density decreases whilst the velocity increases on passing through the pipe, the pressure drop is calculated separately for each pipe section. The various pressure drop equations are all expressed in terms of the pipe diameter so as to simplify the procedures to investigate the influence of pipe diameter.

Now the solids loading ratio can be expressed in terms of equation (6.13) as:

$$\mu = \frac{\dot{G}}{\rho v A}$$

$$= \frac{2.78(4)}{0.96(28)\pi D^2}$$

$$= 0.13/D^2$$

(1) Total pressure drop for a section

The pressure loss for each section is defined as:

$$\Delta p = \frac{\lambda_L \rho v^2 L}{2D}\left(1 + \frac{\lambda_z c}{\lambda_L v}\mu\right) \tag{14.11}$$

$$= \frac{\lambda_L \bar{p}(0.96)(28^2)L}{2D\bar{p}^2}\left(1 + \frac{0.1\bar{p}D}{\lambda_L}(0.69)\frac{0.13}{D^2}\right)$$

$$= 376\frac{L}{D}\left(\frac{\lambda_L}{\bar{p}} + \frac{0.01}{D}\right)$$

(2) Acceleration pressure loss

The acceleration pressure loss is defined as:

$$\Delta p_A = \frac{\dot{G}c}{A} \tag{14.12}$$

$$= \frac{\dot{G}(0.69)v}{\pi D^2/4}$$

$$= 68.3/D^2$$

(3) Lift pressure loss

$$\Delta p_G = \frac{\dot{G}Zg}{Ac} \tag{14.13}$$

$$= \frac{(2.78)(40)(9.81)}{(\pi D^2/4)(0.69)v}$$

$$= 71.8\,\bar{p}/D^2$$

(4) Bend loss

$$\Delta p_B = B(1 + \mu)\rho v^2/2 \tag{14.14}$$

In this example $B = 0.5$

$$\Delta p_B = 0.25(1 + \mu)\rho v^2$$

$$= 0.25\left(\frac{1}{\mu} + 1\right)\frac{\dot{G}}{A}v$$

Since $\mu = 0.13/D^2$ and $v = 20\,\text{m/s}$

$$\Delta p_B = 0.25\left(\frac{D^2 + 0.13}{0.13}\right)\frac{\dot{G}}{\pi D^2/4}\left(\frac{2.8}{p}\right)$$

$$= \frac{190.4}{\bar{p}}\left(\frac{D^2 + 0.13}{D^2}\right)$$

For the average pressure $\bar{p}$ of each section, as a first approximation, assume that the pressure drop varies linearly with the actual pipe length. Then, for an overall system pressure drop of 0.62 atmospheres, referring to Fig. 14.10:

$$\text{average pressure section } 5\text{–}6 = 1 + \frac{7.5}{125}(0.62) = 1.037\,\text{atm}$$

$$\text{average pressure section } 4\text{–}5 = 1 + \frac{20}{125}(0.62) = 1.099\,\text{atm}$$

Thus for any section:

$$\text{average pressure } \bar{p} = 1 + \frac{x}{125}(0.62)$$

where x is the distance in metres from discharge point 6.

$$\text{average pressure in section } 3\text{–}4 = 1.223\,\text{atm}$$

$$\text{average pressure in section } 2\text{–}3 = 1.384\,\text{atm}$$

$$\text{average pressure in section } 1\text{–}2 = 1.533\,\text{atm}$$

(f) Effect of changing pipe diameter

Starting with a 150 mm diameter pipe, the components of the pressure drop can be tabulated (Tables 14.6, 14.7) and the total checked to see if it exceeds 62.8 kPa.

Table 14.6 $D = 150\,\text{mm}$, $\lambda_L = 0.022$

Section	L (m)	x (m)	$\bar{p}$ (atm)	Δp (kPa)	Δp_A (kPa)	Δp_G (kPa)	Δp_B (kPa)	$\sum\Delta p$ (kPa)
1–2	35	107.5	1.533	7.1	3.0			10.1
Bend		90.0	1.446				0.9	0.9
2–3	25	77.5	1.384	5.2				5.2
Bend		65.0	1.322				1.0	1.0
3–4	40	45.0	1.223	8.5		3.9		12.4
Bend		25.0	1.124				1.1	1.1
4–5	10	20.0	1.099	2.2				2.2
Bend		15.0	1.074				1.2	1.2
5–6	15	7.5	1.037	3.3				3.3
							Total	37.4

Table 14.7 $D = 120\,\text{mm}$, $\lambda_L = 0.024$

Section	L (m)	x (m)	$\bar{p}$ (atm)	Δp (kPa)	Δp_A (kPa)	Δp_G (kPa)	Δp_B (kPa)	$\sum\Delta p$ (kPa)
1–2	35	107.5	1.533	10.9	4.7			15.6
Bend		90.0	1.446				1.3	1.3
2–3	25	77.5	1.384	7.9				7.9
Bend		65.0	1.322				1.4	1.4
3–4	40	45.0	1.223	12.9		6.1		19.0
Bend		25.0	1.124				1.7	1.7
4–5	10	20.0	1.099	3.3				3.3
Bend		15.0	1.074				1.8	1.8
5–6	15	7.5	1.037	5.0				5.0
							Total	57.0

Additional losses must be allowed for in filter, silencers and separation equipment, etc.

Note the following points:

(1) Acceleration pressure drop is only accounted for once in the calculation.
(2) The $D = 120\,\text{mm}$ pipe allows a generous margin $(62.8 - 57) = 5.8\,\text{kPa}$.
(3) A 110 mm pipe also provides an acceptable pressure loss, but could result in streamers.
(4) Apart from the acceleration pressure loss, all other losses take into consideration the average pressure $\bar{p}(0.96)$ where 0.96 is the prevailing air density term. Also all terms containing the air velocity v are replaced by $v/\bar{p}$.

14.7 DENSE PHASE PNEUMATIC CONVEYING SYSTEM DESIGN

14.7.1 Introduction

It has been pointed out that there is limited information on dense phase system design procedures. The work reported by Weber [2] provides a method, which appears to yield reasonable results when compared to actual operating systems. The technique needs to be refined in terms of obtaining additional data to facilitate a more accurate assessment of various correction factors.

14.7.2 The problem

Determine the pressure loss in a dense phase pneumatic conveying system, required to transport a powder over a distance of 150 m based on the following information:

Conveying rate, $\dot{G} = 1.2\,\text{t/h}$
Horizontal length, $L = 150\,\text{m}$
Available air flow rate at $100\,\text{kPa}$ and $20°\text{C}$, $\dot{V} = 19\,\text{m}^3/\text{h}$
Maximum pipe size, $D = 36\,\text{mm}$
Particle size, $d = 75\,\mu\text{m}$
Particle bulk density, $\rho_B = 500\,\text{kg/m}^3$
Particle density, $\rho_P = 1190\,\text{kg/m}^3$
Air density, $\rho = 1.2\,\text{kg/m}^3$

14.7.3 The solution

(a) Free fall velocity

From Fig. 14.7(a), for a particle size $d = 75\,\mu\text{m}$ and a particle density $\rho_p = 1190\,\text{kg/m}^3$:

$$w_{f0} = 0.15\,\text{m/s}$$

Now

$$Fr_{f0}^* = w_{f0}/(gD)^{1/2}$$
$$= (0.15)/(9.806 \times 0.036)^{1/2}$$
$$= 0.252$$

(b) Solids loading

$$\mu = \dot{G}/\rho\dot{V}$$
$$= (1.2)(1000)/(1.2)(19)$$
$$\mu = 52.63$$

(c) Conveying air velocity

$$v = \dot{V}/A$$
$$= (4)(19)/\pi(0.036)^2(3600)$$
$$= 5.2 \, \text{m/s}$$

(d) Froude number

$$Fr = v/(Dg)^{1/2}$$
$$= 5.2/(9.806 \times 0.036)^{1/2}$$
$$= 8.8$$

(e) Density ratio, Γ

By definition, the density ratio is given as:

$$\Gamma = 0.5(\rho_1 + \rho_2)/\rho_B$$

where $0.5\,(\rho_1 + \rho_2)$ is the mean air density and ρ_B is the bulk density. Since the air density $\rho = 1.2 \, \text{kg/m}^3$, relating the air density to the pressures

$$\Gamma = (0.5)(1.2)(1 + p_1/p_2)/500$$
$$= 1.2 \times 10^{-3}(1 + p_1/p_2)$$

Hence

$$\mu\Gamma = 0.064(1 + p_1/p_2)$$

(f) The parameter ζ

$$\zeta = 4\lambda_s^* B(Fr)^5 \, \Gamma/(\pi\beta Fr_{fo}^*)$$

From experimental observations, it has been found that:

$$\lambda_s^* \simeq 0.75; \quad \beta \simeq 0.6 \quad \text{and} \quad B = 10^{-3}$$

From which

$$\zeta \simeq 1.6 \times 10^{-3}(Fr)^5\Gamma/Fr_{fo}^*$$

Large values of ζ occur for the transport of fine powders with grain size from 10–$100 \, \mu\text{m}$ at normal pressure and at air velocities in the range 10 to $15 \, \text{m/s}$. Small values are encountered for the same products at the same pipe diameters but operating at higher pressures (several atmospheres) and velocities in the range 3 to $6 \, \text{m/s}$.

Table 14.8 Dense phase conveying parameters

No. Material	L (m)	Z (m)	D (mm)	$\dot{G}$ (t/h)	$\dot{V}$ (m³/h)	Δp (kPa)	v (m/s)	$Fr\Gamma^{1/2}$	$\mu\Gamma$	μ	c/v	ρ_P	ρ_B
1 Cement raw meal	146	—	36	1.4	11.5	200	3.15	0.25	0.25	102	0.88	2690	1000
2 PAN powder	150	—	36	1.2	19	140	3.95	0.40	0.20	53	0.59	1190	500
3 Soda	200	30	100	35	1050	250	18	0.95	0.08	28	0.29	2030	1000
4 Filling material SiO₂	30	—	65	4	100	30	7.3	0.89	0.30	33	0.25	2650	150
5 Moist sand	120	—	100	19.5	300	350	3.75	0.20	0.13	54	0.28	1800	1350
6 Filling material SiO₂	58	—	70	1.4	30	14	2.1	0.175	0.20	39	1.12	2650	270
7 Filling material SiO₂	10	—	70	1.0	29	2.3	2.25	0.175	0.13	29	0.83	2650	270
8 Organic products	37	1.5	66	4.1	63	70	3.6	0.20	0.12	54	0.25	1000	700
9 Soda	25	—	65	20	200	30	13	0.60	0.12	83	0.51	2030	1000
10 Light ash	1200	15	200	50	4000	350	13	0.50	0.03	10	0.52	2350	1200
11 PVC powder	115	20	70	7	240	65	13.5	0.90	0.07	24	0.36	1370	500
12 Rock salt (flexible pipe)	26	2	50	5.8	110	80	11	0.55	0.05	44	0.13	2200	1400
13 Organic products	6.5	—	20	0.4	8	17	6.5	0.70	0.10	41	0.11	1000	600
14 Organic products	25	10	70	17	300	120	13	0.95	0.17	77	0.10	1000	500
15 Alumina	130	15	100	8	300	250	5	0.35	0.12	22	0.15	2480	800
16 Plastic powder	300	—	100	10	310	150	6.8	0.53	0.10	27	0.57	1050	350

Table 14.8 has been drawn up from data [2] representing a number of dense phase conveying systems.

Now

$$\zeta = 1.6 \times 10^{-3}(8.8)^5(1.2 \times 10^{-3})(1 + p_1/p_2)/0.252$$
$$= 0.402(1 + p_1/p_2)$$

(g) Calculation of pressure loss

If p_1 and p_2 are the initial and final pressures then:

$$p_1 = \exp(\beta \mu g L v/RTc)$$
$$p_1/p_2 = \exp[(0.6)(530)(9.806)(150)v/(287)(293)c]$$
$$= \exp[0.6/(c/v)]$$

where

$$R = 0.287\,\text{kJ/kg K} \quad \text{(universal gas constant)}$$

$$T = 273 + 20 = 293\,\text{K}$$

Now by trial and error, selecting values for p_1/p_2, where c/v is obtained from values of $\mu\Gamma$ from Fig. 14.11 we calculate quantities. It can be seen from Table 14.9 that the closest approximation for p_1/p_2 is

$$p_1/p_2 = 2.4$$

Thus the pressure loss across the system is

$$\Delta p = 0.14\,\text{MPa} = 140\,\text{kPa}$$

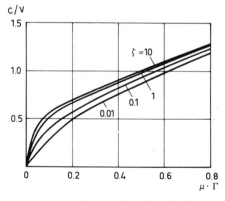

Figure 14.11 c/v as a function of $\mu\Gamma$.

Table 14.9

p_1/p_2	$\mu\Gamma$	ζ	c/v	$\exp[0.6/(c/v)]$
2	0.19	1.77	0.68	2.42
2.2	0.20	1.89	0.68	2.42
2.3	0.21	1.95	0.68	2.42
2.4	0.22	2.01	0.69	2.39
2.6	0.23	2.12	0.70	2.36

Table 14.10

	Δp (MPa)	v (m/s)	μ	c/v
Theory	0.14	5	53	0.69
Experiment	0.14	3.95	53	0.59

Table 14.10 gives theoretical and experimental results for comparison.

14.8 TEST YOURSELF — DILUTE PHASE CALCULATIONS

In order to familiarize yourself with the dilute phase techniques described above, the following system is to be designed (Fig. 14.12):

Material	Sand
Solids mass flow rate	$\dot{G} = 3000\,\text{kg/h}$
Particle density	$\rho_p = 2420\,\text{kg/m}^3$
Particle size	$d = 1\,\text{mm}$
Pipe diameter	$D = 125\,\text{mm}$
Pipe length horizontal	$L = 170\,\text{m}$
Vertical lift	$Z = 30\,\text{m}$
Solids loading	$\mu = 2.8$

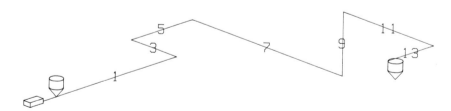

Figure 14.12 Dilute phase system—sand.

Air alone friction loss	$\lambda_{L*} = 0.02$
Friction loss due to solids	$\lambda_Z = 0.007$
Air density	$\rho = 1.23\,\text{kg/m}^3$
Bend radius	$R_B = 1.5\,\text{m}$
Number of bends	6

Solution

(a) Using the Weber method

Transport velocity	$v = 20\,\text{m/s}$
Settling velocity	$w_{f0} = 6.2\,\text{m/s}$
Velocity ratio	$c/v = 0.75$
Solids velocity	$c = 15\,\text{m/s}$
Froude number	$Fr^2 = 326.3$
	$\lambda_Z = 0.012$
Acceleration pressure loss	$\Delta p_A = 246 + 1021.4 = 1267.4\,\text{Pa}$
Lift pressure loss	$\Delta p_G = 1361\,\text{Pa}$
Frictional pressure loss	$\Delta p = 20\,681\,\text{Pa}$
Bend pressure loss	$\Delta p_B = 2775.7\,\text{Pa}$
Total pressure loss	$\Delta p_{tot} = 26.09\,\text{kPa}$

(b) Using the Hinkle method

The following input parameters were used:
maximum velocity at discharge $v = 20\,\text{m/s}$
particle length $l_p = 1\,\text{mm}$

Table 14.11

Section	L (m)	x (m)	$\bar{p}$ (atm)	Δp (kPa)	Δp_A (kPa)	Δp_G (kPa)	Δp_B (kPa)	$\Sigma \Delta p$ (kPa)
13	15	7.5	1.023	4.297				4.297
12		15	1.076				0.442	4.739
11	30	30	1.092	8.521				13.260
10		45	1.138				0.407	13.666
9	30	60	1.183	8.437		2.004		24.107
8		75	1.229				0.376	24.483
7	50	100	1.306	13.906				38.389
6		125	1.382				0.335	38.724
5	20	135	1.413	5.517				44.240
4		145	1.443				0.320	44.561
3	15	152.5	1.466	4.122				48.683
2		160	1.489				0.311	48.994
1	40	180	1.550	10.934	0.802			60.730

Calculations yielded the following results:

Equivalent particle diameter $\qquad d = 1.14\,\text{mm}$
Shape factor $\qquad\qquad\qquad \psi = 0.524$
Drag coefficient $\qquad\qquad\quad C_D = 1.93$
Velocity ratio $\qquad\qquad\qquad c/v = 0.59$
Solids loading $\qquad\qquad\qquad \mu = 2.76$

From Table 14.11 the total pressure loss across the system

$$\Delta p_{tot} = 60.73\,\text{kPa}$$

Note: The two methods yield significantly different values of pressure loss. This discrepancy further illustrates the fact that there is still a large amount of research work to be done to further refine the pressure loss correlations. Other techniques available in the literature produce results which are even more confusing to interpret. In the above example, the authors would select the Hinkle method in preference to the Weber method.

14.9 GAS – SOLID FLOW EXAMPLES

In this section a number of worked examples are provided in an attempt to illustrate the use of equations presented in Chapters 3, 4, 5 and 12. The examples relate to a number of practical conveying situations, and should assist the reader to appreciate more fully the practical implications of the various theories postulated in these chapters.

Chapter 3

Example 1

Consider the vertical flow of particles having a diameter of 250 μm in a 0.05 m diameter pipe. The gas velocity is 1.2 kg/m^3 and the particle density is 2000 kg/m^3. A solid loading of 10 is maintained at a gas velocity of 20 m/s.
    Analyse this flow condition for the possibility of choking.

Solution

The Doig and Roper equation states

$$\log \frac{v}{(gd)^{0.5}} = 0.03\,w_{f0} + 0.25 \log \mu$$

where v is the gas choking velocity.

Using the K parameter classification

$$K = d\left(g\rho\frac{\rho_p - \rho}{\eta^2}\right)^{1/3}$$

$$= 250 \times 10^{-6}\left(\frac{9.8 \times 1.2 \times (2000)}{(10^{-5})^2}\right)^{1/3} = 15.41$$

This indicates an intermediate range

$$w_{fo} = \frac{0.153(9.8)^{0.71}(250 \times 10^{-6})^{1.14}(2000)^{0.71}}{(1.2)^{0.29}(10^{-5})^{0.43}}$$

$$= 1.79\,\mathrm{m/s}$$

Applying these results to the Doig and Roper equation

$$v = 0.099\,\mathrm{m/s}$$

This indicates the present system is well above choking.
   Now apply the Yousfi and Gau, and Yang, criteria to see if choking will occur if the gas velocity is low enough.

$$\frac{w_{fo}}{gd} > 4.0 \qquad \text{Yousfi and Gau}$$

$$\frac{(1.79)^2}{(9.8)(250 \times 10^{-6})} = 1308$$

This indicates that choking will occur.

$$\frac{w_{fo}^2}{gDt} > 0.123 \qquad \text{Yang}$$

$$\frac{(1.79)^2}{(9.8)(.05)} = 6.54$$

This also indicates that choking will occur.

Example 2

Find the relaxation time for the following particles:

Case	$d(\mu m)$	$\rho_p(kg/m^3)$	$\tau(s)$
1	2000	2000	444
2	1000	1000	5
3	500	980	1.36
4	100	1500	0.083
5	10	1000	0.00055

Solution

The equation to calculate the relaxation time is

$$\tau = \frac{d^2 \rho_p}{18\eta}$$

for case 1

$$\tau = \frac{(2000 \times 10^{-6})^2 (2000)}{18(10^{-5})} = 4.44 \times 10^2\,s$$

Example 3

For the particles of the previous example determine the terminal velocities.

Solution

Using the K factor format

$$K = d\left(g\rho \frac{\rho_p - \rho}{\eta^2}\right)^{1/3}$$

Case 1

$$K_1 = 2000 \times 10^{-6}\left(\frac{9.8 \times 1.2(2000 - 1.2)}{(10^{-5})^2}\right)^{1/3}$$

$K_1 = 122$	Newton's range
$K_2 = 4.89$	Newton's range
$K_3 = 24.1$	intermediate range
$K_4 = 5.60$	intermediate range
$K_5 = 0.484$	Stokes

Three different equations will be used:

$$w_{f0} = 1.75\left(\frac{gd(\rho_p - \rho)}{\rho}\right)^{1/2} \qquad \text{Newton's range}$$

$$w_{f0} = 0.153\frac{g^{0.71}d^{1.14}(\rho_p - \rho)^{0.71}}{\rho^{0.29}\eta^{0.43}} \qquad \text{intermediate range}$$

$$w_{f0} = \frac{g(\rho_p - \rho)d^2}{18\eta} \quad \text{Stokes}$$

$$w_{f01} = 0.01\,\text{m/s}$$
$$w_{f02} = 0.005\,\text{m/s}$$
$$w_{f03} = 2.37\,\text{m/s}$$
$$w_{f04} = 0.512\,\text{m/s}$$
$$w_{f05} = 5.4 \times 10^{-3}\,\text{m/s}$$

Chapter 4

Example 1

Consider the horizontal transport of a solid having the density of $1340\,\text{kg/m}^3$ and an average particle size of $250\,\mu\text{m}$. The transport gas is air at atmospheric conditions. It is decided to use a 5 cm diameter copper pipe for transport. The solids flow rate is 1000 kg/h. Determine the energy loss to transport this solid at gas velocities of 10, 20 and 30 m/s.

Solution

As an example in the case the Konno and Saito solid friction will be employed. For horizontal flow

$$\frac{\Delta p}{L} = 2f_L \frac{\rho \varepsilon v^2}{D} + \lambda_Z^* \frac{\rho_p(1-\varepsilon)}{2D} c^2$$

For $v = 10\,\text{m/s}$

$$Re = \frac{0.05 \times 1.2 \times 10}{10^{-5}} = 60\,000$$

$$\frac{\Delta p}{L} = 2\frac{(0.0014 + 0.125Re^{-0.32})}{0.05}(1.2)(10)^2\varepsilon$$

$$+ 4 \times 0.0285(9.8 \times 0.05)^{1/2}\frac{c \times 1340 \times (1-\varepsilon)}{2 \times 0.05}c^2$$

For the particle velocity the Hinkle (IGT) correlation will be employed:

$$c = v(1 - 0.68d^{0.92}\rho_p^{0.5}\rho^{-0.2}D^{-0.54})$$
$$= 10[1 - 0.68(250 \times 10^{-6})^{0.92}(1340)^{0.5}(1.2)^{-0.2}(0.05)^{-0.50}]$$
$$= 9.4\,\text{m/s}$$

and the voidage is

$$\varepsilon = 1 - \frac{1000/3600}{\frac{1}{4}\pi(0.05)^2 \times 9.4 \times 1340}$$
$$= 0.988$$

The loading for the condition is

$$\mu = (1000/3600)/[\tfrac{1}{4}\pi(0.05)^2 \times 10 \times 1.2] = 11.69$$

Substituting these values into the pressure drop equation gives

$$\Delta p/L = 141 \text{ N/m}^3 \qquad \text{at } 10 \text{ m/s}$$

for the other cases

$$\Delta p/L = 209 \text{ N/m}^3 \qquad \text{at } 20 \text{ m/s}$$

$$\varepsilon = 0.994$$

$$\mu = 5.84$$

$$c = 18.8 \text{ m/s}$$

$$\Delta p/L = 311 \text{ N/m}^3 \qquad \text{at } 30 \text{ m/s}$$

$$\varepsilon = 0.996$$

$$\mu = 3.89$$

$$c = 28.2 \text{ m/s}$$

Example 2

For a heavy loaded gas–solid mixture the friction factor found by Mathur and Klinzing has been suggested. Consider the vertical flow of coal of 100 μm diameter at a rate of 10 000 kg/h in a 0.05 m diameter pipe using nitrogen at atmospheric conditions. The solid density is 1280 kg/m^3. The gas velocity is 20 m/s. Determine each pressure drop contribution.

Solution

The pressure drop equation is given as

$$\frac{\Delta p}{L} = \rho_p(1 - \varepsilon) + \rho(\varepsilon) + \frac{2f_L\rho\varepsilon v^2}{D} + \lambda_Z^* \frac{\rho_p(1 - \varepsilon)}{2D}(v - c)^2$$

for 20 m/s

$$Re = \frac{0.05 \times 1.2 \times 20}{10^{-5}} = 120\,000$$

using 15.15 m/s as the particle velocity from measurements:

$$\varepsilon = 1 - \frac{10\,000/3600}{\tfrac{1}{4}\pi(0.05)^2 \times 15.15 \times 1280} = 0.967$$

$$\mu = 26.6$$

$$\frac{\lambda_Z^*}{4} = 0.395(v_\varepsilon - c)^{-1.65}$$

$$\frac{\Delta p_{\text{total}}}{L} = 582 \text{ N/m}^3$$

Individual contributions:

(1) $\rho_p(1 - \varepsilon) = 413 \text{ N/m}^3$

(2) $\rho(\varepsilon) = 11.4 \text{ N/m}^3$

(3) $2f_L \dfrac{\rho\varepsilon(v/\varepsilon)^2}{D} = 99.8 \text{ N/m}^3$

(4) $2\lambda_Z^* \dfrac{\rho_p(1 - \varepsilon)(v_\varepsilon - c)^2}{D} = 57.8 \text{ N/m}^3$

Note the large contribution due to the vertical lift.

Example 3

Consider the transfer of 0.0252 kg/s of 200 μm diameter coal particles by carbon dioxide at an average velocity of 6.1 m/s in a 0.508 m ID pipe. Determine the pressure loss around a 90° bend having a 0.61 m radius of curvature. The gas is at 3441 kN/m^2 and 38 °C. Use the design suggestion and the Schuchart analysis to determine the pressure loss.

Solution

$$\rho = 38 \text{ kg/m}^3$$

$$\text{length of bend} = (\pi/2)(0.61) = 0.598 \text{ m}$$

Design suggestion

$$\Delta p = 2f_L \frac{\rho v_\varepsilon^2 L}{D} + \lambda_Z^* \rho_p \frac{(1 - \varepsilon)c^2 L}{2D}$$

assuming $v \simeq c = 6.1$ m/s and the Konno and Saito friction is

$$\frac{\lambda_Z^*}{4} = 0.0285(gD)^{1/2}/U_p = 0.0033$$

$$\varepsilon = 1 - \dot{G}/A(\rho_p)c = 0.998$$

$$f_L = 0.0028$$

$$R_e = 11.8 \times 10^5$$

$$\Delta p = 149.3 + 11.1 = 160.4 \text{ N/m}^2$$

for a 90° bend

$$(\Delta p)_{\text{bend}} = 20\Delta p_{\text{straight}} = 3208 \text{ N/m}^2$$

Schuchart analysis

$$\left(\frac{\Delta p_{\text{bend}}}{\Delta p_{\text{straight}}}\right)_{\text{solid}} = 210\left(\frac{2R_{\text{B}}}{D}\right)^{-1.15}$$

$$\Delta p_{\text{(bend)solids}} = 6.32\Delta p_{\text{(straight)solids}}$$

$$= 6.32(11.1) = 70.1 \text{ N/m}^2$$

One must add the Δp for the gas alone as it passes through the bend. A variety of expressions could be used for this such as Ito's analysis. Taking the design suggestion for single-phase flow one would have

$$\Delta p_{\text{(bend)gas}} = 20(149.3) = 2986 \text{ N/m}^2$$

adding the solids effect one finds

$$\Delta p_{\text{bend}} = 2986 + 70.1 = 3056 \text{ N/m}^2$$

Example 4

Often the question arises as to which frictional representation should be used for a particular analysis. A comparison will be made between the Konno and Saito and the Yang expressions for vertical flow of a gas–solid system. Consider the case where the following conditions are specified:

$$\rho_{\text{p}} = 1340 \text{ kg/m}^3$$

$$d = 250 \text{ } \mu\text{m}$$

$$\dot{G} = 1000 \text{ kg/h}$$

$$v = 30 \text{ m/s}$$

$$\rho_{\text{f}} = 1.2 \text{ kg/m}^3$$

Using Example 1 as a base the vertical contribution must be added to the expression for $\Delta p/L$. Using the Hinkle (IGT) particle velocity representation one can write

$$\Delta p/L = 311 + \rho_{\text{p}}(1 - \varepsilon) + \rho\varepsilon$$

$$= 311 + 16.1 + 1.2 = 328 \text{ N/m}^3$$

For the Yang expression an iterative technique must be employed since the particle velocity is implicitly related.

$$c = v_{\varepsilon} - w_{\text{f0}}\left(1 + \frac{\lambda_Z^* c^2 \varepsilon^{4.7}}{2gD}\right)^{1/2}$$

$$\lambda_Z^* = 0.0126 \frac{1-\varepsilon}{\varepsilon^3}\left((1-\varepsilon)\frac{Re_{\text{t}}}{Re_{\text{p}}}\right)^{-0.979}$$

where

$$Re_t = \frac{w_{fo}\rho d}{\eta}$$

$$Re_p = \frac{(v_\varepsilon - c)\rho d}{\eta}$$

A Newton–Raphson iterative technique was devised yielding the following results:

$$(\Delta p/L)_{vert} = 315.3\ \text{N/m}^3$$

$$c = 29.9\ \text{m/s}$$

$$\varepsilon = 0.9965$$

Comparing the two results one sees

$$(\Delta p/L)_{K-S} = 328\ \text{N/m}^3$$

$$(\Delta p/L)_Y = 315.3\ \text{N/m}^3$$

Example 5

Using Weber's analysis for the velocity of sound in a gas–solid system, determine this velocity for the following conditions:

(a) $c/v_\varepsilon = 0.5$, $\varepsilon = 0.8$

(b) $c/v_\varepsilon = 0.5$, $\varepsilon = 0.9$

(c) $c/v_\varepsilon = 1$, $\varepsilon = 0.94$

Using Fig. (4.11) for case (a):

$$a_{fs}/a = 0.09$$

$$a = 335\ \text{m/s}$$

at STP for air, therefore

$$a_{fs} = 30.2\ \text{m/s}$$

For case (b):

$$a_{fs}/a = 0.09$$

$$a_{fs} = 0.11 \times 335 = 36.9\ \text{m/s}$$

For case (c):

$$a_{fs}/a = 0.1$$

$$a_{fs} = 33.5\ \text{m/s}$$

Thus one sees a sizeable reduction in the velocity of sound in a two-phase system over that in a single-phase system.

Example 6

Consider a Y expansion unit where the angle between the Y is 45°. All pipe diameters are the same and there is an equal split of volumetric flows. The upstream gas velocity is 20 m/s with a density of 1.2 kg/m³. The solid loading is 5.0. Find the pressure loss across the Y.

$$\frac{\Delta p_{\text{total}}}{\rho v^2/2} = \frac{\dot{V}_2}{\dot{V}_1} - 1.59\frac{\dot{V}_2}{\dot{V}_1} + 0.97(\mu)_2 \left[0.48 \left(\frac{\dot{V}_2}{\dot{V}_1} \right)^2 + 0.09 \right]$$
$$+ (\mu)_2 \left[0.48 \left(\frac{\dot{V}_2}{\dot{V}_1} \right)^2 + 0.09 \right]$$

$$\Delta p_{\text{total}} = (1.2)\frac{(20)^2}{2}[(2)^2 - 1.59(2) + 0.97 + 5(0.48(2)^2 + 0.09)]$$

$$= 2842 \text{ N/m}^2$$

Example 7

Using Yang's format for frictional representation determine the particle velocity of the system.

$$\frac{\lambda_Z^*}{4} = 0.00315\frac{(1-\varepsilon)}{\varepsilon^3}\left(\frac{(1-\varepsilon)w_{\text{f0}}}{v_\varepsilon - c} \right)^{-0.979}$$

and for the particle velocity

$$c = v_\varepsilon - w_{\text{f0}}\left[\left(1 + \frac{\lambda_Z^* c^2}{2gD} \right)\varepsilon^{4.7} \right]^{1/2}$$

In order to solve this implicit system assume a value for *c* first and then calculate ε and v_ε:

$$\varepsilon = 1 - \frac{G0}{cA\rho_p}$$

$$v_\varepsilon = v/\varepsilon$$

With this information λ_Z^* can be found. Insert c, λ_Z^* and ε into the particle equation to see if agreement is achieved. For the iterative process let

$$F_1 = c - v_\varepsilon + w_{\text{f0}}\left[\left(1 + \frac{\lambda_Z^* c^2}{2gD} \right)\varepsilon^{4.7} \right]^{1/2}$$

and

$$\frac{dF_1}{dc} = 1 + \frac{1}{2}\left(1 + \frac{\lambda_z^* c^2}{2gD}\right)^{-1/2} \frac{2\lambda_z^* c}{2gD} \varepsilon^{4.7}$$

For the new estimate of c one uses the Newton–Raphson procedure, thus

$$c_{new} = c_{old} - F_1/(dF_1/dc)$$

The calculations return to the beginning and iterate until $c_{new} - c_{old} < 0.001$.

Example 8

Dixon has developed an expression to predict the maximum loading for gas–solid flow. This expression is given as

$$\mu_{max} = \dot{G}/A\left(\rho v_{mf} + \frac{\varepsilon_{mf}\dot{G}/A}{1 - \varepsilon_{mf}} \frac{\rho}{\rho_p}\right)^{-1}$$

For particles 250 μm in diameter and having a density of 1500 kg/m^3 with the gas density of 1.2 kg/m^3 and the solid flow rate of 100 kg/m^2 s, the value of μ_{max} can be determined.

For small particles

$$v_{mf} = \frac{d^2 g(\rho_p - \rho)}{1650\eta}$$

$$= \frac{(250 \times 10^{-6})^2(9.8)(1500 - 1.2)}{(1650)(10^{-5})} = 0.056 \, m/s$$

The voidage at this condition can be found from Ergun's equation in the form

$$\frac{1.75}{\phi_s \varepsilon_{mf}^3} Re_p^2 + \frac{1.50(1 - \varepsilon_{mf})}{\phi_s \varepsilon_{mf}^3} Re_p^2 - K^3 = 0$$

where

$$Re_p = \frac{v_{mf} d\rho}{\eta}$$

$$\phi_s = \text{sphericity}$$

$$K = d\left(\frac{g\rho(\rho_p - \rho)}{\eta^2}\right)^{1/3}$$

With $\phi_s = 1$

$$Re_p = 1.68$$
$$K = 13.9$$

Thus

$$\frac{4.94}{\varepsilon_{mf}^3} + \frac{423(1-\varepsilon)}{\varepsilon_{mf}^3} - 2686 = 0$$

$$\varepsilon_{mf} = 0.44$$

Therefore

$$\mu_{max} = 100\left((1.2)(0.056) + \frac{(0.44)(100)}{0.56} \frac{1.2}{1500} \right)^{-1}$$

$$= 769$$

For a 0.05 m diameter pipe

$$\dot{G} = 100\left(\frac{\pi}{4}\right)(0.05)^2 = 0.196 \, \text{kg/s}$$

Example 9

For a cyclone separation of interior radius of 0.3 m, find the radial drift time from 0.1 to the radius of the cyclone of three types of particles:

(a) $d = 1000 \, \mu\text{m}, \rho_p = 1000 \, \text{kg/m}^3$

(b) $d = 100 \, \mu\text{m}, \rho_p = 2000 \, \text{kg/m}^3$

(c) $d = 50 \, \mu\text{m}, \rho_p = 2500 \, \text{kg/m}^3$

The transport gas is air at atmospheric conditions.

$$t = \frac{g}{2}\left(\frac{\eta}{\rho_p - \rho}\right)\left(\frac{R_2}{U_{T2}d}\right)^2\left[1 - \left(\frac{R_1}{R_2}\right)^4\right]$$

The tangential velocity U_{T2} is 20 m/s.

Case (a)

$$t = \frac{g}{2}\left(\frac{10^{-5}}{1000 - 1.2}\right)\left(\frac{0.3}{(20)(1000 \times 10^{-6})}\right)^2\left[1 - \left(\frac{0.1}{0.3}\right)^4\right]$$

$$= 4.5 \times (10^{-8})(15)^2(0.9876)$$

$$= 9.99 \times 10^{-6}$$

Case (b)

$$t = \frac{g}{2}\left(\frac{10^{-5}}{2000-1.2}\right)\left(\frac{0.3}{20(100)\times 10^{-6}}\right)^2\left[1-\left(\frac{0.1}{0.3}\right)^4\right]$$

$$= 4.5(0.5 \times 10^{-8})(150)^2(0.9876)$$

$$= 5.0 \times 10^{-4}\,\text{s}$$

Case (c)

$$t = \frac{g}{2}\left(\frac{10^{-5}}{2500-1.2}\right)\left(\frac{0.3}{20(50)\times 10^{-6}}\right)^2(0.9876)$$

$$= 1.6 \times 10^{-3}\,\text{s}$$

Chapter 5

Example 1

A number of cases will be considered to assess if saltation can be anticipated in a gas–solid flow system using the criteria of Owens. Consider a 0.0245 inch pipe. The criteria state that if

$$X = \frac{\rho v^2 f_L}{2\rho_p g d} < 1$$

then saltation is of importance. Table 14.2 gives details of the cases.

(a) Using the Koo equation for f_L

$$f_L = 0.0014 + 0.125 Re^{-0.32}$$

$$Re = (0.0245)(20)(1.2)/10^{-5} = 5.88 \times 10^6$$

Table 14.12

Material	Particle diameter (μm)	Mean velocity (m/s)	Gas pressure (kN/m^2)
(a) Glass	150	20	101
(b) Lead	10	20	101
(c) Iron oxide	50	15	310
(d) Coal	100	14	690

Therefore

$$f_L = 0.0023$$

$$X = \frac{1.2(20)^2(0.0023)}{2 \times 2240 \times 9.8 \times 150 \times 10^{-6}} = 0.1675 \qquad \text{saltation is important}$$

(b) $X = \dfrac{0.023(20)^2(1.2)}{2(11\,300)(9.8)(10 \times 10^{-6})} = 0.498 \qquad \text{saltation is important}$

(c) $f_L = 0.00366$

$$X = \frac{(3.68)(1.5)^2(0.00366)}{2(5120)(9.8)(50) \times 10^{-6}} = 30.1 \qquad \text{saltation not important}$$

(d) $f_L = 0.00366$

$$X = \frac{(8.2)(14)^2(0.00366)}{2(1200)(9.8)(100 \times 10^{-6})} = 2.5 \qquad \text{saltation may not be important}$$

Example 2

Use the method of Rizk and Matsumoto *et al.* to predict the gas velocity at saltation for 1 mm diameter particles with

$$\dot{G} = 1 \, \text{kg/s}$$
$$\rho_p = 1000 \, \text{kg/m}^3$$
$$\rho = 1.2 \, \text{kg/m}^3$$
$$D = 0.1 \, \text{m}$$

Rizk's equation states

$$\mu = \frac{1}{10^\sigma}\left(\frac{v_s}{(gD)^{1/2}}\right)^x$$

for 1 mm diameter particles $\sigma = 3.4$, $x = 3.6$

$$\mu = \frac{1}{10^{3.4}}\left(\frac{v_s}{(9.8 \times 0.1)^{1/2}}\right)^{3.6}$$

$$\frac{1}{\rho A v_s} = \frac{1}{(1.2)(0.00785)v_s} = \frac{1}{2512}\left(\frac{v_s}{0.9899}\right)^{3.6}$$

$$v = 14.9 \, \text{m/s}$$

The Matsumoto *et al.* equation is

$$\mu = \alpha \left(\frac{\rho_p}{\rho}\right)^a \left(\frac{w_{f0}}{10(gD)^{1/2}}\right)^b \left(\frac{v_s}{10(gD)^{1/2}}\right)^c$$

where

$d = 1.1$

$a = 0.55$

$b = -2.3$

$c = 3$

For w_{f0} use the K factor:

$$K = d\left(\frac{gp(\rho_p - \rho)}{\eta^2}\right)^{1/3}$$

$$= 1000 \times 10^{-6}\left(\frac{9.8 \times 1.2(1000)}{(10^{-5})^2}\right)^{1/3} = 48.9$$

Thus the Newton range is applicable

$$w_{f0} = 1.75\left(\frac{gd(\rho_p - \rho)}{\rho}\right)^{1/2}$$

$$= 1.75\left(\frac{9.8 \times 1000 \times 10^{-6}(1000)}{1.2}\right)^{1/2} = 5.47\,\text{m/s}$$

Therefore the basic equation is

$$\mu = \frac{1}{v(1.2)(0.00785)} = 1.11\left(\frac{1000}{1.2}\right)^{0.33}\left(\frac{5.47}{10(0.98)^{1/2}}\right)^{-2.3}\left(\frac{v}{10(0.98)^{1/2}}\right)^{3.0}$$

Solving for v:

$$v = 4.92\,\text{m/s}$$

The difference in the two answers is sizeable; thus one may want to be conservative and employ 14.9 m/s to avoid saltation.

Example 3

Estimation of the acceleration length in a gas–solid system is to be made. In order to approach this the Enick and Klinzing model is suggested

$$\frac{L}{D} = 0.527\left(\frac{D}{d}\right)^{-1.26}\left(1 + Re_g\frac{\dot{G}}{\dot{Q}}\right)$$

For a 7.5 cm diameter tube conveying 300 μm particles at a Reynolds number of 10^5 estimate the acceleration length as a function of loading. Employing the above expression one has

$$L = 0.527(0.075)\left(\frac{0.075}{300 \times 10^{-6}}\right)^{-1.26}(1 + 10^5\mu)$$

$$= (0.0395)(9.5 \times 10^{-4})(1 + 10^5)\mu m$$

Thus

L(m)	Loading
0.375	0.1
3.75	1.0
18.8	5

Example 4

Solids are being transported for 300 m in a horizontal 2.5 cm diameter pipe. The exit pressure is atmospheric. The solids flow is 500 kg/h with a solids to gas ratio of 2.0. Determine the upstream pressure 300 m from the exit. The solids have a density of 1300 kg/m³ and a diameter of 150 μm. Do not ignore compressibility effects.

Solution

From the compressible equation one can write for the isothermal compressible flow

$$p_2 - p_1 = \frac{g(MW)C_2}{RTC_1\alpha}\left(\frac{p_1 - p_2}{2}\right)L + \frac{g(MW)}{RT}\left(\frac{p_1 + p_2}{2}\right)L$$

$$+ 2f_L\frac{C_1^2RT}{D(MW)}\frac{2L}{p_1 - p_2} + \lambda_Z^*C_1C_2\alpha\frac{RT}{2(MW)}\frac{2L}{p_1 + p_2}$$

$$+ C_1^2\frac{RT}{(MW)}\left(\frac{1}{p_2} - \frac{1}{p_1}\right) + C_1C_2\frac{\alpha RT}{(MW)}\left(\frac{1}{p_2} - \frac{1}{p_1}\right)$$

This equation must be solved numerically. Assume the constant α is 0.90 for the equation

$$c = \alpha v_\varepsilon$$

The other parameters for the system are:

$$(MW) = 29 \quad \text{for air}$$

$$T = 20\,°C = 293\,K$$

$$g = 9.8\,\text{m/s}^2$$

$$L = 300\,m$$

$$p_1 = 1.013 \times 10^5\,\text{N/m}^2$$

$$R = 83.12 \times 10^2\,\text{m N/kg mol K}$$

$$f_L = 0.0014 + 0.125(Re_g)^{-0.32}$$

$$\frac{\lambda_z^*}{4} = 0.0285(gD)^{-1/2}/c$$

$$C_1 = 1.2Uf$$

$$\varepsilon = 1 - \frac{\dot{G}}{\rho_p Ac} = 1 - \frac{500/3600}{(1300)\frac{1}{4}\pi(0.025)^2 c}$$

$$\text{Loading} = 1 = \frac{\dot{G}/3600}{v\rho\frac{1}{4}\pi(0.025)^2} = \frac{500/3600}{v(1.2)\frac{1}{4}\pi(0.025)^2}$$

$$v = 118\,\text{m/s}$$

$$c = 106\,\text{m/s}$$

$$\varepsilon = 0.9979$$

$$C_1 = 142$$

$$C_2 = \rho_p c(1 - \varepsilon) = (1300)(106)(0.002) = 275.6$$

Inserting these values and iterating on the equation gives p_2 as $1.673 \times 10^5\,\text{N/m}^2$ or $167.3\,\text{kN/m}^2$.

Example 5

The particle velocity in pneumatic transport is the result of dynamic forces acting between the particles, fluid and pipe walls. Assess the particle velocity of two flow situations assuming that the particles behave as individual entities:

(a) $a = 500\,\mu m$

$v = 20\,\text{m/s}$

$$\rho_p = 2500 \, \text{kg/m}^3$$

$$\rho = 1.2 \, \text{kg/m}^3$$

$$D = 5 \, \text{cm}$$

$$\dot{G} = 2000 \, \text{kg/h}$$

Short of carrying out a detailed experimental evaluation of this system to find c, one must rely on some empirical model. For this case the Hinkle format as modified by IGT is appropriate:

$$c = v(1 - 0.68d^{0.92}\rho_p^{0.5}\rho^{-0.2}D^{-0.54})$$

$$= 20[1 - 0.68(500 \times 10^{-6})^{0.92}(2500)^{0.5}(1.2)^{-0.2}(0.05)^{-0.5}]$$

$$= 16.97 \, \text{m/s}$$

The loading for this situation is

$$\text{Loading} = \frac{\dot{G}}{vA\rho} = \frac{2000/3600}{(20)\frac{1}{4}\pi(0.05)^2(1.2)} = 11.8$$

This is bordering on the medium dense phase regime.

(b) $d = 25 \, \mu\text{m}$

$$v = 30 \, \text{m/s}$$

$$\rho_p = 1000 \, \text{kg/m}^3$$

$$\rho = 1.2 \, \text{kg/m}^3$$

$$D = 7.5 \, \text{cm}$$

$$\dot{G} = 3000 \, \text{kg/h}$$

Since the particle size is less than $40 \, \mu\text{m}$, it is most appropriate to employ

$$c = v - w_{f0}$$

To determine the terminal velocity the characterization parameter K must be first determined:

$$K = d\left(\frac{g\rho(\rho_p - \rho)}{\eta^2}\right)^{1/3}$$

$$= 25 \times 10^{-6}\left(\frac{9.8 \times 1.2(1000 - 1.2)}{(10^{-5})^2}\right)^{1/3}$$

$$= 1.21$$

The Stokes regime is thus applicable so

$$w_{f0} = \frac{d^2 g \Delta \rho}{18\eta} = \frac{(25 \times 10^{-6})^2 (9.8)(1000 - 1.2)}{18 \times 10^{-5}}$$

$$= 0.0340 \, \text{m/s}$$

Thus

$$c = 30 - 0.034 = 29.97 \, \text{m/s}$$

The loading in this case is

$$\mu = \frac{3000/3600}{30(\pi/4)(0.075)^2 (1.2)} = 5.2$$

This loading remains in the relatively dilute phase.

Example 6

Consider the horizontal gas–solid flow of silica particles with an average diameter of 200 μm being transported by air at 30.5 m/s and STP. The relative humidity of the air is 80%. The solids loading is 2.0 in a 0.025 m ID plastic pipe. The air relative humidity is lowered to 40% and the pressure drop is found to increase by 25%. Determine the magnitude of the electrostatic contributions.

Since the loading is relatively low the Konno and Saito frictional representation will be employed:

$$\frac{\Delta p}{L} = \frac{2 f_L \rho \varepsilon v_\varepsilon^2}{D} + 2\lambda_Z^* \frac{\rho_p (1 - \varepsilon) c^2}{D}$$

Using Hinkle (IGT) correlation for Up:

$$c = v(1 - 0.68 d^{0.92} \rho_p^{0.5} \rho^{-0.2} D^{-0.54})$$

$$= 30.5[1 - 0.68(200 \times 10^{-6})^{0.92}(3590)^{0.5}(1.2)^{-0.2}(0.0254)^{-0.54}]$$

$$= 30.5(1 - 0.68(0.000395)(59.9)(0.964)(7.27))$$

$$= 0.887(30.5) = 27.1 \, \text{m/s}$$

$$\text{Loading} = 2 = \frac{\dot{G}}{(\pi/4)(0.0254)^2 (1.2)(30.5)}$$

$$\dot{G} = 0.037 \, \text{kg/s}$$

$$\varepsilon = 1 - \frac{\dot{G}}{Ac\rho_p} = 1 - \frac{0.037}{(0.000645)(27.1)(3590)} = 0.9994$$

$$v \simeq c$$

$$f_L = 0.0014 + 0.125(Re)^{-0.32}$$

$$Re = \frac{(0.0254)(30.5)(1.2)}{(10^{-5})} = 92.9 \times 10^3$$

$$\lambda_z^* = 0.0285(gD)^{1/2}/c = 0.0285(9.8 \times 0.0254)^{1/2}/27.1 = 0.00052$$

$$\frac{\Delta p}{L} = \frac{2 \times 0.0046(1.2)(0.9994)(30.5)^2}{0.0254}$$

$$+ \frac{4(0.00052)(3590)(0.0006)27.1)^2}{2 \times 0.0254}$$

$$= 404 + 64.8$$

$$= 469 \text{ N/m}^3$$

for a 25% increase in $(\Delta p/L)$ due to electrostatics

$$\Delta p/L = 1.25(469) = 586 \text{ N/m}^3$$

thus

$$\left(\frac{\Delta p}{L}\right)_{\text{electro}} = 586 - 469 = 117 \text{ N/m}^3$$

$$= \frac{E_x q}{m_p}(1 - \varepsilon)\rho_p = 117 \text{ N/m}^3$$

$$E_x q = 117 \frac{\pi}{6} \frac{(200 \times 10^{-6})^3(3590)}{(3590)(1 - 0.9994)}$$

$$= \frac{4.9 \times 10^{-10}}{6 \times 10^{-4}} = 8.2 \times 10^{-5}$$

Now considering $q = 10^{-14} \text{ C}$

$$E_x = 8.2 \times 10^9$$

This increased pressure drop caused by the electrostatic forces also affects the particle velocity.

One can develop this effect of electrostatics on the particle velocity at equilibrium as

$$c = v_\varepsilon - w_{f0}\left(\frac{\lambda_Z^* c^2}{2gD} + \frac{E_x q}{gm_p}\right)^{1/2} \varepsilon^{2.35}$$

For these 200 μm diameter particles the characterization factor K is

$$K = 200 \times 10^{-6}\left(\frac{9.8 \times 3590 \times 1.2}{(10^{-5})^2}\right)^{1/3} = 14.8$$

This gives the intermediate range for w_{f0}:

$$w_{f0} = \frac{0.154 g^{0.11} d^{1.14} \rho_p^{0.71}}{\rho^{0.29}\eta^{0.43}}$$

$$= \frac{0.153(5.06)(6.06 \times 10^{-5})(334)}{(1.05)(0.0071)} = 1.47\,\text{m/s}$$

$$c = 30.5 - 14.7\left(\frac{2 \times 0.00052 \times c^2}{(9.8)(0.0254)} + 5.54\right)^{1/2}(0.9994)^{2.35}$$

Chapter 12

Example 1

In attempting to place controls on a pneumatic transport system the time constant and gain factor of the transport line are essential parameters. Both these parameters depend on the solid friction factor. Using the solid friction factor as a constant of 0.003 and the Konno and Saito frictional term determine these parameters. The pipe diameter is 5 cm with the length of 100 m. The solids flow is 3000 kg/h. The particle velocity for a system can be estimated from empirical expressions. The time constant is

$$\tau = \frac{D}{\lambda_Z^* c}$$

and the given factor is

$$K = \frac{1}{\pi \lambda_Z^* \rho_p c L D(1 - \varepsilon)}$$

Assume $c = 5\,\text{m/s}$ and $\rho_p = 1500\,\text{kg/m}^3$

$$1 - \varepsilon = \frac{\dot{G}}{A\rho_p c} = \frac{3000/3600}{(\pi/4)(0.05)^2(1500)(5)} = 0.0565$$

Case (a):

$$f_L = 0.003$$

$$\tau = \frac{0.05}{4(0.003)(5)} = 0.833$$

$$K = \frac{1}{\pi(0.003)(1300)(5)(100)(0.05)(0.0565)}$$

$$= 0.0577$$

Case (b):

$$\frac{\lambda_z^*}{4} = 0.0285(gD)^{1/2}/c$$

$$\tau = \frac{D}{4[0.0285(gD)^{1/2}/c]c} = \frac{D}{4(0.0285)(gD)^{1/2}}$$

$$= \frac{0.05}{4(0.0285)(9.8 \times 0.05)^{1/2}}$$

$$\tau = 0.626\,\text{s}$$

$$K = \frac{1}{\pi(0.0285)[(gD)^{1/2}/c]\rho_p cLD(1-\varepsilon)}$$

$$\frac{1}{\pi(0.0285)(9.8 \times 0.05)^{1/2}(1300)(100)(0.05)(0.0565)}$$

$$= 0.0139$$

Example 2

Consider a volume expansion in a pipeline used in order to damp concentration oscillations in the solids. For a 0.0254 m diameter line consider a 0.05 m expansion section. In order to damp out 75% of the concentration oscillations, what length of the expansion section is needed. The basic equation is given as

$$\frac{\text{Amplitude out}}{\text{Amplitude in}} = \left(\frac{1 + \omega^2 V^2(\rho_p - \rho)^2}{c^2 \rho_p^2 A^2}\right)^{-1/2}$$

The basic parameters are

$$\omega = 10\,\text{cps} = 2\pi(10)\,\text{rad/s}$$

$$\rho_p = 1200\,\text{kg/m}^3$$

$$\rho = 1.2 \, \text{kg/m}^3$$

$$A = (\pi/4)(0.05)^2$$

$$c = 15 \, \text{m/s}$$

$$V = \text{volume of expansion section}$$

Thus

$$0.75 = \left(1 + \frac{(20\pi)^2 V^2 (1200 - 1.2)^2}{(15)^2 (1200)^2 (0.00196)} \right)^{-1/2}$$

$$V = 0.0579 \, \text{m}^3$$

$$L = V/A = 2.95 \, \text{m}$$

14.10 CONCLUSIONS

In this chapter, a number of design techniques have been illustrated in an attempt to provide the reader with an insight into the development of a 'design' philosophy.

The reader is cautioned to use these correlations with care and to rather resort to the use of experimental techniques to obtain reliable design data.

REFERENCES

1. Stephenson, R.L. and Nixon H.E. (1983) *Centrifugal Compressor Engineering*, Hoffman Air and Filtration Division, Clarkson Industries Inc., New York.
2. Weber, M. (1973) *Stromung-Fordertechnik*, Krausskopf Verlag.
3. Butters, G. (ed.) (1981) *Plastics Pneumatic Conveying and Bulk Storage*, Applied Sciences Publishers, Reading.
4. Hinkle, B.L. (1953) *Ph.D. Thesis*, Georgia Institute of Technology.

Index